Concepts and Methods of
Experimental Statistics

H. C. Fryer

Kansas State University

Allyn and Bacon, Inc.
Boston, 1966

To Ruth, Gaye, and Claire

To Ruth

Preface

Increasingly large numbers of people are learning more about the area of applied statistics. One of the most popular of these areas can be described as experimental statistics, because it deals with the concepts and methods of statistical analyses needed when experimental research culminates in the taking of numerical measurements.

Many persons doing experimental research or preparing to do such research must attain a working understanding of the basic concepts in experimental statistics with a minimum of prerequisite work in mathematics and statistics, for they often have not taken two or three one-year sequences in undergraduate mathematics and statistics while seeking an advanced degree in another field.

Over the past twenty-five years a number of books have been written in the general area of statistical methods. Some of these books do not cover enough of the topics which one wishes to learn. Others cover most of the topics one wishes to learn but are written chiefly as reference books or handbooks seeking to give directions for many statistical operations. It seems to me that at the present time there is need for a book on statistical methods which is adequately comprehensive and also primarily a teaching instrument designed to lead the nonmathematical persons into as thorough an understanding of the basic concepts and reasoning of experimental statistics as is possible in what is essentially an introduction for them. After teaching this subject over a period of roughly twenty-five years I have attempted to develop this textbook in experimental statistics for advanced undergraduates and beginning graduate students in the several areas of experimental research. It is not slanted intentionally toward any particular field of applied statistics.

This attempt to present a teaching book in experimental statistics to nonmathematical but mature students necessarily calls upon the intuition, common sense, and ingenuity of the student to bridge some gaps best filled by mathematical reasoning. However, the student is expected to have or to attain some facility with algebra, with summation symbols, and even with a few elementary matrix operations.

Chapter 1 is intended to be more than a cursory introduction to the subject of this book. It is hoped that here the student will gain an insight into the problems, concepts, and procedures of experimental statistics and so acquire a good background for the other chapters, which present in more detail what already has been touched upon in Chapter 1. Certainly the student will not fully understand what is covered in Chapter 1 when he has finished this chapter, but it is hoped, and believed from past experience, that he will be better able to learn the subject of this book than if he were plunged immediately into detailed discussions of sampling, statistical methods, and statistical interpretations. It will be necessary for an instructor using this book as a text to guard against spending too much time on Chapter 1. It is the aim of that chapter to bring the student to as full an understanding as possible of the points made in Section 1.8, the summary, before that student plunges into a deeper and more detailed study of experimental statistics. It is suggested that Sections 1.1, 1.2, and 1.3 be assigned as a group, Sections 1.4 and 1.5 as another, Section 1.6 by itself, and Section 1.7 by itself, Section 1.8 being made the basis of a final summary of Chapter 1. As I see it, the instructor's discussions should be general and unifying, and he should spend a good deal of the classroom time on the problems at the ends of the sections in Chapter 1, with as much class participation as possible. No more than six or seven class periods, including an "idea" examination, should be spent on this chapter.

This book's precursors were used in classes in statistical methods for several years by members of the Department of Statistics at Kansas State University. This use was the basis of several revisions. The classes in which this material was used comprised mostly graduate students from at least twenty-five different departments in agriculture, arts and sciences, commerce, engineering, home economics, and veterinary medicine. This broad background seems to justify the inclusion of problems and illustrations from a wide variety of experimental situations. It also seems to me to justify a sincere attempt to lead students to a basic understanding of the subject rather than to a mere facility with statistical methods, for these students will be called upon later in their professional lives to apply experimental statistics to a very wide range of problems, some not even specifically conceivable at this time.

Anyone writing a textbook on this subject inevitably will be influenced by Snedecor's classic books and also by several other textbooks, reference books, and handbooks in the general area of statistical methods. There is, further, abundant literature on statistical methods in the many fields of experimental research. When these influences are overlain by more than twenty-five years of teaching of experimental statistics to nonmathematical students, it becomes impossible to acknowledge specific debts to specific writers and teachers with whom I have had contact. I do feel a special debt to Professor George W. Snedecor, who was one of my teachers at Iowa State University and whose books we have used at Kansas State University for many years. I am glad, however, to acquit him of all blame for the inadequacies of the present textbook. I am indebted also to the students in my classes and to my colleagues in the Department of Statistics at Kansas State University for calling my attention to errors, to misprints, and to unclear presentations in earlier versions of this book.

I am indebted to the late Sir Ronald A. Fisher, F.R.S., Cambridge, and Dr. Frank Yates, F.R.S., Rothamsted, and to Messrs. Oliver and Boyd Ltd., Edinburgh, for permission to reprint parts of Table XII from their book, *Statistical Tables for Biological, Agricultural and Medical Research.*

Finally, I should like to thank all other persons and organizations who have granted permission to use parts of their publications. These permissions are acknowledged in the appropriate places.

H. C. Fryer
Manhattan, Kansas

Contents

Chapter 7

Sampling More Than Two Normal Populations Simultaneously: Introductory Analysis of Variance

Chapter 8

Models and Expected Mean Squares for the Analysis of Variance for Completely Randomized and Randomized Complete Block Designs

Chapter 9

More Complex Analyses of Variance

Chapter 10
Simple Analysis of Covariance

Chapter 11
Multiple Linear Regression and Correlation Analysis

Chapter 12
Curvilinear Regression Analysis

Chapter 13
The Poisson and Negative Binomial Distributions

Chapter 14
Introductory Discriminatory Analysis

Tables

Chapter 1

Introduction

1.1 STATISTICAL POPULATIONS OF NUMERICAL MEASUREMENTS

For centuries human beings have described themselves, their environments, their possessions, their thoughts, and their actions by means of numerical measurements. This sort of description developed from the necessity to arrange efficiently our activities and to make more rapid the communication of ideas. For example, the density of habitation by man, plants, or animals, in a describable geographical or sociological area usually is measured by counting. Weights describe crops, people, soils, fish, or manufactured products. The economic rewards of labor, investment, professional services, or the production of consumable goods are measured numerically, such that highly complex transactions are carried out and described accurately and efficiently. The increasing availability of high-speed computers and data processors is indicative of the benefits to be derived from numerical description by calculation and the storage of information.

When a person makes numerical measurements of some objects or actions, he does not just measure a conglomeration of them; rather, he has at least previously formulated in his mind a reasonably homogeneous group that he wishes to measure in some specific respect. An economist does not measure the net incomes of a random group of people whom he meets during a tour or on his way from one part of a country to another; instead, he measures net incomes of lawyers in a certain area, of cattlemen in western Kansas, of grocers in Hawaii, etc. There is a definable homogeneity about any group which is measured for any specific characteristic. This homogeneity is the starting point for defining what will be called a *statistical population* or, more briefly herein, a *population.*

There is, however, associated with the concept of a homogeneous group that may be measured in a specific way the full awareness that *no* group is perfectly homogeneous: always there is some variability, even in the most closely knit group. If this were not so, there would be no reason at all for statistical concepts, and all experimental research would be exceedingly simple.

The group of actions, objects, or situations to which a set of numerical measurements pertains can be the basis of defining a statistical population. However, the same group of actions, objects, or situations also can be the basis of defining several different statistical populations. The inhabitants of Australia, for example, could be studied with respect to sex ratio, age, weight, blood sugar, political opinions, amount of education, quality of eyesight, and so forth, ad infinitum. Hence, any particular statistical population which is to be studied must be defined carefully, or considerable confusion may result and thus obscure the purposes of the study. The definition of the population must specify the group of objects or actions to be studied, the particular feature which is to be studied numerically, and the unit of measure to be employed; and these must be specified unambiguously. For example, all the legal residents of the State of Oregon on July 1, 1965, could be the basis of the following rather specific statistical populations, and many more:

(*a*) Their ages to the nearest tenth of a year.

(*b*) Their blood pH's in the usual unit of measure for this chemical characteristic.

(*c*) Their weights to the nearest tenth of a pound.

(*d*) Their pulse rates at 9:00 A.M. (PST).

(*e*) The gross annual incomes of all who were teachers in four-year colleges or universities and had been rehired in writing for the next school year.

(*f*) The political faiths of those at least 21 years of age, with Democrat = 1, Republican = 2, and Other = 3.

Note that each of these statistical populations is a collection of numerical measurements, not of people.

Once a statistical population has been defined unambiguously, it usually is of interest to highlight a few features of it by means of some summary numbers. If the objects, actions, or characteristics are merely to be classified in two or more categories and then the numbers in each class recorded, the data will be called *enumerative data.* For example, if insects are to be sprayed with some insecticide and the numbers Dead and Alive counted after a suitable waiting period, then probably the only summary number of interest would be the percent Dead, for this figure succinctly describes the effectiveness of an insecticide. If the percent Dead for the whole population involved is called p, then we say p is the *population parameter* which describes the potential effectiveness of that spray against the particular species of insect studied. This parameter, p, is sufficient to convey all the information wanted in this situation. For example, if one knows that a certain insecticide kills 95% of the houseflies that it hits, and if the lethal quality of the spray is the only matter of interest, then $p = 0.95$ gives this information fully. Put another way, one can expect that the chances are 95 out of 100 that a randomly chosen housefly sprayed with that particular spray will be killed. If some flies are killed, some are merely made moribund, and others are unaffected, one needs two parameters, namely p_1 = percent killed and p_2 = percent made moribund. Obviously, $100 - p_1 - p_2$ = percent unaffected by the spray. Now, to convey all the information needed about the population one parameter (p) is not sufficient, and two parameters (p_1 and p_2) are required. Such an enumerative population, or one with even more parameters, is called a *multinomial population*; a one-parameter population with p = percent killed is called a *binomial population*. More specific definitions of these two types of enumerative population will be given later.

If the objects or actions upon which a statistical population is based are described numerically by measuring something along a continuous scale of measurement, such as weights in ounces, prices in cents, yields of grain in bushels per acre, or breaking loads of concrete beams in pounds, each statistical population probably will be described by means of averages and measures of variability. Perhaps frequency distributions and graphs also will be employed. That is, one usually is concerned with the general level of the sizes of the numbers in the population and with their variability (or dispersion) around that general level of size. For example, intelligence quotients (I.Q.'s) of people are measured along an essentially continuous scale from 25 to 175, approximately. A psychologist might wish to know whether one group of people has, in general, a higher level of intelligence than another group. One way to express the level of intelligence is to compute an average I.Q. of some sort. The arithmetic mean and the median are two popular averages, but there are others, such as the midrange, the geometric mean, and the harmonic mean.

Even if the general level of intelligence in one group is higher than in another, as measured by I.Q.'s, there will be considerable variation within each group. Some individuals in the group with generally lower intelligence will have I.Q.'s higher than those of some members of the higher-intelligence group. Thus, any acceptable study of the levels of intelligence of two or more groups of people must consider not only apparent differences in general level of intelligence but also the variability within each group. Doing this correctly and efficiently is one of the purposes of statistical analysis.

One of the most common and useful measures of variability in a group of measurements taken on what is regarded as a homogeneous group of objects or actions is the *variance*, σ^2, or its square root, σ, which is called the *standard deviation*. These and other measures of variability will be considered in detail later.

The preceding statements may be illustrated by means of large sets of numerical measurements, which simulate actual statistical populations of numerical measurements. The population of Table 1.11 simulates some actual agronomic data taken during a study at Kansas State University. Several hundred differences in wheat yield between the Pawnee and Tenmarq varieties of wheat grown side by side on pairs of plots in a number of regions in Kansas were used as the starting point for the population. Thereafter, similar data were added in such quantity and in such a way that a population

TABLE 1.11.   FREQUENCY DISTRIBUTION TABLE FOR A NEAR-N(5, 4) POPULATION

X interval		Frequency of occurrence (f)	X interval		Frequency of occurrence (f)
10.8 to	11.2	2	4.3 to	4.7	268
10.2	10.6	10	3.8	4.2	244
9.6	10.0	18	3.3	3.7	210
9.0	9.4	34	2.8	3.2	166
8.4	8.8	61	2.3	2.7	127
7.8	8.2	104	1.8	2.2	104
7.2	7.7	127	1.2	1.6	61
6.8	7.1	166	0.6	1.0	34
6.3	6.7	210	0.0	0.4	18
5.8	6.2	244	−0.6	−0.2	10
5.3	5.7	268	−1.2	−0.8	2
4.8	5.2	287			

Total number in population: 2775

of 2775 measurements was produced, which closely conforms to what is called a *normal population* with a mean of $\mu = 5$ and a variance $\sigma^2 = 4$. Such a population is designated by the symbol N(5, 4). Obviously, this mass of 2775 numbers would be quite incomprehensible until it were summarized in some effective way. One helpful summary is obtained by grouping those 2775 numbers into relatively few classes of numbers and essentially considering all the numbers within any class as being at the midpoint of that class.

With a relatively large set of data one usually tries to form about twenty classes whose widths are about one fourth of the size of the standard deviation. When the numbers in a population are symmetrically arranged with respect to the mean, μ, as is true of any normal population, that μ should be at the midpoint of one of the classes, or there will be some distortion of the distribution curve. Minor adjustments in the lengths of the class intervals used may be advisable, if indicated by some trial-and-error preliminary groupings of the data. In the case of the 2775 numbers described above, the standard deviation is $\sqrt{\sigma^2} = \sqrt{4} = 2$, and one fourth of 2 is 0.5; hence this length of interval was tried with $X = 5$ at the midpoint of one interval. It appeared upon actual trial that an excessively large number of classes would result and that some of the end classes would have very few members of the population in them. For this reason a few of the classes at the extremes of the distribution were increased to a length of 0.6 instead of 0.5. Table 1.11 then was constructed by tallying the individual 2775 numbers into their proper classes and counting them. The frequencies, f's, are these counts for each of the classes.

The following features of the population can be noted in the table rather easily:

(*a*) The highest frequency of occurrence of measurements (X's) comes for the X interval which includes the true mean, $\mu = 5$.

(*b*) The class frequencies are smaller and smaller for measurements farther and farther from the population mean, and this decrease is symmetrical with respect to that mean.

(*c*) A high percent (near 95) of the whole population consists of numbers within two standard deviations ($=4$) of the mean ($=5$), and about two thirds of the members of the population are within one standard deviation ($=2$) of the mean, either way.

Thus, one can say that if a pair of adjoining plots of wheat, one Pawnee and the other Tenmarq, is chosen at random, the most probable difference in yield is $\mu = 5$ bushels per acre favoring Pawnee. Furthermore, large differences (and small differences) equally far from the most probable value, μ, are equally likely to occur. The likelihood of occurrence of such differences is closely related to the standard deviation, σ, in the normal population. This information is deducible either from the frequency distribution in Table 1.11 or from its graph in Figure 1.11. The graph was obtained by plotting the class frequencies over the midpoints of the class intervals, because all X's in an interval are considered, for computational purposes, to be at the midpoints of these intervals. Thereafter a smooth curve was drawn to fit these points as well as possible. This is approximately a normal curve with $\mu = 5$ and $\sigma^2 = 4$, so it is designated a near-N(5, 4) population.

The table and figure display, in general, three interesting features of this population of numbers, namely, its general form, its general level of magnitude, and the dispersion (or variation) of the individual measurements from the general level for the whole group. In other words, the Pawnee variety generally outyielded the Tenmarq variety by about 5 bushels per acre, but the differences in yield varied symmetrically by more than 6 bushels per acre in each direction from the mean, $\mu = 5$. Thus, the *form*, *level*, and *dispersion* of a statistical population are generally of interest, and are displayed to some degree by the frequency distribution table and its graph.

To emphasize the above statements additionally, consider the sketches in Figure 1.12 of other frequency distributions of populations.

The curve A indicates a preponderance of relatively small measurements but also the existence of a few relatively very large measurements. Some salary distributions are of this sort, as are insect counts under certain circumstances.

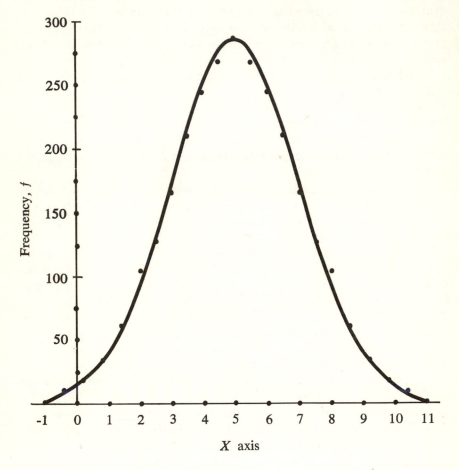

Figure 1.11. Frequency distribution for the population of Table 1.11.

The curve B is basically similar to A but has a preponderance of large numbers. Both A and B are decidedly nonsymmetrical in general form, but the *level* of measurement is much higher in B than in A. As far as these sketches show, there is approximately the same *dispersion* about the respective means.

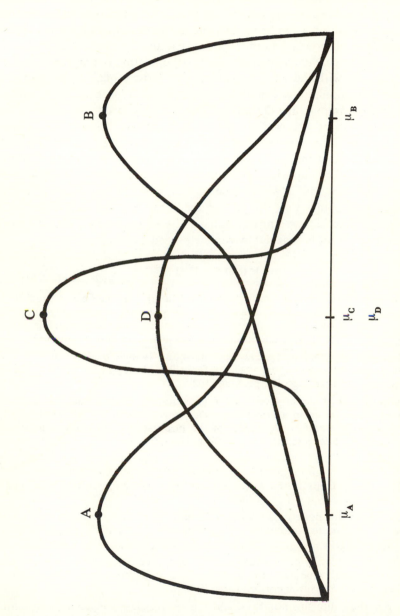

Figure 1.12.   Schematic comparison of populations with different forms, levels, and dispersions.

The curves C and D are symmetrical in *form* and differ in *dispersion* rather than in *level* of measurement.

In terms of the results of random observations on each of the four populations outlined by the graphs in Figure 1.12 one would judge that the most probable observation from A would be close to μ_A, but there is a sizable probability of observing a random X larger than μ_A because the total variability is quite large. Similar remarks hold for population B, the word "larger" being replaced with the word "smaller." The most probable observation is the same for populations C and D, but values of X near μ_D are much less probable from population D than are values near μ_C from population C on any specified future observation of these populations, because the variance of population C is much less than the variance of population D. Thus, it is again observed that the sizes of the population parameters, μ and σ^2 in this discussion, are very important in statistical studies of populations of numerical measurements. This is why so much time is devoted in statistics to studies of population parameters. In fact, if the form and the parameters of a statistical population are known, nothing else of importance remains to be learned that cannot be learned by routine procedures.

PROBLEMS

1. Suppose that an insecticide is known to kill 80% of the fleas it touches, to make another 10% of the fleas moribund, and not to noticeably affect the other 10%. Describe as best you can a statistical population which is appropriate for these results, and state the parameter(s) of this population.

2. Referring to Problem 1, class the moribund (which recover) and the unaffected as Alive, the others as Dead. Describe as best you can this population, and state what the specific parameter(s) are.

3. Suppose that grades on freshman compositions in English classes in a certain large university form a normal population with mean 60 and variance 144. What is the standard deviation of the population? Would you expect to find many grades less than 30 on those papers?

4. Suppose that the breaking loads of a certain type of concrete test beam are known to have approximately an N(550, 900) distribution. What would you expect the strength of the weakest beam to be, approximately? The strongest beam?

5. If a vaccine for polio is said to be 95% sure to produce immunity to Type III polio, how would you describe an appropriate corresponding population?

6. Suppose that a certain lake contains five million white bass. Describe four different statistical populations pertaining to these bass and based on continuous measurements. Also describe three different populations based on enumerative measurements on these bass.

7. Given the following numbers, make a twelve-class frequency distribution table: 4.7, 6.3, 3.6, 4.2, 7.8, 2.3, 4.7, 2.1, 1.6, 6.0, 4.6, 4.2, 3.3, 3.2, 7.6, 2.7, 5.3, 6.9, 6.4, 6.5, 4.7, 0.4, 2.4, 2.2, 7.1, 6.2, 5.7, 6.8, 4.7, 5.4, 2.9, 3.9, 6.6, 1.2, 4.0, 5.6, 2.5, 6.8, 7.3, 2.7, 7.1, 6.4, 4.9, 4.4, 7.1, 6.4, 6.0, 3.2, 6.4, 5.9, 7.1, 8.2, 4.2, 4.8, 5.0, 5.8, 2.2, 5.6, 4.2, 10.6, 5.8, 7.3, 5.9, 6.3, 4.0, 2.0, 4.7,

6.9, 4.8, 3.8, 5.8, 5.7, 6.9, 5.2, 4.9, 5.3, 7.4, 3.1, 5.6, 5.7, 9.0, 6.9, 2.6, 2.9, 3.2, 5.8, 3.2, 3.8, 8.0, 4.9, 3.2, 3.4, 5.6, 4.9, 4.3, 2.5, 5.1, 6.0, 5.3, 3.8, 2.8, 4.5, 5.0, 5.7, 5.5, 5.9, 7.8, 5.3, 6.5, 4.0, 2.7, 7.1, 4.5, 8.8, 0.8, 2.1, 8.2, 5.1, 8.2, 8.6, 2.7, 7.1, 2.6, 6.9, 4.1, 7.2, 4.0, 6.5, 5.3, 0.8, 2.8, 3.6, 5.0, 1.4, 10.2, 7.4, 2.7, 6.8, 3.7, 3.3, 4.0, 7.7, 3.8, 6.9, 2.7, 6.0, 1.8, 2.7, 3.5, 5.1, 3.0, 6.0, 10.4, 4.8, 8.6, 6.1, 5.4, 6.8, 2.5, 4.1, 5.4, 4.1, 6.2, 4.7, 7.9, 7.9, 4.3, 5.6, 3.1, 4.2, 3.8, 7.1, 5.4, 5.5, 2.5, 4.4, 8.4, 8.2, 5.6, 6.3, 6.9, 5.2, 8.0, 4.4, 5.6, 7.6, 5.4, 7.9, 4.7, 7.2, 3.5, 1.2, 4.0, 4.3, 5.4, 2.2, 6.0, 6.3, 3.9, 6.3, 5.1, 2.8, 3.5, 5.1, 4.9, 2.5, 8.4, 4.7, 6.7, 8.0, 5.2, 5.0, 2.4, 6.2, 7.2, 1.6, 3.3, 3.2, 3.9, 4.5, 4.4, −0.4, 7.6, 8.0, 3.5, 8.2, 3.5, 2.7, 7.9, 3.9, 5.5, 4.5, 7.4, 4.2, 6.2, 2.5, 8.8, 5.6, 7.1, 4.6, 7.3, 6.6, 7.8, 5.8, 3.7, 5.0, 6.4, 3.5, 5.2, 6.3, 6.5, 6.7, and 6.9.

8. Describe symbolically two normal populations which have the same level of measurement except that one of them has twice the variance of the other. Do the same with one population having twice the standard deviation of the other.

9. Describe symbolically two different normal populations, each of which should have about two thirds of its members between the limits 10 to 25. How many such populations would it be possible to define symbolically?

10. Do Problem 7 after adding 10 numbers in such a way as to move the high point of the frequency distribution curve noticeably to the right.

11. Do Problem 7 after adding 10 numbers in such a way as to decrease the level of measurement and also to make the frequency curve less symmetrical.

1.2 TYPES OF STATISTICAL POPULATIONS

It has been pointed out that a statistical population must be defined unambiguously before the concept of a population can become a useful part of experimental research. One way to accomplish this aim is to describe mathematical populations by means of a type name and a mathematical expression which includes those parameters of the population that measure level and dispersion. It usually is true that only a few parameters are needed to describe the form, level, and dispersion of a statistical population. The so-called normal population can be described in terms of its arithmetic mean (for level) and its variance (for dispersion). The symbol $N(\mu, \sigma^2)$ indicates that the population is normal in *form* (hence the N), has an arithmetic mean of μ to measure *level* (hence the μ), and has a variance of σ^2 to measure *dispersion* (hence the σ^2). *Any* normal population with these parameters is statistically identical with any other normal population having the same mean and variance, even though the numerical measurements for one population may be based on squirrels and the other on wheat plants. Thus, a great deal of powerful mathematical and statistical theory is brought to bear on many problems of experimental research. The student should try to visualize this subject as a general science in which his or her own special interests lose their particular identities and become special cases of the more general theory and methodology. In this way the trivial or less important aspects of a study which are not profitably studied statistically are sub-ordinated to the major features of the study.

With the preceding general background we shall now introduce in more detail three of the most important types of statistical populations: the *binomial*, the *multinomial*, and the *normal*.

When enumerative data are taken on objects or actions which fall into one of only two classes, a *binomial population* is involved. Its only parameter is *p*, the percentage of the objects which fall into a specified one of these two classes. For example, if a new fly spray truly will kill 90% of all houseflies on which it is sprayed, then $p_{\text{kill}} = 0.90$.

If experiments are performed on a binomial population, a *binomial frequency distribution* can be produced, at least in theory. Thus, the binomial frequency distribution is produced by sampling a binomial population by taking random samples of size *n*. The binomial frequency distribution thus potentially created is denoted by the symbol b(X; *n*, *p*). For example, if it is true that over many trials 90% of all houseflies which come in direct contact with a certain spray will be killed, this does not imply that exactly 90% will be killed on every experiment. If 50 houseflies are to be sprayed during the next experiment, there is no assurance that $X = 45$ flies will be found to have been killed, even though 45 is the most probable X. Obviously, it is quite likely that the number killed will be about 45, and it is extremely unlikely that no flies at all will be killed with such an effective spray, but the actual number, X, which will be killed is a matter of chance to a considerable degree. Mathematical formulas are available which give the relative frequencies with which certain outcomes of experiments of the type being discussed here will occur. The formula which gives the relative frequency with which X flies will be killed out of 50 sprayed with a certain spray which is 90% effective is as follows:

(1.21) $$\text{b}(X; 50, 0.90) = \frac{50!}{X!(50 - X)!} (0.90)^X (0.10)^{50-X}$$

There are tables, such as Romig's 50 − 100 binomial tables (Wiley, New York), which make it very easy to determine the relative frequency. To be specific, the data in Table 1.21 were obtained from Romig's table.

TABLE 1.21. BINOMIAL FREQUENCY DISTRIBUTION TABLE FOR A HYPOTHETICAL EXPERIMENT IN WHICH 50 HOUSEFLIES ARE TO BE SPRAYED WITH A SPRAY WHICH IS 90% EFFECTIVE IN KILLING SUCH FLIES

X (number killed):	0, 1, ⋯, 36	37	38	39	40	41
b(X; 50, 0.90) (rel. freq.):	(0 to 3 decimals)	0.001	0.002	0.006	0.015	0.033

X:	42	43	44	45	46	47	48	49	50
b(X; 50, 0.90):	0.064	0.108	0.154	0.185	0.181	0.139	0.078	0.029	0.005

In terms of percentages it is seen from this table that about 11% of the experiments in which 50 flies are sprayed will result in 43 flies killed among the 50 sprayed; about 15% of these experiments will produce 44 dead flies among the 50 sprayed during each experiment, 18 or 19% of the time 45 flies will be killed (and this is the most probable number), and very rarely will as many as 50 or as few as 40 flies be killed during one of these experiments. It is found by adding the approximate relative frequencies in the table that either the most probable number of flies (45) or within 2 of that number (namely, 43, 44, 46, or 47) will be killed in about 77% of any large number of

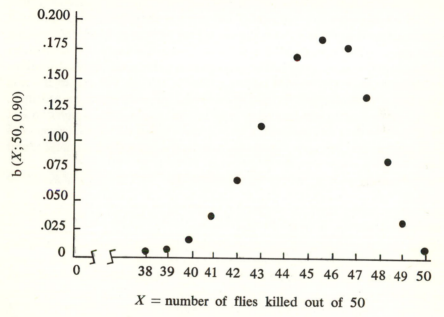

X = number of flies killed out of 50

Figure 1.21. Binomial frequency distribution resulting when a spray which is 90% effective in killing houseflies is sprayed on randomly selected groups of 50 houseflies.

such experiments. Hence, the observed number killed during even such a small experiment as one in which only 50 flies are used will produce a good estimate of the true percentage kill for the spray being tested.

The information shown in Table 1.21 may be given in graphic form, as is done in Figure 1.21. This graph indicates rather clearly that, although any number of flies from none to all fifty could be killed on, say, the next such experiment, it is extremely unlikely that fewer than 40 or as many as 50 will be killed, if the spray being used truly is 90% effective in the sense that over many trials exactly 90% of the flies so sprayed will be killed. The graph also illustrates the rather obvious fact that the "curve" for a binomial frequency distribution, $b(X; n, p)$, is really a set of discrete points; in fact, it consists of $n + 1$ such points, if n is the number of observations made on the *binomial population* during each experiment.

When enumerative data are taken on objects or actions which fall into three or more unique classes, the population is called *multinomial*. Two or more parameters are needed to describe such a population. In general, the number of parameters needed to describe a multinomial population is one less than the number of mutually exclusive classes into which the objects or actions fall. For example, if the members of a well-defined group of human beings in the age class of 21 to 60 years are asked an unambiguous question which they understand and can answer with Yes, No, or Undecided, their replies will fall into three classes. If p_1 is the percent of all replies which fall into the Yes category and p_2 is the percent of all replies which fall into the No category, the percent falling into the Undecided category obviously is $100 - p_1 - p_2$; therefore, the two parameters p_1 and p_2 with their definitions completely define this multinomial population. It does not matter if those answering Yes, No, or Undecided are Russians, aborigines in Australia, Kansas farmers, or well-trained porpoises: the multinomial population is a collection of symbols, say with $1 = $ Yes, $2 = $ No, and $0 = $ Undecided and with p_1 the percent of the symbols which are 1's, p_2 the percent of 2's, and $100 - p_1 - p_2$ the percent of 0's.

If the population of Table 1.11 and Figure 1.11 were truly a normal population, N(5, 4) the formula for its frequency distribution would be:

$$(1.22) \quad f_1 = \frac{1}{\sqrt{2\pi}\,\sigma} \exp\left[-\left\{\frac{(X - \mu)^2}{2\sigma^2}\right\}\right] = \frac{1}{2\sqrt{2\pi}} \exp\left[-\left\{\frac{(X - 5)^2}{8}\right\}\right]$$

The "exp" in the formula is the base for natural logarithms and is approximately $(1 + 1/n)^n$ for large n. The student can verify that exp $= 2.72$, approximately, by using $n = 100$. The π is the familiar ratio of the circumference of any circle to its own diameter and is approximately $3\frac{1}{7}$, or 3.14. It should be noted specifically here that the distribution function for this normal population involves only two parameters: $\mu = 5$ has to do with the general *level* of size of the measurements in the population, whereas the other parameter, $\sigma^2 = 4$, has to do with the *dispersion* of the measurements in the normal population about their own mean. The *form* of the population is *normal*. This implies symmetry about $\mu = 5$, a theoretically infinite extent each way, from $X = \mu = 5$, and a general bell shape.

If values of X are substituted into Formula 1.22, one obtains results such as those shown in Table 1.22. Referring to this table, one could plot f on the vertical scale against X on the horizontal scale and thereby obtain the graph of the frequency distribution curve for an N(5, 4) population. The fact that $f = 0.05$ when $X = 9$ and that $f = 0.02$ when $X = 10$ means, to the accuracy kept, that in an N(5, 4) population measurements in the neighborhood of $X = 9$ occur about two and one-half times as frequently as in the neighborhood of $X = 10$. This illustrates the concept of *population density* in the neighborhood of points. The symmetry of the normal frequency distribution about its mean also is shown by Table 1.22 and its graph, if plotted. It is noted that a random X chosen from an N(5, 4) population is most likely to be close to $\mu = 5$. It is much more likely to be within, say, 0.25 of $\mu = 5$ when $\sigma^2 = 4$ than it would be in the case of an N(5, 16) population, for which $\sigma^2 = 16$, because the latter population is much the more dispersed about its mean, $\mu = 5$.

TABLE 1.22.   SOME VALUES OF THE RELATIVE FREQUENCY
$f = 2f_1$ FOR N(5, 4)

X	f	X	f	X	f
10	0.02	6	0.35	2	0.13
9	0.05	5	0.40	1	0.05
8	0.13	4	0.35	0	0.02
7	0.24	3	0.24	-1	0.00

Formula 1.22 gives specifically the relative frequency with which values in the neighborhood of X occur in a population, but one may wish to know what proportion of a normal population lies between specified limits on X. For example, an agricultural economist might wish to know what proportion of all Kansas net farm incomes lay between $5000 and $10,000 per year during some interesting period of time. To obtain this sort of information it is necessary to construct a *cumulative frequency distribution* starting with the smallest X's. This sort of summarization was done to obtain Table 1.23

TABLE 1.23.   CUMULATIVE FREQUENCY DISTRIBUTION FOR A
NEAR-N(5, 4) POPULATION

X interval		Cumulative interval	Cum f as %	X interval		Cumulative interval	Cum f as %
4.3 to	4.7	-1.2 to 4.7	44.8	10.8 to 11.2		-1.2 to 11.2	100.0
3.8	4.2	,, 4.2	35.2	10.2	10.6	,, 10.6	99.9
3.3	3.7	,, 3.7	26.4	9.6	10.0	,, 10.0	99.6
2.8	3.2	,, 3.2	18.8	9.0	9.4	,, 9.4	98.9
2.3	2.7	,, 2.7	12.8	8.4	8.8	,, 8.8	97.6
1.8	2.2	,, 2.2	8.3	7.8	8.2	,, 8.2	95.5
1.2	1.6	,, 1.6	4.5	7.3	7.7	,, 7.7	91.7
0.6	1.0	,, 1.0	2.3	6.8	7.2	,, 7.2	87.2
0.0	0.4	,, 0.4	1.1	6.3	6.7	,, 6.7	81.1
-0.6	-0.2	,, -0.2	0.4	5.8	6.2	,, 6.2	73.6
-1.2	-0.8	,, -0.8	0.0	5.3	5.7	,, 5.7	64.8
				4.8	5.2	,, 5.2	55.2

from Table 1.11, based on the near-N(5, 4) laboratory population studied earlier. The first column shows the X intervals used to construct the frequency distribution table. The next column shows the cumulative interval, starting with the lowest measurement and including the highest measurement shown in the right-hand end of each cumulative interval. The cumulative frequency from the smallest measurement to the largest given at each right-hand end of an interval is shown, to save space, as a percentage of the total number in the population, 2775 in this case; it is abbreviated "Cum f as %."

Using the right-hand end point of the cumulative interval and the cumulative frequency column, one can read directly the percentage of the measurements in the population which are no larger than any particular end point in the table. For example, 95.5% of the population summarized in the table consists of numbers no larger than $X = 8.2$. Obviously, then, 4.5% of the numbers in this population exceed $X = 8.2$, because $100.0 - 95.5 = 4.5$. The cumulative frequency distribution of this table is shown graphically in Figure 1.22. The cumulative percent, such as 95.5, is plotted over the

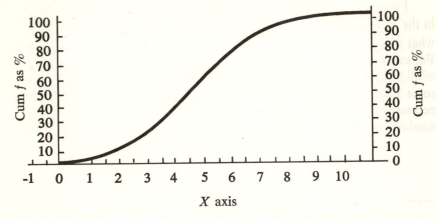

Figure 1.22.　Cumulative frequency distribution of Table 1.23.

largest number for that interval (namely, the 8.2 for percent = 95.5) for the obvious reason that it is only at the *end* of the interval that the frequency within the interval has all been accumulated.

A different normal population is defined with each different set of parameters, (μ, σ^2), simply by substituting different parameters into Formula 1.22. Apparently, this is a disadvantage to one studying normal populations, because it would be much more convenient if there were just one normal, so that one set of tables and graphs would serve for the study of any normal population. This ideal of one *standard normal population* can be attained easily by an algebraic procedure, which merely is a change of scales of measurement for X and its relative frequency, f_1, in Formula 1.22.

If all the X's in any normal population are measured as deviations from the population mean μ rather than from zero, as mankind usually measures, and if the units of measure along the X scale are expressed in multiples of the standard deviation σ, a *standard normal frequency distribution function* is obtained as follows. Let $\lambda = (X - \mu)/\sigma$ in Formula 1.22. This substitution produces the following formula:

$$f_1 = \frac{1}{\sqrt{2\pi}\,\sigma} \exp\left[-\left(\frac{\lambda^2}{2}\right)\right]$$

Hence,

(1.23)
$$f = \frac{1}{\sqrt{2\pi}} \exp\left[-\left(\frac{\lambda^2}{2}\right)\right]$$

where $f = \sigma f_1$, which corresponds to measuring the relative frequency in units of σ also.

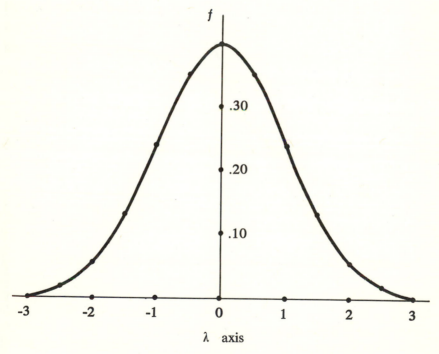

Figure 1.23.   Standard normal frequency distribution.

The standard normal distribution of this formula and the corresponding cumulative frequency distribution are shown in convenient tabular form in Table III for values of λ ranging from -3.0 to $+3.0$. Figures 1.23 and 1.24 present the frequency and cumulative frequency distributions for the standard normal, $N(0, 1)$. The student and the scientific researcher will have much to do with the standard normal distribution throughout almost any appreciable use of statistical methods and concepts.

If experiments are performed on a normal population such that random samples of size n are drawn from an $N(\mu, \sigma^2)$ population, the type of sampling distribution involved will depend upon the quantity which is computed from the sample. For example, if $\bar{x} = \sum(X)/n$ is computed, its distribution is known to be $N(\mu, \sigma^2/n)$, but if $t = (\bar{x} - \mu)/s_{\bar{x}}$ is computed, the distribution of t is something else. This is in contrast to binomial sampling. In binomial sampling usually the only matter of interest is the number of observations (X) which fall into a predetermined one of two possible classes. The sampling of normal and of binomial populations will occupy much of the discussion in this book.

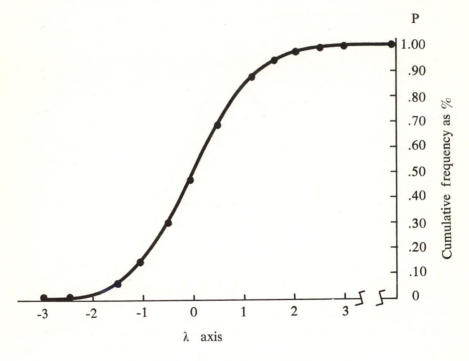

Figure 1.24.   Cumulative standard normal.

PROBLEMS

1. Use Table III to plot the standard normal frequency curve between $\lambda = -3$ and $\lambda = +3$. Check with Figure 1.23.
2. Use Table III to plot the graph of the cumulative normal distribution for the interval $-3 \leqslant \lambda \leqslant +3$. Check with Figure 1.24.

3. Use a sketch of the standard normal frequency distribution to show the percent of *any* normal population in the interval corresponding to $-0.7 \leqslant \lambda \leqslant +1.8$. Use Table III to put a precise percentage on your sketch.

4. Given that X is N(13, 4), what percentage of the population lies in the interval $10 \leqslant X \leqslant 14$? In the interval $14 \leqslant X \leqslant \infty$?

5. If a large number of grades constitute an N(70, 100) population and the instructor wishes to mark 10% "A", what is the actual grade range for an "A"? If he also will mark 25% of the grades "B", what is his entire grading scale for those numerical grades in terms of the usual letter grades A, B, C, D, and F?

6. Suppose that the heights of American males in the age range of 20 to 25 years, inclusive, and over a 50-year period of time are known to constitute an N(69, 9) population, measured in inches. If a person is to be selected at random from this group, all 50 years of those records being used, what is his most probable height? How likely is it that his height will be no more than 69 inches? What is the likelihood that his height will fall between 66 and 72 inches, inclusive?

7. Suppose that the accompanying graph truly represents the frequency distribution of a certain describable statistical population.

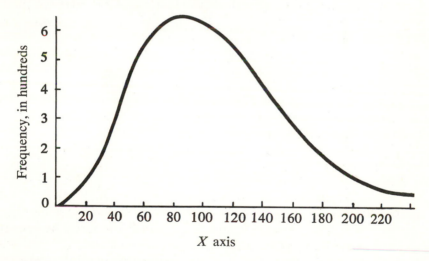

X axis

(a) What would you judge the mean X to be? What sort of a mean are you using?

(b) If an X is to be "drawn" (somehow) at random, what is its most probable size? Its least probable size?

(c) Is this frequency distribution normal? Symmetrical?

(d) What percentage of this population would you judge to have X's less than 60? Between 60 and 120? Greater than 180?

8. If two X's are to be drawn at random from the population whose frequency distribution curve is shown in Problem 7, then

(a) What would you judge is the likelihood that both X's will be greater than 180?

(*b*) What would you judge to be the most likely size of the arithmetic mean of the two *X*'s, where mean = $(X_1 + X_2)/2$?

(*c*) Would you expect the arithmetic mean of those two *X*'s to be as likely to exceed 140 as a single randomly chosen *X*?

1.3 THE SAMPLING OF POPULATIONS WITH UNKNOWN PARAMETERS

So far the discussion has been in the realm of descriptive statistics. It has entered the area of experimental, and sampling, statistics only for background. Although there are some situations in which purely descriptive statistics are needed, it is much more common to need statistical methods appropriate to sampling investigations of one sort or another. This usually is the case when experimental research is contemplated in which numerical measurements will be taken to describe some interesting object, action, or condition, because the results of the experiment usually are considered to be representative of some more general situation. For example, a medical scientist who is trying to develop a new serum of benefit to mankind will try it on a relatively small number of animals or people but will hope that the results so obtained will represent the usefulness of the serum in a much wider application of this drug. When an engineer tests the strengths of a few structural beams, he probably expects his results to be typical of a whole class of such beams. As a final example, if an entomologist or chemist tests the killing power of some toxic compound on houseflies raised in a laboratory, he expects the results to be applicable in people's homes. Thus, all such experiments are *sampling* studies, and it is very important to know:

(*a*) How to take the most useful samples

(*b*) How to draw the most complete but valid conclusions possible from the samples taken.

When an experimenter seeks to derive new knowledge from his research by drawing general conclusions from relatively few observations of some general situation, he is using an inductive rather than a deductive type of inference. Such inductive inferences cannot be exact; there must be some risk or error and some equivocalness in the conclusions drawn. The validation of uncertain inferences is the chief new feature of modern experimental statistics. If John has two apples and Bill has three apples, one can deduce that the two boys together have five apples, *for sure*. However, if John and Bill both become ill an appropriate length of time after attending a party at which some child broke out with the measles, one might *infer* that the two boys have measles, but until this philosophical inference is confirmed by a physician it is subject to being in error. One simply has concluded from previous observations that, when one child breaks out with the measles at a children's party, those attending who have not already had the measles have been exposed and will get the measles after a typical period of time for that disease. It might be said that one formulates a hypothesis when Bill and John get sick, and this hypothesis has to be checked against a diagnosis.

Even though experimental statistics is often regarded as a modern scientific development, it had its roots in the eighteenth century. A paper by Thomas Bayes was published in 1763 (after his death) under the title "An essay solving a problem in the doctrine of chances." This paper concerns the application of the theory of mathematical probability (an old deductive science) to the measurement of the acceptability of hypotheses about the sizes of the parameters of populations which have only been sampled. There was a long period of time between the publication of Bayes' paper and the turn of the twentieth century, when Karl Pearson and Student, in particular, initiated the concepts which have blossomed into modern sampling statistics. Nevertheless, there were isolated attempts to add to the theory of sampling statistics during the nineteenth century, all of which served as background for the rapid development of this science during the twentieth century up to the present time.

One very important field of inductive inference in statistics is the estimation of unknown population parameters. For example, an entomologist who is studying the lethality of a newly developed insecticide does not *know* its potential (true average) percent kill, or he would not be running tests constantly to determine precisely that information, so he conducts relatively small sampling trials to estimate the population parameter, p = true percent kill, for this insecticide. Or, an engineer measures the strengths of sample concrete beams, so he can economically but reliably predict the strengths of materials used in construction.

A second major field of inductive inference in statistics is that of testing reasonable hypotheses against experimental evidence. In statistical studies the hypotheses to be tested almost invariably pertain to the true values of population parameters, although the type of population involved might be the basis of the actual hypothesis tested by sample evidence. Every scientist doing experimental research tests hypotheses, one way or another. For example, if someone suggests that the addition of certain trace elements to the diet of a beef animal will improve its efficiency of gain and thus be of economic advantage, this can be the basis of testing a specific hypothesis regarding a population parameter, namely, the true mean average daily gain for that sort of beef animal under specified conditions and with trace elements added.

Before generally discussing methods of estimating population parameters or ways of testing hypotheses about them, some general points concerning sampling procedures need to be considered, because every decision based upon the evidence obtained from a sample obviously depends upon the adequacy of the sampling process used. Some of the intuitively obvious points about the taking of good samples are:

(*a*) The sample should be so taken that it has the best possible chance to reflect accurately the major features of interest in the population to be sampled. By definition, a sample is *of* something and should not distort the impression given of that something.

(*b*) All available information about the population to be sampled should be employed while the sampling is being planned, but no attempt should be made to cause the sample to reflect any opinions of the sampler.

(*c*) The sample should be taken in such a way that the most reliable and efficient procedures available for analyzing and interpreting sampling data become available for use after the data have been collected.

Suppose, now, that the population to be sampled is well defined, the facilities to handle a sample of size *n* are available, and a size of sample has somehow been determined to be appropriate for the study which is being planned. This means that *n* of the objects or actions which are to provide the basis of the statistical population are going to be measured or classified in some way, and those measurements are to be recorded as the sample from which the corresponding statistical population of measurements will be studied. Aside, possibly, from general information as to the type of population being sampled, the information in the sample is all the information available about the population. How should the specific objects or actions for the sample be chosen from among the whole group actually, or conceptually, available for study?

In order that systematic though unintentional errors may not be introduced by some special scheme of sampling that might occur to the investigator as, say, easiest to use, and in order that the laws of probability may be employed to validate the uncertain inferences which must be made, it is suggested that a *randomized sample* be drawn. A *simple random sample* is defined as any sample so taken that every conceivable sample of that same size initially had the same chance to be drawn from the population to be sampled. For example, suppose that you wished to draw a simple random sample of the registered voters in Oceanside, California, as of October 20, 1965. If the name of each registered voter in that city on that date were to be written on a suitable piece of plastic material and all such objects mixed thoroughly in some container, a simple random sample would be drawn by taking *n* of those pieces from the container without any selection. It seems impossible to believe that under these rules every possible sample of size *n* would not have the same chance to be drawn; hence, we would feel that a simple random sample had been taken. On the other hand, if some of the names were to be omitted, some were to be put in more than once, or the drawer of the sample made any sort of deliberate selection during his drawing, it would not be a random sample. The use of a suitable material, such as the plastic disc, is advisable because such materials as pieces of paper are virtually unmixable, the names tending to stay among those into which they fell.

The true nature of random sampling is made clearer if a few cases of nonrandom and nonsimple random sampling are pointed out.

(*a*) In a certain town there are 1000 persons registered to vote in the next election, and a pollster wishes to study a 10% (100 in this case) sample from the alphabetical list of registered voters. He starts at random among the first ten names and then takes every tenth name thereafter. Is this simple random sampling? No, because only persons whose names are exactly nine names apart on the listing can possibly be in the same sample; therefore, many possible samples could not occur at all, which certainly means that all samples do not have an equal chance to be drawn.

(*b*) A newspaper prints and distributes a ballot which readers are encouraged to fill out and return to the newspaper office. Theoretically, every reader has an equal chance to vote and, if every voter did vote, this would not be a sample at all. Because all voters will not vote and because some potential voters in the area probably do not even take this paper, a *subset* of the potential voters will be obtained. Moreover, only the more eager will vote, some will not know of the voting opportunity, and some will vote more than once. So this obviously is not a procedure for obtaining a simple random sample or even an unbiassed sample of any sort.

Circumstances may make it unwise to take a simple random sample. It may be preferable, instead, to attempt to increase homogeneity within the subsets defined by doing some prior grouping of the objects or actions whose measurements will produce the population. For example, it might be advisable to group the Oceanside voters into four classes, male Democrats, female Democrats, male Republicans, and female Republicans, and then, within each subset, to take a simple random sample. These voters also might be preclassified regarding age, religion, occupation, and many other socio-logical, economic, or political classes. For convenience, we shall use the term "random sample" whenever simple random sampling is done within each of any predefined subgroups pertaining to the population to be created and sampled.

PROBLEMS

1. Suppose that a college newspaper editor wishes to sample student opinion on a certain campus matter. This editor stands on the front steps of the journalism building and asks 50 students chosen "at random" for their answer—Yes, No, or Undecided—to a specific question. Criticize this method of sampling student opinion. What population might this editor be sampling? If he stood in front of the campus post office where all the students went to get their mail, would he be doing better? Would his method now be free of fault in your opinion?

2. Suppose you wish to sample a lake to determine the form, level, and dispersion of the population of the weights of its black bass. How would you direct that the sampling be done, if 500 fish can be examined and you have the resources to obtain these fish in whatever way you think best?

3. Suppose that you have charge of the sampling of the water in a public swimming pool and are to determine whether it is safe in terms of numbers of

certain specific bacteria. This pool is 100 feet by 300 feet, and has an inlet at the south end and an outlet at the north end. How would you have the sampling done? What sort of population would you consider you were sampling?

4. Suppose that you are charged with the responsibility of sampling the grass in the outfield of a certain baseball diamond to see whether it is seriously infested with grubs around the roots. You are allowed to take out twenty-five 1 foot by 1 foot pieces of the sod. How would you choose the places to take these twenty-five sections of sod for inspection?

5. You are asked to sample the milk produced by a certain dairy, to learn whether it contains specific dangerous bacteria. How would you do this sampling?

1.4 ESTIMATION OF POPULATION PARAMETERS BY MEANS OF SAMPLES

It already has been said that statistical populations are characterized by their general *form* (or type, such as normal or binomial), by the general *level* (or magnitude) of measurement within the population, sometimes by the dispersion (scatter or variability) of the measurements in the population about their general level of size, and sometimes by other features. These characteristics of entire populations are measured by means of numbers called *parameters*. There are many conceivable ways by which those relatively fixed features described by population parameters might be estimated from sampling data. Therefore, some criteria must be adopted for choosing the best method of estimation for any given situation. When a sampling situation has been specified clearly, an appropriate general type of statistical population to fit that sampling situation often will suggest itself, but the parameters will be unknown. For example, when almost anything is measured along a continuous scale of measurement under conditions which assure that errors of measurement and of sampling are about as likely to go one way as the other from the true mean measurement, and if it seems likely that the most common measurements are those close to the true mean, one often can assume that a normal population is going to be sampled. Or, if some objects or actions are merely to be classified into two unique classes and counted, and if it seems assured that the potential proportions in those two classes are likely to stay fixed during the experimenter's interest in this situation, one can assume that in all likelihood a binomial population is being sampled. In each case, however, the parameters of the populations will be unknown and must be estimated from the evidence in a sample.

Some of the desirable features which usually should be embodied in the criteria for good estimators of parameters are the following:

(*a*) All the pertinent information available in the sample should be utilized.

(*b*) The estimation procedure to be used should assure estimates which are as unaffected by accidents of sampling (i.e., sampling error) as it is possible to attain. That is, the estimator of the parameter should have potentially low sampling variation.

(*c*) The estimation procedure should be as simple to use as is consistent with (*a*) and (*b*) above.

(*d*) Theoretically, if the procedure for estimating a population parameter were to be repeated many times, the mean of those estimates should coincide with the size of the parameter they are estimating or be a known function thereof. Otherwise, the estimates would be biassed to an unknown degree and, hence, might be useless.

Actually, the four points just listed need to be stated more mathematically before they can be fully useful. It would be going beyond the scope of this course to do so rigorously, but some clarification will be given later. These points embody some of the concepts to be borne in mind with regard to good estimators of population parameters. Estimates of population parameters often are called *statistics*. Their meaning now will be clarified by examples.

Suppose that the ten numbers 4, 8, 11, 3, 6, 5, 14, 7, 10, and 7 constitute a random sample from a well-defined population which can be assumed to be of the normal type. As is well known even without a previous course in statistics, the most popular average to compute as a summary measurement for a group of numbers is the arithmetic mean, commonly called the mean or the *average*, for simplicity. This sort of average is obtained by summing all the numbers and dividing this sum by the size, n, of the group ($n = 10$ in this example). The result is $\bar{x} = 75/10 = 7.5$. The sample mean, $\bar{x}$, is defined symbolically by

$$\bar{x} = \frac{\sum_{i=1}^{n} (X_i)}{n}$$

or, for brevity,

(1.41) $$\bar{x} = \sum (X)/n$$

where the X's are the measurements in the sample taken in their order of observation so that X_1 is the first observation (4, in the above sample), etc., until X_{10} is the tenth and last observation (the second 7 in the above sample). Formula 1.41 merely describes in symbols the arithmetic process used to obtain $\bar{x} = 7.5$.

With a normal population, whose distribution is symmetrical about μ, another possible estimator for μ is the *midrange* (MR). It is defined as the mean of the smallest and the largest members of the sample. For the sample used above,

$$MR = (3 + 14)/2 = 8.5$$

A third average, which is used to estimate a population mean, is called the *median* and is denoted by the symbol md. This estimator is defined from what is called an *ordered array* of the numbers whose median is to be calculated. After the *n* numbers have been arranged in order of size, either ascending or descending, the median is defined as the $[(n + 1)/2]$th number in that array, or computed from that array. If *n* is an odd integer, the median will be the middle number in the array, but if *n* is even, the median will be the mean of the two "middle" numbers in the array. For example, if $n = 10$, the fifth and sixth numbers in the array are the "middle" numbers. For the sample above we have the following:

Ordered array: 3, 4, 5, 6, 7, 7, 8, 10, 11, 14
Corresponding order numbers: 1 2 3 4 5 6 7 8   9 10

TABLE 1.41. SAMPLING DISTRIBUTIONS OBTAINED FOR $\bar{x}$ AND MR ON 1000 RANDOM SAMPLES, EACH OF SIZE $n = 10$, FROM A NEAR-N(5, 16) POPULATION

Class interval for $\bar{x}$ and MR		Observed frequencies of occurrence	
		of $\bar{x}$	of MR
10.25 to	10.74	0	1
9.75	10.24	0	2
9.25	9.74	0	3
8.75	9.24	1	10
8.25	8.74	3	14
7.75	8.24	18	33
7.25	7.74	16	30
6.75	7.24	39	80
6.25	6.74	84	52
5.75	6.24	114	96
5.25	5.74	131	85
4.75	5.24	160	158
4.25	4.74	152	87
3.75	4.24	118	101
3.25	3.74	74	64
2.75	3.24	48	81
2.25	2.74	25	33
1.75	2.24	8	39
1.25	1.74	4	10
0.75	1.24	4	13
0.25	0.74	0	6
−0.25	0.24	1	2
Total:		1000	1000
Mean of 1000 estimates:		4.97	4.94
Variance of 1000 estimates:		1.69	3.16

By definition, the median is the average of the two sevens, so md = 7. Notice that the median is the mean of the fifth and sixth numbers in the ordered array; it is *not* the mean of 5 and 6, as students sometimes conclude.

Three possible estimators of the population mean (μ) now have been suggested. Which of the estimators $\bar{x}$, md, and MR is the best among those three? The answer to this sort of question depends somewhat upon the type of population which was sampled, so we shall assume a normal population in the discussion to follow.

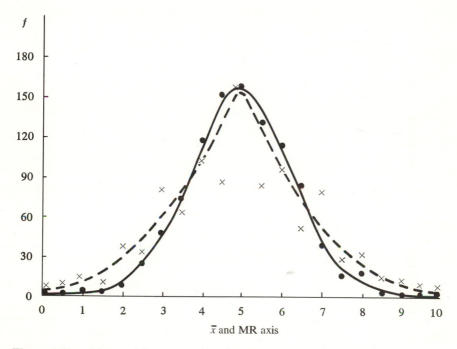

Figure 1.41.   Observed frequency distribution curves of 1000 $\bar{x}$'s and MR's from N(5, 16), $n = 10$: —•— = $\bar{x}$, --x-- = MR.

In the light of the criteria, suggested above, of good estimators of parameters, it appears intuitively that the $\bar{x}$ directly uses more of the information available in the sample than either of the other two, because it uses all the numbers and uses their actual sizes, whereas both the md and the MR do not fully use the actual sizes of all the numbers. One could change the numbers greatly, including their general level of size, without changing the md and the MR. On the other hand, the MR is easier to compute than either the $\bar{x}$ or the md. What about the consistency with which sizes of $\bar{x}$, md, and MR from samples will be close to μ? Table 1.41 gives some empirical information on this question by showing the sampling distributions of $\bar{x}$ and

MR as obtained from 1000 random samples, each of size $n = 10$, from a near-N(5, 16) population. The sampling distribution of the median was omitted from this table to simplify the comparison and because it is intermediate between those of $\bar{x}$ and MR with respect to its sampling variation. The table shows the numerical frequency distributions of $\bar{x}$ and MR; Figure 1.41 presents the distribution curves. Although nothing is proved by tables or graphs, the following conclusions appear justified by the table and the figure.

(a) Both sampling distributions are reasonably symmetrical about the true mean, $\mu = 5$.

(b) The sampling distribution of the $\bar{x}$'s is less erratic than that of MR. There is more concentration of the $\bar{x}$'s near the modal class (4.75 to 5.24) than there is of the other estimator, and the graph of the sampling mean is noticeably smoother than that of the midrange. This is saying that the $\bar{x}$ from a random sample from an N(5, 16) population is more likely to be close to 5 than is the MR (or the md).

The chief feature which distinguishes $\bar{x}$ from the other two estimators of μ is the greater consistency with which the $\bar{x}$ estimates fall near the parameter each is estimating. This feature of estimators is not easily assessed by casual observation of graphs and tables, so it is measured numerically by the sampling variance of each estimator. We shall look first at the sampling variances of the three estimators as computed from the 1000 samples of Table 1.41 and Figure 1.41, which involved samples of size $n = 10$. The computation of this variance was accomplished by (effectively) subtracting the mean for the $\bar{x}$'s, 4.97, from each of the 1000 observed $\bar{x}$'s, squaring these differences, and dividing the sum of those squared differences by 1000. A similar process was applied to the sample midranges. It was learned that the variances are 1.69 and 3.16 for $\bar{x}$ and MR, respectively. The fact that $\bar{x}$ has the lower variance (and this is theoretically true also) means that on any future random sample the estimate of μ obtained from $\bar{x}$ has a higher probability of being near to the true mean it is estimating than does the estimate of μ obtained from the MR. It is customary, therefore, to say that $\bar{x}$ is a more efficient estimator of μ than is MR.

Summarizing the preceding discussion of the three estimators, it is seen that with respect to all the criteria suggested for good estimators, except ease of computation, the sample mean is at least as good as the others and is more efficient than they. Of course, this heuristic sort of reasoning is supplemented by mathematical proof in more advanced courses. The student should note, though, that when viewed in the right light and with some thought the desirable properties of the estimators of parameters suggested above simply are what common sense would demand, namely, that (a) the estimator should not distort the true situation by producing estimators which do not average to the true value of the parameter or to some *known* function thereof, (b) the estimator should be as unaffected by sampling error as possible, and (c), a point not emphasized before, the usefulness of the estimator probably should increase with sample size, for usually the acquisition of more evidence should improve the estimate obtained.

PROBLEMS

1. Suppose the following numbers are the heights of the basketball players on a certain university squad, expressed to the nearest tenth of a foot: 6.9, 5.8, 6.3, 6.3, 6.7, 7.1, 6.7, 6.5, 6.6, 5.9, 6.0, 6.1, 6.4, 6.4, and 6.4.
   (a) Put these numbers into an ordered array and determine their median.
   (b) Compute their midrange (MR) and their arithmetic mean ($\bar{x}$).
   (c) Compute $\sum_{i=1}^{15} (X_i - \bar{x})$ and $\sum_{i=1}^{15} (X_i - \bar{x})^2$.
   (d) Compute $\sum_{i=1}^{15} |X_i - \bar{x}|$, which means to take all $X_i - \bar{x}$ as positive.
   (e) Determine the mode (MO) of these heights, where MO = most frequent measure.
   (f) Which of the averages MR, md, $\bar{x}$, and MO does it seem to you is the most nearly representative of these heights?

2. Suppose that the accompanying sketches are of the sampling distributions of three different sample averages, A_1, A_2, and A_3, estimating the same population parameter, θ.

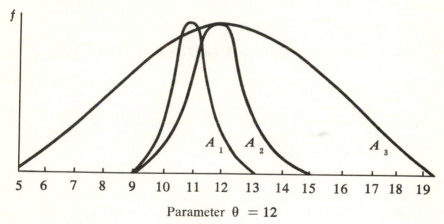

Parameter $\theta = 12$

   (a) Which estimators are unbiassed?
   (b) Which estimator has the greatest sampling variance, in your opinion? Which has the least variance?
   (c) Estimate from the sketch how likely it is that a random sample will produce an A_2 greater than 12. Greater than 14. At least one unit larger than θ.
   (d) Which estimator would you recommend the most highly? Why?

3. Suppose that an insecticide which is *known* to be 95% effective in killing mosquitoes is sprayed on a random sample of 500 mosquitoes, and 460 are killed.
   (a) What is the specific size of the parameter, p?
   (b) What is the specific size of the estimate, $\hat{p}$, of p?
   (c) If a manufacturer merely *claimed* his insecticide was 95% effective on mosquitoes in terms of kill and you obtained the $\hat{p}$ requested in part (a),

would you believe his claim? What if only 440 out of the 500 were killed? At what figure for $\hat{p}$ would you definitely cease to believe the claim of 95% effectiveness? Why?

4. Suppose that the accompanying graphs represent the frequency distributions of three different statistical populations:

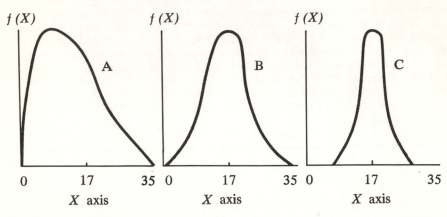

(a) For which population would you expect the sample mean, $\bar{x}$, to be the most reliable estimator of μ? Why?

(b) For which populations would you expect the sample MR to be an unbiassed estimator of μ?

(c) For which populations would you expect the sample values of $s^2 = \sum_{i=1}^{n} (X_i - \bar{x})^2/(n - 1)$ to be the least variable?

5. If a large number of samples, each of size $n = 9$, were to be drawn at random from population B of Problem 4, which of the accompanying graphs would you select as most nearly representative of the sampling distribution of the $\bar{x}$'s to be obtained from those samples? Why?

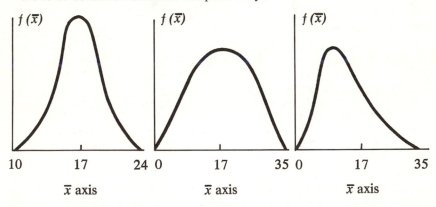

6. If a random sample of size $n = 50$ is to be drawn from N(3.8, 0.81), which of the following is the most likely to occur, in each case separately?

(a) An $\bar{x}$ less than 1.1 or an $\bar{x}$ larger than 4.0?

(b) An $\bar{x}$ closer to 3.8 than the md is, or vice versa?

(c) An MR closer to 3.8 than the $\bar{x}$ is, or vice versa?

7. Sketch what you think would be a reasonable graph of the sampling distribution of $\bar{x}$ for samples of size $n = 16$ from an N(5, 16) population.

8. An unbiassed coin is going to be tossed 100 times; what is your best guess of the number of heads which will be tossed? What would you think if heads appeared on 75 of the tosses?

9. If the coin of Problem 8 were so biassed that heads appeared three times as often as tails, how would you answer the questions of Problem 8?

10. Suppose two dice are to be tossed 100 times. What is your estimate of the number of *sums* of 7 which will be thrown? If the outcomes of the tosses in terms of sums on the two dice are classified as less than 5, as 6 or 7 or 8, or as greater than 8, what type of population is involved? What can you say about the relative frequencies in these classes?

1.5   TESTING HYPOTHESES BY MEANS OF SAMPLES

As noted earlier, a second broad area of experimental statistics besides the estimation of parameters is that of testing hypotheses regarding population parameters. The idea of formulating and testing hypotheses about currently unknown situations is not unique to statistics: it is characteristic of the scientific method of research. For many years scientists have been formulating and testing hypotheses in some manner. Perhaps the relatively new feature of this process for deriving new knowledge is the way the theory of probability and the concepts of statistics are used to determine whether a proposed hypothesis is acceptable in the face of experimental evidence on the matter.

Everyone's everyday life is full of examples of hypotheses about existing conditions. For example, the following statements embody hypotheses:

"A majority of registered Republicans want Mr. X as presidential candidate."

"The poor vote Democratic, the rich vote Republican."

"Gentlemen prefer blondes."

"Wrapping sweet corn ears in cellophane will increase the net profit per ear."

"The youth of today are less physically fit than those of the previous generation."

Each of these "hypotheses" is a statement which some people believe, but which usually has not been established as reasonable. Each, however, could be the subject of a careful statistical study after being put in more precise form.

To illustrate hypothesis testing more specifically, suppose an agriculturalist wishes to learn whether some stated amount of agricultural lime will neutralize a certain type of acid soil. It is already known that liming in *some* amount will do so, but the process of liming and the process of measuring the pH of the soil to see whether it has been neutralized are subject to accidents of sampling. Soils are not perfectly uniform, and man and his measuring devices do not perform perfectly. As a result of the unpredictable errors of measurement, it seems reasonable to assume that the pH readings will be a random sample from a normal population with a mean of 7 (neutral pH), *provided the soil has been made neutral as a result of the liming.*

Suppose, now, that on 10 plots of soil, which represent a certain soil type and have been limed as recommended, the following pH readings were obtained: 6.5, 6.8, 7.2, 6.8, 7.3, 7.7, 6.6, 7.2, 7.4, and 7.2, in the customary units. Is it now reasonable to believe that the population of which these ten numbers are a random sample has a true mean pH = 7? Or, in more appropriate statistical terminology, is the hypothesis $H_0(\mu = 7)$ acceptable or not?

When one is considering the acceptability of a proposed hypothesis, one must also consider what the alternative is to acceptance of that hypothesis. Sometimes the alternative hypothesis is merely the negation of the proposed hypothesis. If the hypothesis "A majority of registered Republicans want Mr. X as presidential candidate" is not acceptable in view of available evidence, the alternative seems obviously to be that less than a majority want him as their presidential candidate. However, the hypothesis "wrapping sweet corn ears in cellophane will increase the net profit per ear" might well have either of two alternatives: either "this process has no effect at all on net profit" or "this process reduces the net profit per ear." It will be seen later that the alternative hypothesis to that being tested must be clearly stated before a dependable testing procedure can be devised.

The mean pH of the hypothetical sample is $\bar{x} = 7.1$, which may indicate slight alkalinity; that is, the liming may have been overdone a bit. If this seems to someone to be a negligible indication of alkalinity, how would he feel about the following sample, presumably from the same population: 7.0, 7.0, 7.0, 7.1, 7.1, 7.1, 7.1, 7.1, 7.0, and 7.1? This sample has *exactly* the same mean as the previous sample. Would the greater uniformity of the second sample of pH readings and the fact that all 10 soil samples were either neutral or alkaline alter the decision to be made? Such questions are in the field of testing statistical hypotheses by means of sampling data. There are existing statistical procedures which help one to decide whether or not a proposed hypothesis is acceptable in view of available sampling evidence.

There are no statistical procedures which will prove or disprove a hypothesis, because sampling data are always subject to error. Nothing can remove all risk of error, when decisions are made from sampling evidence, but the probability of error can be measured and expressed. This fact makes statistical methods of reasoning highly useful tools in scientific research.

Referring briefly again to the illustration regarding soil pH, the student might be surprised to learn that, upon the basis of the most powerful statistical methods available, the hypothesis that the limed soil now is neutral, or that $H_0(\mu = 7)$, is readily acceptable following the first sample discussed above, but from the evidence in the second sample, this same hypothesis would be rejected decisively. In view of the equality of the observed sample means of the two samples, the difference between these two decisions must be the consequence of the difference in variability displayed by the two samples.

If one is sampling populations produced by enumeration under specified conditions, he also may wish to test an interesting and important hypothesis of some sort. For example, a gambler might wish to test a coin to see whether it will turn up heads or tails equally frequently. He tosses the coin fairly 200 times and obtains 110 tails. How does he decide whether this was a sampling accident or an indication that the coin is biassed toward tails? This is a statistical problem of testing the hypothesis that the true proportion of tails is 0.50, that is, of testing $H_0(p_T = 0.50)$. Obviously, even with an unbiassed coin, the result of 200 flips will rarely be exactly 100 heads and 100 tails, so it must be recognized that the number of tails on 200 flips will have a sampling distribution. In general, the distribution of the number of tails to be observed after any coin is flipped n times will depend on the trueness of the coin and the number, n, of flips.

It should be noted from the two preceding examples (and also from a general consideration of experimental research) that one is attempting to make some decisions about population parameters upon the basis of the admittedly uncertain evidence to be found in random samples. This procedure of decision-making is necessary, because sample evidence obviously is all that one can obtain under the conditions of experimental research, which seeks to produce new knowledge. Nevertheless, it must be recognized that risks and possible losses, as well as gains, are involved. For example, consider again the hypothetical experiment on the neutralization of a soil by applying lime. Lime costs money, so you do not wish to overdo it and thus waste money. However, there presumably is something valuable to be gained by neutralizing soil under certain circumstances, or agronomists would not attempt it. With either of the samples used earlier for illustration, the soil actually and truly could have been neutral after the lime had been used. However, with the first sample described the hypothesis $H_0(\mu = 7)$ was accepted as reasonable, so the experimenter probably would have concluded that he used the correct amount of lime. But if the decision were to be made after the results of the second experiment were analyzed, the experimenter would conclude that the liming had been overdone, so he could cut down on the amount of lime applied and thus save some money. This sounds fine, but what if this decision actually is wrong because the sample had by chance misled the experimenter? In this event the reduced amount of lime would leave the soil too acid for optimum crop production, and this loss of yield might well more than offset the money saved on lime.

There are, therefore, two types of error one could make in using sample data to test hypotheses: one can reject a true hypothesis or one can accept a false hypothesis. It is customary to give these possible errors names as follows:

Type I error: to reject a true hypothesis
Type II error: to accept a false hypothesis

For example, rejection of the hypothesis that a certain coin is unbiassed when, in fact, it *is* unbiassed, is a Type I error, whereas the acceptance of the hypothesis that a certain coin is unbiassed when, in fact, it is *not* unbiassed is a Type II error.

In practice one rarely, if ever, knows whether a decision made from the evidence obtained from an experiment, no matter how well run, is correct or is misleading. There must be a balancing of the possible losses and gains from Type I and Type II errors in consideration of their probabilities of occurrence. These obviously are statistical problems.

PROBLEMS

1. Suppose that the accompanying graphs are those of the frequency distributions of two normal populations, as indicated:

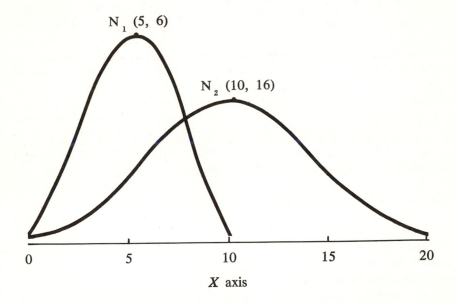

(*a*) From which population is a sample of size $n = 10$ with mean $\bar{x} = 15$ most likely to be drawn? What about the likelihood of $\bar{x} = 10$? Of $\bar{x}$ less than 5?

(b) Which of the following is the more likely to occur: an $\bar{x}$ between 6 and 14 from population N_2 or an $\bar{x}$ between 1 and 9 from population N_1?

(c) If $\bar{x}$ turns out to be 7, which of the hypotheses $H_{01}(\mu = 5)$ or $H_{02}(\mu = 12)$ would you consider the more acceptable, if you knew only that the sample came from some normal population? What if, in addition to normality, you knew only that both populations had variances of 25? Variances of 4?

2. Suppose that it is believed that 40% of all white American citizens have type A blood, and you wish to test this belief by drawing a random sample of size $n = 100$ in a supposedly "typical" American city.

(a) What specific H_0 would you test?

(b) If you reject the H_0 of (a), what do you conclude? If you accept that H_0, what do you conclude?

(c) Suppose that someone conjectures that 43% of all white American citizens have type A blood. Is it possible that this hypothesis and the one of part (a) both would seem acceptable after the sample were drawn? If you drew a sample of 1000 instead of 100, would this tend to help make the choice between $H_{01}(p_A = 0.40)$ and $H_{02}(p_A = 0.43)$ easier?

3. Take a quarter and put a thick area of glue on the tails side near the rim. Flip this coin 100 times, let it fall on a flat hard surface, and record the number of heads. On the assumption that you do not know the glue is on this coin, does $H_0(p_H = 0.50)$ seem acceptable in view of your sampling result? Toss this same coin another 100 times, add these results to those obtained before, and answer the same question. Continue this process until you have $n = 500$ tosses, and then answer the same question.

4. Suppose that a geneticist believes that brown and white coloring in guinea pigs is so inherited that, if brown males are mated to white females, an off-spring designated in advance is equally likely to be brown or white. What specific H_0 should he use when testing this hypothesis? Suppose, on the other hand, this geneticist believes that the probability of a brown offspring is three times as large as for a white offspring; what H_0 would he use? If guinea pigs are born in litters of from 2 to 6 pigs each, would he have to consider the possibility that pigs within the same litter might tend to be all the same color?

5. Suppose that under the general conditions of Problem 4 one has two distinct lines of guinea pigs which have been developed for generations in two different laboratories. What H_0 would this geneticist test to learn whether the two lines were identically alike with regard to the inheritance of brown and white hair colors? Would $H_0(p_{B1} = p_{B2})$ be the same as testing $H_{01}(p_{B1} = 0.50)$ and $H_{02}(p_{B2} = 0.50)$ separately?

1.6 SAMPLING DISTRIBUTIONS

Although quite a bit has been said or implied about them already, the concepts of sampling error and of sampling distributions will be considered a bit more fully, because much of the theory and practice of sampling statistics depends upon these concepts. Any number computable from some or all of the numbers to be obtained from a future sample is called *a statistic* and has a sampling distribution. The usefulness of this statistic depends on its sampling distribution, upon the ingenuity of the statistician and experi-menter, and upon the sampling situation, but *no* statistic is useful unless and until its sampling distribution is known, no matter how ingenious anyone may be.

Given a sampling situation for a well-defined population, much of the decision-making done from sample data is based upon the concept of a sampling distribution. This sampling distribution simply is a description, usually in a mathematical form, of the whole class of such statistics which conceptually could be obtained if this same sampling were to be continued indefinitely under the conditions which defined the population originally. Table 1.61 presents the results of such a sampling process continued for 1250 samples. A laboratory population with 2775 numbers on 2775 plastic discs was constructed to conform as nearly as possible to an $N(5, 16)$ population. Samples of size $n = 10$ were drawn at random from this population and the range, R, and the function, $G = (\bar{x} - \mu)/R$, were computed for each sample. For example, the first sample drawn could have been the following, also drawn at random from that same $N(5, 16)$ population:

$$X_i: \quad 11.0, \ 7.8, \ 6.2, \ 13.4, \ -0.2, \ -1.4, \ 4.2, \ -4.2, \ 2.2, \ \text{and} \ 2.2$$

The smallest number in this particular random sample from $N(5, 16)$ is -4.2

TABLE 1.61.   SAMPLING DISTRIBUTIONS OF THE SAMPLE RANGE, R, AND OF THE FUNCTION, $G = (\bar{x} - \mu)/R$, AS OBSERVED ON 1250 RANDOM SAMPLES OF SIZE $n = 10$ FROM $N(5, 16)$

R class		Frequency	G class		Frequency
23.5 to 24.9		1	0.358 to 0.412		1
22.0	23.4	4	0.303	0.357	8
20.5	21.9	10	0.248	0.302	15
19.0	20.4	17	0.193	0.247	39
17.5	18.9	39	0.138	0.192	73
16.0	17.4	89	0.083	0.137	122
14.5	15.9	107	0.028	0.082	232
13.0	14.4	204	-0.027	0.027	260
11.5	12.9	253	-0.082	-0.028	220
10.0	11.4	235	-0.137	-0.083	143
8.5	9.9	140	-0.192	-0.138	77
7.0	8.4	101	-0.247	-0.193	35
5.5	6.9	42	-0.302	-0.248	16
4.0	5.4	8	-0.357	-0.303	5
	Total f:	1250	-0.412	-0.358	2
			-0.467	-0.413	1
			-0.522	-0.468	1
				Total f:	1250

Mean observed R: 12.3   Mean observed G: -0.002
Variance of R's: 10.22   Variance of G's: 0.0135

and the largest number is $+13.4$; therefore, the range is $R = 13.4 - (-4.2)$ $= 17.6$. This R would have been tallied in the fifth R class from the top in the left half of the table.

The function $G = (\bar{x} - \mu)/R$ will be shown later to be useful for making certain statistical decisions from sample evidence obtained during an experiment, but this really is immaterial in the present discussion. The important point is that the equation for G involves quantities $\bar{x}$ and R whose sizes are dependent upon chance occurrences during sampling; therefore, G must necessarily have a sampling distribution. For the particular sample drawn above,

$$\bar{x} = (11.0 + 7.8 + 6.2 + \cdots + 2.2 + 2.2)/10 = 3.92$$

The true mean is $\mu = 5$; hence, $G = (3.92 - 5)/17.6 = -0.061$. This G would have been tallied in the ninth G class from the top on the right-hand side of the table.

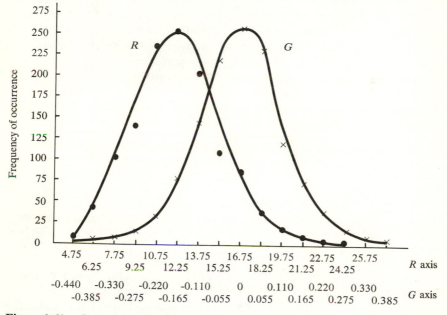

Figure 1.61. Sampling distributions observed for R and G on 1250 random samples from $N(5, 16)$, where $R = $ range and $G = (\bar{x} - 5)/R$; samples of size $n = 10$.

This same type of sampling and computation was done 1250 separate times to produce Table 1.61. Basically, this table is a start on the formation of two new statistical populations: one for the random variable R and the other for the random variable G.

Although the general mathematical formulae for any particular frequency distribution may be hard, or even impossible, to obtain in a convenient form, this process of sampling and computing a function of the sample data *does* produce a statistical population with a frequency distribution. In the case of R and G the statistical populations are useful for making certain decisions from sample data obtained during experimental research, as will be illustrated later.

Figure 1.61 shows the observed sampling distributions of Table 1.61. It is noted that the G distribution is quite symmetrical about $G = 0$, whereas the R distribution tends to be nonsymmetrical, as shown by the fact that the right-hand tail of the curve extends farther from the high point of the frequency curve for modal R than does the left-hand tail of the curve for R.

Common sense tells one that increasing the size of the sample probably will produce sampling distributions with less variance than is found for small samples. It also is reasonable to expect that the actual sizes of the population parameters must have some effect on the sampling distributions of R and G. For example, a population with relatively large variance would be expected to produce a more erratic sampling distribution for the random variable R than would a population with a small variance, if the mean remained the same.

PROBLEMS

1. Toss a set of 6 coins freely 200 times, recording the number of heads each time. Make and graph the sampling binomial distribution so obtained, using the following outline:

   Number of heads: 0   1   2   3   4   5   6
   Number of occurrences in 200 trials:

2. From any newspaper which gives the New York Stock Exchange prices for a given day and the net changes, make a frequency distribution table of the first 300 net changes. Use intervals by eighths, and keep the plus and minus changes separate. Is this a sampling distribution?

3. Take a simple random sample of 100 *lines* of printing in this book and make a sampling distribution table and graph of the number of letters per word.

4. Take a simple random sample of 500 *lines* of printing in this book, and make and graph the sampling distribution of the arithmetic mean of the number of letters per word in lines in this book. Does this distribution appear to be normal? Is it symmetrical or skewed? What population did you sample?

5. Using any newspaper having at least 100 captioned news items or stories, measure the vertical length of each item to the nearest sixteenth of an inch. Then make and graph the frequency distribution of this measurement. Does this distribution look normal? If you did this for 500 newspapers, would the mean lengths of items have a normal distribution? How would the distribution of the mean lengths (no matter what the type of distribution) compare with the distributions of actual lengths in a given newspaper?

1.7 SOME ELEMENTARY CONCEPTS AND RULES OF PROBABILITY

The following should be obvious by now:

(*a*) Experimental research involves experimental units (such as men, pigs, lots of land, plants, or salable goods), which are selected or produced for study by some scheme involving chance events. Not only are they selected at random for an experiment, but their existence, condition, attitude, etc., at the time of the experiment are heavily dependent upon chance.

(*b*) The measurements taken on the sample experimental units are random variables because of (*a*) and because there inevitably will be errors of measurement.

(*c*) Any sensible and useful interpretations of experimental data must be subject to some uncertainty, and the degree of uncertainty must be measured and expressed somehow.

Probability is the means by which we measure uncertainty and express it concisely and usefully. Fortunately, the theory of mathematical probability was quite well developed by 1900, chiefly as a result of mankind's long-standing interest in games of chance. Statistical theory includes the theory of mathematical probability and also concepts of randomization, estimation, and the testing of statistical hypotheses which are recognized as of interest in experimental research.

There are several concepts of probability, but we shall confine attention to a rather natural relative-frequency probability, which can be simulated by experiment. It will be convenient to use coins and dice as tools for introducing some basic concepts of probability which, however, are vital in experimental research.

When someone is about to toss an ordinary coin in the air, let it fall on a flat hard surface, and note whether a head or a tail is uppermost when the coin stops moving, most observers would say that the *outcome* of this experiment is equally likely to be heads or tails. Of course, on any one throw it will be either heads or tails, and on 10 throws it will not often produce exactly five heads and five tails. If this coin were tossed 10,000 times, any observer surely would be astounded to see exactly 5000 heads and 5000 tails. However, the ratio of heads to total number of throws is confidently expected to be very close to 1/2. This, then, is taken to be the probability of tossing a head on any designated future throw of this coin.

If in the process of tossing a coin many times the ratio of the number of heads to the total number of throws deviates notably and persistently from one half, one would conclude that the probability of heads, say p_H, was not equal to 1/2. The ratio might be 0.33 after 5000 throws and stay this value to two decimals on through the 10,000th throw. In such event it would be concluded that this coin was biassed and that for practical purposes $p_H = 0.33$. It would follow that $p_T = 1 - p_H = 0.67$ for tails.

The discussion is saying simply this: if certain describable events can be simulated by some sort of an experiment, we can measure their probabilities of occurrence by means of relative-frequency probabilities which sum to unity.

It sometimes is convenient to describe the totality of all possible events under given circumstances by means of what is called a *sample space*. A sample space has the following features of interest here:

(*a*) Each possible outcome of a specified experiment may be represented by a point in a space which logically is called a *sample space*.

(*b*) Each such point has a probability associated with it, which measures the relative frequency with which the corresponding event occurs during this experiment.

(*c*) The sum of the probabilities associated with the points of the sample space is 1, just as percentages add to 100. With the one unbiassed coin used as illustration earlier, the sample space consists of just two points, each with a probability of 1/2. In the experiment with a biassed coin the sample space also contained but two points, but their probabilities were $p_H = 0.33$ and $p_T = 0.67$ for heads and tails, respectively. Obviously, $p_H + p_T = 1$.

Consider next an experiment in which four unbiassed coins are to be tossed. One coin has 2 (or 2^1) possible outcomes. Two coins have 4 (or 2^2) outcomes, namely HH, HT, TH, and TT. Three coins have 8 (or 2^3) possible outcomes, namely HHH, HHT, HTH, THH, HTT, THT, TTH, and TTT. The four coins to be used in this experiment will have $2^4 = 16$ outcomes, as follows, assuming a penny (p), a nickel (n), a dime (d), and a quarter (q) are used:

p	n	d	q	X = number of heads	Number of events in this class	Probability = relative number of heads
H	H	H	H	4	1	1/16
H	H	H	T			
H	H	T	H	3	4	4/16
H	T	H	H			
T	H	H	H			
H	H	T	T			
H	T	H	T			
T	H	H	T	2	6	6/16
H	T	T	H			
T	H	T	H			
T	T	H	H			
H	T	T	T			
T	H	T	T	1	4	4/16
T	T	H	T			
T	T	T	H			
T	T	T	T	0	1	1/16

It would seem reasonable to say that with the unbiassed coins being used in this experiment each of these 16 possible outcomes of the experiment is equally likely to occur on any one set of throws. If so, one could reasonably assign a probability of 1/16 to each outcome. Furthermore, the *classes of events* shown above logically would be assigned the probabilities at the right. The sample space would consist of 16 points, one for each physically different and identifiable outcome of this experiment. Each of the 16 points would be assigned a probability of 1/16. It then appears that the probabilities for the classes of events are just the sums of the probabilities assigned the corresponding points in the sample space. However, all this is quite intuitive and should be put in a more general and rigorous form. This is done in the following statements.

Rule 1. If the events (or outcomes) E_1, E_2, $\cdots$, E_m are mutually exclusive because no two of them can occur in the same trial of an experiment, the probability that some *one* of E_1, E_2, $\cdots$, E_m will occur on any specifically designated future trial of this experiment is

(1.72) $$\Pr\{E_1 + E_2 + \cdots + E_m\} = \sum_{i=1}^{m} \Pr\{E_i\}$$

For example, $\Pr\{2H \text{ or } 3H\} = 4/16 + 6/16 = 10/16 = 5/8$.

Rule 2. If the outcomes E_1, E_2, $\cdots$, E_m of a specific experiment are independent in the sense that the occurrence or nonoccurrence of any one of them has no relation to the occurrence or non-occurrence of any of the others, then the probability of the simultaneous occurrence of E_1, E_2, $\cdots$, E_m on a future specified trial of this experiment is given by

(1.73) $$\Pr\{E_1 \cdot E_2 \cdot \cdots \cdot E_m\} = \Pr\{E_1\} \cdot \Pr\{E_2\} \cdot \cdots \cdot \Pr\{E_m\} = \prod_{i=1}^{m} \Pr\{E_i\}$$

For example, the probability that on a designated future toss of an unbiassed penny, an unbiassed nickel, an unbiassed dime, and an unbiassed quarter the specific outcome will be:

Coin:	p	n	d	q
H or T:	H	T	H	T

is $\Pr\{H_p \cdot T_n \cdot H_d \cdot T_q\} = \Pr\{H_p\} \cdot \Pr\{T_n\} \cdot \Pr\{H_d\} \cdot \Pr\{T_q\} = (1/2)(1/2)(1/2)(1/2) = 1/16$.

If the coins are biassed such that $\Pr\{H \text{ on penny}\} = 1/3$, $\Pr\{H \text{ on nickel}\} = 1/2$, $\Pr\{H \text{ on dime}\} = 2/3$, and $\Pr\{H \text{ on quarter}\} = 1/4$, then

Pr{HHTT *in order*} = Pr{H_p}·Pr{H_n}·Pr{T_d}·Pr{T_q} = (1/3)(1/2)(1/3)(3/4) = 1/24. For the whole *class* of events (2H, 2T) one has the following:

$$Pr\{H_pH_nT_dT_q \text{ or } H_pT_nH_dT_q \text{ or}\cdots\text{or } T_pT_nH_dH_q\}$$
$$= Pr\{H_pH_nT_dT_q\} + Pr\{H_pT_nH_dT_q\} +\cdots+ Pr\{T_pT_nH_dH_q\}$$
$$= 1/24 + 1/12 + 1/6 + 1/72 + 1/36 + 1/18 = 28/72 = 7/18$$

Finally, for two mutually exclusive classes of events, such as 2H or 3H, one can compute that Pr{2H or 3H} = Pr{2H} + Pr{3H} = 28/72 + 13/72 = 41/72, as the reader can verify by applying Rule 2 to the specific events in those two classes of events and then applying Rule 1 to the mutually exclusive events, 2H and 3H, on one toss of the four coins.

A concept closely related to pure probability theory is that of a *random variable*, also called for brevity a *variate*. If X = the number of heads shown after four coins are tossed, then X equals 0, 1, 2, 3, or 4 with probabilities which depend upon the nature of the coins used. If all four coins are unbiassed in the sense that $p_H = 1/2$ for each coin, then one has the following information with regard to this random variable:

X_i:	0	1	2	3	4	all other values
p_i:	1/16	4/16	6/16	4/16	1/16	0

If the coins are biassed so that Pr{H on penny} = 1/3, Pr{H on nickel} = 1/2, Pr{H on dime} = 2/3, and Pr{H on quarter} = 1/4, then for this different random variable, Y, one has the following complete information:

Y_i:	0	1	2	3	4	all other values
p_i:	6/72	23/72	28/72	13/72	2/72	0

In these simple academic examples, the probabilities for the random variable in question can be worked out directly from an enumeration of all possible outcomes of the experiment and an application of Rules 1 and 2. In practice we usually need to use mathematical functions which describe the probabilities of occurrence of the possible values of the random variable, X, or the occurrence of an X within a specified class of outcomes, such as "weighed between 70 and 79 pounds," "answered Yes to the question asked," and "yielded between 30 and 40 bushels per acre."

If one is dealing with a continuous measurement such as weight, average daily gain, price per pound, or pounds per square inch, how do probabilities become involved, and how can a relative-frequency concept of probability be appropriate? It is reasonable to say that if a random event, such as X = the weight of an animal chosen at random under specified conditions, truly is measured on a continuous scale of measurement, the *exact* weight of this animal is a dimensionless point on a linear scale, say a horizontal line, and therefore logically should be associated with a probability of zero. Hence, when dealing with random variables which are measured on a continuous scale we do not speak of the probability that $X = X_0$, a specific and exact value of X. Instead, we work with the probabilities of classes of events which correspond to values of X within some interval. For example, we might wish to know the probability that a weight of an animal would be found to lie between 40 and 50 pounds, or, in symbols, $\Pr\{40 \leqslant X \leqslant 50\} = (?)$.

A *frequency distribution curve* of a variate describes what is called the *probability density* of that random variable. For example, the standard normal random variable, X, has the frequency distribution curve of Figure 1.71 obtained basically from a mathematical formula and process but readable from Table III.

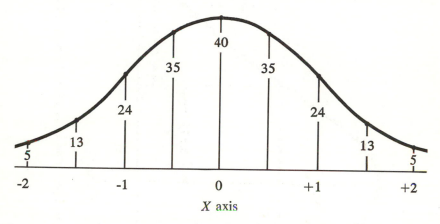

Figure 1.71.   The standard normal frequency distribution curve, showing probability densities at selected points along the X axis.

The numbers on the vertical line are the relative-frequency ordinates for the corresponding values of the random variable, X, which are along the horizontal axis. The numbers on the vertical lines denote the *probability densities* in the neighborhoods of the corresponding specific X's relative to the other X's. For example, X's in the neighborhood of $X = 0$ are about 8 times as likely to be observed in random samples from an $N(0, 1)$ population as are X's in the neighborhood of $X = -2$, according to the figure. Hence, these probability densities indicate relative frequencies of occurrences of values of the random variable, X, in those neighborhoods along the X scale of measurement. This sort of measurement of probability is the same sort as that discussed earlier.

To determine such probabilities as $\Pr\{-2 \leqslant X \leqslant +1\}$, $\Pr\{X \leqslant -0.5\}$, or $\Pr\{X \geqslant +1\}$, for example, one needs to use methods of integral calculus or to consult tables constructed for just this purpose. We shall do the latter. To illustrate, consider an $N(0, 1)$ population again. Figure 1.72 shows some selected areas under the frequency distribution curve for $N(0, 1)$, which

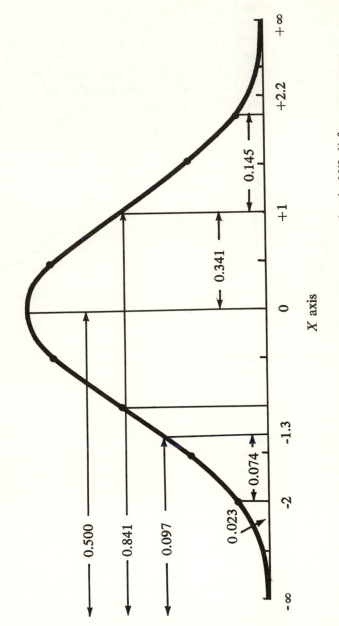

Figure 1.72.   Illustration of probabilities depicted by areas under the N(0, 1) frequency curve.

correspond to probabilities because the sizes of these areas play the role of relative frequencies when the total area under the curve is taken as 1. Table III shows the following, regarding the fractions of N(0, 1) lying between the indicated intervals along the X scale of measurement:

(a) $\Pr\{-\infty \leqslant X \leqslant -2\} = 0.023$ (b) $\Pr\{-\infty \leqslant X \leqslant -1.3\} = 0.097$

(c) $\Pr\{-2 \leqslant X \leqslant -1.3\} = 0.074$ (d) $\Pr\{-\infty \leqslant X \leqslant 0\} = 0.500$

(e) $\Pr\{-\infty \leqslant X \leqslant +1.0\} = 0.841$ (f) $\Pr\{0 \leqslant X \leqslant +1.0\} = 0.341$

(g) $\Pr\{+1.0 \leqslant X \leqslant +2.2\} = 0.145$

With reference to the discussion of the sampling distributions of random variables earlier in this chapter, one may say in terms of probability concepts that, given the mathematical form of any sampling distribution, one can determine the probability that any future sample statistic (such as $\bar{x}$) will have a size within any limits one wishes to specify. Graphically, such a probability is an area under the appropriate sampling frequency distribution curve. These probabilities will be subject to the usual laws of mathematical probability, and they are useful in making statistical decisions from experimental data.

Another type of chance event also deserves consideration before this brief discussion of probability is closed. The chance events considered so far were either mutually exclusive of other events which might occur in the same experiment or were independent of each other. Chance events also can be dependent upon each other's occurrence in such a way that information about the occurrence of E_i is useful in calculating the probability of occurrence of E_j. For example, the probability that a person chosen at random will have blood of type A could depend upon his nationality, which might be readily observable. If so, one might ask, what is the probability that a person chosen at random out of a roomful of others will turn out to have type A blood when we now can observe that he is a Spaniard? This is calling for what is called a *conditional probability*, because a condition has been added after the random drawing; namely, it now is given that the person is a Spaniard. Symbolically, this probability is indicated by $\Pr\{\text{type A} \mid \text{Spaniard}\}$, and it is read "probability of type A given that the person is known to be a Spaniard."

To illustrate specifically the computation of a conditional probability, it is convenient to use the four-coin game discussed earlier. Suppose that four unbiassed coins are tossed, and a small child sees one coin and says something which shows that one coin came up heads. What, now, is the probability that exactly two heads have been thrown, that is, $\Pr\{\text{2H} \mid \text{at least 1H}\} = ?$ Clearly the case TTTT has been eliminated by the child's remark, and this is all the information obtainable from that remark. Hence, we know that only 15 events are now possible, and 6 of these events are in the class (2H, 2T), which is of interest. We are assuming all events to be equally likely; so $\Pr\{\text{2H, 2T} \mid \text{at least 1H}\} = 6/15$. In terms of a sample space, the original set of 16 points each with $p = 1/16$ now has been reduced to a sample space with but 15 points each with $p = 1/15$ by the child's revealing remark.

It rarely is true that events in a sample space are readily counted or have equal probabilities, so there is need for a more general way to compute conditional probabilities. This procedure has been summarized by mathematical methods into a general formula. Let A and B denote two random events which can occur together and which are such that information about event A is relevant to the computation of the probability of occurrence of event B thereafter. Then we can state a third probability rule as follows:

Rule 3. $\Pr\{B \mid A\} = \dfrac{\Pr\{A \text{ and } B\}, \text{ unqualified}}{\Pr\{A\}, \text{ unqualified}}$

where:

$\Pr\{B \mid A\}$ = the conditional probability that B will occur, given the information that A has occurred,

$\Pr\{A \text{ and } B\}$ = the unconditional probability of the joint occurrence of A and B on the same trial of an experiment,

$\Pr\{A\}$ = the unconditional probability of the occurrence of A, nothing said or specified about event B. This is called the *marginal probability* of the occurrence of event A. For the sake of mathematical rigor we must assume that $\Pr\{A\} \neq 0$.

To illustrate Rule 3, consider again the four-coin game during which it was learned accidentally that one coin had turned up heads. Event B = the throwing of 2H, 2T. Event A = the throwing of at least 1H. In this case, the joint occurrence of B and A is identical with the occurrence of B, because 2H is at least 1H, and the occurrence of more than 2H would not be event B. Then, by Rule 3,

$$\Pr\{2H, 2T \mid \text{at least } 1H\} = \frac{\text{probability of 2H, 2T originally}}{\text{probability of at least 1H originally}}$$

$$= \frac{6/16}{15/16} = 6/15 = 2/5, \text{ as computed earlier}$$

Consider next another illustration of conditional probability in which $\Pr\{B\}$ and $\Pr\{B \text{ and } A\}$ are not the same. Suppose that a box contains 15 uniformly made marbles, which have some different colors and different numbers on them as follows:

> White marbles   with   2, 3, 7, and 9
> Blue marbles   with   5, 6, 7, 8, 9, and 10
> Aqua marbles   with   0, 1, 1, 2, and 3

Thus, there are 15 marbles each with one color and one number on it. Suppose, now, that one marble has been drawn at random and has been seen only well enough to be known to be either blue or aqua, and there is no information about the number on it. What is the probability that the unknown number on this marble is a 7 or larger? In this case,

$$\Pr\{B \mid A\} \qquad = \Pr\{\text{no. at least as large as 7} \mid \text{marble not white}\} = (?)$$
$$\Pr\{B \text{ and } A\} = \Pr\{\text{of a nonwhite marble with a number} \geq 7\} = 4/15$$
$$\Pr\{A\} \qquad\quad = \Pr\{\text{before any draw, that a nonwhite marble would be drawn}\} = 11/15$$

Therefore, $\Pr\{B \mid A\} = \Pr\{\text{no.} \geq 7 \mid \text{nonwhite}\} = (4/15)/(11/15) = 4/11.$ This result also is obtainable in this simple case by noting that there are 4 marbles with numbers ≥ 7 among the 11 nonwhite marbles.

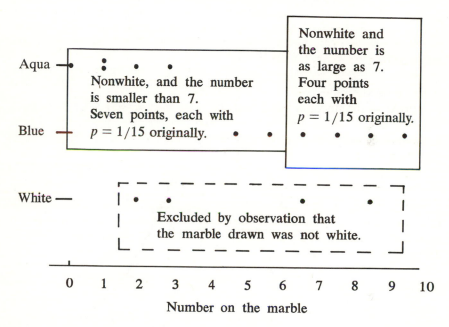

Figure 1.73.   Sample space for events occurring on numbered colored marbles.

The sample space for the marble game may be illustrated as in Figure 1.73. The joint, marginal, and conditional probabilities discussed above are shown in the figure for the events A and B, A, and B | A. It is seen again that probabilities for classes of events are obtained by adding the probabilities for the individual events making up those classes of events. In this particular simple game, this can be done by enumeration. In general, one needs more sophisticated methods, such as integral calculus and the determination of areas under curves.

PROBLEMS

1. Given an unbiassed die, so that it is reasonable to assign a probability of 1/6 to the occurrence of each face on any future toss of this die, what is the probability that an even number ($X = 2, 4,$ or 6) will be thrown on the next random throw of this die? What is the probability that an even sum will be thrown with two such dice? What is the probability that an even number will be thrown on each of the next two successive throws of one of these dice?

2. Suppose that a die is so biassed that $Pr\{1\} = Pr\{2\} = 0.11$, $Pr\{3\} = 0.13$, $Pr\{4\} = Pr\{5\} = 0.20$, and $Pr\{6\} = 0.25$. What is the probability that an odd number will be thrown on the next throw of this die? What is the probability that a number larger than 2 will be thrown? That three successive 6's will be thrown on the next three throws of one die?

3. What is the probability that with dice such as described in Problem 2 a sum of 7 will be thrown on the next throw of a pair of such dice? That a sum of 7 will not be thrown? That a sum of 6 will be thrown on the next throw of these two dice and repeated on the third throw without either a 6 or a 7 being thrown on the second throw?

4. Given the accompanying curve and some areas marked off under the curve, answer the questions below, assuming that the total area under this curve is equal to 1.

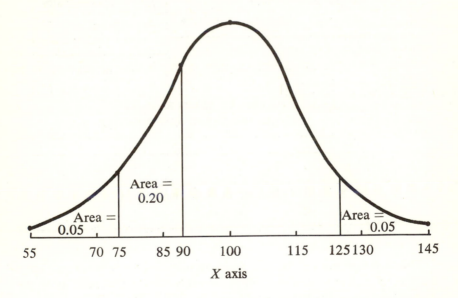

(a) What is the probability that a random observation on this population will produce an $X \leqslant 90$? An X greater than 90?

(b) What is the probability that a random X will lie between 90 and 125?

(c) In your judgment, using areas, what is the probability that a random X will lie between 85 and 115? That this X will exceed 100?

5. Suppose that in a certain geographical region 30% of the adults of voting age are Catholics, 10% are Jews, 40% are either Methodists or Presbyterians,

and the remaining 20% have no stated religion. Suppose also that 55% of these adults are males. If a list of the names of these adults exists and identifies them by numbers between 1 and 100,000 inclusive, what is the probability that a number drawn at random will be that of a Catholic male? A Catholic male or a female Methodist or a female Presbyterian? An "unreligious" male? What assumption are you making about the sex ratios that was not stated specifically in this problem?

6. Referring to Problem 5, suppose that a number is drawn at random and you somehow learn accidentally that it represents a man. What now is the conditional probability that this person known to be a man also is a Jew?

7. Suppose there are 8 Americans on safari in Bechuanaland, one of whom is a physician. The blood types are as follows: 4 are type A, 2 are type O, 1 is type B, and 1 is type AB. However, only the doctor's specific type is known, and it is A. One person other than the doctor gets injured by a lion and must have a blood transfusion in the field, but no blood-typing equipment is available, and the types must match during the transfusion or the man will die. What is the probability of the man's survival if this depends only upon a successful transfusion? What is this probability if the injured man's type were known to be A? Assume the doctor could be a donor.

8. Suppose that it is known that 60% of the wheat brought to a certain elevator is of the variety Concho, 20% is Pawnee, and 20% is Red Chief. Suppose also that, contrary to usual practice, the wheat is in sacks and, hence, the varieties are only mixed in the sense that the sacks are mixed and are indistinguishable in the elevator. What is the probability that a sack chosen at random is Pawnee? That both of two sacks chosen at random are Concho? That a sack chosen at random is either Concho or Red Chief? That a sack chosen at random and known somehow not to be Red Chief actually is Pawnee?

9. Suppose that the accompanying curve is the graph of the frequency distribution of a random variable zeta (ζ).

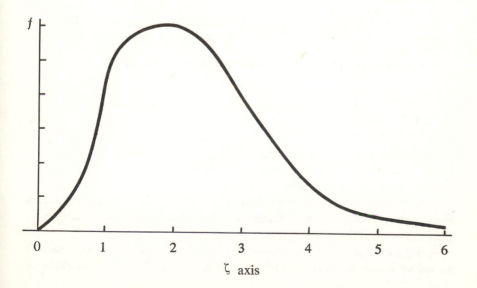

(a) What value, ζ_0, of this random variable would you say would be such that $\Pr\{\zeta \geqslant \zeta_0\} = 0.50$?

(b) Where would you place ζ_1 on the horizontal scale so that $\Pr\{\zeta \geqslant \zeta_1\} = 0.80$?

(c) What two values of zeta, say ζ_1 and ζ_2, would you say would be such that $\Pr\{\zeta_1 \leqslant \zeta \leqslant \zeta_2\} = 0.80$ if you should like $\zeta_2 - \zeta_1$ to be as small as possible? What if $\zeta_2 - \zeta_1$ were to be as large as possible? How many ways could the ζ_1 and ζ_2 be chosen?

10. Suppose that there are 100 walleye pike in a hatchery pond and 20 of them are diseased. If 60 of the pike in this pond are at least 12 inches in length and 40 are less than 12 inches in length, and if the disease in question does not occur in pike less than 12 inches in length, then:

    (a) What is the probability that a pike caught at random will be diseased?

    (b) What is the conditional probability that such a pike will be diseased given that it also is 15 inches in length?

    (c) What is the probability that the fish of (b) will not be diseased?

11. Suppose that among six foreigners seeking admission to the United States from the same foreign country, three are saboteurs. The law permits only three to enter the United States at this time, it is supposed. The saboteurs can only do their sabotage if at least two work together. What is the probability of letting in enough saboteurs to be dangerous, if the three allowed to enter the United States from the foreign country are chosen at random?

12. Assume that a turtle is hatched 50 feet straight away from the edge of a perfectly straight river bank. This baby turtle cannot walk more than 100 feet on dry land without dying, so he must get to the river's edge by walking no more than 100 feet. If he cannot tell where the water is when he starts out and so starts off at random from the place where he is hatched, what is the probability of his survival if he walks in a straight line from the point of hatching until he either reaches the river or dies?

13. Under certain conditions rocks on the ocean floor become agatized; hence, some beds of gravel which are exposed at low ocean tides contain a few agates among many other rocks. If it is supposed (purely for illustration) that one rock in 200 chosen at random is an agate of some sort and that one agate in 50, on the average, is valuable, what is the probability that among 2000 rocks taken at random at least two will be valuable agates? That none will be valuable agates? That at most one will be valuable?

1.8 SUMMARY

It is hoped that the preceding introductory discussions have suggested to the student the following points regarding the field of experimental statistics, or sampling statistics:

(a) It deals with actual or conceptual groups of numerical measurements which pertain to some clearly defined set of objects, actions, or phenomena, which are measurable numerically.

(b) Any population of measurements has a general form, such as normal or binomial, and has characteristics, such as level of magnitude of measurement and dispersion about that level, which are measured by population parameters.

(*c*) Sampling is done from statistical populations with the purpose of making useful decisions, such as estimating population parameters, testing hypotheses about those parameters, or comparing parameters of different populations.

(*d*) Any numerical quantity derived from a sample has a sampling distribution, and it is inferred that knowledge about sampling distributions is required in solving problems in the areas of estimation and testing of hypotheses.

(*e*) The type of inference used with sampling data is inductive and hence subject to error in any conclusion drawn. One major goal of statistical analyses and research is to measure the probability of error and make it as small as possible by good planning and the use of the most efficient procedures possible. Decisions made from experimental research must combine this probability information with practical considerations of losses and gains in order to produce the most "economic" decisions.

REVIEW PROBLEMS

1. If everyone over 25 years of age in Denver, Colorado, on July 1, 1965, had been classified as having graduated from high school ($X = 1$) or not having graduated from high school ($X = 0$), what sort of a statistical population would have been created? What parameter(s) would this population have?

2. If the people in Problem 1 had been classified as Not High School Graduates ($X = 0$), High School Graduates but Not College Graduates ($X = 1$), and College Graduates ($X = 2$), what sort of statistical population would this process have defined? How many parameters would it take to define this population?

3. If you had been asked to sample the population of Problem 1, how would you have gone about it if you had been studying the attitudes of those residents toward a specific political question?

4. Write the following 25 numbers on 25 uniform and easily mixed objects (one number per object), and then compute the mean = $\mu = 5$ and variance = $\sigma^2 = 2.76$:   6.5, 1.2, 4.0, 5.2, 2.7, 5.4, 4.3, 5.8, 6.9, 5.1, 3.0, 4.4, 3.9, 7.0, 3.7, 7.2, 5.4, 7.9, 4.1, 6.0, 6.8, 2.1, 4.4, 6.5, 5.5.

5. Compute the range and standard deviation for Problem 4.

6. Draw a random sample of size $n = 5$ from the objects prepared for Problem 4, and compute the sampling mean, $\bar{x}$. Next, repeat this sampling operation 19 times, so that you end with 20 random samples each of size $n = 5$. During the sampling, draw one number at a time randomly, put it back and stir the objects well before taking out another number at random. Repeat this operation until for each sample five numbers have been drawn, the population being of its original composition just before each draw. This procedure produces one sample of size $n = 5$.

7. Compute the mean and standard deviation of the 20 sample means obtained for Problem 6. Compare each with the population parameter being estimated.

8. Compute the midrange (MR) for each of the 20 samples taken in Problem 6, and compare their average with the true mean of this population.

9. Compute the standard deviations of the 20 MR's of Problem 8, and compare their sizes with that of the population standard deviation. How would you expect these standard deviations of the 20 MR's to compare with the standard deviation of the 20 sample means from these same samples?

10. Compute the median for each of the 20 samples taken in Problem 6. Then compute the mean and standard deviation of these 20 sample medians. How would you expect this standard deviation to compare with that of the MR's? That of the $\bar{x}$'s?

11. Referring to Table 1.41, what is the empirical probability that a random sample of size $n = 10$ from N(5, 16) will have a mean ($\bar{x}$) at least as large as 6.25? Smaller than 2.25? Within 0.25 of the true mean?

12. Answer the questions of Problem 11, but for the midrange (MR) as estimator.

13. Use Table 1.61 to answer the following. If a random sample of size $n = 10$ is to be drawn from N(5, 16) and then $G = (\bar{x} - 5)/R$ is to be computed, what is the approximate probability that the G will be positive? Will be within 0.027, either way, of 0? Will be between -0.247 and $+0.247$?

14. Suppose that under the conditions of Problem 13 one mistakenly used $\mu = 6$ instead of the true value, $\mu = 5$. What effect do you think this error would have on the sampling distribution of the G? Give reasons for your answer.

15. Suppose that someone said that he knew that the true mean of a certain normal population was $\mu = 10$, and thereafter you took a random sample of size $n = 10$ from that population, computed the G, and got $G = 0.750$, using the μ he suggested. Would you conclude that he had given you the correct mean of the population or not? Could you be sure, either way? Give reasons for your answers.

16. Try to devise some other average than the mean, median, or midrange, and apply it to the 20 samples of Problem 6.

17. Try to devise a method of measuring dispersion other than standard deviation, variance, or range, and then apply it to the samples of Problem 6.

18. Referring to Problem 4, what is the probability that a number chosen at random from among those 25 numbers listed will have a size less than 4? Less than 5? At least as large as 4.1? Between 4 and 5, inclusive? Between 4 and 5, exclusive?

19. Referring to the questions of Problem 18, would the probability be the same, less, or larger in each instance if the mean of a sample of size $n = 3$ were used instead of a single draw? Why?

20. Which of the following quantities would have sampling distributions, where any quantity involving X is dependent upon the sample observations in some way and all symbols not involving X, either *directly or indirectly*, are regarded as constants?

(a) $(\pi - 2)/\bar{x}$ (b) $(2e - 3)/\mu$ (c) $(X_3 + X_4)/2$
(d) $(\bar{x} - \mu)/\sigma$ (e) $(md - \bar{x})/2\sigma$ (f) $(17 - \sigma^2)e^\mu$
(g) $mv^2/2$ (h) $(2\sigma^2 - R)/md$ (i) $(X_1 + X_3 + X_5)/3 - \mu$
(j) $\sin h\bar{x}$

21. Relative to Problem 20, you should be able to state the distribution type, or function, for three of the nonconstant quantities listed, if all X's are from $N(\mu, \sigma^2)$. Can you? If so, which, and what?

22. Compute function (a) of Problem 20 for each of the 20 samples of Problem 6, and find their average.

23. Do as in Problem 22 for part (i) of Problem 20, and comment on the results as generally as possible.

24. Do as in Problem 22 for part (h) of Problem 20.

25. Which of the following statements do you regard as true statements?
    (a) If you visualize all the human males in the U.S.A. right now who have had at least five fillings of any sort put into their teeth as forming a homogeneous group in some sense, their heights in centimeters at noon today (CST) will form a statistical population.
    (b) If X is the number of heads obtained when five coins, which are unbiassed, are tossed fairly, then $Y = 2X - 1$ also is a random variable.
    (c) The mean of the Y of part (b) for samples of size $n = 4$ has a sampling distribution.
    (d) $\Pr\{0 \leqslant X \leqslant 4\} = 0.67$ if the random variable X has an $N(3, 4)$ distribution.
    (e) According to the accompanying sketch of the distribution of some random variable X, the probability that two random observations both will be > 5 is < 0.50.

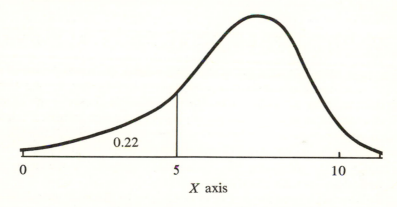

(f) If you reject a false hypothesis, you commit a Type II error.

Chapter 2

Sampling Binomial and Multinomial Populations

2.1 BINOMIAL FREQUENCY DISTRIBUTIONS

It has been said already that when every object or action which is admissible under specified conditions of an experiment or other investigation is to be classified uniquely into one of only two possible classes—such as male or female, success or failure, dead or alive, yes or no—the statistical population defined therefrom is called a binomial population, provided the proportions in the two possible classes remain fixed for some useful period of time. The only necessary parameter for a binomial population is the percent, p, in a specified one of the two classes.

Suppose that a random sample of size n is to be drawn from a binomial population and the number falling into the class with true percentage p is to be recorded as a sample number, X. Clearly, aside from trivial cases, the X could turn out by chance to have any size from 0 to n inclusive, no matter what the size of p. For, if there are as many as n members of the population in each class, one *could* draw by chance 0, 1, 2, $\cdots$, or n from either class. Thus, the chance variable X takes on the values 0, 1, 2, $\cdots$, n with some probability dependent upon n and p. The frequency distribution of this X is called a *binomial frequency distribution*, and is denoted by the symbol $b(X; n, p)$, for obvious reasons. As with any other frequency distribution, its actual or conceptual constitution will be a statistical population with at least one parameter, such as the mean or variance, which will be of statistical

52

interest in some type of research. This population will be of the discrete, or enumerative, type, because the random variable X can assume only isolated positive values. These points were illustrated in Section 1.2 by visualizing an experiment with a spray assumed to be 90% effective in killing houseflies. In that experiment a binomial population with $p = 0.90$ was being sampled with $n = 50$, so the random variable X could have any of the values $0, 1, 2, \cdots, 49$, and 50.

The important features of any binomial distribution are measurable by means of the binomial series for $(q + p)^n$, studied in elementary algebra. For example, if $n = 3$, it is well known that

$$(q + p)^3 = 1q^3 + 3q^2p + 3qp^2 + 1p^3$$

whatever be the values of q and p. In statistical work associated with a binomial frequency distribution, $p =$ the probability of an event under study and $q = 1 - p$. The binomial series given above symbolically describes every sampling event possible when samples of size $n = 3$ are drawn from a binomial population with a fixed parameter, p. Specifically, if $p =$ percent A's in a population, where A stands for some attribute, such as Dead in a fly spray experiment, then:

(*a*) There is just one way that the three members of a sample of size $n = 3$ all will be classified as not-A, namely: the first member drawn is not-A, the second member is not-A, and the third member is not-A. This fact corresponds to the coefficient 1 for q^3. Furthermore, it can be shown that the probability of this event is $1q^3$ or, more simply, q^3, if the p and q be expressed as fractions or decimals instead of percentages. This agrees with Rule 2 of Section 1.7 because the results of the three draws just described are outcomes of three independent random events, each with probability q; therefore, $\Pr\{q \cdot q \cdot q\} = q^3$. Moreover, there is just one way that three not-A's can occur, so $\Pr\{3 \text{ not-A's on 3 draws}\} = 1 \cdot q^3$.

(*b*) There are exactly three ways a random sample of size $n = 3$ can have exactly two not-A's and one A, namely: the first member is not-A, the second member is not-A, and the third member is A; or, the first member of the sample is not-A, the second is A, and the third is not-A; or, the first member of the sample is A and the other two are not-A. The second term in the binomial series for $(q + p)^3$ is $3q^2p$, which corresponds to the fact that there are three mutually exclusive ways to obtain exactly two not-A's. The probability of this occurrence can be shown to be $3q^2p$ by the following reasoning and the use of Section 1.7. The following specific outcome of three draws: first draw is not-A, second is not-A, third is A, involves three independent events whose probabilities are q, q, and p, respectively. Hence, $\Pr\{\text{not-A, not-A, and A } in \ this \ order\} = q \cdot q \cdot p = q^2p$. Similarly,

$$\Pr\{\text{not-A, A, not-A } in \ this \ order\} = q \cdot p \cdot q = q^2p, \text{ and}$$
$$\Pr\{\text{A, not-A, not-A } in \ this \ order\} = p \cdot q \cdot q = q^2p \text{ again.}$$

The following three outcomes of three draws *in order* are mutually exclusive events on any one specified set of three draws:

$$\text{not-A,} \quad \text{not-A,} \quad \text{A}$$
$$\text{not-A,} \quad \text{A,} \quad \text{not-A}$$
$$\text{A,} \quad \text{not-A,} \quad \text{not-A}$$

Therefore the probability of the occurrence of some one of these three mutually exclusive events, each of which produces two not-A's and one A, is, by Rule 1 of Section 1.7,

$$\text{Pr\{two not-A's and one A in } some \text{ order\}} = 3q^2p$$

In a similar manner, the third and fourth terms of the series for $(q + p)^3$ describe the other two possible classes of samples and give their probabilities of occurrence, when p and q are expressed as fractions so that the probability will be expressed in its usual fraction form.

The facts noted for $n = 3$ are true for the general sample size, n; hence, the series

$$(2.11) \quad (q + p)^n = 1q^n + nq^{n-1}p + \frac{n(n-1)}{2!} q^{n-2}p^2 + \cdots$$
$$+ \frac{n!}{X!(n-X)!} q^{n-X}p^X + \cdots + 1p^n$$

gives the relative frequency of occurrence (to be called the *probability*) of samples of size n which will have $X = 0, 1, 2, \cdots$, or n, respectively, if p is the constant probability of occurrence of the event A on any specified future observation of the binomial population with parameter p.

In brief, Formula 2.11 is said to describe the *binomial frequency distribution* for any p and integral positive n, because it completely describes the relative frequency of occurrence of each possible event from samples of size n which could be drawn from a binomial population with parameter p. As stated before, we shall denote such a binomial frequency distribution by the symbol $b(X; n, p)$ where X is the number of occurrences of the event whose constant probability is p from trial to trial. The X also will be called a *binomial variate*.

The coefficients in the series of Formula 2.11 give the number of mutually exclusive ways each possible event can occur. For example, one could obtain 2 occurrences and $n - 2$ nonoccurrences of an event with constant probability p in $n(n-1)/2$ mutually exclusive ways. In general, the event could occur exactly X times out of n trials in

$$\frac{n!}{X!(n-X)!}$$

ways. It is convenient to use the symbol $\binom{n}{X}$ for this number. It should be obvious that $\binom{n}{X} = \binom{n}{n-X}$, because the factors in the denominator merely would be reversed. Thus,

$$\binom{n}{X} = \frac{n!}{X!(n-X)!}, \qquad \text{whereas} \qquad \binom{n}{n-X} = \frac{n!}{(n-X)!\,X!}$$

which are identical numbers. It is customary to call $\binom{n}{X}$ *the number of combinations of n objects* (interpreted broadly) *taken X at a time.*

To illustrate the above discussion, suppose an unbiased coin is to be tossed and the result of each toss is to be classified as a Head or a Tail. The results of all conceivable tosses of this coin classified as H or as T (and numerically designated as 1 or 0, respectively, for mathematical completeness) constitute a binomial population. However, if attention is fixed on subsets of six tosses, each drawn at random from this population by making the tosses in sets of six, a binomial frequency distribution $b(X; 6, 1/2)$ with $X = 0$, $1, \cdots, 6$, is obtained. The terms of the following binomial series give, by application of Formula 2.11, the specific relative frequencies (or probabilities) of occurrence of each of the seven possible outcomes of a set of six tosses.

$$(2.12) \quad \left(\tfrac{1}{2} + \tfrac{1}{2}\right)^6 = 1\left(\tfrac{1}{2}\right)^6 + 6\left(\tfrac{1}{2}\right)^5\left(\tfrac{1}{2}\right)^1 + 15\left(\tfrac{1}{2}\right)^4\left(\tfrac{1}{2}\right)^2 + 20\left(\tfrac{1}{2}\right)^3\left(\tfrac{1}{2}\right)^3$$

$$+ 15\left(\tfrac{1}{2}\right)^2\left(\tfrac{1}{2}\right)^4 + 6\left(\tfrac{1}{2}\right)^1\left(\tfrac{1}{2}\right)^5 + 1\left(\tfrac{1}{2}\right)^6$$

$$= \frac{1}{64} + \frac{6}{64} + \frac{15}{64} + \frac{20}{64} + \frac{15}{64} + \frac{6}{64} + \frac{1}{64}.$$

The series on the right-hand side of this formula produces the following information:

(a) In the long run, 1/64 of such sets of six tosses will show 0 Heads, so X will be 0 on 1/64 of the tosses. This also is the probability that X will be 0 on a designated *future* set of six tosses.

(b) The relative frequency with which sets of six tosses of an unbiassed coin will produce exactly 1 Head and 5 Tails is 6/64.

(c) In a similar manner it is concluded that the relative frequencies with which sets of six tosses of an unbiassed coin will produce 2, 3, 4, 5, and 6 Heads are 15/64, 20/64, 15/64, 6/64, and 1/64, respectively.

Table 2.11 has been made to summarize the immediately preceding statements and to demonstrate why the mean size of X is simply $\mu = np$. The rationalization of the last column of the table is simply as follows. On 1/64 of a very large number of sets of tosses, 6 Heads will be obtained, so 1 time in 64 the average number of Heads per set of six tosses is 6. However, since this only occurs 1 time in 64, this average is given a weight (or importance) of only 1/64, as shown in the last column of the table. The other possible results of six tosses are treated similarly, and the results for all seven ($=n + 1$) possibilities added. Obviously, the average, $np = 3$ Heads per set, might not be obtained exactly on any finite number of sets of tosses, but for the population of X's under the circumstances stated the true mean is $\mu = np$ after a sufficiently large number of tosses (this is proved rigorously in more mathematical courses). Hence, we write for a binomial variate X:

(2.13) $$\mu_X = np$$

It also has been shown mathematically that the true variance of a binomial variate X is

(2.14) $$\sigma_X^2 = npq$$

Although these two formulas are not being derived herein, they are easy to use and are important formulas to keep in mind.

TABLE 2.11. FREQUENCY DISTRIBUTION TABLE FOR $b(X; 6, 1/2)$ AND DEMON-STRATION OF THE CALCULATION OF THE MEAN NUMBER OF OCCURRENCES OF AN EVENT WITH CONSTANT PROBABILITY OF H $= p = \frac{1}{2}$ ON EACH TRIAL

Sample	X	Relative frequency (P)	(P) (number of Heads) = PX
6H, 0T	6	1/64 or 1.6% approx.	6/64
5H, 1T	5	6/64 or 9.4% ,,	30/64
4H, 2T	4	15/64 or 23.4% ,,	60/64
3H, 3T	3	20/64 or 31.2% ,,	60/64
2H, 4T	2	15/64 or 23.4% ,,	30/64
1H, 5T	1	6/64 or 9.4% ,,	6/64
0H, 6T	0	1/64 or 1.6% ,,	0/64

Total: 192/64
$= 3 = \mu$
$= 6(\frac{1}{2}) = np$

Tables exist which show the specific numerical binomial frequency distributions for many combinations of n and p, that is, for many $b(X; n, p)$ distributions. Table 2.12 has been constructed to illustrate some $b(X; n, p)$ frequency distributions specifically and also to show, for a given n, how different binomial frequency distributions compare and contrast.

It is rather obvious from common sense and from looking at this table that small X's are much more likely to be observed when p is small, and large X's when p is large. For example, $X = 0$ will occur on about 0.122 of any large number of sets of 20 observations taken when $p = 0.10$, but X will virtually never be 0 when p is 0.90. On the other hand, when n is 20 and p is 0.90, X will be 20 about 1 time in 8, but if p is 0.10, X will virtually never be

20. The contrast between $b(X; 20, 0.30)$ and $b(X; 20, 0.50)$ is, as one would expect, much less marked than between $b(X; 20, 0.10)$ and $b(X; 20, 0.90)$. The outcome $X = 8$ is about as likely to be observed from $b(X; 20, 0.30)$ as from $b(X; 20, 0.50)$, the respective relative frequencies for $X = 8$ are 0.114 and 0.120, but the outcome $X = 6$ is much more likely to be observed from $b(X; 20, 0.30)$ than from $b(X; 20, 0.50)$, for the respective relative frequencies are 0.192 and 0.037.

TABLE 2.12. COMPARISON AND CONTRAST OF FOUR SELECTED BINOMIAL FREQUENCY DISTRIBUTIONS WITH n ALWAYS 20

$b(X; 20, 0.10)$		$b(X; 20, 0.30)$		$b(X; 20, 0.50)$		$b(X; 20, 0.90)$	
X	b	X	b	X	b	X	b
0	0.122	0	0.001	0		0	
1	0.270	1	0.007	1		1	
2	0.285	2	0.028	2	0.000	2	
3	0.190	3	0.072	3	0.001	3	
4	0.090	4	0.130	4	0.005	4	
5	0.032	5	0.179	5	0.015	5	
6	0.009	6	0.192	6	0.037	6	
7	0.002	7	0.164	7	0.074	7	
8	0.000	8	0.114	8	0.120	8	
9		9	0.065	9	0.160	9	
10		10	0.031	10	0.176	10	
11		11	0.012	11	0.160	11	
12		12	0.004	12	0.120	12	0.000
13		13	0.001	13	0.074	13	0.002
14		14	0.000	14	0.037	14	0.009
15		15		15	0.015	15	0.032
16		16		16	0.005	16	0.090
17		17		17	0.001	17	0.190
18		18		18	0.000	18	0.285
19		19		19		19	0.270
20		20		20		20	0.122
Total:	1.000		0.999		1.000		1.000

The Department of Commerce "Tables of the Binomial Probability Distribution" were used to obtain the relative frequencies in this table. The relative frequency was obtained from $b(X; 20, p) = \binom{20}{X} p^X (1 - p)^{20-X}$ by using $p = 0.10, 0.30, 0.50,$ and 0.90 in turn.

One can also study Table 2.12 in terms of the X most likely to be obtained from a random sample of size $n = 20$ from a specific binomial population. For example, if $p = 0.10$, the X with the highest relative frequency is $X = 2$, for which $b(2; 20, 0.10) = 0.285$, but if $p = 0.30, 0.50$, and 0.90 in turn, the most probable X's are 6, 10, and 18, respectively. It is observed that in all cases the most probable X for a given p is just $20(p)$. Specifically:

$$2 = \text{most probable } X \text{ for } p = 0.10, \quad \text{and} \quad 2 = 20(0.10)$$
$$6 = \text{most probable } X \text{ for } p = 0.30, \quad \text{and} \quad 6 = 20(0.30)$$
$$10 = \text{most probable } X \text{ for } p = 0.50, \quad \text{and} \quad 10 = 20(0.50)$$
$$18 = \text{most probable } X \text{ for } p = 0.90, \quad \text{and} \quad 18 = 20(0.90)$$

Figure 2.12 displays the frequency graphs for Table 2.12. These illustrate several points important in experimental research which involves the sampling of binomial populations. A sample of size n drawn at random from any binomial population produces a numerical value, X, which is a member of *some* binomial frequency distribution, $b(X; n, p)$ with p unknown. This is inevitable, and the making of decisions from such sample evidence must take this fact into account. Some of the points which bear on decisions made from binomial samples (and which are illustrated in Figure 2.12) are as follows:

(*a*) Only when $p = 0.50$ is the frequency distribution graph symmetrical so that the most probable X is in the middle of the range of values possible for $b(X; 20, 0.50)$. (When n is odd, there will be two "most probable" X's in the "middle.")

(*b*) When p is near either end of its possible range (namely, near 0 or near 1), the random X's are more closely grouped about the most probable X than when p is at or near 0.50. This observation corresponds to the mathematical fact that the variance of X is a maximum when $p = 1/2$ (see Problem 18, this section).

(*c*) If an X has been found to be 4 in a sample of size $n = 20$, it clearly is more likely that p is near 0.10 than that p is near 0.90, but *p could have been any size between* 0 *and* 1.

(*d*) If an X from a random sample of size $n = 20$ is found to be 8, a decision between $p = 0.30$ and $p = 0.50$ is subject to far more risk of error than a decision between $p = 0.30$ and $p = 0.90$ would be, because the frequency distributions for $p = 0.30$ and $p = 0.50$ overlap very much more than those for $p = 0.30$ and $p = 0.90$.

The points just illustrated will be seen to be involved, when one estimates p or tests hypotheses about p by means of sample data.

Table 2.13 was constructed as a partial generalization of Table 2.12. It shows 28 binomial frequency distributions in the 28 columns in the body of the table. Each distribution has $n = 20$, but the parameter p varies from near 0 to near 100%. *Each column is a single specific binomial frequency distribution* with the zeros, to two decimals, omitted after the first such term at each end of each distribution. No probability for this table is *exactly* zero, however.

If one chooses any X and reads from left to right in the table opposite

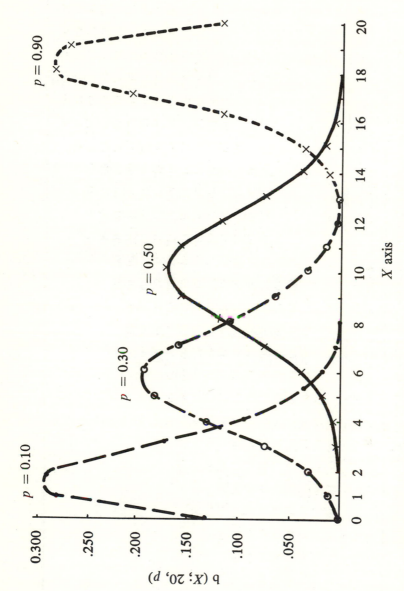

Figure 2.12.   The b(*X*; 20, *p*) distributions of Table 2.12 illustrating shape and overlap.

TABLE 2.13.   BINOMIAL FREQUENCY DISTRIBUTIONS $b(X; 20, p)$, WHEN $n = 20$ AND p HAS VALUES RANGING FROM 0.05 TO 0.95 AS INDICATED, STEP BOUNDARIES ROUGHLY DELINEATING THE 90% CONFIDENCE INTERVALS

p = the percent in the population having the specified attribute

Sample X	5	10	15	20	22	25	30	35	36	38	40	42	45	47	50	52	55	60	62	65	70	75	76	78	80	85	90	95
0	.36	.12	.04	.01	.01	.00	.00																					
1	.38	.27	.14	.06	.04	.02	.01	.00	.00																			
2	.19	.29	.23	.14	.10	.07	.03	.01	.01	.01	.00																	
3	.06	.19	.24	.21	.18	.13	.07	.03	.03	.02	.01	.01	.00	.00														
4	.01	.09	.18	.22	.21	.19	.13	.07	.06	.05	.03	.02	.01	.01	.00	.00												
5	.00	.03	.10	.17	.19	.20	.18	.13	.12	.09	.07	.06	.04	.03	.01	.01	.00											
6		.01	.05	.11	.14	.17	.19	.17	.16	.14	.12	.10	.07	.06	.04	.03	.01	.00										
7		.00	.02	.05	.08	.11	.16	.18	.18	.18	.17	.15	.12	.10	.07	.06	.04	.01	.01	.00								
8			.00	.02	.03	.06	.11	.16	.17	.18	.18	.18	.16	.15	.12	.10	.07	.04	.02	.01	.00							
9				.01	.01	.03	.07	.12	.13	.14	.16	.17	.18	.17	.16	.15	.12	.07	.05	.03	.01	.00						
10				.00	.00	.01	.03	.07	.08	.10	.12	.14	.16	.17	.18	.17	.16	.12	.10	.07	.03	.01	.01	.00				
11						.00	.01	.03	.04	.05	.07	.09	.12	.14	.16	.17	.18	.16	.14	.12	.07	.03	.02	.01	.01			
12							.00	.01	.02	.02	.04	.05	.07	.09	.12	.14	.16	.18	.18	.16	.11	.06	.05	.03	.02			
13								.00	.01	.01	.01	.02	.04	.05	.07	.09	.12	.17	.18	.18	.16	.11	.10	.08	.05	.02		
14									.00	.00	.00	.01	.01	.02	.04	.05	.07	.12	.14	.17	.19	.17	.16	.14	.11	.05	.01	
15												.00	.00	.01	.01	.02	.04	.07	.09	.13	.18	.20	.20	.19	.17	.10	.03	
16														.00	.00	.01	.01	.03	.05	.07	.13	.19	.20	.21	.22	.18	.09	.01
17																	.00	.01	.02	.03	.07	.13	.15	.18	.21	.24	.19	.06
18																			.01	.01	.03	.07	.08	.10	.14	.23	.29	.19
19																					.01	.02	.03	.04	.06	.14	.27	.38
20																								.01	.01	.04	.12	.36

this X, one sees again that *any* random X from a sample *could* have come from *any one* of many b(X; 20, p) distributions, but it is more likely to have come from certain populations than from others. In fact, given sufficient accuracy in the table, there always will be a largest relative frequency for each X, and this largest relative frequency will occur under that p which equals X/n. For example, with $n = 20$ and $X = 9$ the largest relative frequency opposite (to the right) $X = 9$ is the 0.18 under $p = 45\%$, and $X/20 = 9/20 = 0.45 = 45\%$. The British statistician, the late R. A. Fisher, apparently took this sort of fact as the basis of his method of maximum likelihood for estimating population parameters. Thus, if a random sample of size $n = 20$ produces $X = 9$, the method of maximum likelihood chooses $\hat{p} = 9/20 = 0.45$ as the estimate of the unknown parameter, p, in the binomial population so sampled, *because* such a choice of $\hat{p}$ maximizes the likelihood of occurrence of a sample with $X = 9$. As can be seen, the term "likelihood" is used to designate the probability of occurrence of the sample. For binomial frequency distributions this probability is, as noted earlier,

$$b(X; n, p) = \binom{n}{X} p^X q^{n-X}$$

Methods of calculus lead to the fact that $\hat{p} = X/n$ maximizes this function for a given X and n.

Table 2.13 also shows a step boundary, which includes between its top and bottom boundaries, *in each column separately*, at least 90% of the possible occurrences of the X's. For example, in the column under 22 the sum of the relative frequencies between the top and bottom boundary lines is:

$$0.10 + 0.18 + 0.21 + 0.19 + 0.14 + 0.08 = 0.90$$

and this includes the occurrence of X's from 2 to 7 inclusive. Thus, it is seen that values of X between 2 and 7 inclusive will be observed 90% of the time in samples from b(X; 20, 0.22). Put another way, there are 9 chances out of 10 that the next random sample of size $n = 20$ from a binomial population with $p = 0.22$ will produce $X =$ some number from 2 to 7 inclusive. All the other 15 possible sizes of X, that is 0, 1, 8, 9, 10, 11, $\cdots$, 19, and 20, considered together will occur only 1 time in 10, on the average.

The percentages of X's within the vertical boundaries of the columns in Table 2.13 usually do not add exactly to 0.90, but the general principles expressed above still hold true. These principles will be used later to develop the idea of a confidence interval on a population parameter, p.

PROBLEMS

1. If exactly two thirds of the inhabitants of a large midwestern area have an I.Q. (Intelligence Quotient) above 85, what is the probability that a person

chosen at random from that group will have an I.Q. below 86? If the people in this area were to be classified into two groups, I.Q. below 86 and I.Q. at or above 86, what binomial population could this define? Could several binomial populations be defined from this same I.Q. classification of the inhabitants of that area? Could several nonbinomial populations be so defined?

2. If 20 names were to be drawn at random from the binomial population described in Problem 1, what is the probability that X would be 10, where X is the number of people in the sample who have I.Q.'s above 85 and p is rounded off to the accuracy maintained in Table 2.13?

3. Suppose that it is known that 42% of the White Rock chickens raised under certain specified conditions will weigh less than 725 grams at eight weeks of age. Define a binomial population suggested by that fact. Referring to Table 2.13, read off the respective probabilities that among 20 such chicks chosen at random 6, 7, 8, or 9, respectively, will weigh less than 725 grams. Note that this problem asks for four separate probabilities of four separate events.

4. Suppose that you have taken a random sample of 20 observations from a binomial population with unknown parameter, p, and that you find that $X = 9$. What is your best estimate of the size of p? Why? What are some very unlikely values for p?

5. Suppose that 60% of the registered voters in a specified area are Democrats. What is the probability that 20 voters chosen at random from that area will include exactly 8 Democrats? What is the most likely number of Democrats to be in this sample? What is the probability that the Democrats (who are, in fact, in the majority in the area sampled) will be in the minority in the sample to be drawn?

6. Suppose that you were sent into a community to determine public opinion regarding the necessity for flood control of a certain specific sort for that area. How would you obtain your sample so that it would have the best chance to be representative of the whole community, even though you could question but 1% of the inhabitants of legal voting age? Would you take the sample vote by families? By individuals? By using a telephone listing of inhabitants? By using the tax rolls? By asking the man in the street? By other means?

7. Referring to Problem 6, would it make any difference in the results of your sampling if you did it just after a bad drought or just after a bad flood? Would you be sampling the same or different populations in those instances?

8. Suppose that a roving reporter is going into a certain city to ascertain public opinion on a matter of foreign policy. He will walk about the streets asking persons at random a specific question requiring one of three answers: Yes, No, or No Opinion. Will it make any difference what hours of the day between 7 A.M. and 6 P.M. he does this interviewing? Would the day of the week matter? Would the type of city—that is, industrial, college site, farming community, rich suburb, and the like—have anything to do with the answers to the previous questions? If so, what? What type of statistical population is he sampling? What are the parameters involved?

9. Suppose that a company which is manufacturing candies develops a new product which its originators believe is especially good. Which of the following possible ways of testing public reaction to the new candy would you prefer to use, and why?
(a) Sit back and see how the sales go.

(b) Have some trained persons offer samples to the public, and ask people to taste the candy, record their reactions on a card, and give the card directly to the company's representative.

(c) Place in the first 10,000 packages of candy manufactured for public consumption a stamped and addressed card with the request that the purchaser record his or her opinion on the card and mail it.

(d) Ask a panel of expert candy tasters to decide the matter.

(e) Do (d) first and then (a).

(f) Do (d) and then (b), except for having the card dropped into a box in the store away from the company's representative, so the customer will know that the representative will not know what the customer said.

(g) Do (f) first and then (c).

(h) Do something else. Specify.

10. Suppose that an engineering firm wishes to test the strengths of two types of structural beam produced and recommended by two different companies. Which of the following sampling procedures would you recommend, if the engineering company conducting this investigation has two testing laboratories, each with its own operating personnel available for use?

(a) Ask each company to send a specified number of beams for testing, and have each laboratory test half of each company's beams.

(b) Do as in (a), but have one laboratory test one company's beams and the second laboratory test the other company's beams.

(c) Go into the public market and purchase the necessary number of beams of each type, and then do as in (a). (Assume the beams could be so purchased.)

(d) Do as in (c), but replace (a) by (b).

(e) Do something else. Specify.

11. An agronomist wishes to run yield, protein, and test weight studies on a proposed new variety of wheat, before this variety is released to the public. He proposes to use a standard and widely planted variety of wheat for comparison with the new one. Plenty of land is available for this study, but the land is quite nonuniform in soil qualities, moisture content, and exposure to weather. Which of the following outlines for this study do you prefer, and why?

(a) Plant the new variety on the east half of the available land, the standard variety on the west half (or vice versa, as decided by flipping an unbiassed coin), harvest and measure the wheat from each half for yield, protein, and test weight, and study these records.

(b) Divide the available land into 20 equal-sized plots, and plant 10 of the plots to each variety, choosing the variety for any plot by drawing the variety names "from a hat" at random. Then make the required measurements for each plot separately, and study these statistically.

(c) Do as in (b), but first group the plots into 10 pair of plots, so that each pair has the two varieties grown side by side.

(d) Save the land for some other purpose, send out samples of each wheat seed to each of 10 farmers, and ask them to report the yields and test weights, and send samples in for protein analysis.

12. According to Table 2.13, on what percent of all sampling experiences would it be wrong to assume that X will not be smaller than 5 or larger than 12 if $p = 0.40$ and $n = 20$?

13. With the same background as in Problem 12, what percent of the time would one be wrong if one assumed that X would not have a value outside the step

boundaries of Table 2.13 if p were some one number between 0.40 and 0.50? What if p were between 0.70 and 0.90? What if no limitations were put on p other than $0 \leqslant p \leqslant 1$?

14. Suppose that a manufacturing process is producing an item which actually turns out to be below acceptable standards one time in each 10 items produced, on the average; that is, $p = 0.10$ for defective items. How likely is it that among 20 of these items selected at random none will be a defective item? What is the most likely number to be found defective?

15. Suppose that a student is taking a true-false examination containing 20 statements to be marked "T" or "F." If he knows nothing about the subject at all, he should have a probability $p = 1/2$ to mark a particular statement correctly. Under this assumption, and assuming independence of action on each item, what is the probability that he will mark exactly 14 items correctly? That he will mark *at least* 14 correctly? What is his most probable score?

16. Referring to Problem 15, suppose that a very large number of students, each of whom knew nothing about a certain subject, were to take an examination on that subject. Within what range, out of 20, would you think *about* 88% of the scores would fall? Is this a unique range, or could you think of another?

17. Make up a problem involving sampling a binomial population with $n = 20$, and use Table 2.13 to solve it.

18. Graph $V = npq$ (on vertical axis) for $n = 20$ and $p = 0.1, 0.2, 0.3, 0.4, 0.45, 0.5, 0.55, 0.6, 0.7, 0.8,$ and 0.9, thus illustrating the fact that the maximum variance occurs when $p = 1/2$.

19. Graph npq (on the vertical axis) against np for $n = 20$ and $p = 0.1, 0.2, 0.3, 0.4, 0.5, 0.6, 0.7, 0.8,$ and 0.9. Also plot the straight line between the points $(0, 0)$ and $(6, 6)$, thus illustrating with $n = 20$ the general fact that the variance of any binomial variate is always less than the mean.

2.2 POINT ESTIMATION OF THE BINOMIAL PARAMETER p FROM SAMPLE EVIDENCE

Any statistical population has a frequency distribution and one or more parameters. If a sample of size n is drawn from a statistical population, one can use that sample evidence to estimate the population parameter or parameters. In this connection it should be remembered that the computation of any number from the sample data produces a member of another population which also has a distribution and one or more parameters.

A binomial population has one parameter, p, and an almost trivial frequency distribution, for there are but two different members of a binomial population, such as male and female represented by 0's and 1's. The frequency distribution is simply the proportions of 0's and 1's, for example, p and $1 - p$.

If a random sample of size n is drawn from a binomial population with parameter p, and if X is the number of occurrences of some specified one of two possible events, whose relative frequency in the binomial population is p, then X is a member of another population, namely the $b(X; n, p)$ defined earlier.

The general problem of estimation under these circumstances is to make the most useful and reliable statement or statements one can about p and to express the reliability of such statements by means of probability statements. In the present section of this book a specific value, $\hat{p}$, will be assigned to p as being the best single *point estimate* available from the sample data. In the next section limits will be set on p, and a probability statement pertaining to the reliability of this *interval estimate* will be given.

In either approach, the *point estimate* or the *interval estimate*, the value or values assigned to p upon the basis of evidence from a sample of size n are subject to error, because they are based on a random variable. This situation requires the use of inductive inference rather than deductive inference. When one attempts to induce a general fact from a sample of instances, one is on uncertain grounds.

It is useful sometimes to distinguish between the process used to estimate a parameter and the result obtained by applying this process to a specific sample. The process is summarized in a rule for computing an *estimator* of the parameter. Application of this rule to specific sampling data produces an *estimate* of the parameter. For example, the rule for estimating p by the method of maximum likelihood is to use the *estimator* defined in the formula

$$\hat{p} = X/n$$

Given a sample of size $n = 20$, on which X turned out to be 13, application of this formula produces the maximum-likelihood *point estimate* of p:

$$\hat{p} = 13/20 = 0.65$$

It was suggested in Chapter 1 that such criteria as ease of computation, unbiassedness, efficiency, and the utilization of all available information should be used to determine which of several possible estimators one should employ in a particular situation. However, given that X Heads were obtained on n random tosses of a coin which is not necessarily unbiassed, it would be hard to see how any specific estimator of the parameter p, could be better than

(2.21) $$\hat{p} = X/n$$

Clearly, it is easy to compute, and it is the observed relative frequency of occurrence of Heads. The meaning of the term *maximum-likelihood estimator* was illustrated from Table 2.13 for a discrete enumerative random variable. It is seen from that table that in each column, which is a separate frequency distribution, the largest relative frequency (or probability) is opposite that X which is such that X/n is as nearly equal to p as the accuracy maintained in the table permits. For example, in the column below $p = 20\%$, the largest probability seen is 0.22, and it is opposite $X = 4$. With $X = 4$ and

$n = 20$, $X/n = 4/20 = 0.20 = 20\%$. Thus it is seen that the method of maximum likelihood does just what it says: it chooses that estimate, $\hat{p}$, of the parameter p which maximizes the likelihood of occurrence of the particular sample upon which the estimate is being based.

Although the mathematics of the theory of estimation by the method of maximum likelihood is beyond the level of this book, it can be said here that likelihood estimators satisfy most of the criteria previously discussed as desirable attributes of estimators; hence, such estimators are widely used in experimental statistics.

One important question remains to be discussed about the point estimator $\hat{p} = X/n$: How reliable is this estimator in the sense of consistently being close to the size of the parameter p being estimated? The variance of $\hat{p}$ can be shown to be

(2.22) $$\sigma_{\hat{p}}^2 = pq/n$$

which will be quite small if n is at all large. In practice, p and, hence, q are unknown and have to be estimated from the sample themselves; so that $\sigma_{\hat{p}}^2 = \hat{p}\hat{q}/n$ is used as an estimate of $\sigma_{\hat{p}}^2$. In any event, something must be done to measure and express the reliability of any proposed estimate of a population parameter. The variance (or the standard deviation, if preferred) of the $\hat{p}$ could be computed as indicated above, but it has been found to be preferable in many situations to compute an *interval estimate* of p instead of the point estimate $\hat{p}$, so nothing more will be said here about $\hat{p}$ and its standard deviation. The interval estimate will state only that p lies between two specific limits. This statement will be subject to some risk, or error, as are all inductive inferences, but the reliability of the statement will be measured in terms of probability, so one will know the risk being taken of making an error. For example, an engineer might state that the strength of a certain type of concrete structural beam lies between 1000 and 1200 pounds, and not attempt to pinpoint its strength more closely, but he would wish to know how reliable those limits are. This is a reasonable point of view, because all concrete structural beams of the same dimensions do not have the same strength. An engineer is chiefly concerned with the average, or potential, strength of beams of a given type or, perhaps, only with the minimum strength under specified conditions. If he can make the statement that the true average strength under study lies between 1000 and 1200 pounds, and if he has, say, 95 chances out of 100 of being right, then this interval estimate of the parameter can be quite useful.

PROBLEMS

1. As far as you can tell from Table 2.13, what is the maximum-likelihood estimate of p if $X = 9$ from a sample of size $n = 20$? If $X = 11$ from a sample of 20? If $X = 6$ when $n = 20$?

2. If $p = 0.30$, how large must n be to make the variance of $\hat{p} = X/n$ no more than 10% of the size of the parameter?

3. If 14 A-type plants are found in a random sample of 70 plants of a certain variety of wheat, what is the point estimate of p, the true percent of A-type plants in the binomial population sampled? Is this the maximum-likelihood estimate of p?

4. Suppose that in a room holding 125 "typical" legal voters, 14 have not made up their minds regarding their choice between two candidates for President of the United States two months before an election is to be held. What is the maximum-likelihood point estimate of $p =$ percentage of voters who are undecided at this time? What is the binomial population so sampled?

5. Estimate the standard deviation of the estimate $\hat{p}$ in Problem 4.

6. Suppose there is a bin full of two-inch spherical fishing floats in a certain sporting goods store. If you examine a simple random sample of 100 of these floats and find 7 with serious defects, what is the maximum-likelihood estimate of the proportion of nondefective floats in that bin? What is the estimated variance of that estimate?

7. Suppose a bin as in Problem 6 truly contains 6.5% defective floats. What is the variance of the maximum-likelihood estimate $\hat{p}$ obtainable from a sample of size $n = 50$? Of $n = 25, 36, 64, 81, 100$, in turn? Graph the relationship between $\sigma_{\hat{p}}^2$ (on vertical axis) and size of sample, n.

8. Do Problem 7, but replace "variance" with "standard deviation."

9. Suppose that as you walk down a street in a certain city you observe that 16 out of 90 ladies met are wearing some shade of blue. Assuming this is a random sample of that city, what is the maximum-likelihood estimate of the true percentage of the ladies wearing some shade of blue during that time?

10. If a coin is so biassed that the probability of heads is $p_H = 1/3$, what is the standard deviation of the number of heads thrown on sets of 9 tosses of this coin?

2.3   INTERVAL ESTIMATION OF THE PARAMETER p

Although the method of maximum likelihood produces excellent point estimates of population parameters, these point estimates (or point estimates made by any other procedure) are virtually certain to be in error to some degree. It is as though one were shooting with a rifle at a point on a straight line. Theoretically, a point has no dimensions and could not be hit, so the probability that one would hit an exact point is zero. However, one could talk about the probability of hitting within one inch of a chosen spot, and this essentially is what we do in interval estimation of a population parameter. Interval estimates are less specific regarding the magnitude of the parameter, but they have the great virtue of including an exact probability statement that the interval computed really will include the size of the parameter which is being estimated. That statement of probability is called a *confidence coefficient*, $1 - \alpha$, because it measures the degree of confidence that the experimenter has in the statement that the population parameter actually does lie within the stated confidence interval. The $1 - \alpha$ can be chosen arbitrarily as any probability between 0 and 1, exclusive of these end points. Usually, the confidence coefficient is chosen as 0.90, 0.95, or 0.99. It also is common to express the confidence coefficient as being 90, 95, or 99%.

Even though the choice of $1 - \alpha$ is arbitrary, it should be noted that the choice which is made will affect the length of the confidence interval to be obtained. Moreover, the length of a confidence interval affects its usefulness. Obviously, a longer confidence interval permits a less definite, and therefore less useful, statement about the parameter than does a shorter interval.

The experimenter usually has control over another matter which affects lengths of confidence intervals, namely the sample size, n. The larger the n, the shorter the confidence interval, on the average, for a given sampling situation, because there is more evidence on which to base the estimation of the interval.

The actual (but unknown) size of the parameter being estimated (besides that of other parameters, possibly) also has some effect on lengths of confidence intervals, but the experimenter often has no control over this feature. In normal sampling (to be covered in later chapters) the experimenter may be able to exert a useful influence on a parameter, say the variance, of a normal population by good design, and thereby shorten the average lengths of confidence intervals obtained from sampling data.

One point of view taken in interval estimation essentially is this: having set up rules for operation, taken a sample, and obtained an interval statement for the parameter being estimated, what binomial parameters, p_i, should one *accept* as possible? Obviously, the parameter is being treated as a variable from this point of view, and some bounds are going to be put on this variable, with an attendant risk of error, in order that a useful decision may be made. This, very crudely, is the *fiducial-limits* point of view initiated by the late Sir Ronald A. Fisher.

The *confidence-interval* point of view, originated by J. Neyman and E. S. Pearson, regards the binomial parameter as fixed and chooses the bounds on p (now called a confidence interval) so that the relative frequency with which sample confidence intervals will include the true p is at least $1 - \alpha$.

In most experimental situations the fiducial limits and the confidence interval are identical. In view of the fact that it seems more natural to take the point of view that an experimenter or other sampler is sampling a specific population with fixed parameter or parameters the confidence-interval procedure will be followed herein. There are also sampling situations in which one-sided limits are needed—that is, only a lower or an upper bound—and the fiducial procedure does not produce optimum lower or upper bounds.

In the latter situation one obtains either a lower bound or an upper bound with an associated degree of confidence expressed in the confidence coefficient

$1 - \alpha$. Because these bounds are considered in many cases to be the best lower and upper bounds, separately, which one can obtain with a given $1 - \alpha$, they will be designated as the *greatest lower bound* ($GLB_{1-\alpha}$) and the *least upper bound* ($LUB_{1-\alpha}$), respectively. A drug manufacturer of vaccines probably would want the $GLB_{1-\alpha}$ on the effectiveness of his product, while an animal scientist might prefer the $LUB_{1-\alpha}$ on the percentage of beef animals which had an unsafe concentration of some chemical in their meat, because he could hope, with confidence $1 - \alpha$, that no more than $LUB_{1-\alpha}$ of the beef animals carried seriously contaminated meat.

The two-sided confidence intervals which take their risk of error, α, from both extremes of the binomial distribution will be called *central* confidence intervals and denoted by $CI_{1-\alpha}$. The lower and upper limits on this central interval are denoted by L and U, respectively.

Suppose that a random sample of 20 observations from a binomial population with unknown parameter p produced $X = 8$ members which had the attribute A which an experimenter was studying, whereas the other 12 members of the sample were not-A. If reference is made to Table 2.13, it is seen that, within the limits of the two-place accuracy of that table, the sampling result $X = 8$ could have occurred from many binomial populations. If p actually were as low as 0.15, samples with $X = 8$ would occur only 1 time in 100, on the average, but they *would* occur. Samples of size $n = 20$ are most likely to produce $X = 8$ when the population percent, p, is about 40 to 42, according to Table 2.13. Clearly, the experimenter is faced with a situation which requires that he accept some risk of error, no matter what decision is made. Moreover, it is apparent that, the less risk of error he is willing to take, the more indefinite he must be about the unknown parameter, p. As noted previously, the larger the confidence coefficient, $1 - \alpha$, he uses— and it is open to arbitrary choice—the longer and less useful the confidence interval will be. At the same time, the risk of being wrong about whether p is in an interval computed from a sample is less for the longer interval, so one must balance the greater definiteness inherent in short intervals against the greater risk of error. This balance obviously depends upon the consequences of error.

The problem of the interval estimation of a population parameter has been solved by scientifically ignoring a known proportion of the rarer occurrences in binomial frequency distributions. Referring to Table 2.13 again, suppose that one has decided that it is appropriate to run a risk of 1 chance in 10 that the confidence interval obtained from the sampling evidence will fail actually to include p. One way this decision can be put into effect is to exclude from further consideration the extreme 5% (or less, if 5% cannot be attained exactly) from each end of every possible binomial frequency distribution. This process is illustrated by the two step boundaries drawn into the table. Outside those boundaries lies a percentage not to exceed 10%, of all possible binomial sampling experience covered by the table. Consequently, if one makes decisions on the assumption that those cases do not occur, those decisions will be wrong no more than 1 time in 10, on the average.

If, on a particular random sample of size $n = 20$, X turns out to be 8, we shall only consider as possible magnitudes for the p those p's which pertain to relative frequencies *inside* the step boundaries. This produces the following 90% confidence interval for p, the true percentage A's in the binomial population:

$$\text{CI}_{90}: \quad 25 \leqslant p \leqslant 60\%$$

It then would be assumed that the true percent of A's in the binomial situation sampled is in the range of 25 to 60%, inclusive. One's confidence in this conclusion is measured by odds of at least 9:1 or by a confidence coefficient, $(1 - \alpha) \geqslant 0.90$, because no more than 10% of all possible sampling experiences with $n = 20$ were excluded from consideration in setting up the step boundaries. Quite often less than 10% of the possible X's were excluded, as a result of the discontinuity of the distributions and the low degree of accuracy kept.

Table 2.31 is an extension of that portion of Table 2.13 which provides

TABLE 2.31.   EXTENSION OF TABLE 2.13 ILLUSTRATING THE CALCULATION OF L AND U FOR A CI_{90} WHEN $n = 20$ AND $X = 8$

X	$p=.20$	$p=.21$	$p=.215$	$p=.22$	$p=.23$	$\cdots$	$p=.59$	$p=.60$	$p=.605$	$p=.61$	$p=.62$
4	.218	.217	.215	.213	.207	$\cdots$	.000				
5	.175	.184	.188	.192	.198	$\cdots$	.002	.001	.001	.001	.001
6	.109	.123	.130	.136	.148	$\cdots$	.006	.005	.004	.004	.003
7	.055	.065	.070	.076	.088	$\cdots$	.018	.015	.013	.012	.009
(8)	.022	.028	.031	.035	.043	$\cdots$	.042	.035	.033	.030	.025
9	.007	.010	.012	.013	.017	$\cdots$	.080	.070	.066	.062	.054
10	.002	.003	.004	.004	.006	$\cdots$	.127	.117	.112	.107	.097
11		.001	.001	.001	.002	$\cdots$	.166	.160	.156	.153	.144
12					.000	$\cdots$	.179	.180	.180	.179	.177

$\sum b(X; 20, p)$ above step boundary: .026 .021 .051 .046 .038

.031 .042 .048 .053 .035 $\sum b(X; 20, p)$ below step boundary

an approximate CI_{90} on p if X is found to be 8 on a random sample of size $n = 20$ from some binomial population with unknown parameter p. In the preceding paragraph the CI_{90} was crudely estimated to be $25 \leqslant p \leqslant 60\%$. An improved estimate is made from Table 2.31 by using smaller intervals between p's and by using three-decimal accuracy. It is clear that the L and U (lower and upper bounds) are those values of p which are as small and as large, respectively, as possible and still have $X = 8$ exactly on the step boundary. Hence, we want the sum of the $b(X; 20, p)$ below the step boundary as close to 0.050 as possible when $p = L$, and the sum of $b(X; 20, p)$ above the step boundary to be as close to 0.050 as possible when $p = U$.

When these concepts are applied in Table 2.31, the CI_{90} on p becomes, as given in Table IV.

$$22 \leqslant p \leqslant 61$$

The procedure just illustrated for obtaining a central confidence interval is unnecessarily crude and laborious, so simpler and more accurate methods are available. It was used only to clarify the manner in which an interval estimate of p is obtained. Tables covering some of the more common experimental situations have been constructed. Tables IV, V, and VI are three such. They were constructed by using the principles described above but taking advantage of the existence of tables of binomial frequency distributions for a wide range of p's and sample sizes. The construction of these tables can be accomplished several ways. One process will be discussed briefly in the following paragraphs.

It would seem from the above that L should be determined by so choosing p that $\sum_{i=x+1}^{n} b(i; p, n) \leqslant \alpha/2$ and by choosing U in a similar manner so that $\sum_{i=x}^{n} b(i; p, n)$ is $\geqslant (1 - \alpha/2)$. This procedure, however, is somewhat indefinite, and:

(*a*) In the former case the lower limit, L, should be excluded from the confidence limits, because $X + 1$ is outside the central $1 - \alpha$, whereas in the latter case U apparently should be included in the confidence limits, because X is within the central $1 - \alpha$ of events.

(*b*) If $X = 0$, the $\sum_{i=x}^{n} b(i; p, n)$ always is 1.

(*c*) For sample sizes usually involved in experimental research, the central $1 - \alpha$ includes more than $1 - \alpha$ of the possible X's, a situation which tends to widen the confidence limits.

Hence, after some preliminary investigations it was decided that the confidence intervals to be presented in Tables IV, V, and VI would be derived from the following formulas, which can be read from existing binomial tables:

When $\sum_{i=x}^{n} b(i; p, n) = \alpha/2$ as nearly as possible by choice of p, this $p = L$. This causes the sum of probabilities for events above the central $1 - \alpha$ of possible events (larger X's) to be as close to $\alpha/2$ as possible by use of summations.

When $\sum_{i=x+1}^{n} b(i; p, n) = (1 - \alpha/2)$ as nearly as possible by choice of p, this $p = U$. This action causes the sum of probabilities of events below the central $1 - \alpha$ of possible events (smaller X's) to be as near to $\alpha/2$ as possible with tabular summations.

Tables IV, V, and VI were derived originally in this way, the L and U being taken to the nearest whole percent. One could debate whether the L and U should be included in the confidence interval or excluded therefrom. Although there seems to be some reason to exclude them, other small inaccuracies, such as rounding off to the nearest percent, make this seem a useless refinement, so for teaching purposes it is probably less confusing to include the L and U as part of the interval, because this is the natural interpretation made by the student.

The intervals in Tables IV, V, and VI also were checked by means of formulas for exact confidence intervals on p which involve the F distribution of Table XII. These formulas are as follows (see Bowker and Lieberman, for example):

$$(2.31) \qquad L = \frac{X}{X + (n - X + 1)\, F_{\alpha/2}[2(n - X + 1),\, 2X]}$$

for the lower limit and

$$(2.32) \qquad U = \frac{(X + 1)\cdot F_{\alpha/2}[2(X + 1),\, 2(n - X)]}{(n - X) + (X + 1)\cdot F_{\alpha/2}[2(X + 1),\, 2(n - X)]}$$

for the upper limit, where $X =$ observed number with, say, attribute A, $n =$ sample size, and $1 - \alpha =$ the confidence coefficient.

For example, if $n = 100$, $\alpha = 0.10$, and X is found to be 25, then by Table XII

$$F_{0.05}[2(100 - 25 + 1),\, 50] = F_{0.05}(152,\, 50) = 1.50,$$
$$F_{0.05}[2(25 + 1),\, 2(100 - 25)] = F_{0.05}(52,\, 150) = 1.43$$

and therefore

$$L = \frac{25}{25 + 76(1.50)} = 0.18$$

$$U = \frac{26(1.43)}{75 + 26(1.43)} = 0.33$$

as in Table IV for $n = 100$ and $X = 25$. Tables IV, V, and VI were checked by means of Formulas 2.31 and 2.32, and corrected so the reader can verify them easily.

Tables IV, V, and VI are extremely easy to use. For example, suppose that a random sample of size $n = 50$ has been drawn from a binomial population based upon animals classified as either Dominant or Recessive and that 9 out of the 50 were of the Recessive type. Looking in Table IV opposite $X = 9$ and under $n = 50$, one finds that $L = 11$ and $U = 29$ or, symbolically,

$$\text{CI}_{90}: \qquad 11 \leqslant p \leqslant 29\%$$

It is concluded with 90% confidence that the true percentage of Recessives in the animal population sampled is some number from 11 to 29, inclusive, but not necessarily an integer.

From Table V one would conclude in a similar manner, but with 95% confidence, that p lies in the interval $9 \leqslant p \leqslant 31\%$ Recessive when $X = 9$ and $n = 50$. This interval is longer than the CI_{90} for the obvious reason that less risk has been taken of an erroneous decision with the consequent need to be more equivocal about the true size of p. If one wishes to have 99%

assurance that a sampling result has not misled him, the confidence interval lengthens to

$$\text{CI}_{90}: \qquad 7 \leqslant p \leqslant 36\% \text{ Recessive}$$

If an experimenter wishes (or needs) to have a relatively short and perhaps more useful confidence interval, he can take one or both of the following actions: accept greater risk of error by choosing a larger α and take a larger sample. If a sample of 500 had been taken instead of only 50, as above, and if X/n had been the same relative size (namely 0.18), the following confidence intervals would have been obtained from Tables IV, V, and VI respectively:

		Risk of error
$\text{CI}_{90}:$	$15 \leqslant p \leqslant 21\%$	1 in 10
$\text{CI}_{95}:$	$15 \leqslant p \leqslant 22\%$	1 in 20
$\text{CI}_{99}:$	$14 \leqslant p \leqslant 23\%$	1 in 100

The lengths of those intervals are 6, 7, and 9 units as compared with the lengths of 16, 20, and 26 units, respectively, obtained when the sample size was only $n = 50$. It is seen in this example that decreasing the risk of error tenfold will have much less effect on the length of the confidence interval than will increasing the sample size tenfold. However, matters of convenience and economy and the seriousness of being wrong must all be considered before a course of action is chosen.

If the noncentral limits of $\text{GLB}_{1-\alpha}$ or $\text{LUB}_{1-\alpha}$ arc preferred, one uses Table IV when $\alpha = 0.05$, Table V when $\alpha = 0.025$, and Table VI when $\alpha = 0.005$. One also could use Table 2.13 when $n = 20$ and put in only one step boundary for each α. Preferably, one could use Formulas 2.31 and 2.32 with α replaced by 2α and L and U replaced by $\text{GLB}_{1-2\alpha}$ and $\text{LUB}_{1-2\alpha}$, respectively.

PROBLEMS

1. Suppose that you buy a bushel of peaches and find that of the 150 fruits in the basket 10 are rotten. If one can assume sensibly that these 150 peaches are a random sample of the peaches a certain store is selling in a given season, what is the maximum-likelihood point estimate of the true percentage of rotten peaches being sold by this store in this season? What is the CI_{95} on that same parameter to the nearest whole percent? How would you interpret this interval to someone?

2. Would the answers given to Problem 1 necessarily apply to next season's sales? To another store in this same city this year?

3. If you had done the sampling suggested in Problem 1, would you believe the storekeeper's statement that among all of his sales this season no more than 5% of the peaches sold were rotten? Give a reason for your answer.

4. Usually, when one is going to study a binomial population by taking a random sample, it is well to determine the size of the sample to be taken upon the

basis of the usefulness of the estimate one will thereafter obtain for p. If one must obtain a confidence interval less than 10 units long, or if that interval estimate will be so indefinite as to be useless, it is idle to take a sample of size $n = 20$ and set $1 - \alpha = 0.95$, because, as Table IV shows, *all* CI_{95}'s for $n = 20$ are longer than 10 units. What size of sample should one take in these circumstances? Would it help to know that the p certainly was below 0.10? Or between 0.40 and 0.60? If so, how does it help in each instance?

5. Suppose that 100 bolts have been taken at random from a large batch of bolts and that $X = 2$ have been found to be defective under a specific definition of this term. What is the 90% confidence interval on the true percent defective in the batch so sampled? What information does this interval give?

6. Suppose that a random sample of 50 apples has been taken from a certain large tree. If 5 of the apples in this sample have a certain specific blight, what percentage of blighted apples do you estimate for the whole tree, if you safely can accept a risk of 1 chance in 10 that your answer is wrong? Do likewise with a risk of 1 in 100.

7. If a sample of 250 gun barrels from a large shipment has been examined for defects and none found defective, place 99% confidence limits on the percent defective in the whole batch. Would a sample of size $n = 250$ be large enough, if the acceptable proportion defective is only 1%?

8. Suppose that of 100 cattle selected at random from a very large number of cattle in a certain locality 15 have been found to be tubercular reactors. What is the upper 95% confidence limit on the true percentage of TB reactors in the area sampled?

9. Calculate directly from the binomial series for $(q + p)^6$ the 75% confidence interval on p if 3 out of 6 items in a random sample have a specified attribute A. Obtain limits on p to the nearest multiple of 5. Use the process shown in Table 2.13.

10. Suppose that an entomologist wishes to learn what percent of the corn plants in a large field are infested to some degree by the southwestern corn borer. He thinks the percentage is between 20 and 80, but he wishes to reduce this uncertainty to an interval of not over 15 percentage units. If he is willing to accept a risk of 5 in 100 of drawing an erroneous conclusion about the true percentage infestation by this corn borer, how large a sample must he take?

11. Suppose that you are helping to administer a farm management association and wish to learn what percentage of its members use a certain practice recommended to poultrymen. If a random sample of poultrymen in the area to which the recommendation has been made shows that 200 out of 250 in this sample do follow the association's recommendation, what can you say about the true percentage of poultrymen in the whole area who follow the association's recommendation in the respect studied?

12. Suppose that a public-opinion poll concerning a gubernatorial race shows that 160 out of 300 votes are for candidate Doe. What is the greatest lower bound on Doe's true percentage of the votes at that time in that city if α is taken as 0.10? What is the least upper bound on Doe's opponent's true percentage of the votes? What conclusions can you draw?

13. Suppose that during the first two weeks of the fishing season on a certain lake the following catches have been made: 35 northern pike, 60 black bass,

25 drum, and 180 crappie. Assuming this is a good sample and that conditions stay the same, how could you use a 95% confidence interval to compute your most optimistic probability of catching a black bass on your next try? Your most pessimistic probability? The central CI_{90} on your probability? Do the same for catching either a northern pike or a black bass.

14. Suppose that you have obtained 40 seeds from a Joshua tree and have found that 32 of them germinated. Assuming these are typical Joshua tree seeds from that tree, what is the greatest lower bound on the true percentage germination for that Joshua tree's seeds if $\alpha = 0.05$? What is the central CI_{90}?

15. Suppose that, when a certain procedure for displaying head lettuce to the public was tried on 100 head, the equivalent of 5 head was lost as a result of spoilage over a three-day period. If the net profit on a head of lettuce is 10 cents (ignoring overhead and other storewide expenses) what is the most optimistic estimate of spoilage loss under this display procedure with $\alpha = 0.05$? What is the most pessimistic estimate?

16. Suppose that you take a random sample of 50 bolt-and-nut combinations from a large bin in a hardware store and find that with four pairs the nut will not screw entirely down on the threads of the bolt. What is the CI_{90} on the true percentage of such faulty pairs in the whole bin? If there were only 25 bolt-nut pairs left in the bin when you had completed your sampling, how would this affect you conclusions?

17. Suppose that an animal scientist wishes to conduct an experiment on newborn Poland China pigs and needs eight pigs in one litter. If records on 50 Poland China sows show that 32 had eight or more pigs on their second farrowing and this scientist has four such sows about to farrow, what is the most optimistic probability that he will get at least one eight-pig litter for his experiment? Use a confidence interval with a confidence coefficient of 0.90. Do the same for his most pessimistic probability. What if he needs two eight-pig litters?

2.4 TESTING HYPOTHESES ABOUT p BY MEANS OF CONFIDENCE INTERVALS

In some types of scientific research the experimenter has a specific hypothesis about the population parameter which is being studied and wishes to test this hypothesis against actual observations made on the population during an experiment. For example, he may expect an equal division of the sexes among certain plants or animals by virtue of some logical reasoning from past experience. If so, he would wish to know whether the sample evidence bore out the theory that $p_M = 1/2$, where p_M was the true fraction classified as Males. Samples rarely reproduce population ratios exactly, so the experimenter essentially asks whether the observed departure from theoretical expectation is reasonably assignable to sampling error, that is, to chance. If not, according to a probability level chosen to measure reasonableness satisfactorily, the experimenter will wish to reject the hypotheses $H_0(p_M = 1/2)$, where p is the proportion of males in the population being studied. One could as well use $p_F = 1/2$ for Females.

When an experiment has been conducted to test a stated hypothesis and the data from this experiment are at hand, a decision then needs to be made about the hypothesis, H_0. At the outset of a study there must be one or more alternatives to H_0, for there would be nothing to test unless one faced the question "If H_0 is not true, what is?" It will be seen that even the manner in which H_0 should be tested depends on the logical alternatives to H_0. The alternative hypothesis will be denoted by H_a.

It also should be recognized that nothing is going to be *proved* unequivocally by any experiment, because the true situation sampled is, and shall remain, unknown. All that can be hoped for is to reach a logical and objective conclusion which has an appropriate probability of being so close to the exact truth that the "error" is unimportant to the experimenter. For example, if it is concluded that $H_0(p = 1/2)$ is an acceptable hypothesis compared to the alternative $H_a(p = 3/4)$, this does not imply that p could not be 0.51 or perhaps even 0.55, but it does imply that $H_0(p = 1/2)$ definitely is preferable to the conclusion $H_a(p = 3/4)$. If there are other reasonable alternatives besides $p = 3/4$, then the alternative hypothesis should include them.

The following summarizes the terminology to be employed. It will be said that the hypothesis H_0 being tested is accepted if H_0 is deemed preferable to the alternative, H_a, and it will be said that H_0 is rejected if, as a result of an experiment and statistical analysis, H_0 is not preferable to H_a. These preferences are based on regions of rejection of a predetermined size α, which are so chosen as to give the test as much power as possible to reject false hypotheses.

It would be inappropriate herein to deal extensively with the subject of *simple* versus *composite* hypotheses, but these terms will be defined and illustrated. A *simple hypothesis* about a parameter is any hypothesis which completely defines the population. For example, $H_0(p = 1/2)$ for a binomial population completely defines that population from the statistical point of view. Given any chosen sample size, n, it also completely defines the binomial frequency distribution, $b(X; n, p)$.

Any statistical hypothesis which is not simple is called a *composite hypothesis*. For example, $H_0(p \geqslant 1/2)$ does not define a single binomial population; in fact, infinitely many binomial populations have $p \geqslant 1/2$. As might be expected, it often is much more difficult to deal fully with composite hypotheses than with simple hypotheses. Unfortunately, in a sense, many practical hypotheses are composite.

Whenever a hypothesis is accepted or rejected, this decision is liable to two sorts of error, as noted in Chapter 1. The hypothesis H_0 may be rejected, when it actually is correct. This is called an *error of the first kind*, or a *Type I error*. If the hypothesis, H_0, is accepted when, in fact, it is false, an *error of the second kind*, or a *Type II error*, has been committed. Type I errors are traditionally more feared than Type II errors, presumably because it is reasoned that any hypothesis worth testing should be based upon considerable thought and, perhaps, experimental evidence. Actually, this point of view may be wrong, because a specific H_0 may be tested just because it is convenient. For example, a person may test the hypothesis that a newly discovered genetic trait of economic importance is so inherited that it is convenient to use $H_0(p = 1/2)$ instead of attempting to guess what the specific probability is. If so, the experimenter surely would be at least as anxious not to conclude falsely that $p = 1/2$ (a Type II error) as he would be to avoid rejecting $H_0(p = 1/2)$ when it is true (a Type I error). It merely is convenient to test $H_0(p = 1/2)$ because it seems close to the truth and can be explained readily.

Because the probability of committing a Type I error (falsely rejecting H_0) can be computed from the appropriate sampling distribution for the cases we shall consider, its value is fixed at a level we denote by the Greek letter α (alpha), and thereafter the best region of rejection is determined in some sense of "best." For example, if one wishes to test $H_0(p = 1/4)$ for a binomial population by drawing a random sample of size $n = 20$, then the binomial frequency distribution $b(X; n, p) = b(X; 20, 0.25)$ and is completely specified by H_0. In fact, this distribution is shown with two-decimal accuracy in Table 2.13 under $p = 25\%$. To test $H_0(p = 1/4)$, one must choose a set of values of X such that, if any one of them is obtained in the sample drawn, this event will cause H_0 to be rejected. Such a set of X's is called a *region of rejection* and is denoted by the Greek letter omega, ω. The size of any region of rejection is simply the probability, α, that X will fall in ω *if H_0 is true*, which would cause the rejection of H_0.

Suppose we choose $\alpha = 0.10$ and decide to use the region of rejection

$$\omega_1: \quad X \geqslant 8$$

which is of size $\alpha = 0.10$, as can be verified in Table 2.13. Another possible region of rejection of size $\alpha = 0.10$ is

$$\omega_2: \quad X \leqslant 2 \quad \text{and} \quad X \geqslant 10$$

and a third region, also of size $\alpha = 0.10$, is

$$\omega_3: \quad X = 2 \quad \text{or} \quad X = 9$$

Any of these three regions could be used to test $H_0(p = 1/4)$ and would have a probability, $\alpha = 0.10$, of committing a Type I error. Which region of rejection should one use?

The rather obvious and logical answer is that one should use that region which has the smallest probability of allowing a Type II error. A Type II error can be committed only if H_0 is false. Furthermore, the probability that a Type II error will be committed depends on how wrong H_0 is. Thus, we can talk about Type II error only in relation to admissible alternatives of H_0. It is customary to let β be the probability of a Type II error, and to call

$1 - \beta$ the *power* of the test. The power obviously is the probability of detecting a false H_0.

Suppose that, actually, $p = 30\%$. With ω_1 the probability that the *untrue* $H_0(p = 1/4)$ will be rejected is the probability that X will be 8 or larger when $p = 0.30$; that is, $1 - \beta_1 = 0.11 + 0.06 + 0.03 + 0.01 = 0.21$. Thus, the power of the region of rejection ω_1 is 0.21 against the simple alternative $H_a(p = 0.30)$. For ω_2 and ω_3 the powers are $1 - \beta_2 = 0.03 + 0.01 + 0.03 + 0.01 = 0.08$ and $1 - \beta_3 = 0.03 + 0.06 = 0.09$, respectively. Hence, ω_1 is decidedly the best region of rejection for testing the simple hypothesis $H_0(p = 1/4)$ against the simple alternative $H_a(p = 0.30)$, because this test of significance has 21 chances in 100 of detecting the falsity of H_0 when, in fact, $p = 0.30$, whereas the other two have only 8 and 9 chances per 100, respectively. It is noted that in this instance, in which the true size of p is larger than that supposed in H_0, the best region of rejection is the one based solely on some larger sizes of X. That is, ω is in the right-hand tail of the graph of $b(X; n, p)$.

If p actually is 20%, the following information can be read directly from Table 2.13:

$$\text{With } \omega_1, \quad \Pr\{\text{reject false } H_0\} = 0.03$$
$$\text{With } \omega_2, \quad \Pr\{\text{reject false } H_0\} = 0.21$$
$$\text{With } \omega_3, \quad \Pr\{\text{reject false } H_0\} = 0.15$$

The probability of a Type I error is $\alpha = 0.10$ for all three regions of rejection. Hence, it now is seen that the best one of these three regions is ω_2, which includes $X \leqslant 2$. If α had been 0.11, another region, ω_4, where $X \leqslant 3$, would have had the power $1 - \beta = 0.41$ to reject the false $H_0(p = 0.25)$.

If there is logical reason to believe strongly, in advance of the taking of the sample, that if H_0 is false it errs in the direction of being too small, one should use a *one-tail region of rejection*, such as ω_1 or ω_4. A similar statement holds when the logical alternative of H_0 is $H_a(p < p_0)$, where $0 < p_0 < 1$. If, however, there is no logical reason to choose an alternative in one direction, one should use a *two-tail region of rejection*, such as ω_2.

The confidence intervals studied in the previous section offer a ready means of testing hypotheses about p. For example, if α is chosen as 0.10 and n as 20, the $H_0(p = 1/4)$ can be tested against $H_a(p \neq 1/4)$ as follows, assuming that the random sample produced $X = 6$. Table IV shows that the 90% confidence interval on the parameter p is

$$\text{CI}_{90}: \quad 14 \leqslant p \leqslant 51\%$$

and it includes the p stated in H_0; therefore, H_0 is accepted. The use of a confidence interval of this sort to test an H_0 is a two-tail test of significance, because in obtaining the confidence intervals shown in Table IV equal risk of a Type I error was taken from each tail of each binomial distribution as nearly as possible.

If it is desirable to test $H_0(p = 1/4)$ versus $H_a(p > 1/4)$, one should use a one-tail test by means of a GLB_{90}. This requires either a CI_{80} table for p or the use of Formula 2.31 with $\alpha = 0.20$. The latter is the easier, especially in view of the lack of CI_{80} tables. With $\alpha = 0.20$, $X = 6$, and $n = 20$, by the application of Formula 2.31 one obtains

$$L = GLB_{90} = \frac{6}{6 + 15F_{.10}(30, 12)} = 0.17$$

The hypothesis $H_0(p = 1/4)$ is above this lower bound; hence, H_0 is accepted. If, however, X had turned out to be 10, $GLB_{90} = 0.34$ and $H_0(p = 1/4)$ would be rejected in favor of $H_a(p > 1/4)$.

There are many practical situations in which one wishes to test the composite hypothesis $H_0(p \leqslant p_0)$ against the composite alternative $H_a(p > p_0)$ or the reverse, $H_0(p \geqslant p_0)$ versus $H_a(p < p_0)$. For the one-parameter binomial population a test of this sort is quite easy. It depends upon the truth of the following mathematical theorem (see Mood-Graybill, *Introduction to the Theory of Statistics*, 2nd edition, McGraw-Hill, New York, 1963, p. 295).

Theorem.   Suppose the probability density function $f(X)$ for a one-parameter population can be written in the form:

(2.41) $f(X) = s(p) \cdot U(X) \cdot \exp \{v(X) \cdot t(p)\}$

where $s(p)$, $U(X)$, $v(X)$, and $t(p)$ are functions only of p, X, X, and p, respectively. Then, if there exists a constant c such that $\Pr\{[v(X) > c] \mid p_0\} = \alpha$, the region of rejection for testing $H_0(p \leqslant p_0)$ versus $H_a(p > p_0)$ is

$$\omega: \qquad v(X) > c$$

To illustrate, consider the binomial probability function $f(X) = b(X; n, p)$. This function involves only one parameter when the sample size n has been chosen. It can be written in the form suggested by the theorem or as given in Formula 2.42:

$$b(X; n, p) = (1 - p)^n \cdot \left[\frac{n!}{X!(n - X)!}\right]\left(\frac{p}{1 - p}\right)^X$$

(2.42) $b(X; n, p) = (1 - p)^n \cdot \left[\dfrac{n!}{X!(n - X)!}\right] \cdot \exp \{X \log_e [p/(1 - p)]\}$

$$= s(p) \cdot [U(X)] \cdot \exp \{v(X) \cdot t(p)\}$$

where $s(p) = (1 - p)^n$, $U(X) = \binom{n}{X}$, $v(X) = X$, and $t(p) = \log [p/(1 - p)]$.

Therefore, one needs to find a constant c such that $\Pr\{(X > c) \mid (p = p_0)\} = \alpha$; that is, the integer c is to be so chosen that the binomial variate X has the probability α of exceeding that c on a specified future random sample if $p = p_0$, as in H_0.

To illustrate the preceding discussion specifically, suppose $\alpha = 0.05$, $p_0 = 0.10$, and $n = 20$. Then we wish to test $H_0(p \leqslant 0.10)$ against $H_a(p > 0.10)$. By the theorem outlined earlier, we essentially need to determine c such that

$$\Pr\{v(X) > c \mid p = 0.10\} = 0.05$$

With the binomial frequency distribution $b(X; 20, 0.10)$,

$$\Pr\{(X > c) \mid (p = 0.10)\} = 0.05$$

requires that c be 4 (see Table 2.13) because

$$\Pr\{(X > 4) \mid (p = 0.10)\} = 0.04^+$$

whereas $\Pr\{(X > 5) \mid (0.10)\}$ is only 0.01 and

$$\Pr\{(X > 3) \mid (p = 0.10)\} = 0.13$$

Because the n is only 20, we cannot get Pr any closer to 0.05 than what using $X = 4$ gives us. Hence, the region of rejection for testing $H_0(p \leqslant 0.10)$ against $H_a(p > 0.10)$ with $\alpha = 0.05$ and $n = 20$ is one in which X is *greater than* 4; that is,

$$\omega: \quad X \geqslant 5$$

If one were to approach this same problem of testing $H_0(p \leqslant 0.10)$ against $H_a(p > 0.10)$ by means of noncentral confidence intervals, he would set $\alpha = 0.05$, choose $n = 20$, and obtain an X from a random sample. The *lower* limit of Table IV for a central confidence interval would be the GLB_{90} on p. If this p were > 0.10, then H_0 would be rejected; if not, H_0 would be accepted. One sees from Table IV under L and for $n = 20$ that, if $X \leqslant 4$, the figure is less than 10 and, if $X > 5$, the lower limit is > 10. At $X = 5$ the lower limit is 10. Considering the discontinuity of $b(X; 20, p)$ and the large gaps for $n = 20$, this is not a serious disagreement with the ω stated above, namely $X \geqslant 5$, for rejecting $H_0(p \leqslant 0.10)$. Thus, the noncentral CI_{90} test appears to be equivalent to the test embodied in Equation 2.41.

PROBLEMS

1. According to certain genetic theory, if a heterozygous red-eyed fruit fly is mated to a white-eyed fruit fly, one half of the offspring are expected (statistically) to be white-eyed. Suppose that among 500 such offspring 240 are found to be white-eyed. Does the CI_{90} on the true proportion, p, of white-eyed individuals in the group sampled indicate that the genetic theory is correct? What is the region of rejection in this test?

2. Suppose that 15 of 100 concrete test beams have been found to be lighter than is acceptable for such beams and that these 100 beams reasonably can be considered representative of the general type of concrete beam produced

by a certain company. On the basis of this sampling evidence would you accept or would you reject $H_0(p = 0.10)$ versus $H_a(p \neq 0.10)$, where p is the true percentage of lighter-than-acceptable beams in the group sampled? State the significance level and region of rejection used. Could another region of rejection be used with α still 0.10?

3. If in the situation of Problem 2 the sample size had been 200 and 15% of the beams had been too light, how would your conclusions have changed?

4. Suppose that there are but two candidates for a certain political office and that in a random sample of 150 voters in that area 80 are for Mr. Jones and 70 favor his opponent. Would you accept the hypothesis that 51% of all the voters in that area favor Jones' opponent?

5. If 52 students in a biology class of 200 have type A blood, would you accept $H_0(p_A = 0.35)$ over against $H_a(p_A \neq 0.35)$ if $\alpha = 0.10$ and the class is representative of a binomial population with parameter p_A? What if the alternative hypothesis were $H_a(p_A < 0.35)$?

6. Suppose that a plant pathologist takes a random sample of 300 plants from a field of a certain variety of wheat and finds that 42 plants have a certain race of smut. If α is chosen as 0.05, would you accept $H_0(p_S = 0.10)$ over against $H_a(p_S > 0.10)$, where p_S is the true percentage of smutted plants in that field?

7. The maturity date of some agronomic crops is determined as that date on which half the plants are in bloom. If an agronomist takes a random sample of 200 plants in a certain field of sorghum and finds 90 in bloom, is $H_0(p_B = 0.50)$ acceptable against $H_a(p_B < 0.50)$ if $\alpha = 0.10$ and p_B is the true percent of the plants in bloom when the sample was taken? What if $H_0(p_B \geqslant 0.50)$ is tested?

8. Some counties in certain states try to keep the assessed valuations of properties at 30% of actual sale value. If a random sample of 100 pieces of property in a given county is found to have 60 properties essentially at 30% and 40 definitely below 30%, is $H_0(p_{30} = 70)$ acceptable against $H_a(p_{30} < 70)$, where p_{30} is the true percent of properties assessed at essentially 30% of sale value, and with α as 0.10? What if $H_0(p_{30} \geqslant 70)$ is tested?

9. Suppose that a freight car load of boys' bicycles is sampled by inspecting 50 bicycles for serious defects. If 3 of the bikes are defective, what is the GLB_{90} on the true percentage of defective bikes in this car? Would $H_0(p_D = 0.2)$ be acceptable at the 10% level of significance, as against $H_a(p_D > 0.2)$?

10. Suppose that in a random sample of 300 one-inch firecrackers taken from a large shipment 25 will not explode. Test $H_0(p_{NG} = 0.5)$ versus $H_a(p_{NG} > 0.5)$ if $\alpha = 0.05$ and p_{NG} as the true percent of No-Goods in the shipment.

11. Suppose that when a set of five six-sided dice is tossed fairly 250 times, the following results are obtained on the 1250 faces turning up:

Number up:	1	2	3	4	5	6
Percent of time:	17.4	15.7	17.2	14.9	18.2	16.7

Because no adjustment has been made on these dice for the fact that five and six hemispherical pockets were taken out of the five and six sides, respectively, and only two and one such pockets from their respective opposite sides, one might expect 5's and 6's to appear more frequently than other numbers. Use these data to test the hypothesis that the probability of a 5 or a 6 on any one such die is $p_{5 \text{ or } 6} = 1/3$ versus $H_a(p_{5 \text{ or } 6} > 1/3)$ by means of a 90% confidence interval.

12. Suppose that power-steering units are being inspected at the end of a production line and either passed or rejected. If a random sample of 200 units shows 15 were rejected, is $H_0(p_R = 5)$ acceptable against $H_a(p_R > 5)$ if $\alpha = 0.10$ and p_R is the true percentage of rejects being produced during the period of time sampled?

13. Use Equation 2.41 to test $H_0(p \geqslant 0.51)$ against $H_a(p < 0.51)$ with the information in Problem 4.

14. Use Equation 2.41 to test $H_0(p_S \leqslant 10)$ against $H_a(p_S > 10)$ with the information of Problem 6.

15. Use Equation 2.41 to test $H_0(p_{30} \geqslant 70)$ against $H_a(p_{30} < 70)$ under the conditions of Problem 8.

16. Use Equation 2.41 to test $H_0(p_D \leqslant 2)$ against $H_a(p_D > 2)$ with the information of Problem 9.

17. Use Equation 2.41 to test $H_0(p_{NG} \leqslant 5)$ against $H_a(p_{NG} > 5)$ under the conditions of Problem 10.

18. Use Equation 2.41 to test $H_0(p_{5 \text{ or } 6} > 1/3)$ against $H_a(p_{5 \text{ or } 6} \leqslant 1/3)$ under the conditions of Problem 11.

2.5   TESTING HYPOTHESES ABOUT THE BINOMIAL PARAMETER p WITH THE CHI-SQUARE TEST

The chi-square test of significance in some respects is more flexible than the confidence-interval procedure described in Section 2.4. Moreover, the chi-square distribution has a number of other uses in experimental statistics, so it is a good tool to learn early. It was introduced as a means of testing hypotheses by Karl Pearson in 1900 ("On the criterion that a given system of deviations from the probable in the case of a correlated system of variables is such that it can be reasonably supposed to have arisen from random sampling" the London, Edinburgh, and Dublin *Philosophical Magazine and Journal of Science*, 50: 157–175, 1900), but its mathematical distribution was derived earlier by F. R. Helmert in 1876, apparently with no idea of its use as a test of significance.

Basically, the chi-square distribution provides a means of comparing numbers of observable sampling occurrences with the theoretical frequencies of occurrence of these same events under some particular hypothesis. For example, if the expected proportion of males in a genetic population of some sort is one half, so that $p = 1/2$, and if $n = 80$ in a particular sampling study, the best estimate of the number of males and females in a future sample of size $n = 80$ is 40 of each sex. Obviously, though, this result (40 of each sex) will not be obtained on all samples of 80, because there will be sampling variation from the expected ratio, even though it be the correct ratio for the whole group being sampled. Hence, given the results of a particular sampling with $n = 80$, one must decide whether to assume that the observed departure from 40 of each sex is a chance event or the consequence of the ratio's being other than 1:1 in the population sampled. If the latter is true, then the hypothesis $p = 1/2$ for males is false and should be rejected.

Many functions of the sample numbers and their expected values in two binomial classes, such as male and female, could be used to test a hypothesis. Each such function would have its own sampling distribution, so one could define one or more regions of rejection in terms of values of X which would produce an α of any predetermined size. The real problem is to choose that test of significance which, for a given probability of a Type I error, namely α, is the least likely to commit a Type II error by accepting a false hypothesis. As noted before, this involves a choice of a statistical test criterion for comparing observed data with theory. This choice is made by choosing that region of rejection of size α which has the lowest β, the probability of allowing the acceptance of a false H_0, considering the alternatives to H_0.

It has been found that for many situations met in experimental research the best function of theory and observation to use is defined as*

$$(2.51) \quad X^2 = \sum \left(\frac{(\text{observed number in } i\text{th class} - \text{theoretical number in } i\text{th class})^2}{\text{theoretical number in } i\text{th class}} \right)$$

summed over all classes. When a binomial population is to be sampled, the summation given above will involve just two classes of observation, such as Males and Females, so $i = 1$ and 2 only. More generally, X^2 will be the sum of s terms, one for each of s classifications into which the sample data can be classified. If the only restriction placed on the theoretical numbers is that they conform to a stated theory and sum to the total number in the sample, then X^2 is said to have $s - 1$ degrees of freedom (for brevity, "degrees of freedom" will be denoted by DF. If, however, there is a total of m restrictions on the theoretical numbers, including the requirement that they sum to the total sample size, then X^2 is said to have $\nu = s - m$ DF, and is written as X_ν^2. The basic idea of *degrees of freedom* is to indicate the number of possible *chance differences between theory and observation*. The more degrees of freedom an X_ν^2 has, the larger it can be solely by chance; hence, as shown in Table XI, the size of X_ν^2 due to chance alone increases as you read downward in any column.

To illustrate these statements, suppose that a sample of size $n = 80$ is drawn from a binomial population which theoretically has a 1:1 ratio as, for example, when an equal division of the two sexes is expected theoretically. If the sample produced 50 Males and 30 Females, is the hypothesis $H_0(p = 1/2)$ acceptable as against $H_a(p \neq 1/2)$, where p is the probability that a

* The X^2 notation is due to W. G. Cochran, *Biometrics*, December 1954, p. 418.

random observation of this group will produce an individual classed as Male? Using Formula 2.51, one obtains

$$X^2 = \frac{(50 - 40)^2}{40} + \frac{(30 - 40)^2}{40} = \frac{(10)^2}{40} + \frac{(-10)^2}{40} = 5.00, \qquad \text{with 1 DF}$$

The 1 DF comes from the fact that $s = 2$ and $m = 1$ because the sum of the theoretical numbers is required to equal the sum of the observed numbers; hence $v = s - m = 2 - 1 = 1$ DF. How often would the quantity X^2 with 1 DF get as large as 5.00 or larger, if one is using the correct hypothesis and sampling a binomial population? As usual, the answer to such a question depends upon the nature of the sampling distribution of X_v^2 *when the correct hypothesis is used to compute the theoretical numbers for the class of observations.*

In 1876 Helmert derived the distribution of the sum of the squares of n independent standard normal variates. Essentially, and for our purposes, he derived the distribution of

$$(2.52) \qquad \chi_n^2 = \sum_{i=1}^{n} \left(\frac{y_i - \mu_i}{\sigma_i} \right)^2$$

where the y_i are n independent $N(\mu_i, \sigma_i^2)$ variates. This distribution turns out to be closely similar to that of the X^2 of Formula 2.51, but this fact was not appreciated for nearly twenty-four years, until Karl Pearson independently derived an approximation to the sampling distribution of the X^2, which he had defined in a direct attempt to test such an H_0 as that above. Helmert's distribution commonly is called the chi-square distribution and is readily available in tables. For almost any size of sample in which an experimenter would have any real faith, this tabular distribution is an excellent approximation to the true sampling distribution of X^2. Because the mathematical chi-square (χ^2) distribution fits so many different X^2 distributions, we shall speak of the chi-square test generally, even though we use the symbol X^2 to stand for the sampling quantity which we compute. It should be remembered, however, that the distribution of χ^2 is a mathematical distribution which, fortunately, corresponds quite closely to the sampling distribution of X^2, even though X^2 inherently has a discontinuous distribution.

In those few instances in which this agreement between X^2 and χ^2 is believed to be poor, Yates' correction for continuity may be used (*Supp. J. Roy. Stat. Soc.* 1: 217, 1934). It is limited to cases with 1 DF; and consists of subtracting 0.5 from each difference between observation and theory; that is,

$$(2.53) \quad \text{Corrected } X^2 = X^{2\prime} = \sum \left(\frac{(| \text{ observed number } - \text{ theoretical number } | - 0.5)^2}{\text{theoretical number}} \right)$$

where | observed number − theoretical number | is the positive difference between observation and theory, summing over all classes. For example, if one applied this correction for continuity to the sex-ratio example, one, would compute

$$X_1^{2\prime} = \frac{(\,|\,50 - 40\,| - 0.5)^2}{40} + \frac{(\,|\,30 - 40\,| - 0.5)^2}{40} = \frac{2(9.5)^2}{40} \cong 4.51$$

Such a correction seldom is needed in practice.

In a comparatively nonmathematical course it is informative to verify certain mathematical concepts empirically by taking actual samples in sufficient numbers to obtain a satisfactory approximation to the distribution, which also could be derived mathematically. In view of the interest in the testing of statistical hypotheses, a sampling study was conducted under two relevant circumstances, namely:

(a) The hypothesis $H_0(p = p_0)$ which is used to compute the theoretical numbers in X^2 is exactly right, so that *all* variation from expectation is caused entirely by chance occurrences during sampling. The sampling distribution so obtained should verify approximately that distribution outlined in a chi-square table, such as Table XI,

(b) The hypothesis $H_0(p = p_0)$ is untrue by a *known* amount. In this event, a decision to accept H_0 commits an error of Type II. The distribution obtained in this circumstance is not the X_v^2 distribution. It is its failure to display known features of the X_v^2 distribution that gives the chi-square test its power to detect false hypotheses. Obviously, the farther the H_0 is from the truth, the farther the sampling distribution obtained when H_0 is false will deviate from the tabular chi-square distribution.

The sampling done for this Monte Carlo type of study of the X_1^2 and pseudo X_1^2 distributions simulates some genetic research in which for (a), above, the true genetic ratio is 9:7. For (b), above, the true ratio also is 9:7, but an error in theory is supposed to have led the experimenter to assume that a 3:1 ratio exists in the population he is sampling. Symbolically, the situation is this:

For (a), $H_0(p = 9/16)$ is true and is assumed to be true.
For (b), $H_0(p = 3/4)$ is assumed to be true but is false, because the ratio actually is 9:7.

Thus, in (a) the expected numbers for Formula 2.51 are calculated with the correct parameter p, whereas in (b) the theoretical numbers are computed on the hypothesis that $p = 0.75$, which is as badly in error as the difference between a 9:7 ratio and a 3:1 ratio.

Table 2.51 shows observed cumulative frequency distributions for X^2 under the two circumstances described earlier. Figure 2.51 presents this same general information visually.

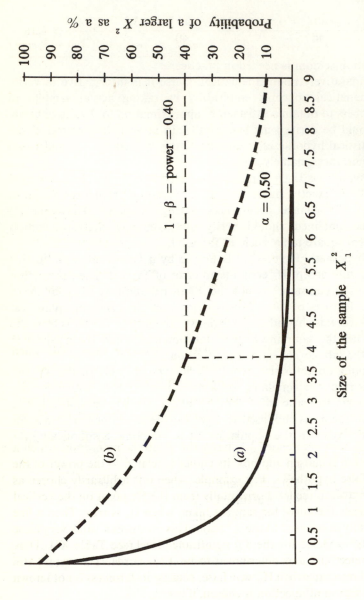

Figure 2.51. Distribution of sample X_1^2 when $H_0(p = 9/16)$ is true and when $H_0(p = 3/4)$ is false because p actually is 9/16: based on more than 3800 samples of sizes ranging from $n = 12$ to $n = 32$, but all with 1 DF. The (a) curve approximates that which could be obtained from Table XI with 1 DF. Curve (a) is H_0 (3:1) false and curve (b) is H_0 (9:7) true.

TABLE 2.51.   EMPIRICAL CUMULATIVE SAMPLING DISTRIBUTIONS OF X^2 WHEN $H_0(p = 9/16)$ IS TRUE, AND WHEN $H_0(p = 3/4)$ IS FALSE BECAUSE $p = 9/16$

Cumulative X^2 interval		(a) $H_0(p = 9/16)$ *is true*		(b) $H_0(p = 3/4)$ *is false because* $p = 9/16$	
		Cum f	100 − % *cum f*	*Cum f*	100 − % *cum f*
0.000 to	10.828	3841	0.0	3908	0.0
0.000	10.827	3835	0.2	3729	4.6
0.000	8.000	3820	0.5	3378	13.6
0.000	6.635	3804	1.0	3216	17.7
0.000	5.412	3784	1.5	2915	25.4
0.000	4.000	3664	4.6	2332	40.3
0.000	3.841	3617	5.8	2332	40.3
0.000	3.300	3617	5.8	2179	44.2
0.000	2.706	3516	8.5	1737	55.6
0.000	2.249	3386	11.8	1724	55.9
0.000	1.642	3072	20.0	1288	67.0
0.000	1.074	2818	26.6	937	76.0
0.000	0.455	2177	43.3	508	87.0
0.000	0.148	853	77.8	266	93.2
0.000	0.064	822	78.6	189	95.2

Sample sizes varied from 12 to 32, but there always was 1 DF.

Even a casual inspection of the table may be sufficient to convince one that the X_1^2's tend to be relatively much larger when H_0 is false than when it is true. For example, about 40% of the X_1^2's are *larger* than 3.841 when this H_0 is false, whereas only 5.8% of them *exceed* 3.841 when the true hypothesis is used to compute the theoretical numbers for Formula 2.51. Essentially, this is the basis upon which we are able to detect false hypotheses. The figure shows this situation quite clearly, because the two curves are decidedly different.

Figure 2.51 also is intended to clarify the arbitrary manner in which a region of rejection is chosen and how its choice is related to the power of the test to detect false hypotheses. For example, when α is arbitrarily chosen as 0.05, a line is drawn to the left horizontally from the 5% point on the vertical scale until it meets the curve for samples taken when H_0 is true. Then a line is drawn vertically downward to the X^2 scale. This produces a value very close to the tabular $\chi^2 = 3.841$ for the 5% significance level (see Table XI). Thus the region of rejection, ω, is determined to be $X^2 \geqslant 3.841$. This would still be the region of rejection when H_0 were false, because its falseness is not known at the time the region of rejection is chosen, if ever.

The power of a test of significance, such as the chi-square test, to detect false hypotheses also depends upon the size of the region of rejection chosen in advance of the taking of the sample. If one is willing to take a greater risk of committing a Type I error, the probability of detecting a false hypothesis, and thereby of avoiding a Type II error, is increased. This can be seen graphically from Figure 2.51 by using $\alpha = 0.10$ and going through the construction described above to determine graphically the power of the X^2 test. It is found that the power to avoid a Type II error increases from approximately 0.40 to approximately 0.55 if one is willing to take a risk of 1 in 10 of a Type I error instead of a risk of only 1 in 20.

Table 2.52 was constructed to provide more nearly exact information on this point for a range of sample sizes and levels of significance. It illustrates several points:

TABLE 2.52.   EXACT RELATION BETWEEN THE POWER, $1 - \beta$, OF THE CHI-SQUARE TEST, THE SIGNIFICANCE LEVEL, α, AND SAMPLE SIZE n IF p IS ASSUMED 3/4 WHEN, IN FACT, IT IS 9/16

Significance level (α)	Size of sample taken				
	16	32	48	80	100
0.100	0.405	0.711	0.854	0.896	0.995
0.050	0.405	0.579	0.776	0.856	0.985
0.010	0.230	0.438	0.569	0.776	0.948
0.001	0.041	0.194	0.342	0.648	0.818

Used tables of $b(X; n, p)$.

(a) The probability of detecting that a hypothesis is as erroneous as $p = 3/4$ when the true size of p is 9/16 is poor for any acceptable significance level, when the sample size is as small as $n = 16$.

(b) The smaller the α adopted, the lower the power of the chi-square test to detect a false hypothesis. In fact, there is virtually no power with samples as small as $n = 16$ if α is taken as 0.001.

(c) The experimenter can offset somewhat the ill effects of a low significance level by taking larger samples. Hence, if an experimenter wishes to be especially cautious about Type I errors, he should take an especially large sample, to guard better against Type II errors. Although these conclusions were drawn with reference to the chi-square test and sampling from binomial populations, these same ideas are generally applicable to other tests to be studied later.

It was stated earlier that other tests of $H_0(p = p_0)$ besides using the X^2 criterion could be devised and that the reason for choosing X^2 was that it is believed to have greater power to detect false hypotheses than other possible tests have. Figures 2.52 and 2.53 illustrate this point. Figure 2.52 is similar to Figure 2.51 but involves three cases: when $H_0(p = 3/4)$ is true, when $H_0(p = 9/16)$ is false because $p = 3/4$, and when $H_0(p = 15/16)$ is false because $p = 3/4$. The probability distributions graphed in Figure 2.52

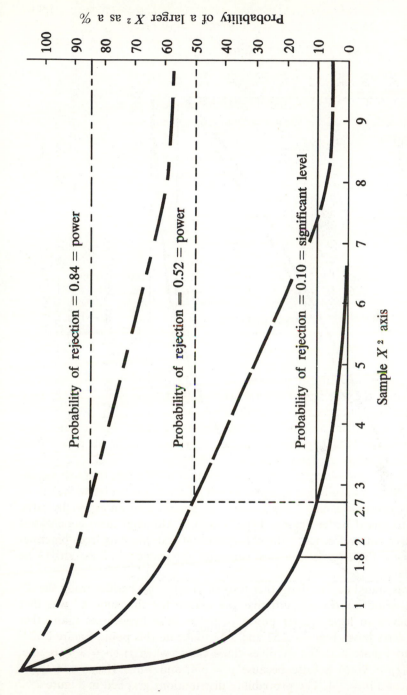

Figure 2.52. Cumulative distributions of X^2 under three specified sampling situations; $n = 20$ for all samples (compare with Figure 2.53). Curve —·— is H_0 (15:1) false, curve ——— is H_0 (9:7) false, curve --- is H_0 (3:1) true.

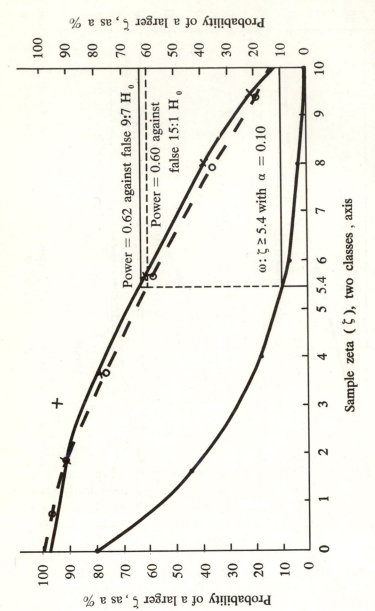

Figure 2.53. Cumulative distributions of $\zeta = \sum |\text{observed } i - \text{theoretical } i|$, when $n = 20$ and specified H_0's are tested (compare with Figure 2.52). Curve ———·—— is H_0 (15:1) false, curve ———×—— is H_0 (9:7) false, curve ——————·—— is H_0 (3:1) true.

for the situations in which H_0 is false were obtained by using a table like Table 2.13, but with p either 9/16 or 15/16, to compute the probabilities for the various X^2's which could occur. Then a smooth curve was drawn through the points obtained. The graph for the situation in which H_0 is true was obtained by using points from the tabular chi-square distribution with 1 DF in Table XI and then making a curve smooth through these points, as in the other cases. The scale at the right gives the probability of getting a *larger* X^2 under the specified sampling conditions, as did Figure 2.51.

Figure 2.53 is analogous to Figure 2.52, but it pertains to the use of another test criterion computed from the sample observations, namely:

(2.54) $\zeta = \sum$ (absolute difference, observed number − expected number)
$= \sum |\text{observed number} - \text{expected number}|$

which simply is the sum of the numerical amounts by which the observed and theoretical numbers disagree in the s classes of observations. For the example considered earlier, in which n was 80 and the theoretical ratio was 1:1, ζ is $10 + 10 = 20$. Obviously, this is a much easier computation than that needed to obtain the X^2 for this same sample. Why use the more difficult procedure? Because it is generally believed that the power of the chi-square test is enough greater than that of the zeta test to more than offset this extra labor. This will be illustrated to some degree in the subsequent discussion.

Before the zeta test could be used in practice, the sampling distribution of zeta would have to be known and readily available. This distribution has been obtained for the cases studied in Figure 2.53 by again using probability distributions such as those in Table 2.13. The data in Table 2.53 were used to plot Figure 2.53.

A 10% level of significance was used in Figure 2.53, and the corresponding region of rejection was determined as illustrated in Figure 2.51. The ω resulting was $\zeta \geqslant 5.4$. The following information then was obtained by drawing a straight line vertically upward from $\zeta = 5.4$ to each of the cumulative distribution curves for ζ when the hypothesis being tested was as false as noted on the figures.

(*a*) If $H_0(p = 9/16)$ is false because p actually is 3/4, the zeta test will reject this false hypothesis with probability $1 - \beta = 0.62$, as nearly as can be told from the graph. Reference to Figure 2.52 shows that this is somewhat better power than for the chi-square test under the same circumstances.

(*b*) If $H_0(p = 15/16)$ is false because p actually is 3/4, the zeta test will reject this false hypothesis about 60% of the time, whereas the chi-square test has a power of 0.84, which is 40% higher than that of zeta. It may be noted, however, that $p = 9/16$ and $p = 15/16$ are, in a real sense, equally false when in fact $p = 3/4$, so the zeta test is more sensitive to the degree of falseness here.

It also should be noted that the zeta test depends on the sample size (in contrast to X^2) and would be difficult to use because a new table would be needed for almost every sampling situation. It might be possible, though, to remedy this difficulty satisfactorily, so one should not lose sight of the fact that the major reason for using the X^2 criterion instead of the ζ criterion is that the former is believed generally to have the greater power to detect false hypotheses and thus avoid Type II errors when the α level of Type I error is fixed.

TABLE 2.53. EXACT ZETA DISTRIBUTION WHEN $n = 20$ AND H_0 IS, SUCCESSIVELY, 3A:1a, 9A:7a, AND 15A:1a WITH H_0(3A:1a) ALWAYS TRUE

Sample observed		Probability of sample with $p = 0.75$	Values of ζ on indicated H_0's			Zeta class	Probability of a larger ζ when $p = 0.75$ but H_0 is:		
X	$(20 - X)$		9:7	3:1	15:1		9A:7a	3A:1a	15A:1a
0	20	0.00				17.50			0.01
1	19	,,				15.50	0.01		0.02
2	18	,,				13.50	0.03		0.05
3	17	,,				11.50	0.10		0.11
4	16	,,				10.00		0.01	
5	15	,,				9.50	0.23		0.22
6	14	,,				8.00		0.02	
7	13	,,				7.50	0.42		0.39
8	12	,,				6.00		0.07	
9	11	0.00				5.50	0.62		0.59
10	10	0.01	2.50	10	17.50	4.00		0.20	
11	9	0.03	0.50	8	15.50	3.50	0.79		0.78
12	8	0.06	1.50	6	13.50	2.50	0.90		
13	7	0.11	3.50	4	11.50	2.00		0.46	
14	6	0.17	5.50	2	9.50	1.50	0.91		0.91
15	5	0.20	7.50	0	7.50	0.50	0.97		0.98
16	4	0.19	9.50	2	5.50	0		0.80	
17	3	0.13	11.50	4	3.50				
18	2	0.07	13.50	6	1.50				
19	1	0.02	15.50	8	0.50				
20	0	0.00							

Zeta $= \sum |$ observed number $-$ theoretical number $|$ over all classes. Probabilities of samples obtained from Table 2.13.

PROBLEMS

1. Suppose that all the registered voters in a large city are classified as either Democrat or Republican, the very small number in neither class having been excluded from the proposed study. Suppose that a simple random sample of 100 voters is taken and is found to have $X = 56$ Democrats. Test $H_0(p = 0.50)$ against the alternative $H_a(p \neq 0.50)$, using 0.95 protection against committing a Type I error.

2. According to certain simplified genetic theory, if a heterozygous red-eyed fruit fly is mated to a homozygous white-eyed fruit fly, one half of the offspring are expected (statistically) to be white-eyed. Suppose that among 500 offspring from such matings 240 are found to be white-eyed. Does this result justify rejection of $H_0(p_W = 0.50)$ tested against $H_a(p_W \neq 0.50)$, if one is satisfied with 90% protection against Type I error? What if 95% protection against Type I error is demanded? What if $H_a(p_W < 0.50)$ is used?

3. Suppose that 15 out of 100 concrete test beams have been found to be too light to meet specifications for such beams. Assuming acceptable random sampling, would you accept or would you reject $H_0(p_1 = 0.10)$ when tested against $H_a(p_1 \neq 0.10)$, where p_1 is the true fraction of beams which are too light in the population sampled? State the significance level used and the specific region of rejection involved. Could more than one region of rejection be used, each with $\alpha = 0.10$? If so, what is the basis for choosing any specific one of them?

4. If in the situation of Problem 3 the sample size had been 200 and 15% of the beams again had been too light to meet standards, what effect would the larger sample size have had on the chi-square test? What does this suggest with regard to the calculation of χ^2 from percentages?

5. Suppose that there are but two candidates for a certain political office and that in a random sample of 150 voters 80 are for Jones and 70 favor his opponent. Would you accept the hypothesis that 51% of the voters favor Jones' opponent? Use $\alpha = 0.10$.

6. The sugar pine is a valuable source of lumber but also is highly susceptible to the white pine blister rust disease. Suppose that a geneticist claims to have developed a 90% resistant strain of sugar pine. When he runs an experiment to test this claim, he finds that 65 trees out of a sample of 500 exposed to the disease did develop this blister rust. Test his claim against $H_a(p_R \neq 0.90)$, using a 10% region of rejection. What if $H_a(p_R < 0.90)$ is the alternative?

7. Suppose that, on a sample of size $n = 20$, $X = 13$. With $\alpha = 0.10$, use the zeta test to test $H_0(p = 0.50)$ against $H_a(p \neq 0.50)$, and draw appropriate conclusions.

8. Referring to Problem 7, devise some other test criterion besides either X^2 or ζ, which you think would reflect differences between theory and observation, and then test the hypothesis given in Problem 7.

9. Do Problems 7 and 8 with $H_a(p = 0.60)$, and draw all appropriate conclusions.

10. Do Problem 1 by both the chi-square test and a CI_{95}, and discuss the two results of testing the same H_0.

11. Do Problem 5 by both the chi-square test and a CI_{90}. Discuss results.

12. Suppose that a geneticist has a theory that, when two strains of guinea pigs are crossed, half the offspring should be black and half should be white. He makes the appropriate matings and obtains 68 black and 52 white. If you employ the chi-square test and maintain 90% protection against a Type I error, do you accept the geneticist's hypothesis? Do this problem also by means of a CI_{90}.

13. Suppose that a confection manufacturer intends to produce a Halloween mixture of jelly beans in which half the beans are licorice and half are orange. If a random sample of 300 of these jelly beans shows 160 licorice, has the manufacturer succeeded in maintaining a 50:50 mixture? Choose $\alpha = 0.10$.

14. If the male-to-female sex ratio in a certain geographical area actually is 52:48, how large a random sample would it require to cause rejection of $H_0(p_M = p_F = 1/2)$ in favor of $H_a(p_M \neq 1/2)$, if α is chosen as 0.10 and 52% of the sample is male?

15. Suppose that at the time a certain public opinion poll is to be taken 55% of the voters actually would vote Yes on a certain bond issue if *all* could be polled. How large a sample would it take to cause the rejection of $H_0(p_Y = p_N = 1/2)$ in favor of $H_a(p_Y \neq 1/2)$ with a 10% region of rejection, if 55% of the sample do answer Yes? Could this problem be solved by means of a CI_{90}? If so, could the CI_{90} solution be better than the chi-square approach?

16. Do Problem 7 using the chi-square test with the correction for continuity.

17. It has been estimated that 15% of white American citizens have Rh negative blood. This is an important matter, because some combinations of Rh negative and Rh positive parentage can cause blood troubles in the offspring. If in a sample of 300 white Americans 52 have Rh negative blood, is $H_0(p_N = 15)$ acceptable over $H_a(p_N \neq 15)$ if α is 0.10 and p_N is the true percentage of white Americans with Rh negative blood? Could this problem be done with a confidence interval? Would the chi-square test and a confidence-interval test give precisely the same conclusion?

18. Do Problem 15, but use $H_a(p_Y > 1/2)$.

2.6 TESTING A HYPOTHESIS THAT TWO RANDOM SAMPLES CAME FROM THE SAME BINOMIAL POPULATION

If an experimenter is going to draw random samples from two apparently different binomial situations, he may wish to decide whether the apparently different circumstances actually do produce distinguishably different binomial populations with respect to some specific measurement. For example, an entomologist might be studying two chemically different fly sprays to determine whether the known chemical differences produce two separate binomial populations based on two classes of flies, those Dead after being sprayed and those Alive after being sprayed with one of the formulations. One could argue that, if the sprays were chemically different, there must be *some* difference in toxicity. However, without discussing that point at all, a difference in toxicity is not usefully made the object of experimental research, unless attention is confined to *detectable differences* in effect under standard and reasonably comprehensive testing procedures. As usual with samples of size *n*, all possible numbers of Dead flies among *n* sprayed could be obtained with *either* spray, so the hypothesis $H_0(p_1 = p_2)$ will have to be tested with the usual need for a region of rejection which maximizes the power of the test used. However, there will be no predetermined value of either p_1 or p_2 to be tested, as there was in Section 2.5.

As another example, suppose that a psychologist has devised a procedure for teaching white rats to run mazes swiftly and wishes to test his new training method against a standard method. One type of test would be to set a time during which each rat must complete the run and record how many out of n rats did complete the run during the allotted time. The test would involve two different binomial populations if the teaching methods truly were different, but only one binomial population if the two teaching methods were not different as regards the success of the rat in running the maze in the allotted time. It is hoped in setting up such an experiment that samples will enable the experimenter to distinguish between those two situations.

The records from a test of the sort just visualized might be as follows:

Method of teaching	In the allotted time the run was: Completed	Not completed	Total
New	40	10	50
Standard	35	15	50
Total	75	25	100

Of the rats trained by the new method 80% successfully completed the run, compared to 70% under the older, standard method, but how likely is this difference, or an even larger difference, to occur when two such groups have been trained under the *same* method? In other words, is the observed difference in performance just a chance event which occurred during sampling of the same binomial population, or not?

Usually it is not reasonable to assume that some theoretical percentage of the rats taught by either method should complete the run in the allotted time, so there is no basis for calculating theoretical numbers in advance as soon as the sample size is known. Hence, we do not test such a hypothesis as $H_0(p = p_0)$. Instead, we test the hypothesis that success in finishing the run is independent of the method under which a rat was trained for this test. If p_{NM} is the probability that a rat chosen at random was trained by the new method, and if p_C is the probability that a rat chosen at random will complete the run, nothing being known about the method under which it was trained, then we test the hypothesis that the probability that a rat chosen at random after the test will fall into the upper left-hand corner of the data table above (that is, will be a rat trained under the new method and finishing the maze in the allotted time) is just $p_{NM} \cdot p_C$. More generally, it is assumed that $p_{ij} = p_i \cdot p_j$, as discussed in Chapter 1 for independent events. If, in fact, the probability that a rat chosen at random will finish the run in a specified time is dependent upon the method by which it was trained to run mazes, then $H_0(p_{ij} = p_i \cdot p_j)$ is false and should be rejected.

The two-way, or double, classification table summarizing the hypothetical rat maze study is called a two-by-two (2×2) *contingency table*. Table 2.61 is such a table. It was presented first as a summary of a study of two possibly different binomial populations. However, it essentially is also a sample from a *multinomial population* with the following probabilities for the four cells of the table, *provided* $H_0(p_{ij} = p_i p_j)$ *is true* (SM below is for "standard method" and NC for "not completed"):

$$p_1 \quad \text{(upper left)} \quad = p_{NM} \cdot p_C$$
$$p_2 \quad \text{(upper right)} = p_{NM} \cdot p_{NC}$$
$$p_3 \quad \text{(lower left)} \quad = p_{SM} \cdot p_C$$
$$p_4 \quad \text{(lower right)} = p_{SM} \cdot p_{NC}$$

Each of these probabilities is unknown and hence must be estimated before H_0 can be tested.

Before proceeding further with a test of $H_0(p_{ij} = p_i p_j)$, where i is the row number in the contingency table and j is the column number, it is interesting to consider the alternative situation, namely $H_a(p_{ij} \neq p_i p_j)$. What effect does it have on the 2×2 contingency table if H_a is true? This effect is illustrated in Table 2.61.

TABLE 2.61. ILLUSTRATION OF CONTINGENCY TABLES WHEN
$p_{ij} \neq p_i \cdot p_j$, WHERE $i = 1.2$.

	Case 1		Case 2	
	A_1	A_2	A_1	A_2
B_1	Larger numbers of events than if $p_{11} = p_1 \cdot p_1$	Smaller numbers of events than if $p_{12} = p_1 \cdot p_2$	Smaller numbers of events than if $p_{11} = p_1 \cdot p_1$	Larger numbers of events than if $p_{12} = p_1 \cdot p_2$
B_2	Smaller numbers of events than if $p_{21} = p_2 \cdot p_1$	Larger numbers of events than if $p_{22} = p_2 \cdot p_2$	Larger numbers of events than if $p_{21} = p_2 \cdot p_1$	Smaller numbers of events than if $p_{22} = p_2 \cdot p_2$

The A_i and B_i, $i = 1$ and 2, are two related classifications of the items being enumerated, e.g., A_1 = Republican, A_2 = Democrat, B_1 = Rich, B_2 = Poor, in a community in which these classifications would be related.

With either case 1 or case 2 the differences between the observed and the corresponding theoretical numbers will be greater than they would be under completely random variation, on the average; hence, the X^2 will tend to be excessively large.

With larger contingency tables with more rows (r) and columns (c) such as 2×3, 3×3, $4 \times 5, \cdots$, $r \times c$, the same general effect would be produced by dependencies among classifications. Moreover, and as expected, the interpretation of the larger contingency tables is more difficult, but the best region of rejection, ω, still is of the form $X_v^2 \geqslant X_0^2$, where $v = (r - 1)(c - 1)$ for an $r \times c$ contingency table.

If the two rat-maze samples shown earlier did, in fact, come from the same binomial population based on completing or not completing the run, the best point estimate of the parameter p_C would be the maximum likelihood estimate, $p_C = 75/100 = 0.75$. On the hypothesis that $p_{C,NM} = p_C \cdot p_{NM}$ the theoretical number of rats trained by the new method which should complete the run in the allotted time is $(50/100)(75/100)(100)$, which is 37.5. This is the theoretical number for the upper left-hand cell of the contingency table shown above. Each of the other three theoretical numbers could be computed in a similar way. However, it is implicit in the estimation procedure used that the sum of the theoretical numbers in each row of the contingency table will equal the sum of the observed numbers in that row. The same is true for the columns; hence, the other three theoretical numbers in this 2×2 contingency table are more easily obtained by subtraction. Thus, for the upper right-hand cell,

$$\text{Theoretical number} = 50.0 - 37.5 = 12.5$$

Similarly, theoretical numbers for the other cells are computed as $75.0 - 37.5 = 37.5$ and $50.0 - 37.5 = 12.5$, again. It is noted that each theoretical number differs from the corresponding observed number by 2.5, one way or the other. Therefore, the X^2 will have but 1 DF because there really is just one *chance* difference between theory and observation, namely that they disagree by the amount 2.5. It also is noted that the sums of the theoretical numbers must equal the sums of the observed numbers for each of two rows in the contingency table and for each of two columns. This would seem to make the number of classes (s) and the number of restrictions (m) both equal 4 and leave no degrees of freedom for X^2, but it is easy to verify that if the sums of the theoretical and of the observed numbers in the two rows are made equal and these sums for either column are made equal, then the sums for the second column automatically are equal. This fact reduces m to 3 and leaves $s - m = 4 - 3 = 1$ DF again.

The calculation of the X^2 is as follows:

$$X_1^2 = \frac{(40 - 37.5)^2}{37.5} + \frac{(35 - 37.5)^2}{37.5} + \frac{(10 - 12.5)^2}{12.5} + \frac{(15 - 12.5)^2}{12.5}$$
$$= 1.33, \quad 1 \text{ DF}$$

Is an X_1^2 of this size unusual when the hypothesis being tested is correct and there is but one degree of freedom? If so, the hypothesis probably should be rejected, depending, of course, upon the size of the region of rejection chosen for this study.

The sampling distribution for the sort of X^2 computed above is just the same as for any other X^2 with one degree of freedom for chance differences between the theoretical and the observed numbers, so a table is again used for approximating this distribution.

It is seen in Table XI that if H_0 is exactly true and there is but one degree of freedom for disagreement between theory and observation, then

$\Pr\{X_1^2 \geqslant 1.33\} = 0.25$, and so there is no reasonable size for α which would cause $H_0(p_{NC} = p_{NM} \cdot p_C)$ to be rejected. It is concluded that the two training methods are essentially equal in producing success in running the maze being studied.

From the computational point of view it is worth while to point out that the computation of the theoretical numbers for the cells of a contingency table can be accomplished quite simply. The following computation, shown earlier as (50/100)(75/100)(100), can be simplified by noting that it is just

$$\frac{(\text{total for row 1})(\text{total for column 1})}{\text{grand total}}$$

In general, the theoretical number for the cell in the ith row and the jth column is

(2.61) $$\text{Theoretical } n_{ij} = \frac{(\text{total for row } i)(\text{total for column } j)}{\text{grand total}}$$

Often the enumerative data from an experiment are expressed in percentages. The X^2 should not be calculated from such percentages without a proper correction for the fact that the sample size has thereby been assumed to be $n = 100$. The correction is a simple one, as shown by the following formula:

(2.62)   Corrected $X^2 = (n/100)(X^2$ computed from the percentages)

Obviously, if the actual sample size is less than 100, the uncorrected X^2 will be too large, because the sample size has been artificially increased to 100. If n is larger than 100, the sample size has been artificially reduced when percentages have been used. As seen in Equation 2.62, the factor $n/100$ makes the proper adjustment for the effects of using percentages.

In some instances one may have a specific theoretical value for p (say $p = p_0$) and have taken two random samples which could be from this specific binomial population. However, the two samples usually have been taken under different circumstances, which *could* have caused their respective populations to be different. If it is of special interest to determine whether sample 1 and sample 2 each came from a binomial population with $p = p_0$ and whether, if they both probably did *not* come from the specified population, their populations differ from it the same way; then, to answer these questions, one can use a *heterogeneity* X^2. For example, suppose a geneticist conjectures that, if the double recessive aa is less viable than the dominants AA and Aa, the degree of lessened viability will not depend on environment, he could set up an experiment to test this hypothesis. If A = both AA and Aa and if a = aa, the data taken would be numbers of A and a types, respectively, surviving, so he could test $H_0(p = \frac{3}{4}A)$ versus $H_a(p \neq \frac{3}{4}A)$, for example. He might obtain such data as the following, for which X^2 also is shown for each *row* of data, including the data pooled from both environments:

	Survival			
Environment	A	a	*Total*	*Row* X^2, 1 DF
Cool	165	35	200	6.00
Warm	162	38	200	3.84
Total	327	73	400	9.72

It appears from the data that each environment produces about the same result, namely that $H_0(p = \frac{3}{4}A)$ is unacceptable. The pooled data also produce a pooled $X^2 = 9.72$, with 1 DF, which reënforces the rejection of H_0.

It can be shown mathematically that the sum of independent chi-squares (and, by analogy, X^2's) is also a chi-square with a number of degrees of freedom equal to the sum of those for the chi-squares added. Thus the total $X^2 = 6.00 + 3.84 = 9.84$ is an X^2 with 2 DF. This X^2 supports the previous rejection of H_0. Hence, it certainly would be concluded that H_0 is not acceptable. How do we formally and objectively test the general hypothesis that the two environments are associated with the same degree and direction of disagreement with H_0? The *heterogeneity* X^2, which is the total X^2 minus the pooled X^2, is used for this test. Its DF is the total DF minus the DF for the pooled X^2. In the hypothetical experiment discussed above we find that heterogeneity $X^2 = 9.84 - 9.72 = 0.12$, with 1 DF, which is nonsignificant even with $\alpha = 0.50$. It is concluded that the two different environments cause survivals to deviate from the 3A:1a ratio in essentially the same manner, if, indeed, environment really is a factor at all.

Suppose, now, that the data had been as follows:

	Survival			
Environment	A	a	*Total*	*Row* X^2, 1 DF
Cool	165	35	200	6.00
Warm	138	62	200	3.84
Total	303	97	400	0.12

In this experiment, pooled $X^2 = 0.12$ with 1 DF, total $X^2 = 9.84$ with 2 DF, as before, and heterogeneity $X^2 = 9.72$ with 1 DF. It again is concluded that the 3A:1a ratio is not acceptable for either environment. Furthermore, the deviation from the 3:1 ratio depends on the kind of environment. Apparently, the cool environment is much more favorable to the dominant type A, than is the warm environment.

In a way, the heterogeneity X^2 is a test of the hypothesis that two samples came from the same binomial population, but it is *not* identical with the contingency X^2 introduced first in this section, because the contingency

X^2 does not impose a predetermined hypothetical probability. It tests $H_0(p_{ij} = p_i p_j)$ without specifying their sizes, in contrast to the heterogeneity test which does employ specific parameters.

For the data given above the theoretical numbers in the cells for a contingency X^2 are as follows, on the hypothesis that survival is independent of these environments, so that $p_{AC} = p_A \cdot p_C$, for example, where p_{AC} is the probability that a random observation is both A and under the cool environment:

	A	a
C	151.5	48.5
W	151.5	48.5

Hence, $X_1^2 = (13.5)^2(2/151.5 + 2/48.5) = 9.91$ with 1 DF. This X_1^2, with $\alpha = 0.05$, say, leads to the rejection of $H_0(p_{AC} = p_A \cdot p_C)$, so it is concluded that environment does affect survival. However, this study of the possible effects of environment on survival was strictly a study of association between environment and survival; it was not based upon a preconceived 3A:1a ratio. In fact, the study could be made without the experimenter's having any idea at all about the A: a ratio.

PROBLEMS

1. Random samples of eight-week records of male and female White Rock chickens raised at Kansas State University produced the following data on chick mortality:

By 8 weeks:

Sex	Died	Survived	Total
Male	46	227	273
Female	30	297	327

Use the chi-square distribution to decide whether there probably is a fundamental difference in chick mortality associated with sex in this breed. Could you have made this decision with two confidence intervals? Could you use the zeta test here?

2. Suppose that two independent samplings a week apart at a fish ladder beside the Bonneville Dam in Oregon produced the following information about the breeds of salmon coming through the ladder:

Number of:

Sampling	Chinook	Non-Chinook	Total
First	60	25	85
Second	90	25	115

Is the hypothesis that the percentage of Chinooks stayed the same during the time between samplings an acceptable hypothesis in view of these data?

3. Suppose that some entomologists investigated yellow and spruce pines in a certain forest to see how many trees were being seriously attacked by certain insects. Assume that they gathered the following data from proper random samples of 250 trees of each species:

	Damaged:		
Species	Badly	Not badly	Total
Yellow pine	58	192	250
Spruce pine	78	172	250

Does this evidence justify acceptance of the hypothesis that the two species are equally susceptible to this sort of insect damage? State your H_0 specifically and also the region of rejection.

4. Suppose that two random samples of voter preference for two candidates for a public office are taken, one being in cities of at least 25,000 residents and the other among residents not in any incorporated city or town. If the results of this poll are as given below, would you believe the statement that place of residence, as represented by the two studied, is unrelated to voter preference between these two candidates?

	Number favoring:		
Residence	Mr. A	Mr. B	Total
City of over 25,000	1200	1300	2500
Unincorporated	1050	950	2000

5. Suppose that a poll of 100 college students chosen at random on a certain campus revealed that 40 opposed a specific proposal for a change in student government. Does this result contradict the assertion that 48% of that student body oppose the change? That 51% oppose the change?

6. Suppose that a new fly spray has been compounded and you wish to see whether it loses any of its toxicity during one month of storage under specified conditions. Assuming flies of the same average susceptibility can be obtained for the two tests a month apart and being given the results below, what do you conclude about the effects of this type of storage on the toxicity of this spray?

	Flies which were:		
Test	Dead	Alive	Total
First	480	20	500
Second	380	20	400

7. Given the following for sample X^2, each with 1 DF, classify each as probably due to chance or not, if an event which is as unlikely as 1 in 10 is said not to be a chance event: 3.9, 7.1, 0.95, 2.1, 15.2, 8.7, and 1.28. Do the same, supposing 2 DF and 4 DF in turn.

8. Suppose that a certain type of manufacturing process produces a product which, upon inspection at the end of the inspection line, will be classed either as Satisfactory or as Unsatisfactory, and that two management systems produced the following results. Test the hypothesis that these management systems have the same effect on the percentage of Unsatisfactory items:

Item was:

System	Unsatisfactory	Satisfactory	Total
A	6	94	100
B	12	138	150

Let $\alpha = 0.10$ and draw appropriate conclusions.

9. Suppose that a person wishes to test the relative palatabilities of two brands of food on his one goldfish. It has been determined already that this fish cannot eat more than 20 particles a day of this sort of food and, by using different colors of food, one can count the uneaten particles left by this fish after a 10-minute feeding interval. For ten successive days 10 particles of each brand of food are mixed carefully without crushing the particles and placed on the water of the fish bowl, and the uneaten particles are counted after ten minutes. The results of this study are supposed to be as follows:

	Eaten	Uneaten	Total
Brand A	72	28	100
Brand B	63	37	100

(*a*) Assuming no serious deficiencies in the method of experimentation, what conclusions do you draw, and why?

(*b*) What criticisms do you have of this experimental procedure?

10. Suppose that a geneticist has two hypotheses about the ratio of the genotypes A and a under different environments and in different regions, namely (1) that the ratio A:a may depend on whether the environment is relatively cool or warm within a given region and (2) that the comparison of the A:a ratios in warm and in cool environments may depend upon the region in which the two genotypes have developed. To test these ideas he is assumed to have run two experiments with the following results on the hypothesis $H_0(3A:1a)$ and with $\alpha = 0.10$:

In region R_1			*In region R_2*		
Environment	A	a	Environment	A	a
Cool	240	60	Cool	240	60
Warm	165	35	Warm	135	65

Test the geneticist's conjecture and draw all appropriate conclusions, remembering that genetic theory suggests that the true basic ratio is 3A:1a.

11. Make up an example involving two independent experiments, a 2:1 hypothesis and a significant heterogeneity chi-square test with $\alpha = 0.10$.

12. Given the following hypothetical data on three independent experiments, each intended to test $H_0(9AB:7non\text{-}AB)$, perform all useful and valid additional chi-square tests and draw appropriate conclusions.

Experiment	AB	Non-AB	X_1^2
No. 1	100	60	2.54
No. 2	125	115	1.69
No. 3	160	160	5.08
Pooled data	385	335	2.26

13. Given the following hypothetical data assumed taken in a study of the relationship between race and voter preference:

Race

Party	A	B	Sum
Dem.	242	258	500
Rep.	158	142	300
Sum	400	400	800

Test $H_0(p_{ij} = p_i \cdot p_j)$ against $H_a(p_{ij} \neq p_i \cdot p_j)$, where p_i, p_j, and p_{ij} have the meanings given in this section, relative to party and race. Use $\alpha = 0.05$.

14. Suppose that the quality control officer of a corporation wishes to see if quality of production is dependent on the time of day during which items are produced. He takes a sample of 200 in the mornings over a week's period and classifies each item as Defective or Satisfactory. He does the same in the afternoons of the same week. Given the following data, test the hypothesis that quality of production is independent of the time of day in which production occurred.

Item was:

Time	Satisfactory	Defective	Sum
A.M.	182	18	200
P.M.	170	30	200
Sum	352	48	400

Use 90% protection against Type I error.

15. Could Problem 14 be done satisfactorily by means of confidence intervals? Explain.

16. It seems possible that the incidence of mental illness is associated with home environment; for example, homes with both parents present as compared with so-called broken homes. Given the following hypothetical data, supposedly taken as a random sample from both broken and unbroken homes,

Cases of:

Home	Mental illness	Normality	Sum
Normal	70	8930	9000
Broken	20	980	1000
Sum	90	9910	10,000

test the hypothesis that there is no association between broken homes and mental illness, using $\alpha = 0.10$.

2.7 SAMPLING A MULTINOMIAL POPULATION

Whenever enumerative data are to be classified into three or more mutually exclusive classes, a multinomial population is being dealt with, if the true proportions in the classes stay fixed. Voters' opinions quite often are enumerated under three headings: Yes, No, and No Opinion, or For Mr. Doe, For Mr. Roe, and Undecided. The faces of dice are classified under six headings: 1, 2, 3, 4, 5, and 6; the sums of two dice, under 2, 3, 4, 5, 6, 7, 8, 9, 10, 11, and 12. The number of such illustrations is almost infinite.

A multinomial population actually consists of, say, s classes of marks: for example, $2 = $ Yes, $1 = $ No, and $0 = $ No Opinion, in the proportions $p_1:p_2:(1 - p_1 - p_2)$. If any other three-class situation has those same proportions, it constitutes precisely the same multinomial population as the one on public opinion.

If one draws a sample of size n from a multinomial population with s classes of attributes, the members of the sample will be classified into s, or fewer, classes with n_1 in class 1, n_2 in class 2, $\cdots$, and n_s in class s. The number of possible and distinguishable samples of size n is the number of ways n objects can be distributed among s classes. Suppose n physical objects are at hand and that s boxes are numbered and each will contain any number of objects up to and including n. If object 1 is picked up, there is a choice of s boxes into which it can be put. If object 2 is picked up next, there also is a choice of s boxes into which it can be put, regardless of the final placing of object 1. Hence, the first two objects could be placed in the boxes in $s \cdot s = s^2$ different ways, as long as the objects and boxes are distinguishable. For all n objects, there are s^n different ways they can be placed in the s boxes.

It is noted at this point that, if $s = 2$, one is dealing with a binomial population. Furthermore, as just noted,

$$\binom{n}{0} + \binom{n}{1} + \binom{n}{2} + \cdots + \binom{n}{n} = (1 + 1)^n = 2^n$$

To describe the outcome of a sampling of a multinomial population, one needs to say how many objects fell into each box, that is, how many events occurred in each of the s classes. This was done during the discussion of binomial sampling by means of the number of combinations of n objects taken X at a time, $\binom{n}{X}$. With s classes and $s > 2$, this description naturally becomes more complicated, but it follows similar lines. To illustrate this and to derive a useful formula, attention is drawn again to the s box model and the collection of n objects representing the sample. In how many ways could one choose n_1 objects from among n to be put in box 1? Obviously, one is just dividing the n objects into two groups: those for box 1 and those not for box 1; hence, the required number is merely $\binom{n}{n_1}$. After box 1 has been taken care of, there are $n - n_1$ objects yet to be placed in boxes. In how many ways can n_2 of these remaining $(n - n_1)$ objects be selected for box 2? Again, this clearly is a combinations problem, and the number of ways is $\binom{n - n_1}{n_2}$. In a similar manner one finds there are $\binom{n - n_1 - n_2}{n_3}$

ways to put n_3 objects in box 3, thereafter $\binom{n - n_1 - n_2 - n_3}{n_4}$ ways to put

n_4 objects in box 4, and so on until there simply are n_s left for box s. It is seen that $n_1 + n_2 + \cdots + n_s$ must be n.

If the choice of n_1 objects to be placed in box 1 can be made in $\binom{n}{n_1}$

ways and *thereafter* the choice of n_2 objects for box 2 can be made in $\binom{n - n_1}{n_2}$

ways, it is rather obvious that the n_1 choices for box 1 and the *subsequent* n_2

choices for box 2 can be made in $\binom{n}{n_1}\binom{n - n_1}{n_2}$ ways. By a similar manner of

reasoning it is seen that n_1 objects can be placed in box 1, n_2 in box 2, n_3 in box 3, $\cdots$, n_{s-1} in box $(s - 1)$, and n_s in box s in

$$\binom{n}{n_1}\binom{n - n_1}{n_2}\binom{n - n_1 - n_2}{n_3}\cdots\binom{n - n_1 - \cdots - n_{s-2}}{n_{s-1}}\binom{n - n_1 - \cdots - n_{s-1}}{n_s}$$

ways. When these symbols are replaced by factorials—and one recalls that $n - n_1 - \cdots - n_s = 0$—then one has

$$\frac{n!}{n_1!(n - n_1)!} \times \frac{(n - n_1)!}{n_2!(n - n_1 - n_2)!} \times \frac{(n - n_1 - n_2)!}{n_3!(n - n_1 - n_2 - n_3)!} \times \cdots$$

$$\times \frac{(n - n_1 - \cdots - n_{s-2})!}{n_{s-1}!(n - n_1 - \cdots - n_{s-1})!} \times \frac{(n - n_1 - \cdots - n_{s-1})!}{n_s!0!}$$

which reduces to

(2.71) $$\binom{n}{n_1, n_2, \cdots, n_s} = \frac{n!}{n_1!n_2!\cdots n_s!}$$

If one takes the point of view that n objects are being tossed into s boxes one at a time in such a way that the probability that an object about to be tossed will fall into box i is p_i, where i is any number from 1 to s, then the *multinomial probability function* is

(2.72) $$\binom{n}{n_1, n_2, \cdots, n_s}p_1^{n_1} \times p_2^{n_2} \times \cdots \times p_s^{n_s}$$

where, obviously, $\sum_{i=1}^{s} p_i = 1$ and $\sum_{i=1}^{s} n_i = n$. If $s = 2$, one obtains the binomial probability function discussed earlier. Just as it is true that $\sum_{i=1}^{n}\binom{n}{i}p^i(1 - p)^{n-i} = 1$, so is it true that

(2.73) $$\sum_{\substack{\text{all possible sets} \\ n_1, \cdots, n_s}} \left[\binom{n}{n_1, n_2, \cdots, n_s}p_1^{n_1} \times p_2^{n_2} \times \cdots \times p_s^{n_s}\right] = 1$$

To illustrate the foregoing discussion, consider an unbiassed die which is to be tossed 5 times. Assume one is interested in the numbers of 1's, 2's, 3's, 4's, 5's, and 6's thrown. In terms of the notation of this section, $n = 5$, $s = 6$, $p_1 = p_2 = \cdots = p_6 = 1/6$. There are $s^n = 6^5 = 7776$ ways these dice can fall. The multinomial probability function is

$$\binom{5}{n_1, \cdots, n_6} \frac{1}{6^5}$$

in this case, in which all $p_i = 1/6$. In simpler form the multinomial probability function is $0.01543/(n_1!n_2!\cdots n_6!)$ to five decimals. The probability of throwing three 1's, one 4, and one 6 on the next set of throws, say, is $0.01543/(3!0!0!1!0!1!) \simeq 0.00064$, where the symbol "$\simeq$" means "approximately equal to."

If the die used is biassed, or if one uses five equally biassed dice, the p_i will have some sizes other than 1/6, but the procedure for solving problems on the basis of Equation 2.72 is the same.

Suppose one wished to test a hypothesis about a multinomial population. For example, suppose one has five dice which one believes are unbiassed, but one wishes to test $H_0(p_1 = p_2 = \cdots = p_6)$ against H_a(some p_i unequal). Suppose that on 250 tosses of all five dice simultaneously one obtains the following.

Face uppermost:	1	2	3	4	5	6
Number of occurrences:	217	196	215	186	227	209

The total number of occurrences adds to 1250, because five dice were each tossed 250 times. The expected number of occurrences for each face under H_0(all $p_i = 1/6$) is 1250/6 = 208.3, to one decimal; hence, applying the chi-square test,

$$X^2 = \frac{(217 - 208.3)^2 + (196 - 208.3)^2 + \cdots + (209 - 208.3)^2}{208.3}$$
$$\simeq 5.37, \quad \text{with 5 DF}$$

The probability of such an X^2 or a larger one is well above any reasonable significance level, so H_0 is accepted.

Besides those already described there are many experimental situations in which multinomial populations are involved. For example, a geneticist may reason that an identifiable trait may be so inherited that a $1:2:1$ or a $9:3:3:1$ ratio is expected. The former ratio could occur when a one-gene heterozygote is distinguishable from both the homozygous dominant and the homozygous recessive. The latter could occur when two independent genes produce the trait. In each of these experimental situations multinomial populations are involved.

Suppose that the dominant type is denoted by AA and the recessive by aa and the heterozygote by Aa, and that one wishes to test

H_0(1 AA : 2 Aa : 1 aa) against its negation. Suppose the following data have been gathered to test this H_0:

	AA	Aa	aa	*Sum*
Observed	120	210	70	400
Theoretical	100	200	100	400

The $X^2 = 20^2/100 + 10^2/200 + 30^2/100 = 13.50$ with 2 DF, because there are three observed classes and only one restriction, namely that the sum of the differences be 0. If α has been chosen as 0.05, the region of rejection, ω, is $X_2^2 \geqslant 4.605$; therefore the observed X^2 is far out into the region of rejection and H_0(1 AA : 2 Aa : 1 aa) is rejected decisively. It appears that dominant genes may be beneficial to survival; or there may be another explanation.

If two genes are involved *independently* in the inheritance of a certain genetic trait, one might reasonably place offspring in four mutually exclusive classes, as follows:

> Class AB: has at least one of each of A and B
> Class Ab: has A but not B
> Class aB: has B but not A
> Class ab: has only recessives

This genetic situation is associated statistically with a multinomial population for which $s = 4$. If the two genes are inheritedly independent of each other, and if the production of offspring and their survival to the point of observation is purely a chance event, one can reason that 9/16 of the offspring should be AB, 3/16 should be Ab, 3/16 should be aB, and only 1/16 should be ab, *on the average*. Obviously, these ratios rarely will occur in any one experiment, but the theory justifies testing the hypothesis H_0(9 AB : 3 Ab : 3 aB : 1 ab). Suppose an experiment has produced the following data:

	AB	Ab	aB	ab	*Sum*
Number observed	49	20	24	3	96
Number expected	54	18	18	6	96

The $X^2 = 25/54 + (4 + 36)/18 + 9/6 = 4.185$, with 3 DF. If $\alpha = 0.10$, then ω is $X_3^2 \geqslant 6.251$; therefore, H_0 is readily accepted. This does not *prove* that the ratio is exactly $9:3:3:1$; but it does say that according to the evidence at hand H_0 is acceptable. It would be astounding if this ratio, or any other, were *exactly* realized in nature, so one might argue that any such H_0 would be "disproved" if one took a sufficiently large sample. This often is true, but unless there is a better H_0 or unless the experimenter wishes to undertake a large-sample estimation of the parameters (p_{AB}, p_{Ab}, p_{aB}, and p_{ab}) he may well find that these procedures fill a real need in his experimental research.

PROBLEMS

1. If an unbiassed die is to be tossed six times and the numbers of occurrences of 1's, 2's, $\cdots$, and 6's are to be recorded, what is the multinomial probability function involved?

2. If two unbiassed dice are to be tossed three times and the numbers of occurrences of 1's, 2's, $\cdots$, and 6's recorded, how does the corresponding multinomial population differ from that in Problem 1?

3. Referring to Problem 1, compute the probability of the outcome: no 1's, two 2's, two 3's, no 4's, one 5, and one 6.

4. Referring to Problem 1, compute the probability of throwing all of any one number.

5. Referring to Problem 1, compute the probability that no number appears more than once. More than twice.

6. Suppose that the die of Problem 1 is biassed as follows: $p_1 = 0.12$, $p_2 = 0.14$, $p_3 = 0.16$, $p_4 = 0.18$, $p_5 = 0.19$, and $p_6 = 0.21$. What now is the multinomial probability function?

7. Do Problem 3 under the assumptions of Problem 6.

8. Do Problem 4 under the assumptions of Problem 6.

9. Do Problem 5 under the assumptions of Problem 6.

10. Suppose that a scientist conjectures that a certain genetic ratio is 2 AA:2 Aa:1 aa. If he obtains from a properly conducted experiment the results 80 AA, 72 Aa, and 38 aa, is his conjecture acceptable with 90% protection maintained against Type I error?

11. Suppose that a political analyst and pollster conjectures late in an election campaign that *at that time* the voters would vote as follows: For Jones 43%, For Smith 50%, Undecided 7%. If a poll has been taken at that time without his knowledge and shows For Jones 1102 votes, For Smith 1200 votes, Undecided 298 votes, is his conjecture acceptable if α is chosen as 0.10?

12. Suppose that a tetrahedron has the numbers 1, 2, 3, and 4 on its sides and it is known that each number is equally likely to appear after any specified future toss of this tetrahedron. If it is to be tossed seven times, what is the probability that only even numbers will be thrown?

13. Referring to Problem 12, what is the probability that the sum of the seven tosses will be 14? Will be 6? Will be 20?

2.8 ASSESSING THE EVIDENCE FROM SEVERAL INDEPENDENT SAMPLES FROM BINOMIAL OR FROM MULTINOMIAL POPULATIONS

If one has conducted two or more independent tests of the same binomial or multinomial hypothesis, it may be of interest to study their results with regard to some of the following questions:

(*a*) As a group do these experiments show any systematic departure from predetermined, a priori, hypothetical ratios?

(*b*) Were the individual experiments consistent among themselves in their agreement, or disagreement, with the stated a priori hypothesis regarding one or more parameters, p_i?

(*c*) If the answer to (*a*) is that the experiments are in general agreement relative to the a priori hypothesis, what is the decision on H_0 *over all* the experiments?

(*d*) If the situation is such that there is no a priori hypothesis, did the experiments constitute random sampling from the same binomial, or multinomial, population with parameter or parameters unspecified?

Some of these questions were discussed in the previous section, but that discussion was limited to two samples and to binomial populations. The present section will be more general.

The first question asked is answered by pooling the data from all experiments and doing one X^2 test on these combined data. For example, consider the following hypothetical data supposedly from four independent tests of $H_0(p_A = 2/3)$ versus $H_a(p_A \neq 2/3)$:

Experiment no.	A	Not-A	X^2 and DF	
1	90	30	3.75,	1 DF
2	68	22	3.20,	1 DF
3	110	40	3.00,	1 DF
4	45	15	1.82,	1 DF
Pooled data	313	107		

Pooled-data $X^2 = (313 - 280)^2/280 + (107 - 140)^2/140 = 11.67$, with 1 DF. This X^2 would be significant at any usual level of significance, so, even though no single experiment clearly rejected H_0 with $\alpha = 0.05$, the pooled data indicate strongly that there is an excess of A in the population over the assumed 3A : 1 (3A to 1 not-A) ratio.

It also is noted in the table that the X^2's from experiments 1, 2, and 3 are larger than the X^2 from experiment 4. Does this indicate that the experiments are disagreeing with $H_0(p = 2/3)$ differently? Or is this apparent disagreement merely a sampling occurrence? To test this general hypothesis, we compute the heterogeneity X^2:

$$\text{Sum of experiment } X^2\text{'s} = 11.77, \text{ with 4 DF}$$
$$\text{Pooled-data } X^2 = 11.67, \text{ with 1 DF}$$

$$\text{Difference} = \text{heterogeneity } X^2 = 0.10, \text{ with 3 DF}$$

In some of these calculations it was assumed that the sum of the independent X^2's is another X^2, the DF of which is the sum of the separate DF. This can be proved to be true. It also was assumed that this total X^2 minus the pooled X^2 is another X^2, the DF of which is the total DF minus the DF of the pooled-data X^2's. This also is true, but will not be proved here.

It is concluded from these results that the hypothesis, $H_0(p = 2/3)$, is unacceptable and that the p probably is larger than 2/3. The four experiments are in general agreement on this conclusion, when due allowance is made for sampling error. This is essentially the answer to question (c).

With regard to question (d), the hypothesis to be tested would be that the four experiments constitute four random samples from the same binomial population. More specifically, the hypothesis, $H_0(p_{A_1} = \cdots = p_{A_4} = p)$, should be tested against H_a(some p_{A_i} are unequal). In this circumstance the maximum-likelihood estimate of that common p is obtained from $\hat{p} = 313/420 = 0.7452$, so the expected number of A's on 120 observations is $120(0.7452) = 89.4$ to one decimal, which is identical with the calculation $(313)(120)/420 = 89.4$ used earlier. This merely is another point of view which highlights the estimation of p from pooled data. Similar computations produced the following table, in which the theoretical (expected) numbers appear in parentheses:

Experiment no.	A	Not-A	Sum
1	90 (89.4)	30 (30.6)	120
2	68 (67.1)	22 (22.9)	90
3	110 (111.8)	40 (38.2)	150
4	45 (44.7)	15 (15.3)	60
Sum	313	107	420

With $\alpha = 0.05$, the region of rejection, ω, for an X^2 with 3 DF is $X_3^2 \geqslant 7.81$.

It is found by the usual procedure that

$$X_3^2 = \frac{0.36}{89.4} + \frac{0.36}{30.6} + \frac{0.81}{67.1} + \frac{0.81}{22.9} + \cdots + \frac{0.99}{15.3} \ll 7.815$$

which is the X_3^2 at the 5% level; therefore, $H_0(p_{A_1} = \cdots = p_{A_4})$ is accepted readily. As a matter of fact, this H_0 also would have been accepted readily with $\alpha = 0.10$. This X^2, which is called a contingency X^2, is not equal to the heterogeneity X^2, even though, broadly speaking, both are used to test the hypothesis that the same binomial population was sampled during each experiment. However, the contingency X^2 is not based on an a priori ratio for the binomial population, whereas the heterogeneity X^2 is so based. If a heterogeneity X^2 is significant, it is concluded that the independent experiments disagree differently with the stated a priori probabilities. If a contingency X^2 is significant, it is concluded that different binomial populations were sampled without any restrictions on the parameter p.

The ideas just discussed relative to the sampling of binomial populations apply, with obvious adjustments, to the sampling of two or more multinomial populations. Suppose that the legal voters in two areas, one rural and the other urban, in the Ohio River Valley are asked a question to which any one of three answers is acceptable: Yes, No, and Undecided. The purpose of this sampling study is to see whether the type of area, rural or urban, affects the answers to the question to be asked. Assume that the following data were obtained under proper random sampling:

		Answer was:		
Area	*Yes*	*No*	*Undecided*	*Totals*
Rural	145 (148.1)	125 (144.4)	30 (37.5)	300
Urban	250 (246.9)	180 (190.6)	70 (62.5)	500
Total	395	305	100	800

On the hypothesis of no association between Answer and Area, the theoretical number of Yeses by Rural respondents is:

$$\frac{395}{800} \cdot \frac{300}{800} \cdot \frac{800}{1} = 148.1, \quad \text{to one decimal}$$

Similarly, the theoretical number of Undecided answers from Rural respondents is:

$$\frac{100}{800} \cdot \frac{300}{800} \cdot \frac{800}{1} = 37.5, \quad \text{to one decimal}$$

Using the border totals for rows and columns, all the other theoretical numbers are determined to be as shown in parentheses in the two-by-three contingency table. The X_2^2 is then computed as follows:

$$X_2^2 = \frac{(-3.1)^2}{148.1} + \frac{(10.6)^2}{114.4} + \frac{(-7.5)^2}{3.75} + \frac{(3.1)^2}{246.9} + \frac{(-10.6)^2}{190.6} + \frac{(7.5)^2}{62.5}$$
$$= 4.07, \quad \text{with 2 DF}$$

If $\alpha = 0.10$, the region of rejection is:

$$\omega: \quad X_2^2 \geq 4.61$$

Hence, it is concluded that the type of area studied probably has little or no effect on a person's response to the question asked in this hypothetical study.

The theoretical numbers for the preceding example also can be computed by first estimating the probabilities for Yes, No, and Undecided from $p_Y = 395/800 = 0.4938$, $p_N = 305/800 = 0.3812$, and $p_U = 1 - p_Y - p_N = 0.1250$ and calculating the theoretical number of Yes-Rural answers as 0.4938 (300) = 148.1 (as before), etc., on the hypothesis that Area and Answer are unrelated classifications.

As another, and somewhat different, illustration of sampling multinomial populations, consider a genetic study for which logical a priori probabilities can be suggested. In a number of situations in which one major gene is involved, it can be reasoned theoretically that the mating Aa × Aa will produce three distinguishable types of offspring in the ratios 1 AA : 2 Aa : 1 aa. However, it also is reasonable that various genetic and environmental factors, or some combination thereof, could alter these ratios significantly.

Suppose that Aa × Aa matings have produced the following data on some identifiable trait:

| | | *Number of:* | | |
Environment	AA	Aa	aa	Totals
1	50	120	30	200
2	37	75	48	160
3	95	165	60	320
Pooled	182	360	138	680

On the assumption of independence between the type of offspring and the environment in which they were produced, the usual calculations produce the following table:

Environment	X^2	DF	ω with $\alpha = 0.05$
1	12.00	2	$X_2^2 \geqslant 5.99$
2	2.14	2	$X_2^2 \geqslant 5.99$
3	7.97	2	$X_2^2 \geqslant 5.99$
Total	22.11	6	$X_6^2 \geqslant 12.59$
Pooled data	8.05	2	$X_2^2 \geqslant 5.99$
Heterogeneity	14.06	4	$X_4^2 \geqslant 9.49$

It is concluded that: (a) the environment does affect the departure of the observed numbers from the theoretical 1:2:1 ratios and (b) the 1 AA : 2Aa : 1 aa hypothesis is only acceptable under environment 2.

The degrees of freedom for a contingency X^2 often have been figured in terms of numbers of chance differences between the observed and the theoretical numbers by noting that the differences $0_i - T_i$ must add to zero for each row and for each column. This places $r + c - 1$ restrictions on the differences between theory and observation, because one of the sums follows from the others. There are $(r)(c)$ differences in an $r \times c$ contingency table, so that with these restrictions there are $rc - r - c + 1 = (r - 1)(c - 1)$ DF for any $r \times c$ contingency table. It is easier to calculate the DF this way, so this formula usually is employed instead of figuring out the number of chance $(0_i - T_i)$'s directly.

PROBLEMS

1. If a scientist has developed a technique for making a measurement by which two scientific methods may be compared, it is necessary first to show

that this technique produces repeatable results. If it does not, there is no basis for comparing two *possibly* different scientific methods. To illustrate, suppose that four random samples intended to be from the same binomial population have produced the following data:

Sample	Class A	Class not-A	Total
First	130	70	200
Second	120	80	200
Third	126	74	200
Fourth	135	65	200
Total	511	289	800

Is the hypothesis $H_0(p_1 = p_2 = p_3 = p_4 = p)$ acceptable over the alternative that some of the p's are unequal, if p_i is the true percent A's in the ith population sampled? Use a 10% region of rejection

2. Lerner and Taylor published the following data on chick mortality in Volume 60 of the *Journal of Agricultural Science:*

	Number of progeny which:		
Sire	Died	Lived	Total
G 14	22	65	87
G 36	44	35	79
G 52	17	45	62
H 8	22	39	61
Total	105	184	289

Do you conclude that the sire affects the chick mortality, or not?

3. Suppose that three independent samplings at the same fish ladder produced the following records:

	Fish classified as:		
Sampling	Chinook	Not Chinook	Total
First	60	25	85
Second	70	30	100
Third	52	18	70
Total	182	73	255

Is the hypothesis that the percentage of Chinooks stayed the same during the three samplings an acceptable one according to these data? What is the heterogeneity X^2 relative to the hypothesis that 75% of these fish are Chinooks during each separate sampling?

4. The lodgepole needle miner in its caterpillar form destroys the foliage of the lodgepole pine. A proper malathion spray applied by helicopter will kill a high percentage of these insects. The important question is, Will the damage to the trees be reduced appreciably? Suppose a random sample of 500 trees from

a sprayed and from an unsprayed area of trees produced the following data on damaged and undamaged trees in each area:

Number of trees found to be:

Area	Damaged	Undamaged	Total
Sprayed	182	318	500
Unsprayed	230	270	500
Total	412	588	1000

Is this convincing evidence of the effectiveness of the spraying?

5. If a geneticist theorizes that a certain parental combination should produce progeny in the ratio of 1 Dominant to 2 Intermediate to 1 Recessive, he visualizes a multinomial population with $p_D = 1/4$ for Dominant, $p_I = 1/2$ for Intermediate, and $p_R = 1 - 1/4 - 1/2 = 1/4$ for Recessive (automatically). If among 100 progeny from such parentage he finds 23 Dominant, 57 Intermediate, and 20 Recessive, should he accept or should he reject the hypothesis $H_0(p_D = 1/4, p_I = 1/2)$ as against the hypothesis $H_a(H_0$ wrong) if he uses a 10% region of rejection? Could you use an "extended" zeta test on this problem? Do you *know* whether the test you do use is the best one for this situation?

6. A political scientist wishes to know whether public opinion regarding a Wilderness Bill before Congress depends upon the respondent's sex or political party, or both. To the question, "Do you favor passage of the Wilderness Bill by Congress?" the following replies are assumed recorded:

Group	Yes	No	Undecided	Total
Female Democrat	78	20	52	150
Female Republican	90	50	60	200
Male Democrat	85	35	40	160
Male Republican	90	80	50	220

Is the hypothesis that neither sex nor political party is associated with the respondents' opinions on this Wilderness Bill an acceptable hypothesis?

7. Suppose there are two mountain streams which run quite close together in a certain area but whose headwaters are far apart. You wish to know whether the trout populations in these two streams are the same as regards the true proportions of four species: rainbow, cutthroat, brook, and Dolly Varden trout. Given the following sampling data and assuming proper sampling procedures, what would you conclude about the equality or inequality of the proportions of those four species in the area defined?

Number of trout which were:

Stream	Rainbow	Cutthroat	Brook	Dolly Varden	Total
No. 1	73	49	68	10	200
No. 2	70	80	85	15	250
Total	143	129	153	25	450

8. It is approximately right to assume that the A-B blood groups are inherited by human beings in a simple Mendelian manner so that AO × AO should produce offspring of whom three fourths are type A and one fourth are type O. If on a random sample of 400 children from this sort of parentage 312 are type A and 88 are type O, does this evidence justify rejection of the hypothesis that 75% are type A in the group which was sampled?

9. Suppose that genetic theory suggests that the mating Aa × Aa should produce distinguishable offspring in the ratio 1 AA : 2 Aa : 1 aa. If a random sample of 200 offspring from that mating contained 60 AA : 105 Aa : 35 aa, is the genetic theory acceptable, if a 10% region of rejection is used?

10. Suppose that surgeons have developed three different methods of treating a certain serious heart ailment and that over a period of years, during which all three methods were being used impartially on a homogeneous group of people, the following data were gathered:

Number of:

Treatment used	Recoveries	Deaths	Total
No. 1	21	24	45
No. 2	16	26	42
No. 3	19	20	39
Total	56	70	126

Would you statistically accept $H_0(p_1 = p_2 = p_3)$ over the alternative that some of the p's are unequal, using $\alpha = 0.10$, if p_i were the probability of recovery under treatment i?

11. There has been some study of the effects of environmental temperature upon the chances of surviving traumatic shock. Sometimes dogs are used to study this relationship. Suppose that a number of dogs have been experimentally injured enough to produce traumatic shock and then have been placed in recovery pens under different temperatures. It is supposed that the groups of dogs later treated differently were first randomly divided into three recovery groups and then the following data were obtained:

Recovery temperature	Number of dogs which:		
	Died	Survived	Total
Hottest	18	7	25
Medium	13	12	25
Coolest	9	16	25
Total	40	35	75

Is recovery from traumatic shock probably associated with the environmental temperature or not, according to these data?

12 Suppose that five drugs designed to prevent carsickness and seasickness are tested on a large group of men by putting the men into mechanical devices which simulate the movements which usually cause such sickness. Each man was given one of the drugs at random but the five drugs were being used

equally often. Given the following numbers, presumably from this test, what do you conclude about the comparative effectiveness of these drugs?

Number of men who were:

Treatment	Sick	Not sick	Total
Drug No. 1	51	24	75
Drug No. 2	40	35	75
Drug No. 3	28	47	75
Drug No. 4	45	30	75
Drug No. 5	23	52	75
Total	187	188	375

13. Suppose a plant breeder is working with an economically important trait, which he expects theoretically to segregate in the ratio 1A:2B:1C. During three independent experiments, each designed to test this same hypothesis, he obtains the following results:

Number of:

Experiment	A	B	C	Total
Fall	75	137	68	280
Winter	90	152	58	300
Spring	90	200	110	400
Total	255	489	236	980

Use the X^2 criterion to draw all possible useful conclusions from these data with a region of rejection of size $\alpha = 0.05$.

14. Suppose that a certain manufactured item can be usefully classified as Excellent, Fair, or Reject. If two different plants are producing this item, a comparison of the qualities of production at the two plants could be made from sampling data such as the following:

Item is:

Plant	Excellent	Fair	Reject	Sum
No. 1	152	36	12	200
No. 2	143	42	15	200
Sum	295	78	27	400

Test the general hypothesis that the quality of production is the same from the two plants.

15. Suppose that public opinion polls are taken one month and two months before a general election, with the following results on a question which could be answered Yes, No, Undecided:

Answer:

Time	Yes	No	Undecided	Sum
One month	205	190	45	440
Two months	205	280	75	560
Sum	410	470	120	1000

Do you think the public opinion in the area sampled changed significantly during that one-month period?

2.9 SAMPLING BINOMIAL POPULATIONS WITH LARGE SAMPLES: RELATION TO THE NORMAL POPULATION

It already has been pointed out that when samples of size n are drawn at random from a binomial population with parameter p, the number of occurrences of the event in question is a random variable X which has a binomial frequency distribution $b(X; n, p)$. Geometrically, this frequency distribution consists of but $n + 1$ points, corresponding to $X = 0, 1, 2, \cdots, n$. The probabilities (ordinates) associated with these $n + 1$ points are given by $b(X; n, p) = \binom{n}{X} p^X (1 - p)^{n-X}$. With n successively equal to 5, 10, 20, and 100 and with p always equal to 0.50, one obtains the relative frequency distributions of Table 2.91. The graphs are shown in Figure 2.91. Even

TABLE 2.91.   RELATIVE FREQUENCY DISTRIBUTIONS, WHEN $b = b(X; n, 0.50)$ AND $n = 5, 10, 20,$ AND 100 IN TURN

\(n = 5\)		\(n = 10\)		\(n = 20\)		\(n = 100\)	
X	b	X	b	X	b	X	b
0	0.03	1	0.01	5	0.01	38	0.004
1	0.16	2	0.04	6	0.04	39	0.007
2	0.31	3	0.12	7	0.07	40	0.011
3	0.31	4	0.21	8	0.12	41	0.016
4	0.16	5	0.25	9	0.16	42	0.022
5	0.03	6	0.21	10	0.18	43	0.030
		7	0.12	11	0.16	44	0.039
		8	0.04	12	0.12	45	0.048
		9	0.01	13	0.07	46	0.058
				14	0.04	47	0.067
				15	0.01	48	0.074
						49	0.078
						50	0.080
						51	0.078
						52	0.074
						53	0.067
						54	0.058
						55	0.048
						56	0.039
						57	0.030
						58	0.022
						59	0.016
						60	0.011
						61	0.007
						62	0.004

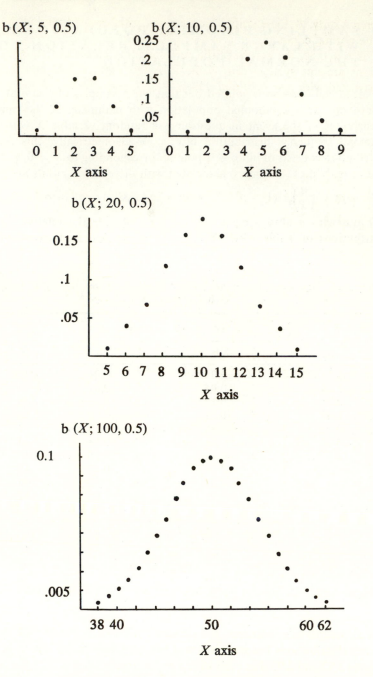

Figure 2.91. Graphs for the binomial frequency distributions of Table 2.91.

when n is only 10, these graphs have a shape which should remind the reader of the normal curve.

If $p \neq 0.50$, the graphs of the corresponding binomial frequency distributions are not symmetrical. Table 2.92 and Figures 2.92 and 2.93 were constructed with $p = 0.20$ and $n = 5, 10, 20,$ and 100, as before. It is seen

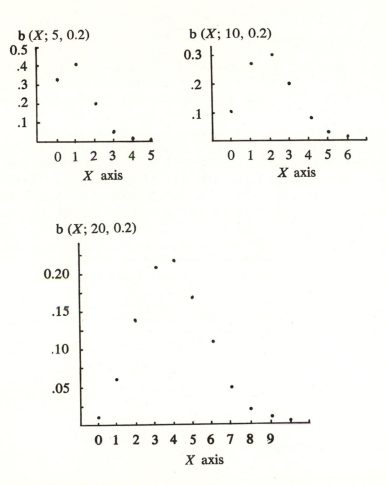

Figure 2.92. Graphs for Table 2.92 with $n = 5, 10,$ and 20, and $p = 0.20$.

that as sample size increases, the skewness (lack of symmetry) of these frequency distributions becomes less and less pronounced. In fact, it is seen in Figures 2.92 and 2.93 that even with p as far from 0.50 as is 0.20 the binomial frequency distribution is quite symmetrical when $n = 20$ or more. With $n = 100$ the lack of symmetry becomes essentially negligible for many practical purposes. It also should be noted again that for $n \geqslant 20$ the graph

of b(X; n, p) suggests the shape of the normal frequency distribution curve
quite clearly.

It can be shown, with certain restrictions on the smallness of p relative
to the size of n, that

(2.91) $$\binom{n}{X} p^X (1-p)^{n-X} \cong \frac{1}{\sqrt{2\pi npq}} \exp -\{(X-np)^2/2npq\}$$

for n sufficiently large. In other words, the binomial b(X; n, p) $\cong$ the normal
N(np, npq) for n sufficiently large. How large n must be depends on how good
an approximation a situation demands and on the size of p. It is surprising,
however, how fast the approximation improves as n increases.

Table 2.93 shows the approximation for stated combinations of n and p.
When p is 0.50, b(X; n, 0.50) is symmetrical. Naturally, the normal distribution, which always is symmetrical, fits b(X; n, p) better when $p = 0.50$ than
when $p \neq 0.50$. As seen in the table, N(5, 2.5) fits b(X; 10, 0.50) very well
even with $n = 10$, and N(10, 5) fits b(X; 20, 0.50) almost exactly to two
decimal places. But N(5, 4.50), for which $n = 50$, does not fit b(X; 50, 0.10)

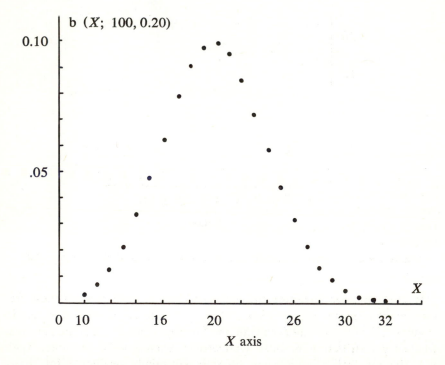

Figure 2.93.   Graph for Table 2.92 with $n = 100$ and $p = 0.20$.

quite as well as the normal fits the binomial when n is only 10. Even so, the approximation of the $N(np, npq)$ distribution to the $b(X; n, p)$ distribution is excellent in all cases shown. Before excellent tables of $b(X; n, p)$ existed, it

TABLE 2.92. TABLES OF BINOMIAL FREQUENCY DISTRIBUTIONS $b(X; n, p)$ WHEN $p = 0.20$ AND $n = 5, 10, 20,$ AND 100 IN TURN

$n = 5$		$n = 10$		$n = 20$		$n = 100$	
X	b	X	b	X	b	X	b
0	0.33	0	0.11	0	0.01	10	0.003
1	0.41	1	0.27	1	0.06	11	0.007
2	0.20	2	0.30	2	0.14	12	0.013
3	0.05	3	0.20	3	0.21	13	0.022
4	0.01	4	0.08	4	0.22	14	0.034
		5	0.03	5	0.17	15	0.048
		6	0.01	6	0.11	16	0.063
				7	0.05	17	0.079
				8	0.02	18	0.091
				9	0.01	19	0.098
						20	0.099
						21	0.095
						22	0.085
						23	0.072
						24	0.058
						25	0.044
						26	0.032
						27	0.022
						28	0.014
						29	0.009
						30	0.005
						31	0.003
						32	0.002

was quite important to be able to approximate $b(X; n, p)$ and $\sum [b(X; n, p)]$ over a suitable range by means of the well-established normal tables. This is much less necessary now, for tables of the latter also are quite common.

If one does need to approximate $\sum_{X = k_1}^{k_2} b(X; n, p)$, a simple adjustment should be made for the fact that $b(X; n, p)$ is discontinuous and $N(np, npq)$ is continuous. The adjustment, and also the reason for it, are illustrated in Figure 2.94.

To see how well the normal approximation of this figure fits the $\sum_{X=3}^{9} b(X; 25, 0.30)$, consider the following facts, which the reader can check.

(a) With no more than two-decimal accuracy, $\sum_{X=3}^{9} b(X; 25, 0.30) = 0.80$.

(*b*) The area under N(7.5, 5.25) from $X = 2.5$ to $X = 9.5$ corresponds to the area of N(0, 1) from $\lambda_1 = -2.19$ to $\lambda_2 = +0.88$, and this area is 0.81, where λ is the standard normal variate.

TABLE 2.93.   RELATION   BETWEEN $b = b(X; n, p)$ AND $N = N(np, npq)$ FOR INDICATED n AND p

$p = 0.50, n = 10$			$p = 0.50, n = 20$			$p = 0.20, n = 20$		
X	b	N	X	b	N	X	b	N
0	0.00	0.00	5	0.01	0.01	0	0.01	0.02
1	0.01	0.01	6	0.04	0.03	1	0.06	0.05
2	0.04	0.04	7	0.07	0.07	2	0.14	0.12
3	0.12	0.11	8	0.12	0.12	3	0.21	0.19
4	0.21	0.21	9	0.16	0.16	4	0.22	0.22
5	0.25	0.25	10	0.18	0.18	5	0.17	0.19
6	0.21	0.21	11	0.16	0.16	6	0.11	0.12
7	0.12	0.11	12	0.12	0.12	7	0.05	0.05
8	0.04	0.04	13	0.07	0.07	8	0.02	0.02
9	0.01	0.01	14	0.04	0.03	9	0.01	0.00
10	0.00	0.00	15	0.01	0.01	10	0.00	0.00
			16	0.00	0.00			

$p = 0.20, n = 10$			$p = 0.30, n = 25$			$p = 0.10, n = 50$		
X	b	N	X	b	N	X	b	N
0	0.11	0.09	1	0.00	0.00	0	0.01	0.01
1	0.27	0.23	2	0.01	0.01	1	0.03	0.03
2	0.30	0.32	3	0.02	0.03	2	0.08	0.07
3	0.20	0.23	4	0.06	0.05	3	0.14	0.12
4	0.08	0.09	5	0.10	0.10	4	0.18	0.17
5	0.03	0.02	6	0.15	0.14	5	0.18	0.19
6	0.01	0.00	7	0.17	0.17	6	0.15	0.17
7	0.00	0.00	8	0.17	0.17	7	0.11	0.12
			9	0.13	0.14	8	0.06	0.07
			10	0.09	0.10	9	0.03	0.03
			11	0.05	0.05	10	0.02	0.01
			12	0.03	0.03	11	0.01	0.00
			13	0.01	0.01	12	0.00	0.00
			14	0.00	0.00			

This surely is a satisfactory approximation and was accomplished for a nonsymmetrical binomial frequency distribution with n as small as 25 and p equal to 0.30.

To summarize the foregoing and simultaneously present a more mathematical point of view, the following can be said. Any $b(X; n, p)$ variate for which n and p are not excessively small (say $n \geqslant 20$ and $0.10 \leqslant p \leqslant 0.90$) can be transformed to an $N(0, 1)$ variable by the formula $\lambda = (X - np)/\sqrt{npq}$. If one wants to compute $\sum_{X=k_1}^{k_2} b(X; n, p)$, it is best to use $k_1 - 0.50$ and $k_2 + 0.50$ as the extremes instead of $X = k_1$ and k_2, respectively.

One other matter regarding the normal approximation to a binomial frequency distribution should be discussed. It may be that one is interested

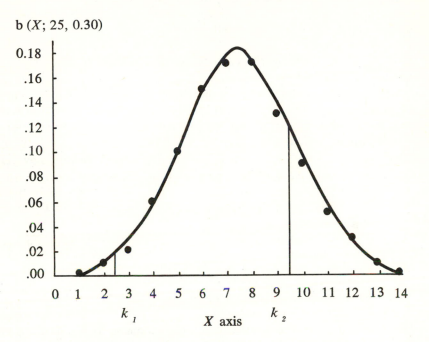

b $(X; 25, 0.30)$

Figure 2.94.   Illustration of benefit from using limits of $k_1 - 0.50$ to $k_2 + 0.50$ to approximate k to the $\sum_{X}^{k_2} = k_1$ $[b(X; n, p)]$; $n = 25$, and $p = 0.30$.   Specifically, $\sum_{X}^{9} = 3$ $[b(X; 25, 0.30)] =$ area   under $N(7.5, 5.25)$ between $X = 2.5$ and 9.5.

in the fraction X/n rather than in X itself. In view of the fact that $(X - np)/\sqrt{npq}$ has approximately the $N(0, 1)$ distribution, it follows, by dividing numerator and denominator by n, that $(X/n - p)/\sqrt{pq/n}$ also is an $N(0, 1)$ variate to a good degree of accuracy. Thus, any table for $N(0, 1)$ can be used for certain other problems basically involving $b(X; n, p)$.

It follows from the foregoing discussion that with two independent random samples from binomial populations one can study the difference between two X's or between two sample ratios X_1/n_1 and X_2/n_2 by means of the standard normal tables. First, however, it is necessary to present a theorem about the variance of the difference between two random variables. This theorem is very important in statistics and is essentially as follows:

Theorem.   If v_1 and v_2 are two independent random variables with variances σ_1^2 and σ_2^2, respectively, the variance of $v_1 - v_2$ or of $v_1 + v_2$ is $\sigma_1^2 + \sigma_2^2$.

The variance of X_i/n_i for a random sample of size n_i is pq/n_i, as shown earlier. Therefore, for two independent random samples of sizes n_1 and n_2 the variance of the difference $d = X_1/n_1 - X_2/n_2$ is

$$(2.92) \qquad\qquad \sigma_d^2 = pq\left(\frac{1}{n_1} + \frac{1}{n_2}\right)$$

if the two samples are from the same binomial population so that only one parameter p is involved.

After normal sampling has been more fully discussed in Chapters 3 and 4, the information in this section will be used to test the difference between two binomial ratios, that is, to test $H_0(p_i = p_j)$. This has been done already by the chi-square test, but the sign of the difference, $d = X_1/n_1 - X_2/n_2$, was lost in that procedure. Further, one-tail regions of rejection now can be used. One also can place a $CI_{1-\alpha}$ on $p_i - p_j$, as will be seen later.

PROBLEMS

1. Suppose that two random samples each of size $n = 20$ are to be drawn from a binomial population with $p = 0.4$. What is the variance of the difference $X_1 - X_2$, when X_i, where $i = 1, 2$, is the number in sample i with attribute A ? What is the standard deviation of $X_1 - X_2$?

2. Referring to Problem 1, what is the standard deviation of the difference $X_1/20 - X_2/20 = 1/20(X_1 - X_2)$?

3. Suppose that a random sample of 20 observations is to be taken from a binomial population whose parameter is, *unknown to the sampler*, actually $p = 0.4$. What is the probability that the *estimated* standard deviation will exceed 0.10 ?

4. Calculate the variance of $X/10$ for $p = 0.3, 0.35, 0.4, 0.45, 0.5, 0.55, 0.60, 0.65,$ and 0.70, thereby empirically verifying for a sample of size $n = 10$ the fact that the maximum variance of X/n occurs at $p = q = 1/2$.

5. If $p = 0.4$, $n = 20$, and $X = 9$, verify that $b(9; 20, 0.4) \cong N(np, npq)$ for $X = 9$.

6. Compare $\sum_{X=7}^{10} [b(X; 10, 0.5)]$ with the area under $N(5, 2.5)$ between $X = 6.5$ and $X = \infty$. Can you rationalize the use of $X = 6.5$ instead of $X = 7$ as the left-hand limit? Would it matter much whether you used $X = 10.5$ instead of ∞ as the right-hand limit?

7. If a random sample of size $n = 35$ is to be drawn from a $b(X; 35, 0.60)$ population, what is the probability that the fraction X/n will fall between 0.55 and 0.65 ?

8. Suppose that the true percentage of the voters in a certain city who favor candidate Jones is $p = 0.52$. What is the probability that a random sample of size $n = 100$ taken in that city will show $X/n > 0.50$, that is, that the sample

will show Jones the favorite? What is the probability that X/n will be < 0.50 and fail to indicate Jones' true popularity?

9. If two random samples of sizes $n_1 = n_2 = 50$ are to be taken from $b(X; 50, 0.45)$ independently, what is the probability that the difference $X_1/50 - X_2/50$ *in that order* will be smaller than 0.22?

10. If a random sample is to be taken from $b(X; 100, 0.60)$, what is the probability that $57 \leqslant X \leqslant 66$?

REVIEW PROBLEMS

1. Suppose that a sociologist makes a survey of the use of deep-freeze units by rural residents of 10 southwest Kansas counties. He obtains from county offices a complete list of all households outside all city limits in the area and then takes a random sample of 150 households. He finds the following with respect to ownership of deep-freeze units: 95 do own such units and 55 do not. Compute a 90% confidence interval on the true percentage of households in this area which do own deep-freeze units at the time the survey was made. Assume that this sample essentially is from an infinite population.

2. Referring to Problem 1, suppose the same sort of sample were taken *within* the limits of cities in this same area in such a way as to represent all cities in this area. Also suppose that 73 out of 150 were found to own deep-freeze units. Does this evidence justify the conclusion that a higher percentage of the rural families own deep-freeze units than of the people within city limits?

3. Referring to Problem 1, suppose that the rural residents of these 10 counties all are classifiable as predominantly either cattle ranchers or wheat farmers. Suppose then, that if each of the households is given a double classification, one obtains the following 2×2 contingency table:

Type of farm	Own a deep-freeze	Do not own a deep-freeze	Total
Cattle farm	45	15	60
Wheat farm	50	40	90
Total	95	55	150

Is it reasonable, statistically, to conclude that ownership of a deep-freeze does not depend upon the type of farm, as here represented?

4. Suppose there are 100 frogs in a small, easily observed, pond, and it is known that there are two and only two species of frog in this pond. However, these species are visually indistinguishable. It is learned by careful observation that some of the frogs consistently croak before they hop and the others do not. It also is seen that some frogs distinctly and consistently lie lower in the water than the others. When these two characteristics are summarized for all 100 frogs in the pond, the following 2×2 contingency table is obtained:

	Position in water:		
Croaking before hopping	Low	Normal	Total
Does croak	25	30	55
Does not croak	30	15	45
Total	55	45	100

(a) Are the frog's position in the water and the practice of croaking before hopping associated traits, assuming that these 100 frogs are a random sample in some meaningful sense?

(b) Could these data help identify the two species in the pond?

(c) What additional information should one obtain about these frogs to improve the studies of (a) and (b)?

5. Suppose that a house-owner has arrangements in his yard for feeding wild birds when there is snow on the ground and that he provides three foods: peanut butter, a fat-seed mixture, and a mixture of dry grains. Suppose this person's home is so located that a large number of birds have access to the feeders. It is recorded over a period of time that the following species of birds were seen eating the different foods the indicated numbers of times on different visits to the feeders:

Species	Peanut butter	Fat-seed mix	Dry grains	Total
Cardinal	15	20	65	100
Starling	70	35	75	180
Titmouse	80	15	5	100
Chickadee	90	20	10	120

(a) Is there an association between species of bird and choice of food?

(b) Which species probably are alike in their choices of food and which are different?

(c) What if only a few birds of each species had access to these feeders but each made many trips? How would this affect the meaning of these data?

6. Suppose that 100 laboratory rats are placed in a situation in which, after going along a narrow chute for 10 feet, they suddenly come out facing a glass wall which forced them to turn either left or right. There are two species of rats in this group. It turns out that the following record is made after each rat has run through the test once:

	Rat turned:		
Species	Left	Right	Total
A	35	16	51
B	25	24	49
Total	60	40	100

(a) Do you conclude that direction of turning under these circumstances is related to species?

(b) What if you now are told that two thirds of the rats in species A are females; whereas the species B rats are divided, 25 males to 24 females?

(c) What if, instead of (b), you find that all rats are females but two thirds of the species A rats are 30 days old and the rest 45 days old, whereas all of the species B rats are 45 days old?

7. Suppose that a manufacturing process is producing square-headed, threaded iron bolts. These bolts are supposed to be three inches long and one-half inch in diameter and to have one inch of threading of a specified sort. Define six different binomial populations based on inspection of these bolts. Also

define two different binomial frequency distributions, each of which pertains to one of the six binomial populations you defined.

8. Referring to Problem 7, define what you think might be a normal population pertaining to that manufacturing process. Why should the manufacturer be concerned about the variance of the population you define?

9. Referring to Problem 7, describe a central and then a noncentral confidence interval which probably would be of interest in a study of the quality of bolt produced.

10. Referring to Problem 8, describe a confidence interval which should be of interest in a study of the population you define.

11. Many of the items on a Strong Interest Inventory require the subject taking the test to mark his preference regarding an item as *L* for like, *I* for indifference and *D* for dislike. Suppose that a group of sophomore men and a group of sophomore women in a certain university have produced the following record from such a test with respect to one particular item:

		Response:		
Sex	*L*	*I*	*D*	*Total*
Male	700	300	100	1100
Female	300	25	75	400
Total	1000	325	175	1500

Using $\alpha = 0.10$ and assuming these are proper random samples, would you conclude that their responses are unrelated to their sex or not?

12. Referring to Problem 11, place a central 90% confidence limit on the true percentage of females represented by this sample who are indifferent regarding the item tested. Interpret this interval as usefully as you can. How could a shorter interval have been obtained?

13. Suppose that for head-on collisions of cars investigated by highway patrols over a wide area the following data were obtained pertaining to the effectiveness in reducing fatalities of seat belts *on the driver* of the automobile:

		Driver:	
Driver had:	*Killed*	*Lived*	*Total*
Seat belt on	40	60	100
No seat belt on	240	160	400
Total	280	220	500

What can you conclude statistically, and what assumptions did you have to make to reach those conclusions?

14. The female cowbird is known for its practice of laying eggs in other birds' nests. Suppose that of 300 nests inspected in a certain area 105 contained one or more cowbird eggs. What is the greatest lower bound on the percentage of nests in the area which have been thus parasitized by cowbirds, if you use a confidence coefficient of 0.95? What H_0 could you test with this confidence interval?

15. Suppose that for the 300 birds' nests of Problem 14 the following classification by species of bird owning the nest was obtained:

The nest was:

Species	Parasitized	Not parasitized	Total
Bluebird	10	20	30
Robin	30	40	70
Cardinal	25	35	60
Brown thrasher	10	30	40
Mourning dove	50	30	80
Other	10	10	20
Total	135	165	300

Does it seem justifiable to conclude that the species of bird owning the nest is unrelated to frequency of parasitization by cowbirds?

16. What would be some of the sampling problems involved in such a study as envisioned in Problems 14 and 15?

17. What is the probability that a random chi-square with 3 DF will be larger than its number of degrees of freedom? In general, what can you say about the probability that a random chi-square will be larger than its number of degrees of freedom? What about a random X^2?

18. Why are the values of χ^2 larger and larger as you read downward in any column of Table XI?

19. If, on a random sample of size $n = 75$ from a binomial population, X is found to be 15, what is the central CI_{90} on p? What does this interval tell you?

20. Referring to Problem 19, what is the greatest lower bound on p with confidence coefficient 0.95? What does it tell you?

21. Suppose that all the registered voters in a large city are classified either as Democrat or as Republican, the small number which fall into neither class being excluded from the study. If a simple random sample of 100 is taken and it is found that $X = 56$ people classified as Democrat, what is the CI_{95} on p, the true percentage Democrat in the group sampled? How should these limits be interpreted? What is the lower limit on percentage Democrat in the population if α is taken as 0.05?

22. Suppose that under the conditions of Problem 21 a simple random sample of size $n = 500$ had been taken, and again 56% of the sample had been classified as Democrat. What is the CI_{95} now? Why is this confidence interval shorter than in Problem 21? Would it usually be shorter than a CI_{95} based on 100 observations? Would it always be shorter?

23. The CI_{95} of Problem 21 includes the possibility that $p \leqslant 0.50$, even though the point estimate, $\hat{p} = 0.56$, suggests that the Democrats are in the majority. Is this contradictory?

24. The minimum-length CI_{90} for Problem 21 is $47 \leqslant p \leqslant 64\%$ Democrat. Would the CI_{80} *from the same sample* have a shorter or a longer range of possibilities for the parameter p? Why? Would your answer also hold for the sample of Problem 22? Could the CI_{80} sometimes be wider and sometimes narrower than the CI_{90} if the same population were being sampled each time but different samples were taken for each CI? Justify your answer.

25. If one is going to sample a vaccine for safety to humans, how many individual dosage units must one take as a minimum sample size without finding any which are unsafe ($X = 0$), before one can conclude with 95% confidence that $p = 0$, assuming that the accuracy of our tables is sufficient for the purpose at hand? How large a sample would it require to assure one with 95% confidence that no more than 1% of the units were unsafe, if $X = 0$?

26. Suppose that a random sample of 250 Germans in a specific geographic area showed that 101 of them had type O blood. Place central 95% limits on the true percentage of those Germans having type O blood, and interpret this interval. Place a least upper bound on the true percentage of Germans having type O blood, keeping α at 0.05.

27. Suppose that 100 eggs are selected at random from a large shipment and that 5 are found to be stale. What would you set as the upper limit on the percentage of stale eggs in the whole batch sampled, if there is no use at all for a lower limit? Use $1 - \alpha = 0.90$. Also test $H_0(p \leqslant 0.07)$ against $H_a(p > 0.07)$, and draw conclusions.

28. If 250 one-pound cartons of butter are to be selected at random from a carload and examined for mold particles, what is the maximum number of cartons which can be found to contain too much mold, before you should conclude that 5% or more of the cartons in the carload probably contain too much mold? Use $\alpha = 0.10$.

29. Suppose that a concern which manufactures roller bearings must meet a standard of 95% classed as Acceptable according to prescribed measurements. If a sample of 250 contains 3 classed as Unacceptable, is the shipment up to standard?

30. Suppose that a random sample of 100 lake trout shows that 8 have been attacked seriously by the lamprey. If one uses a confidence coefficient of 0.95, is the assertion that 10% of the trout in the lake sampled have been attacked seriously by the lamprey eel an acceptable statement? What about a statement that less than 12% of the trout have been so attacked?

31. Referring to Problem 30, how large a sample would one need to take before the observing that 8% of the trout were seriously attacked by lampreys would allow the conclusion that $p < 0.12$ with $\alpha = 0.12$?

32. Suppose that a person seeking to sell a section of timberland says that no more than 5% of the trees (by number) are alder, the remainder being Douglas fir. If one defines in advance a method of taking a random sample in this area and finds that 20 trees out of 500 in the sample are alder, is the owner's statement credible on the basis of a noncentral 95% confidence interval?

33. Referring to Problem 32, how would you define a sampling scheme for this study?

34. It usually is stated that about 15% of all U.S. Caucasians have Rh negative blood; that is, $p_N = 0.15$. If a random sample of 100 non-Americans has only 10% who are Rh negative, is $H_0(p_N = 0.15)$ acceptable against the alternative that $p_N < 0.15$?

35. Suppose that a large stand of lodgepole pine has been marked into one-section (square-mile) subunits by means of the usual section markers. If 100 such sections drawn as a random sample of the whole area of lodgepole pine showed that 15 sections were seriously infested with the lodgepole needle miner, do you believe that no more than 10% of the sections sampled were seriously infested by the lodgepole miner? Explain your conclusion.

36. Use the normal distribution to compute $\sum_{X=5}^{18} b(X; 50, 0.4)$.

37. If a random sample of size $n = 60$ is to be drawn from the binomial population with $p = 0.55$, what is the probability that the observed ratio $X/60$ will have a value below 0.50?

38. If two random samples of sizes 40 and 45, respectively, are to be drawn from the binomial population with $p = 0.55$, what is the probability that the difference $X_1/40 - X_2/45$ will be positive? Will be between -0.02 and $+0.01$?

39. What is the probability that the $X/60$ of Problem 37 will be either <0.50 or >0.60?

40. Suppose that one is going to take a random sample from the binomial population with $p = 0.25$. How large a sample should one take in order that $\Pr\{(0.23 < X) \mid (n < 0.27)\} = 0.90$?

Chapter 3

Sampling One Normal Population, $N(\mu, \sigma^2)$

3.1 DEFINING AND SAMPLING THE POPULATION

If an experimenter is going to measure some objects or actions along a continuous scale of measurement, such as feet, centimeters, pounds, or seconds, he may be sampling a normal population. There are other types of populations of continuous measurements, of course, but the concept of the normal frequency distribution did have one of its origins in the theory of errors of physical measurement. An Englishman, A. de Moivre, who is credited with being the first to derive the formula for the normal frequency curve early in the eighteenth century, discovered this distribution while working on problems in games of chance, which actually involve discrete events. However, P. S. Laplace and K. F. Gauss later independently rediscovered the normal curve as the frequency curve for errors of measurement in some problems in the physical sciences. So many applications of the normal frequency distribution have been found in the biological, sociological, and physical sciences, and in the humanities, that this concept surely is one of the most important in the whole field of experimental statistics.

Even though it frequently is likely that a normal population is involved during a scientific experiment, there are infinitely many different normal populations, because there are infinitely many combinations of μ and σ^2

in $N(\mu, \sigma^2)$. Furthermore, the same set of objects or actions can become the basis for defining several different statistical populations of measurements to be taken on these objects or actions. Hence, the definition of a particular statistical population which is to be studied must be precise and unambiguous. For example, to state that the population consists of all eight-week weights of chickens is insufficient, because there are many different breeds of chickens, many ways to feed them, and many ways to take care of them. It is necessary to state all pertinent matters which conceivably might affect weight materially at that age. On the other hand, one could be so specific about matters which could affect the eight-week weights of chickens that only one chicken met the requirements. Obviously, in practice a happy medium must be struck. Perhaps it would be sufficient to restrict study to the eight-week weights of White Leghorn females which had been raised under stated conditions with respect to housing, weather, and diet.

Once that normal population which is to be studied by sampling has been defined unambiguously, the problem of sampling it must be solved. For the simplest cases considered in this chapter, this theoretically should be easy: under the conditions which define the population, draw completely at random n of the actions or objects to be measured, measure each in the specified way, and record these measurements as $X_1, X_2, \cdots, X_n$ in the order in which they were drawn (or measured). This is the sample. The experimenter should not exclude from measurement some of the objects or actions drawn in the sampling because they seem unusual to him, provided they belong to the circumstances and activities which were specified in defining the population to be sampled. For example, if a cereal chemist is studying the effects of a certain ingredient on the volumes of loaves of bread made from Pawnee wheat flour according to a specific formula and with a definite baking procedure, he should keep in his sample *all* loaves baked under these specifications even though one or two loaves look punier than expected. If he accidentally drops the dough for one loaf on the floor and steps on it, he should not even complete the baking of that loaf, because he failed to follow the specified baking procedure with that potential loaf at that point.

The existence of tables of random numbers (see, for example, Fisher and Yates, *Statistical Tables for Biological, Agricultural and Medical Research,* Oliver and Boyd, London) facilitates the drawing of random samples without any chances being taken on unconscious human biasses. For example, if 500 chickens are available for a certain study and all fulfill the specifications for the study, a random sample of 25 can be taken by numbering the chickens from 1 to 500 and then using a table of random numbers to draw a sample of size $n = 25$. The specified measurement then would be taken, and the measurements would constitute the statistical sample from the corresponding population.

PROBLEMS

1. Assuming that the weights of pigs often are essentially normally distributed, specifically define a population by specifying all factors which you think reasonably might affect weight.

2. Describe in detail a method of taking a simple random sample of size $n = 20$ from the population you defined in Problem 1.

3. Assuming that numerical grades from hour examinations in elementary statistics conform to an $N(65, 100)$ distribution and assuming that the instructor in charge of assigning grades to the papers from a large group of students wishes to convert the number grades into letter grades, 10% getting A's, what is the grade range for an A? For an F? (It is assumed that the letter grades are A, B, C, D, and F.)

4. Define a population of intelligence quotient scores, and associate it with a specific group of people.

5. Draw a random sample of size $n = 25$ from the table of random numbers in the Fisher-Yates statistical tables, and then tell how this sample of random numbers can be used to draw a random sample from any one of the populations defined above.

6. Suppose that an industrial process is producing a cog which is supposed to have a one-eighth-inch hole in its center. How would you sample the end product preparatory to checking the diameter specification?

7. Suppose that a company is producing plastic hose which is intended to be one-half inch in inside diameter. How would you sample this production to see if it met this specification?

8. If a drug manufacturing company is producing 50-milligram thiamine chloride tablets, there should be a check on the actual content of the tablets to be sold. How would you sample a large batch of such tablets?

9. How would you sample the water supply in one specific residence in a given city? In the whole city?

10. The air around you is composed of chemical elements. How would you sample it for percent oxygen?

11. When a new street is being paved in your city, the company doing the job is supposed to meet certain specifications. How and when would you determine by sampling whether or not these specifications were being met?

3.2 POINT ESTIMATION OF THE POPULATION MEAN (μ) AND VARIANCE (σ²) OF AN N(μ, σ²) POPULATION

This subject was covered earlier, in the introduction to experimental statistics, so only a review summary will be given here, to emphasize important points. The maximum-likelihood estimator of μ was defined by

(3.21)
$$\bar{x} = \frac{1}{n} \sum_{i=1}^{n} (X_i)$$

in the general introduction of the process of estimating parameters. It also was pointed out, and illustrated empirically, that the $\bar{x}$'s obtainable by repeated sampling of N(μ, σ^2) with samples of size n form another normal population, namely N($\mu, \sigma^2/n$). The estimator, $\bar{x}$, is an unbiassed and highly efficient estimator of μ and is widely employed in experimental statistics.

The median (md), also defined earlier, is another unbiassed estimator of μ. Why, then, is $\bar{x}$ so frequently the preferred estimator of μ? The variance of $\bar{x}$ is less than that of md for any but the trivial sample size, $n = 2$. For large n and normal samples, $\sigma^2_{md} \simeq (\pi/2n)\sigma^2 = (\pi/2)\sigma^2_{\bar{x}}$; therefore

(3.22) $\sigma^2_{md} = 1.57\sigma^2_{\bar{x}},$ approximately

Hence, in a very real sense the sample median is more than 50% *less* reliable than the sample mean as an estimator of the population mean, μ. The sample median fluctuates more widely than the sample mean from sample to sample and hence has a lower probability of being arbitrarily near to μ when any specified future sample is obtained. For this reason the sample median usually is considered a poorer estimator of μ than the sample mean, $\bar{x}$, if one is sampling a normal population.

The sample midrange, MR, also defined and discussed earlier, is even simpler to compute than the median or the mean and is also an unbiassed estimator of μ. The MR is a better estimator of μ than is the md for samples of sizes no larger than $n = 5$ or 6, but its efficiency relative to both $\bar{x}$ and md falls off rapidly as the sample size is increased, as was shown earlier.

It already has been said that the method of maximum likelihood chooses that estimate of a parameter which maximizes what is called the *likelihood* of the sample. For a random sample $X_1, X_2, \cdots, X_n$ from a normal population with mean $= \mu$ and variance $= \sigma^2$ the likelihood function is

$$L = \left(\frac{1}{\sqrt{2\pi}\,\sigma} \exp -\{(X_1 - \mu)^2/2\sigma^2\}\right) \cdot \left(\frac{1}{\sqrt{2\pi}\,\sigma} \exp -\{(X_2 - \mu)^2/2\sigma^2\}\right) \cdots$$

$$\left(\frac{1}{\sqrt{2\pi}\,\sigma} \exp -\{(X_n - \mu)^2/2\sigma^2\}\right) = \frac{1}{(\sqrt{2\pi}\,\sigma)^n} \exp -\{(1/2\sigma^2) \sum_1^n (X_i - \mu)^2\}$$

because the n independent X's satisfy the requirements for computing the probability of occurrence of independent events stated in Rule 2 (Chapter 1). It can be shown by calculus and by using $\log_e L$ that the maximum-likelihood estimators of μ and σ^2 are:

(3.23) $\hat{\mu} = \bar{x} = \sum_1^n (X_i)/n$

(3.24) $\hat{\sigma}^2 = \sum_1^n (X_i - \bar{x})^2/n$

It turns out that these two maximum-likelihood estimators differ in one basic feature, which sometimes is important: the $\bar{x}$ is an unbiassed estimator, whereas the $\hat{\sigma}^2$ is a biassed estimator in the sense that the long-run average of $\bar{x}_i$ over many samples is equal to the parameter μ. The long-run average of sample values of $\hat{\sigma}^2$ is

$$E\{\hat{\sigma}^2\} = \frac{n-1}{n}\ \sigma^2$$

where E means "expected value of." Therefore the quantity

(3.25)
$$s^2 = \frac{\sum\limits_{1}^{n}(X_i - \bar{x})^2}{n-1}$$

is used as an *unbiassed* estimator of σ^2. It will be seen in subsequent discussions that s^2 is used more frequently in the problems to be considered herein than is the maximum-likelihood estimator shown in Equation 3.24.

The reader already has encountered the concept of the number of degrees of freedom in the sections on the chi-square test. This concept also is useful with s^2. Because the deviations, $X_i - \bar{x}$, on which the value of s^2 depends, always sum to zero, the value of s^2 depends on only $n-1$ chance differences between random X's and their own mean, $\bar{x}$. Therefore, s^2 is said to have $n - 1$ DF.

Some points regarding the point estimators $\bar{x}$, $\hat{\sigma}^2$, and s^2 are illustrated by means of the following random sample of size $n = 10$ drawn from an N(5, 4) population:

X: 7.6, 9.0, 2.0, 5.0, 4.7, 6.1, 7.3, 2.6, 4.1, and 5.3

The three estimates of μ and σ^2 are

$$\bar{x} = 5.37, \qquad \hat{\sigma}^2 = 4.3641, \qquad \text{and} \quad s^2 = 4.8490$$

On another and entirely independent sample from the same normal population, the sample and estimates of μ and σ^2 were:

X: 5.4, 5.2, 4.8, 7.7, 0.8, 6.9, 7.9, 7.2, 3.7, and 3.3

for which $\bar{x} = 5.29$, $\hat{\sigma}^2 = 4.5769$, and $s^2 = 5.0854$. In general, every random sample from an N(5, 4) population would produce different values for $\bar{x}$, $\hat{\sigma}^2$, and s^2. Over many such samples $\bar{x}$ would average 5 and s^2 would average 4, but the average $\hat{\sigma}^2$ would be $[(n-1)/n]\sigma^2 = (9/10)(4) = 3.60$; that is, $\hat{\sigma}^2$ is a biassed estimator of σ^2. The s^2 would have $n - 1 = 9$ DF for each sample because $\sum_{i=1}^{10}(X_i - \bar{x})$ always equals zero.

PROBLEMS

1. What is the theoretical variance of the sample mean for samples of size $n = 6$ from N(8, 12)? For samples of size $n = 36$? What is the approximate sampling variance of the sampling median for samples of size $n = 36$?

2. Given an N(8, 12) as the parent population, plot on the vertical axis the theoretical variance of $\bar{x}$ for $n = 4, 9, 16, 25$, and 36, plotted on the horizontal axis. What conclusions can you draw?

3. What are the implications of Problem 2 on the usefulness of taking larger and larger samples?

4. Given $X_i = 2.6, -1.3, 2.0, 5.2, 3.1, 0.3, 4.0$, and 2.5, compute the three most common estimates of the true mean, μ.

5. Given the following data from *paired* observations supposedly taken on twin pairs of animals, (a) obtain the best point estimate of the true average *difference* $X_A - X_B$ and (b) obtain the best point estimate of the difference between the true means of the two populations sampled:

X_A:	28.2	25.5	37.6	33.2	24.8	29.3	30.4
X_B:	26.7	24.9	38.0	30.0	24.7	27.6	29.5

6. Do Problem 5, using the median as the estimator.

7. Do Problem 5, using the midrange as the estimator.

8. Referring to the data in Problem 4, compute the values of $\hat{\sigma}^2$ and s^2. What is the true average value of such $\hat{\sigma}^2$'s? Of the s^2's? How many DF does each s^2 have?

9. Do as in Problem 8 for the difference $X_i = X_{Ai} - X_{Bi}$.

10. Subtract 27.0 from each X_A of Problem 5 and then compute the maximum-likelihood estimate of the variance of $X_i - 27$ for the population sampled. How is the variance of $X - 27$ related to the variance of X? Compute s^2 from the $\hat{\sigma}^2$ you already have calculated.

11. Prove algebraically that

$$\sum_{i=1}^{n} (X_i - \bar{x})^2 \equiv \sum_{i=1}^{n} (X_i^2) - n\bar{x}^2 = \sum_{i=1}^{n} (X_i^2) - \left(\sum_{i=1}^{n} X \right)^2 / n$$

12. Given the random sample 4.3, 2.5, 6.7, 5.8, and 5.7 from an N(μ, σ^2) population, calculate the unbiassed estimate of σ^2 and give its degrees of freedom.

3.3 INTERVAL ESTIMATION OF THE MEAN (μ) OF AN N(μ, σ^2) POPULATION

It is necessary to take a somewhat different approach from that used with the discrete binomial sampling distribution, yet the new procedure for interval estimation to be presented in this section will closely resemble the binomial procedure in its general line of reasoning. Sampling a binomial population produces a binomial frequency distribution which can be used directly in the computation of confidence intervals on the binomial parameter, p. When a normal population is to be sampled, there is a rather wide choice of sampling statistics which could be involved. Moreover, the process of estimation is additionally complicated by the fact that there are two parameters which usually are not known. It has been found that the general problem of interval estimation of normal parameters is to find a sampling quantity which has the following attributes under repeated sampling experiences.

(*a*) It is a function of the parameter which is being estimated and also of the sample observations; for example, the $G = (\bar{x} - \mu)/R$ introduced earlier involves the parameter μ and the sample statistics $\bar{x}$ and R.

(*b*) This function of the parameter and the sample statistics has a sampling distribution which has been obtained, or is obtainable, and this sampling distribution *does not include any unknown parameters*. This is a mathematical concept which will be illustrated in subsequent discussions. As is suggested by these statements, we shall not attempt to estimate two unknown parameters simultaneously.

In 1908 Student (whose real name was William S. Gosset but who preferred to publish under this pseudonym for many years) proposed the use of the ratio

$$(3.31) \qquad\qquad z = (\bar{x} - \mu)/s$$

where s is the square root of the unbiassed estimator of σ^2 for testing hypotheses about μ (see Student, "On the probable error of a mean," *Biometrika* 6:1, 1908). In the nineteen-twenties R. A. Fisher generalized z by defining a statistic which he called t. There is a general mathematical definition of a t variate, but we shall use several specialized forms in this book. The one which corresponds closely to Student's z is as follows:

$$(3.32) \qquad\qquad t = \frac{\bar{x} - \mu}{s/\sqrt{n}}$$

which shows that this t is $\sqrt{n} \times z$. It is seen that it is a function of μ and of the measurements taken in the sample. Moreover, it can be shown that its sampling distribution is known and that it does not involve any unknown parameters, such as μ and σ^2. The mathematical form of the frequency distribution of t is given in the following equation for a sample of size n, to illustrate specifically the points discussed above.

$$(3.33) \qquad f(t) = \frac{\overline{|n/2}}{\sqrt{\pi(n-1)}\,\overline{|(n-1)/2}} \cdot \frac{1}{[1 + t^2/(n-1)]^{n/2}}$$

where the symbols $\overline{|n/2}$ and $\overline{|(n-1)/2}$ stand for gamma functions whose values can be determined by means of mathematical tables. If $n = 10$, the formula becomes

$$(3.34) \qquad\qquad f(t) = \frac{0.3880}{(1 + t^2/9)^5}$$

It is noted in Formulas 3.33 and 3.34 that there are no unknown parameters when $f(t)$ is regarded as a relationship between n and t.

Formula 3.34 makes it easy to graph the sampling distribution of the statistic t defined by Formula 3.32 when n is 10 and $\bar{x}$ is the arithmetic mean of 10 normally distributed X's. If $t = 0$, f(0) = 0.3880/(1 + 0)⁵ ≃ 0.39 to two decimals. If $t = 1/2$, then f(1/2) = 0.388/(1 + 1/36)⁵ ≃ 0.34. If $t = 1$, then f(t) ≃ 0.23. If $t = 3/2$, then f(3/2) ≃ 0.13. If $t = 2$, then f(2) ≃ 0.06. It is obvious from any graph of t that:

(*a*) The function f(t) is symmetrical about a vertical line through $t = 0$ in the sense that f(t) is the same size for $t = -k$ and for $t = +k$, k being any positive real number.

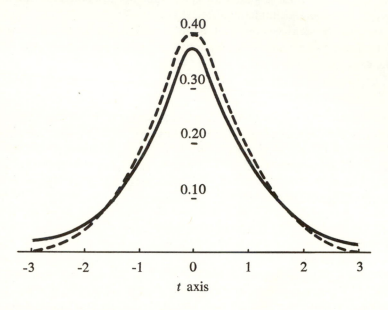

Figure 3.31.   The t distribution with 9 D (———) compared to the standard normal frequency distribution (---).

(*b*) As t is taken larger and larger, f(t) decreases, and this decrease is especially rapid around $t = \pm 1$.

These features remind one of those of the standard normal distribution, N(0, 1).

The graph of the t distribution with 9 DF is shown in Figure 3.31. The graph of the standard normal distribution also is shown in that figure, for comparison. Obviously, the t distribution differs from the standard normal only because the sampling variance is used in its denominator instead of the true variance, σ^2. Hence it is not surprising that, as the sample size is increased, the t distribution approaches that of the standard normal, because $s_{\bar{x}}$ approaches the parameter $\sigma_{\bar{x}} = \sigma/n$ as n approaches ∞.

It is noted in Figure 3.31 that the distributions of the normal and t

variables are much alike. Their worst dissimilarity occurs in the tails of the distributions and in the middle. In view of the fact that regions of rejection commonly are taken in the tails of distributions, the normal is not a satisfactory approximation to the t distribution until n is fairly large.

It can be shown mathematically that the t distribution is symmetrical about $t = 0$ with true mean $\mu_t = 0$ and true variance $\sigma_t^2 = \nu/(\nu - 2)$, where $\nu = n - 1$ in the Formula 3.32. In general, the number of degrees of freedom for this t is $\nu = n - 1$. It also should be emphasized here that the sampling distribution of t does not depend upon any particular size for μ: it only requires that the size used for μ in Formula 3.32 be correct. As long as the X's are drawn from some $N(\mu, \sigma^2)$, and n is 10, the frequency distribution of t is as given in Formula 3.34. This also is true of any other form of the t variate, as long as the number of degrees of freedom is 9.

It can be seen in Figure 3.31 that the t distribution presents an opportunity for probability reasoning that is quite similar to that offered by the binomial frequency distribution which was used to obtain a confidence interval on the binomial parameter, p. Any size of t can be obtained between $-\infty$ and $+\infty$ solely as a result of sampling variation. However, those t's whose sizes are near to zero are much more likely to occur during a sampling of an $N(\mu, \sigma^2)$ population than are t's far from zero. Unless some of the possible sampling sizes for t are scientifically ignored, no decision about the size of μ can possibly be made, but if certain extreme sizes for t (say, the "outer $2\frac{1}{2}\%$" at each end of the distribution) are eliminated from consideration, a very useful statement can be made about μ. Of course, such a procedure will run a risk of 5 in 100 of an error, because 5% of the possible t's are being ignored. This sort of reasoning is entirely analogous to that used in defining step boundaries in Table 2.13 and using them to determine confidence intervals, CI's, on the parameter p. Now we wish to use a similar argument and obtain CI's on μ. Because the t distribution is continuous, we can obtain a CI_{95}, for example, which really does run a risk of 5 in 100 of failing to include μ. With the binomial situation and small samples the risk of not including p merely was $\leqslant 5$ in 100 when a CI_{95} was being computed.

The analogy between the present discussion of CI's and those of a binomial parameter is shown in the accompanying sketch (p. 140, top) for a CI_{90}. Basically, the only difference between the procedure for obtaining a $CI_{1-\alpha}$ for the binomial parameter p and the procedure for obtaining a $CI_{1-\alpha}$ for the normal parameter μ comes from the discontinuity of the binomial frequency distribution.

To illustrate the determination of a central confidence interval on μ, suppose a sample of size $n = 10$ is to be taken from an $N(\mu, \sigma^2)$ population. The accompanying sketch (p. 140, bottom) of the t distribution with $\nu = 9$ DF shows how a 5% risk of a Type I error can be taken equally among the extreme $2\frac{1}{2}\%$ of all possible t_9's in each tail of the distribution. The

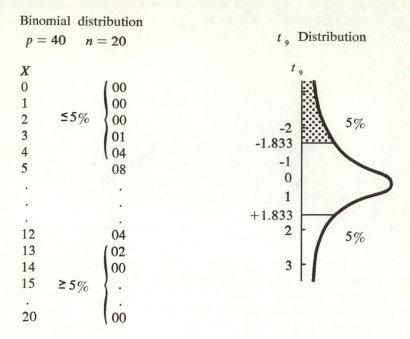

Binomial distribution

$p = 40 \quad n = 20$

t_9 Distribution

information in this sketch can be shown in symbols and a statement as follows: The inequality $-2.262 < t_9 < +2.262$ will be true for 95% of all conceivable samples of size $n = 10$ from any one N(μ, σ^2) population; that is, the inequality

$$-2.262 < \frac{\bar{x} - \mu}{s_{\bar{x}}} < +2.262$$

will be true for 95% of all such samples. Hence, the probability that a designated *future* sample (say, the next) of size $n = 10$ will be such that this inequality is true is 0.95. Therefore, if one has taken a random sample of size

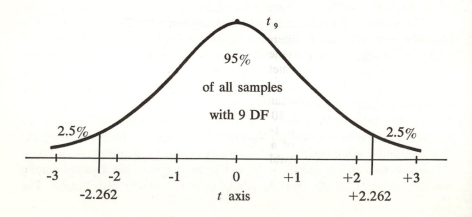

$n = 10$ from an $N(\mu, \sigma^2)$ population and assumes that with the $\bar{x}$ and s^2 computed from these data the following inequality is true,

$$(3.35) \qquad -2.262 < \frac{\bar{x} - \mu}{s/\sqrt{10}} < +2.262$$

then the risk of error is usefully described by the odds $1:20$, or the probability 0.05. As an equivalent statement, it can be said that, unless a rare 1-in-20 sample has been obtained from the extremes of the t_9 distribution, the following inequality is true:

$$(3.36) \qquad \bar{x} - \frac{2.262s}{\sqrt{10}} < \mu < \bar{x} + \frac{2.262s}{\sqrt{10}}$$

This inequality is merely a rearrangement of Inequality 3.35.

To illustrate these remarks, suppose a random sample of size $n = 10$ is going to be drawn from a particular $N(\mu, \sigma^2)$ population. At this time, *before the sample is drawn*, the probability is 0.95 that the $\bar{x}$ and s that will be computed from the sample will be such that Inequality 3.36 will be true. Now, suppose that the sample is drawn and it has produced the following data:

X: 5.4, 9.8, 10.2, 2.6, 7.0, 5.4, 4.2, 7.8, 4.6, and 10.6

It is found that $\bar{x} = 6.76$, $\sum (X - \bar{x})^2 = 69.1840$, $s = 2.77$, and $s/\sqrt{10} = 0.877$. Therefore, the 95% confidence interval on the true mean of the population sampled is $6.76 - 2.262(0.877) \leqslant \mu \leqslant 6.76 + 2.262(0.887)$, which reduces to

$$CI_{95}: \qquad 4.78 \leqslant \mu \leqslant 8.74$$

This is an interval estimate of μ which is associated with a risk of 1 chance in 20 of failing to include the true size of μ as a result of being based upon an especially unusual sample. This is what was previously called a *central confidence interval*, because the risk of error was deliberately taken equally from the two extremes of the t distribution. In view of the symmetry of the t distribution, such a procedure produces an interval which will, on the average, be of minimum length.

The general discussion of confidence intervals for the parameter of a binomial distribution fits that for confidence intervals on μ, because the concepts involved are the same. A summary of some of the salient points is as follows, as they relate to normal sampling:

(*a*) The length of any confidence interval is important, because the shorter confidence interval represents a more definite statement about the parameter and hence a more useful statement for the same α (the risk of error).

(*b*) The smaller the arbitrarily chosen α the longer the confidence interval, everything else being equal.

(*c*) The larger the sample size the shorter the confidence interval, on the average.

(*d*) The smaller the σ^2 in $N(\mu, \sigma^2)$ the shorter the confidence interval on μ, on the average. This is not applicable to binomial sampling except for the fact that the size of p does affect the length of the confidence interval somewhat.

(*e*) The fiducial limits on μ and the confidence interval on μ usually will be the same if a minimum-length (central) confidence interval is computed. However, the probability points of view are different.

(*f*) The experimenter should have some idea of how short a confidence interval must be to serve its purposes. Then n, α, and perhaps σ^2 should be adjusted, so that the sample will be likely to produce a useful confidence interval. An experimenter usually can obtain some information about σ^2 and then experiment with likely values of s^2 and n, to see what lengths of interval are likely with various sample sizes. It also may be that σ^2 can be reduced by using more homogeneous experimental units.

It might be that the circumstances under which a statistical study is being made will make it more logical to compute a *noncentral confidence interval*. For example, one might wish only to set either a lower or an upper limit, with some predetermined probability of error. For a problem with 10 observations tables of t show that there is 1 chance in 20 that a random sample of size $n = 10$ will produce a t at least as large as $+1.833$; hence, the inequality

$$-\infty \leqslant \frac{\bar{x} - \mu}{s/\sqrt{10}} \leqslant +1.833$$

has 19 chances out of 20 of being correct when a random sample is taken and the $\bar{x}$ and s computed from that sample are inserted into this inequality. Therefore, by clearing fractions and rearranging this inequality one obtains the following noncentral 95% confidence interval on the population mean:

(3.37) $\bar{x} - 1.833(s/\sqrt{n}) \leqslant \mu \leqslant +\infty$

In the terms used previously, it is said that the *greatest lower bound* on the parameter μ with confidence coefficient 0.95 is

$$\text{GLB}_{95} = \bar{x} - 1.833s/\sqrt{n}$$

In particular, for the data following Inequality 3.36 it is found that Inequality 3.37 becomes

(3.38) $5.15 \leqslant \mu \leqslant +\infty$

Unless a rare 1-in-20 sample was obtained, the true population mean, μ, is at least as large as 5.15 units. No known fiducial limits correspond to the noncentral limits of Inequality 3.38, so we take the point of view that Inequality 3.37 will produce an interval which does include the fixed parameter, μ, 19 times out of 20 on the average.

As is seen from the previous discussion, if we take the risk of error entirely from the extreme *right-hand* end of a t distribution, as in the accompanying figure, we shall obtain a *lower limit* on μ from $\text{GLB}_{1-\alpha} = \bar{x} - t_{2\alpha} \cdot s_{\bar{x}}$. Similarly, if we take the entire α risk from the *left-hand* end of a t distribution, we shall obtain the *upper* bound $\text{LUB}_{1-\alpha} = \bar{x} + t_{2\alpha} \cdot s_{\bar{x}}$. These results are entirely analogous to those obtained for noncentral confidence limits for the binomial parameter, p.

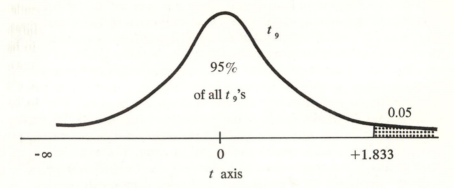

A minimum-length central CI on μ can be used to test hypotheses about μ when a two-tail alternative hypothesis is logical. For example, the interval

$$\text{CI}_{95}: \qquad 4.78 \leqslant \mu \leqslant 8.74$$

obtained earlier from the application of Inequality 3.36 to a hypothetical sample can be used to test $\text{H}_0(\mu = \mu_0)$ against $\text{H}_a(\mu \neq \mu_0)$. If, before the sample was taken, someone thought $\mu = 6$ was a reasonable hypothesis and that the only sensible alternative was that $\mu \neq 6$, α being chosen as 0.05 and the above CI_{95} resulting from a sample, then the hypothesis $\text{H}_0(\mu = 6)$ would be accepted simply because $\mu = 6$ lies within the 95% limits obtained. If $\mu = 3$ had been tested against $\mu \neq 3$, then $\text{H}_0(\mu = 3)$ would have been rejected upon the basis of this sample evidence.

Hypotheses can be tested by means of noncentral confidence intervals on the parameter μ. In connection with these tests it should be noted that, if $\text{H}_0(\mu = \mu_0)$ or $\text{H}_0(\mu \leqslant \mu_0)$ is being tested against a one-sided alternative, the H_0 and the alternative both may be partially within the limits of the noncentral confidence interval. However, the H_0 is accepted unless the noncentral confidence interval *excludes* H_0. For example, suppose that one is sampling a hot mix of asphalt paving material for percentage asphalt and has the hypothesis that the percentage is no more than 6. If $\text{H}_0(\mu \leqslant 6)$ is to be tested against $\text{H}_a(\mu > 6)$, a noncentral confidence interval should be used. Suppose that with $\alpha = 0.05$, the CI'_{95} is $4 \leqslant \mu < +\infty$. Even though H_a also lies in this interval, this CI'_{95} does not exclude $\text{H}_0(\mu \leqslant 6)$; therefore H_0 is accepted. If, however, the CI'_{95} had been $8 < \mu < +\infty$, then H_0 would have been excluded and been rejected in favor of the alternative hypothesis, $H_a(\mu > 6)$.

One can visualize another sort of "confidence interval," which is somewhat different from any previously described but has the same major features. Suppose one is interested in obtaining some useful limits on the value to be obtained for an *individual member* of a normal population with unknown mean and variance, the individual to be drawn at random from an $N(\mu, \sigma^2)$ population. Suppose, then, that an $N(\mu, \sigma^2)$ population is at hand to be sampled, and that (*a*) random sample of size n is to be drawn and thereafter (*b*) a single random draw is visualized. Question: What sort of a confidence interval can one place on this single future X_i, *before it is drawn*, on the basis of the information in the sample of n drawn first?

A useful application might be as follows. One wishes to buy a Kansas farm but wants to know what meaningful range of cash incomes can be expected for one's cash income the first year on the basis of an available sample of, say, 25 similar farms. Assuming that circumstances stay essentially the same, so that this future cash income reasonably can be assumed to be a sample from the same population of cash incomes as that sampled, this person's first year's income can be assumed to be a single observation to be drawn from this same population. This sort of information would be useful to a prospective buyer, for it would at least warn him of the possible low and high incomes he might plan on during that first year when he was getting started.

If X is the value of the single future random draw and $\bar{x}$ is the mean of the future random sample of size n to be drawn as the basis for placing limits on X, the difference, $X - \bar{x}$, is the difference between two independent random variables; hence its variance is the sum of the variances of the two parts. Thus, $\sigma^2_{X-\bar{x}} = \sigma^2 + \sigma^2/n$. In view of the fact that the population variance is not known, it will be estimated by $s^2 + s^2/n$, as might be expected. Then it is not surprising that the ratio

$$(X - \bar{x})/s\sqrt{1 + 1/n}$$

has the t distribution with $n - 1$ degrees of freedom, because $\mu_X = \mu_{\bar{x}} = \mu$, so the true mean of $X - \bar{x}$ is zero. It then is concluded, before any samples are taken, that

$$\Pr\{-t_\alpha s\sqrt{1 + 1/n} \leqslant X - \bar{x} \leqslant t_\alpha s\sqrt{1 + 1/n}\} = 1 - \alpha$$

or, in another form, the confidence interval on X is as follows:

$$(3.39) \qquad CI_{1-\alpha}: \qquad \bar{x} - t_\alpha s\sqrt{1 + 1/n} < X < \bar{x} + t_\alpha s\sqrt{1 + 1/n}$$

To illustrate, suppose that the random sample turns out to be 4.5, 5.7, 5.2, 6.2, and 4.9, so that $n = 5$, $\bar{x} = 5.3$, $s = 0.44$, $t_{0.05} = 2.2$, $st_{0.05} = 0.97$, and $\sqrt{1 + 1/n} \cong 1.1$. Then the CI_{95} is $4.2 < X < 6.4$. By contrast, the central

CI_{95} on μ would be $4.9 < \mu < 5.7$, a relatively much shorter interval, as one would expect, because μ is the true mean of a group of farm incomes rather than of only one farm income.

PROBLEMS

1. Suppose that 12 Marine Corps recruits are firing at targets on the rifle range, and on the first round of shots the radial distances of their bullet holes from the center of the bull's-eye are as follows *in order* from recruit 1 to recruit 12:

   X: 2.3, 0.7, 3.5, 1.2, 2.0, 5.2, 4.1, 3.2, 0.8, 1.0, 2.0, and 3.6 inches

   It will be assumed that, if these recruits were to fire many rounds each in a short time and without additional instruction, they would produce a $N(\mu, \sigma^2)$ population of X's. Compute a CI_{90} and also a CI_{95} on the μ on the basis of this sample. Interpret this interval clearly.

2. Referring to Problem 1, suppose a group of pretty girls comes to the firing range to watch the shooting just after the data in Problem 1 are taken. The recruits then make the following scores on the next round and *in the same order as above*, from recruit 1 to recruit 12:

   X: 5.3, 1.3, 8.9, 6.3, 2.1, 4.0, 6.7, 5.3, 8.8, 0.3, 5.5, and 5.0 inches

   Compute the minimum-length CI_{95} on the true average *increase in inaccuracy* (as measured) caused by the presence of the girls, presumably.

3. Referring to Problem 1, compute the noncentral confidence interval on μ which has a confidence coefficient of 0.90 and gives the least upper bound on μ. What information does this LUB_{90} convey?

4. Do as in Problem 3 for the greatest lower bound on μ.

5. Do as in Problem 3 for the data of Problem 2.

6. Do as in Problem 4 for the data of Problem 2.

7. Suppose that an entomologist is interested in the weights of bumblebees of the species *Bombus americanorum*, so he catches 20 of these bees at random in a large alfalfa field and obtains the following weights in milligrams:

   X: 325, 360, 290, 250, 300, 305, 310, 265, 330, 285, 340,

   310, 295, 310, 305, 350, 320, 300, 285, and 260

   Compute and interpret a minimum-length 95% confidence interval on μ, assuming these weights constitute a properly taken random sample from some $N(\mu, \sigma^2)$ population. Compute also the GLB_{95} on μ and interpret it.

8. Given that $\bar{x} = 31$, $s_{\bar{x}} = 0.884$, and $n = 11$ from a random sample from an $N(\mu, \sigma^2)$ population, use a confidence interval to test $H_0(\mu = 33)$ against the alternative $H_a(\mu > 33)$ with $\alpha = 0.10$. Draw conclusions.

9. Given that the 95% confidence interval $17.3 \leqslant \mu \leqslant 25.1$ pounds was computed from a random sample from an $N(\mu, \sigma^2)$ population, is $H_0(\mu = 20)$ acceptable over the alternative $H_a(\mu \neq 20)$? Is $H_0(\mu = 25)$ also acceptable over $H_a(\mu \neq 25)$? Can both H_0's be acceptable?

10. Referring to Problem 1, how would your computations and procedures change if you somehow knew that $\sigma^2 = 2.0$?

11. Given $n = 20$, $\sum (X) = 80$, and $\sum (X_i - \bar{x})^2 = \sum (x_i^2) = 100$ from a random sample from some N(μ, σ^2) population, compute the central CI_{90} on μ and use it to test $H_0(\mu = 5)$ against $H_a(\mu \neq 5)$. Also test H_0 against $H_a(\mu < 5)$.

12. Do Problem 11, given $\sigma^2 = 5$.

13. Suppose that an improved method of cultivating wheat has produced an average of 5 bushels per acre more yield than an older method on a sample of 21 plots. Also assume that the standard deviation for this sample is $s = 5$ bushels per acre. What are the 90% central confidence limits on the true average additional yields produced by the new method as compared with the older method? If the new method costs $5 per acre more to use than the older one, what do you conclude about the probable economic advantage or disadvantage from using this new method, if wheat currently is selling for $2.25 per bushel? Would a noncentral limit be more useful to answer this question? Discuss.

14. Suppose that in Problem 13 s had been 10 bushels per acre. Show how this increase in sampling variability among the 21 plots changes your answers to the questions asked in Problem 13. Derive a general formula which shows how the length of the CI changes as the s changes, if n remains fixed.

15. Suppose that chemical analysis shows that the mean percent protein for 16 wheat samples is 14.28 and that the estimated standard deviation for the population of $\bar{x}$'s is $s_{\bar{x}} = 0.40$. What conclusions do you draw from the central 95% confidence interval on the true mean μ?

16. If the basal metabolisms for a random sample of twenty-five 16-year-old girls in Kansas produced $\bar{x} = 45.80$ calories per square meter per hour, with $s = 0.50$, what are the 90% confidence limits on the true mean basal score for such girls? What information does this interval provide that would help in setting up a standard for such girls?

17. Suppose that during a recent period of strong prices twenty-five 450-pound choice steer calves were purchased on October 15th, wintered on silage and one pound of cottonseed meal per day, and then sold on April 15th as choice stocker steers. If the average net income per animal was $\bar{x} = \$95$ with $s = \$10$, place a CI_{90} on the true average net income per animal for such steers. Also compute the GLB_{95} on the true average net income, and draw appropriate conclusions.

18. Suppose that some educators test two proposed teaching procedures in the following way.

   (a) All available records and the opinions of teachers are applied to the selection of 20 students who, as a group, are excellent representatives of students who will be studying materials to be taught in the subsequent test of the two methods.

   (b) Two equally difficult sections of subject matter are carefully chosen.

   (c) The group of 20 students is taught one section by method A: the other section of material, by method B.

   (d) Two equally difficult examinations, one on each section of the subject matter, are formulated by competent teachers and then given to this group of students.

   (e) The average difference, each student against himself, between the two test scores is used as the measure of the difference between the two methods of teaching.

If the following test scores are obtained during this study, what conclusions do you draw about the comparative effectivenesses of methods A and B?

| | Grade on: | | | Grade on: | |
Student	Method A	Method B	Student	Method A	Method B
1	90	85	11	81	78
2	72	73	12	83	83
3	86	80	13	75	71
4	78	75	14	85	80
5	97	95	15	72	69
6	85	81	16	100	90
7	64	50	17	88	82
8	69	65	18	77	65
9	86	70	19	80	70
10	79	70	20	73	65

19. A study was made to determine whether tomatoes growing high up on the plant have more ascorbic acid than those growing lower down on the same plant. All plants were staked. To study this matter, 10 pair of red-ripe tomatoes were taken from 10 plants, one member of each pair being taken from the fifth cluster from the bottom of the plant and the other from the seventh cluster of the same plant. Each of the tomatoes from the seventh cluster had more ascorbic acid than its paired mate from the fifth cluster of the same plant by the following respective amounts, in milligrams per 100 grams:

X: 6.6, 11.6, 10.9, 7.4, 8.8, 10.3, 7.4, 7.8, 5.8, and 4.0

Given that $\sum (X) = 80.6$ and $\sum (X^2) = 700.46$, compute the central CI_{90} on the true average amount by which the ascorbic acid content of tomatoes on the seventh cluster is greater than that on the fifth cluster. Compute also the GLB_{90}. Draw appropriate conclusions. To what general botanical situation do these results apply? Should the variety of tomato have been specified? How about the cultural conditions?

20. Suppose that a highway commission is interested in the strength of concrete which it wishes to use for some paving projects and that this commission has concluded that the 7-day tensile strengths of standard test samples will be the best criterion of quality. Suppose also that 10 of the standard testing models gave the following results: $\bar{x} = 438.9$ pounds per square inch and $s = 47.0$ pounds per square inch. What valid and useful conclusions could they draw concerning the true average tensile strength of the concrete tested?

21. Suppose that a sociologist has conjectured that the average rent for two-room furnished apartments in a certain section of a given city is $90 per month. A random sample of 20 apartments shows $\bar{x} = \$82.50$ and $s = \$8.00$. Use a 90% confidence interval to determine whether the hypothesis $H_0(\mu = \$90)$ is acceptable over $H_a(\mu < \$90)$. Over $H_a(\mu \neq \$90)$.

22. Suppose that a timber cruiser has judged that the average breast-high diameter of a given stand of timber is two feet. Is the timber cruiser's estimate reasonable if 31 trees selected at random had $\bar{x} = 2.5$ feet and $s = 0.8$ feet?

23. Suppose that a store conducts a study of the comparative net profits from ears of corn sold in cellophane packs and from loose ears in the husks. The

experiment is conducted during the 26 business days of one month in the corn season. At the end of each day the net profit per ear is figured for each way of presenting the corn to the buying public. It was found that the average advantage from using the cellophane pack was $\bar{x} = 2$ cents, with a standard deviation of 0.5 cent. There was good reason to believe that these data were from a normal population. When sampling variation is given proper consideration, is the observed average advantage from the cellophane pack statistically significant with $\alpha = 0.10$? Should cost of the cellophane be taken into account? Could you calculate how much wrapping the corn in cellophane could cost per day and still leave a net profit from its use?

24. If in a certain investigation it was found that $\bar{x} = 1.5$ and $s = 3$, how large must the sample size have been to cause rejection of $H_0(\mu = 0)$ versus $H_a(\mu \neq 0)$ with $\alpha = 0.05$?

25. If, in a sampling study for which the t distribution is appropriate, $n = 28$ and $s = 5$, how large must $\bar{x}$ be before the hypothesis $H_0(\mu = 0)$ versus $H_a(\mu \neq 0)$ will be rejected at the 5% level? At the 10% level? What if $H_a(\mu > 0)$ is used?

26. Suppose that 27 pair of plants of a certain species have been selected for close similarity with respect to stated criteria and have been planted in pairs as close together as is appropriate for this species. One member of each pair has had some boron added to the fertilizer applied around the plant; otherwise, the plants are treated identically. The 27 plants having boron outgrew their paired partners by an average of 3.6 centimeters during a specified period of time. The standard deviation was $s = 1.2$ centimeters for the *difference* boron minus no boron. Is this sufficient evidence to justify the assertion that the addition of boron in the amount studied will produce superior growth under the growing conditions maintained during this study? In practice, how should one use the cost of the boron in making a decision about using it?

27. J. A. Beerbower in *In Search of the Past* gives the following measurements, in millimeters, of the lengths of the upper-cheek teeth of the extinct mammal *Ptilodus montanus*:

$$X: \quad 3.0, \ 2.8, \ 3.4, \ 3.2, \ 3.0, \ 2.9, \ 3.1, \ 2.9, \ 3.1, \ 3.0, \ 3.0,$$

$$2.6, \ 3.3, \ 2.9, \ 3.0, \ 2.8, \ 2.9, \ 2.7, \ 2.9, \ 2.8, \text{ and } 3.1$$

Compute and interpret a CI_{90} on the true mean length of such teeth, assuming normality of distribution. Compute and interpret the LUB_{90} on this same parameter, and discuss the information provided by these two intervals.

3.4 INTERVAL ESTIMATION OF THE POPULATION VARIANCE, σ²

A confidence interval for the population variance, σ^2, is obtained much as is the confidence interval for the population mean, μ, but the distributions used are not symmetrical; hence minimum-length (central) confidence intervals will not be obtained. Such intervals can be obtained approximately, but the gain usually is slight, considering the extra computations involved.

The usual procedure for obtaining a confidence interval is followed:

(*a*) Devise a function of the sample X's and the parameter to be estimated, in such a way that the sampling distribution of this function can be obtained.

(*b*) Among the many such functions usually obtainable, choose one whose sampling distribution does *not* involve any unknown parameters, including the one to be estimated.

(*c*) Use the most efficient one of the functions from (*b*), in the sense that it produces the shortest intervals on the average.

Mathematical statisticians have found that the quantity $(n-1)s^2/\sigma^2$ has properties of (*a*) and (*b*) and approaches the property of (*c*) quite closely for almost any useful sample size. Moreover, its distribution already is known and fully tabulated, because

(3.41) $(n-1)s^2/\sigma^2 = $ a χ^2_{n-1} variate

As has been implied, if not noted, earlier, the chi-square distribution depends only on the number of degrees of freedom, which is $n-1$ in this instance.

Because $(n-1)s^2 = \sum_{i=1}^{n}(X_i - \bar{x})^2 = \sum(x^2)$, for brevity, we have in this instance $\chi^2 = \sum(x^2)/\sigma^2$ with $n-1$ DF or, as is more useful here, $1/\chi^2 = \sigma^2/\sum(x^2)$. If, as before, we "ignore" 0.025 of the possible sampling events at each end of the chi-square distribution, we arrive at the following formula for a 95% confidence interval on the population variance, σ^2:

(3.42) CI_{95}: $\dfrac{\sum(x^2)}{\chi^2_{0.025}} \leqslant \sigma^2 \leqslant \dfrac{\sum(x^2)}{\chi^2_{0.975}}$

where $\chi^2_{0.025}$ is such that $\Pr\{\chi^2 \geqslant \chi^2_{0.025}\} = 0.025$; similarly for $\chi^2_{0.975}$. Graphically, we have the sketch given here.

With the sample of the procedure for computing a 95% confidence interval on the population mean, used in this illustration, the s^2 had $n-1$ DF $= 9$ DF. This also is the number of degrees of freedom for the chi-square

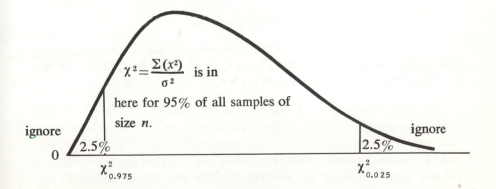

in this situation, so $\chi^2_{0.025} = 10.0$ and $\chi^2_{0.975} = 2.70$, as seen from Table XI of the chi-square distribution. Consequently, the CI_{95} on the population variance is obtained from

$$\frac{69.1840}{19.0} \leqslant \sigma^2 \leqslant \frac{69.1840}{2.70}$$

and the final interval is

$$CI_{95}: \qquad 3.64 \leqslant \sigma^2 \leqslant 25.62$$

It is concluded with the confidence represented by odds of 19:1 that the true population variance is no smaller than 3.64 and no larger than 25.62. If one were satisfied with a 90% confidence interval, it would be 4.09 $\leqslant$ $\sigma^2 \leqslant 20.77$, which is 5.30 units shorter than the CI_{95} obtained from the sample. In other words, the reward for taking a greater risk of an error is to get a shorter, and therefore less equivocal and more useful, confidence interval. If the interval still is too long, it can be shortened by taking larger samples, by taking measures which reduce σ^2, and by choosing a larger α.

As noted earlier, the confidence interval computed from Formula 3.42 is not of minimum length, as a consequence of the asymmetrical nature of the chi-square distribution, but a minimum-length CI is not easily obtained though it is possible to get one. Moreover, if even a moderate-sized sample is taken, the chi-square distribution is close enough to being symmetrical for the difference between the CI obtained as given above and the CI obtained by the more tedious method, which produces a CI of minimum length, to be usually not worth the extra effort.

As with CI's and μ, one can use a CI on σ^2 to test a specific hypothesis, $H_0(\sigma^2 = \sigma_0^2)$, against $H_a(\sigma^2 \neq \sigma)_0^2$ simply by observing whether the CI does or does not contain σ_0^2.

Noncentral confidence limits for σ^2 also can be computed and can be used in the estimation of lower and upper bounds on σ^2. The reasoning used to get such limits is illustrated by the sketch (p. 151) of a chi-square sampling distribution when χ^2 has 14 DF, as s^2 would have from a sample of size $n = 15$. Table XI indicates that the inequality

$$7.79 < \chi^2_{14} < +\infty$$

has 90 chances out of 100 of being true for any specified future random sample. In view of the fact that $\sum_{i=1}^{15}(X_i - \bar{x})^2/\sigma^2$ has the χ^2_{14} distribution, the inequality

(3.43) $$7.79 < \frac{\sum\limits_{i=1}^{15}(X_i - \bar{x})^2}{\sigma^2} < +\infty$$

also has probability 0.90 of being true for, say, the next random sample of size $n = 15$, to be drawn from some particular N(μ, σ^2) population.

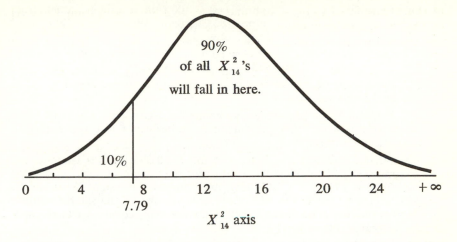

When Inequality 3.43 is rearranged by inverting each term, reversing the inequality signs (which is required when reciprocals are taken), and multiplying through by $\sum_{i=1}^{15}(X_i - \bar{x})^2$, it gives

$$(3.44) \qquad 0 < \sigma^2 < \frac{\sum_{i=1}^{15}(X_i - \bar{x})^2}{7.79}$$

Thus, a least upper bound with confidence coefficient $1 - \alpha = 0.90$ has been obtained on σ^2 from a sample of size $n = 15$. More generally, the following two inequalities give a $\text{LUB}_{1-\alpha}$ and a $\text{GLB}_{1-\alpha}$, respectively, on σ^2 for any random sample of size n from an $N(\mu, \sigma^2)$ population:

$$(3.45) \qquad \text{LUB}_{1-\alpha} = \frac{\sum_{i=1}^{n}(X - \bar{x})^2}{\chi^2_{1-\alpha}}, \qquad \text{for } \nu = n - 1 \text{ DF}$$

$$(3.46) \qquad \text{GLB}_{1-\alpha} = \frac{\sum_{i=1}^{n}(X_i - \bar{x})^2}{\chi^2_{\alpha}}, \qquad \text{for } \nu = n - 1 \text{ DF}$$

PROBLEMS

1. Given the following random sample, X, from an $N(\mu, \sigma^2)$ population, compute a CI_{90} on the parameter σ^2 and state what information this interval provides: 30, 28, 33, 35, 29, 30, 31, 32, 26, 36, and 31. You are given that $\sum(X) = 341$, $\sum(X^2) = 10{,}657$, and $(341)^2 = 116{,}281$.

2. Given $\bar{x} = 31$, $s_{\bar{x}} = 0.884$, and $n = 11$ for a random sample from an $N(\mu, \sigma^2)$ use a CI_{95} to test $H_0(\sigma^2 = 2.5)$ against $H_a(\sigma^2 \neq 2.5)$. Against $H_a(\sigma^2 > 2.5)$.

3. Assume that the same sample variance was obtained as in Problem 2, but with $n = 25$. What effect does this change have on the CI_{95}? What if you were told that the population sampled was $N(30, \sigma^2)$?

4. Given $n = 20$, $\sum (X) = 80$, and $\sum (x^2) = 100$ from a random sample from an N(μ, σ^2), compute and interpret the CI_{90} on σ^2. What is the LUB_{90} on σ^2?

5. Using Problem 4, would you accept $H_0(\sigma^2 = 10)$ and not $H_a(\sigma^2 \neq 10)$ if $\alpha = 0.05$? What if the alternative hypothesis were $H_a(\sigma^2 > 10)$?

6. If you sample the same N(μ, σ^2) population repeatedly, what percent of the CI_{90}'s you compute on the population variance would you expect to fail to include the true variance, σ^2?

7. If in Problem 6 you had sometimes computed a CI_{90} on μ and other times computed a CI_{90} on σ^2, could you still solve Problem 6 if it were revised to include μ and σ^2 *together*?

8. Given that $\bar{x} = 35$ and $s = 10$ for a sample of 10 observations, compute and interpret the 90% confidence interval on the population variance, σ^2. Do the same for $n = 15$ and $n = 20$ in turn, and compare the results. What are the implications regarding the relation between the size of the sample and the width of the confidence interval, everything else being equal? Are these implications reasonable to you?

9. Use the results in the first part of Problem 13, Section 3.3, to compute a CI_{90} on σ^2.

10. Do Problem 14, Section 3.3, for the parameter σ^2 instead of μ.

11. Do Problem 15, Section 3.3, for σ^2 instead of μ.

12. Do Problem 16, Section 3.3, for the true variance, σ^2, instead of the true mean, μ.

13. Do Problem 17, Section 3.3, for σ^2 instead of μ.

14. Using the data and computations of Problem 19, Section 3.3, compute and interpret the CI_{90} on σ^2. Compute and interpret the LUB_{90} on σ^2 also.

15. Use the data in Problem 21, Section 3.3, to test $H_0(\sigma^2 = 40)$ against $H_a(\sigma^2 \neq 40)$. Against $H_a(\sigma^2 > 40)$.

16. Use the data of Problem 22, Section 3.3, to compute a CI_{95} on σ^2.

17. If in a certain investigation $\bar{x} = 1.5$ and $s = 3$, how large must the sample size, n, be before $H_0(\sigma^2 = 5)$ will be rejected if $H_a(\sigma^2 \neq 5)$ is the alternative hypothesis and α is 0.10?

18. Use the data of Problem 27, Section 3.3, to place a CI_{90} on σ^2. Interpret this interval clearly.

3.5 TESTING HYPOTHESES ABOUT μ BY MEANS OF THE t DISTRIBUTION

The sampling variate $t = (\bar{x} - \mu)/s_{\bar{x}}$ was presented in Formula 3.32 as a basis for computing a confidence interval on μ. The reader already is aware that, if the true value of μ is substituted into that formula, the distribution of t is found in available tables. If an incorrect value of μ is used, the distribution is called a *noncentral t* distribution. Thus, one hopes to detect the use of an incorrect μ, as in $H_0(\mu = \mu_0)$, by comparing sampling results with those which are known to hold if the μ truly does equal μ_0.

As before, one tests a proposed hypothesis, $H_0(\mu = \mu_0)$, against an alternative, H_a, and this test is performed by choosing a region of rejection, ω, based on the known t distribution and noting whether the same t at hand does or does not fall in ω. As a matter of fact, any test of an H_0 is simply a choice of a region of rejection, and the choice can be made in many ways. The best way to choose ω, if there clearly is a *best* way, is to choose the region of rejection which, for a given α, makes the probability of a Type II error, β, as small as possible. This is a mathematical problem beyond the level of this book, but one may say the following, which is entirely analogous to statements made previously about binomial sampling:

(*a*) If $H_0(\mu = \mu_0)$ is tested against $H_a(\mu \neq \mu_0)$, one should take the risk of a Type I error equally in the extreme tails of the t distribution and thus perform a two-tail test of H_0.

(*b*) If $H_0(\mu = \mu_0)$ or $H_0(\mu \leqslant \mu_0)$ is tested against $H_a(\mu > \mu_0)$, one should take all risk of Type I error from the right-hand end of the t distribution with the appropriate degrees of freedom. If the H_0 is $\mu \leqslant \mu_0$, the probability of a Type I error will be $\leqslant \alpha$.

(*c*) If $H_0(\mu = \mu_0)$ or $H_0(\mu \geqslant \mu_0)$ is tested against $H_a(\mu < \mu_0)$, one should take all risk of a Type I error from the left-hand extreme of the t distribution. Again, if H_0 is $\mu \geqslant \mu_0$, the probability of a Type I error is $\leqslant \alpha$.

The reasoning behind these three rules is as follows, when the t variate has the form of Formula 3.32. In a slightly different form,

(3.51)
$$t = \frac{\bar{x}}{s_{\bar{x}}} - \frac{\mu}{s_{\bar{x}}}$$

Under the hypothesis $H_0(\mu = \mu_0)$

$$\xi = \frac{\bar{x}}{s_{\bar{x}}} - \frac{\mu_0}{s_{\bar{x}}}$$

If the μ_0 truly is equal to μ, then ξ is equal to t, and this variate has the tabular distribution given in Table VII. If μ_0 is less than μ, so that $H_a(\mu > \mu_0)$ should be chosen instead of $H_0(\mu = \mu_0)$ or $H_0(\mu \leqslant \mu_0)$, then ξ is larger than the true t, because too small a number has been subtracted from $\bar{x}/s_{\bar{x}}$. Hence, all risk of Type I error should be taken at the extreme right-hand end of the t distribution, to best avoid Type II errors. This is a one-tail test.

On the other hand, if μ_0 is greater than μ, so that $H_a(\mu < \mu_0)$ should be chosen instead of $H_0(\mu = \mu_0)$ or $H_0(\mu \geqslant \mu_0)$, then ξ is smaller than the true t, because too much has been subtracted from $\bar{x}/s_{\bar{x}}$. Hence, all risk of Type I error should be taken at the extreme left-hand end of the t distribution, to best avoid Type II errors.

If there is no reason to suspect that either $\mu_0 < \mu$ or $\mu_0 > \mu$ is the more likely alternative to H_0, then one has no reason to do other than take the risk of a Type I error equally from the extremes of the t distribution and thus perform a two-tail test of H_0.

The preceding remarks are equally relevant for testing H_0's by means of confidence intervals or directly from Formula 3.32. Figure 3.51 has been

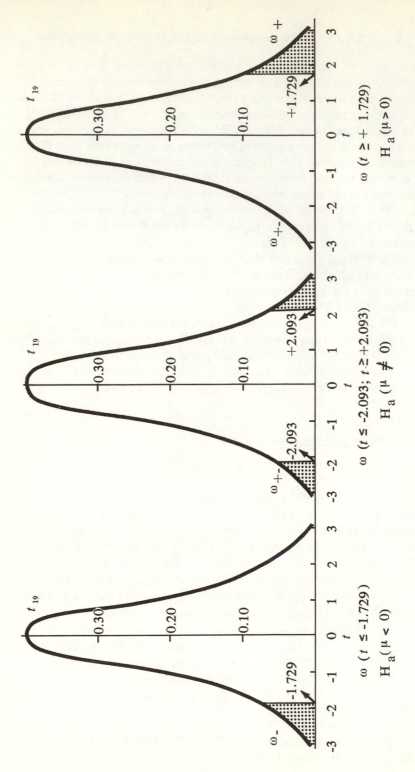

$\omega(t \leq -1.729)$

$H_a(\mu < 0)$

$\omega-$ -1.729

$\omega(t \leq -2.093; t \geq +2.093)$

$H_a(\mu \neq 0)$

$\omega+-$ -2.093 $+2.093$

$\omega(t \geq +1.729)$

$H_a(\mu > 0)$

$\omega+-$ $+1.729$ $\omega+$

t_{19}

0.30

0.20

0.10

constructed to illustrate how the risks of Type I error should be taken in a test of $H_0(\mu = \mu_0)$ against $H_{a_1}(\mu \neq \mu_0)$, $H_{a_2}(\mu < \mu_0)$, and $H_{a_3}(\mu > \mu_0)$. One may, if one wishes, think of H_0 as $\mu \geq \mu_0$ or $\mu \leq \mu_0$, remembering that α then is less than or equal to the stated size.

To illustrate the preceding discussion specifically, suppose that an engineer wishes to study the strengths of concrete beams made with two different aggregates. Because the making of a concrete beam might be unavoidably different from time to time, a paired-comparisons experiment will be conducted. A pair of concrete beams will be made, one beam with each aggregate, n times. The only intentional difference between the members of each pair will be the type of aggregate used in mixing the concrete. Each beam will be intended to be $6\frac{1}{4} \times 6\frac{1}{4} \times 24$ inches, will be cured according to standard practices, and will be broken 14 days after it is made. The standard beam-testing equipment will be used with all beams. Obviously, there will be unpredictable errors in measurement and in the construction of the beams. It will be assumed that experience has shown that the breaking loads of beams made as nearly alike as possible will belong to a normal population of measurements.

When this experiment is completed, data of the sort shown below will have been obtained on the breaking loads of concrete test beams. Within each pair of beams the only anticipated difference will be one associated with the use of two different aggregates. The differences between pairs, if any true difference exists, will not be expected to distort the study of the two aggregates, because only the *difference* between members within the same pair will be measured and studied. Following are some data assumed to have been obtained from such a study, in which breaking load is measured to the nearest pound.

	Pair no.:											
	1	2	3	4	5	6	7	8	9	10	11	12
Br. load, agg. 1:	865	865	720	755	750	940	885	810	692	695	855	880
Br. load, agg. 2:	887	860	805	880	870	965	900	755	795	725	880	845
Diff., $X = X_2 - X_1$:	22	−5	85	125	120	25	15	−55	103	30	25	−35

Simple arithmetic produces the following results: $\sum(X) = 455$, $\bar{x} = 37.91$ pounds, $\sum(X^2) = 54{,}993$, $(\sum X)^2/12 = 17{,}252.08$, $\sum(x^2) = 37{,}740.92$, and $s = 58.6$ pounds. What the engineer conducting this study wants to know is this: do these two aggregates produce any detectable effect on the breaking loads of concrete test beams and, if so, how much? One way to answer both questions simultaneously is to compute an appropriate confidence interval. If, considering all pertinent circumstances and common practices, it is decided that a central 95% confidence interval best suits the situation, the following

---

Figure 3.51.   Regions of rejection when the hypothesis $H_0(=0)$ is being tested against the indicated alternative hypothesis; $\alpha = 0.05$, $n = 20$.

computations are obtained, as previously illustrated. For a t with 11 DF, the probability is 0.95 before the sample is taken that the following inequality will be true, according to Table VII:

$$-2.201 \leqslant (\bar{x} - \mu)/s_{\bar{x}} \leqslant +2.201$$

After some simplifications and rearrangements, this inequality becomes

$$\bar{x} - 2.201 s_{\bar{x}} \leqslant \mu \leqslant \bar{x} + 2.201 s_{\bar{x}}$$

After the sample has been taken (by doing the experiment described above) and it is found that $\bar{x} = 37.91$ pounds, $s_{\bar{x}} = 16.9$ pounds, the following CI_{95} is obtained on the true average difference in breaking load associated with these two different aggregates:

$$CI_{95}: \qquad 0.7 \text{ lb.} \leqslant \mu \leqslant 75.1 \text{ lbs.}$$

Unless a rare 1-in-20 sample has been obtained, this inequality is true.

With these limits on the true average difference in breaking load between beams made with aggregate 2 instead of aggregate 1, about all one can say is that beams made with aggregate 2 are at least a little stronger than those made with aggregate 1; and the amount of the average difference probably does not exceed 75 pounds, in terms of breaking load. If the costs of using these aggregates are the same, aggregate 2 most certainly would be used, but if aggregate 2 costs more than aggregate 1 or is much less convenient to use for some reason, the economics of the situation will determine the decision between these two aggregates.

The confidence-interval procedure illustrated above provides that a quick test of any predetermined hypothesis may be made simply by noting whether or not the hypothetical size of μ lies within the limits computed from the sample evidence. For example, if the hypothesis had been $H_0(\mu = 0)$, it would have been rejected at the 5% level of significance, because the value $\mu = 0$ is not within the confidence limits determined by the sample.

Another, and somewhat less realistic, way to test an H_0 for the immediately preceding concrete-beam example is to use $t = (\bar{x} - \mu)/s_{\bar{x}}$ directly with $\mu = \mu_0$. If it is wondered whether the two aggregates are, perhaps, precisely equal to each other, one could propose the hypothesis $H_0(\mu = 0)$. Unless one has some logical reason to suspect that, if μ is not equal to zero, it is, say, greater than zero, it is best to use the alternative hypothesis, $H_a(\mu \neq 0)$. This decision suggests a two-tail test with $\alpha = 0.05$, as before, and with the region of rejection:

$$\omega: \qquad |t| > +2.201$$

because t has 11 DF. With $\bar{x} = 37.91$ and $s_{\bar{x}} = 16.9$, one computes $t = (37.91 - 0)/16.9 = 2.243$. This value of t is in the region of rejection, and hence H_0 is rejected, as it was with the central CI_{95} test.

One also might logically test $H_0(\mu = 0)$ against $H_a(\mu > 0)$. In this test the region of rejection for the appropriate one-tail test is $t > 1.80$ with 11 DF and $\alpha = 0.05$. The t is the same as for the two-tail test, namely $t = 2.243$; hence, H_0 is confidently rejected.

There would seem to be no sensible reason to test $H_0(\mu \leqslant 0)$ against $H_a(\mu > 0)$, but the test would be the same as just performed, except that α would be $\leqslant 0.05$.

PROBLEMS

1. Using the data of Problem 1, Section 3.3, test $H_0(\mu = 34)$ against $H_a(\mu \neq 34)$ by the t test. Then do the same for $H_a(\mu > 34)$ as the logical alternative to H_0, using $\alpha = 0.05$.

2. Use the data of Problem 4, Section 3.4, to test $H_0(\mu = 2)$ against $H_a(\mu > 2)$ by the t test, using a 10 percent region of rejection.

3. Suppose that a home economist wishes to compare the effects on shear in steaks of two methods of cooking a certain type of beefsteak. In view of the bilateral symmetry of a beef animal, she pairs the steaks to be cooked. To assure additionally that no bias or other distortion of conclusions will be produced by an unexpected source of variability, the decision about which method to use on the left-hand steak of each pair is made by flipping an un-biassed coin. The decision about which steak will be cooked first is made in this random manner. Suppose that the differences in shear between methods A and B, or $X = X_A - X_B$, are found to be 1.3, 0, 2.1, 0.5, -0.3, 0.4, 1.0, -0.2, 1.6, 0.7, 0.2, and -0.5 in the units used to measure shear. Is $H_0(\mu = 0)$ acceptable over $H_a(\mu > 0)$ with $\alpha = 0.10$? What do you conclude about the two methods of cooking beefsteaks of the sort studied?

4. If α had been 0.01 in Problem 3, what conclusions would you have drawn? What factors do you think should determine the size of the region of rejection in such an experiment?

5. During the winter tomatoes often are shipped quite green and allowed to ripen in the package. Aside from matters of flavor and appearance, it is of interest to know what effect this practice has on the vitamin C content of the tomatoes. In a certain experiment (Fryer *et al.*, "Relation between stage of maturity and ascorbic acid content of tomatoes," *Proc. Am. Soc. Hort. Sci.* 64: 365, 1954) two tomatoes were picked from the same cluster on the plant, one tomato being red-ripe and the other being mature but showing no red or yellow color. The red-ripe member of each pair was analyzed for ascorbic acid immediately. The green member of each pair was ripened at room temperature out of the sun until red-ripe before its vitamin C content was determined. Then the difference in vitamin C between the members of these pairs was calculated and designated by X_i, where $i = 1$ to 18. The following results were obtained: $\sum (X) = 49.37$ milligrams per 100 grams favoring the red-ripe tomato of the pair and $\sum (X^2) = 387.5911$. Determine statistically whether there probably is no loss of vitamin C during the ripening process from green-but-mature to red-ripe, using the alternative that the red-ripe tomatoes have the greater ascorbic acid concentration.

6. Do Problem 17, Section 3.3, by the t test. State H_0 and H_a carefully.

7. Do as in Problem 6 for Problem 19 of Section 3.3, using the hypothesis that the true mean difference is 7 milligrams per 100 grams.

8. Do Problem 2, Section 3.3, with $\mu = 90$ as the hypothesis to be tested, first using $H_a(\mu \neq 90)$, then using $H_a(\mu > 90)$, and finally using $H_a(\mu < 90)$.

9. Do Problem 22, Section 3.3, by the t test with $\mu = 2$ versus $\mu > 2$.

10. Do Problem 23, Section 3.3, by the t test with $\mu = 0$ cents as the hypothesis to be tested against an alternative hypothesis of your own choice.

11. Do Problem 26, Section 3.3, with $H_0(\mu = 0)$ versus $H_a(\mu > 0)$, using t.

12. Suppose that on 10 observations from a $N(\mu, \sigma^2)$ population one obtained $\sum (X) = 130$ and $\sum [(X_i - \bar{x})^2] = 114$. Test $H_0(\mu = 11)$ against $H_a(\mu \neq 11)$, and draw appropriate conclusions. Use the t test first and then a CI_{95}.

13. How would the solution for Problem 12 change if you drew that random sample from $N(\mu, 16)$?

14. Do Problem 12 for the alternative hypothesis $H_a(\mu > 11)$.

3.6 TESTING HYPOTHESES ABOUT THE TRUE MEAN OF $N(\mu, \sigma^2)$ BY MEANS OF THE G DISTRIBUTION

The most difficult computation during the use of the t distribution for tests of significance or to compute confidence intervals is the determination of $s_{\bar{x}}$. With small samples this computation can be avoided by using the sample range, R, as the measure of variability in place of the $s_{\bar{x}}$, but this is done at some cost in terms of the power of the test so obtained. The ratio

(3.61) $G = (\bar{x} - \mu)/R$

is analogous to the t ratio used before, but it has a different sampling distribution from that of t. As was mentioned, if the sampling distribution of G is available, and if it does not require knowledge about unknown parameters, then the G distribution can be used both for tests of significance and for constructing confidence intervals. An outline of part of the sampling distribution of the G of Formula 3.61 is given in Table IX for sample sizes to $n = 20$, after which size it is not advisable to use the G because R becomes too unreliable as a replacement for $s_{\bar{x}}$. Note that G does not have degrees of freedom: the actual sample size is used.

The range, R, depends directly upon only two of the sample observations; hence, it is logical that the G distribution does not provide as powerful a test of significance as does the t test nor as short a confidence interval, on the average. E. Lord (*Biometrika* 34: 66, 1947) and K. C. S. Pillai (*Ann. Math. Stat.* 22: 469, 1951) have shown that for small samples, such as those covered by Table IX, the G distribution provides a satisfactory substitute for the t distribution. The G distribution is especially useful in exploratory, or screening, types of experiments, during which it may be more efficient to use a slightly less powerful but more rapid and economical statistical procedure.

To illustrate the usefulness of the G distribution, consider the sample of paired observations studied earlier in a simulated experiment of the strength of concrete test beams. The pertinent data are $n = 12$, $\bar{x} = 37.9$ pounds, and $R = 180$ pounds. Therefore, $G = (37.9 - \mu)/180 = 0.211$, if the μ is taken equal to 0 to test $H_0(\mu = 0)$ against $H_a(\mu \neq 0)$. Table IX indicates that with $n = 12$, G would be numerically as large as 0.211, or larger, between 2 and 5% of the time, if the H_0 is correct. Hence, if one has chosen an α of 0.05 or larger, the $H_0(\mu = 0)$ would be rejected with $H_a(\mu \neq 0)$ as the alternative hypothesis.

The availability of the G distribution is somewhat limited, so that the size of the region of rejection must be one of 0.10, 0.05, 0.02, 0.01, 0.002, or 0.001. Aside from this limitation, the same use of one-tail and two-tail tests as for the t distribution is possible.

A 95% confidence interval on μ can be computed from the G distribution in a manner which is wholly analogous to that used with the t distribution. The general interval so obtained is

$$(3.62) \qquad \text{CI}_{95}: \qquad \bar{x} - R(G_{0.05}) \leqslant \mu \leqslant \bar{x} + R(G_{0.05})$$

in which the $G_{0.05}$ is obtained from a two-tail table of G. For the concrete-beam problem considered earlier one gets a CI_{95} of 3.0 pounds $\leqslant \mu \leqslant 72.8$ pounds. The confidence interval obtained from this particular sample turns out to be a little shorter than that obtained from the t distribution but, as stated earlier, on the average the reverse will be true. Pillai (*Ann. Math. Stat.* 22: 469–72, 1957) has shown mathematically that for $n = 12$, as above, the CI_{95} based on the t distribution will be only 98% of the length of the CI_{95} based upon the G distribution, on the average. In fact, for all sample sizes for which the use of G is recommended at all (namely, through $n = 20$) the CI_{95}'s based on the t distribution are expected to average 1 or 2% shorter than the corresponding CI's based on the G distribution. If CI_{90}'s are computed, the comparative lengths are even closer together. All relevant matters considered, it appears that, if n is no larger than 20, the G test and confidence intervals derived from the G distribution are extremely useful, unless circumstances justify the utmost in precision and power.

If noncentral confidence intervals are appropriate for a given situation, they can be obtained from G distributions even more readily than from t distributions. In general, the $\text{GLB}_{1-\alpha}$ will not be quite as large nor the $\text{LUB}_{1-\alpha}$ quite as small as would be obtained from the t distribution.

Tests of $H_0(\mu = \mu_0)$ against $H_a(\mu > \mu_0)$ or $H_a(\mu < \mu_0)$ or of $H_0(\mu \leqslant \mu_0)$ against $H_a(\mu > \mu_0)$, etc., can be made as with the t distribution but with a small loss of power, necessary if Type II errors are to be avoided.

PROBLEMS

1. Do Problem 1, Section 3.3, using the G distribution.

2. Do Problem 2, Section 3.3, using the G distribution.

3. Do Problem 17, Section 3.3, using the G distribution.

4. Use G and the data of Problem 1, Section 3.3, to compute a CI_{80} on μ, and interpret the interval so obtained.

5. Use G and the data of Problem 3, Section 3.5, to compute a CI_{90} on the true average difference of method A minus method B.

6. Do Problem 19, Section 3.3, by the G test with $H_0(\mu = 7)$ versus $H_a(\mu \neq 7)$ and $\alpha = 0.05$. Do the same with $H_a(\mu > 7)$, and draw appropriate conclusions.

7. Do Problem 20, Section 3.3, by means of the G distribution.

8. Suppose that a college is attempting to learn whether instruction of a certain type probably will improve its students' ability to think critically, even during the first year in college. Also assume that tests exist which will reliably measure such abilities. These tests are to be given every student at the beginning and at the end of the first school year for the student. If the following *differences* between the last and the first scores of each student were obtained, would the G test lead to the acceptance or the rejection of the hypothesis that the teaching procedure employed failed to improve the student's ability to think critically?
X: 5, 0, 10, -4, -6, 8, 1, 7, -10, 0, 3, 5, -1, 8, 4, 0, -3, 7, 7, and 9
Use two different alternative hypotheses, in turn.

9. Make up and solve a problem similar to Problem 8, using the same $\bar{x}$ but producing a G about twice as large. About half as large.

10. Suppose that two methods of computing basal metabolism for 11 subjects produced the following pairs of records, in calories per square meter per hour:
I: 31.42, 30.90, 34.92, 30.59, 30.53, 33.08, 32.61, 30.46, 30.55, 33.19, and 29.22
II: 30.73, 31.44, 32.82, 31.80, 29.16, 32.96, 32.32, 30.76, 27.65, 32.54, and 29.30
Use G to test $H_0(\mu = 0)$ versus $H_a(\mu \neq 0)$ where μ is the true average difference in basal score for the same person by the two methods of measurement. Use $\alpha = 0.10$ for the G test, and then compute a CI_{90} on μ and test H_0 with it.

11. Given $R = 12$, do Problem 12, Section 3.5.

12. Given $R = 12$, do Problem 14, Section 3.5.

3.7 TESTING HYPOTHESES ABOUT THE NORMAL PARAMETER σ^2 BY MEANS OF THE CHI-SQUARE DISTRIBUTION

There are some occasions on which an experimenter may wish to test one of the hypotheses $H_0(\sigma^2 = \sigma_0^2)$, $H_0(\sigma^2 \leqslant \sigma_0^2)$, or $H_0(\sigma^2 \geqslant \sigma_0^2)$ against a suitable alternative hypothesis, which probably will be composite. These tests were discussed in Section 3.4 from the point of view of confidence intervals, $GLB_{1-\alpha}$'s and $LUB_{1-\alpha}$'s and those procedures usually are not only sufficient but may give useful additional information. However, it is worth while to see how the chi-square distribution can be used directly to test an H_0 about the population variance.

It has been noted before that if a random sample of size n is to be drawn from an $N(\mu, \sigma^2)$ population, the statistic $\sum\limits_{i=1}^{n} (X_i - \bar{x})^2 / \sigma^2$ is a χ_{n-1}^2

variate; hence chi-square tables are available to make desirable probability statements about $\sum (X_i - \bar{x})^2/\sigma^2$. In particular, one can so choose a and b that

$$\Pr\left\{ a < \frac{\sum (X_i - \bar{x})^2}{\sigma^2} < b \right\} = 1 - \alpha$$

as one would wish to do to define a region of rejection. If one wished to take an α level risk of Type I error equally from the two tails of the χ^2_{n-1} distribution, one would choose $a = \chi^2_{1-\alpha/2}$ and $b = \chi^2_{\alpha/2}$. If one wished to take all the risk of a Type I error from among the largest χ^2_{n-1}'s, one would choose $a = \chi^2_\alpha$ and $b = +\infty$.

The region of rejection one would want for a test of an H_0 would logically and conveniently be on $\sum (X_i - \bar{x})^2$, because this is the quantity routinely obtained from the sample; hence, one chooses the regions of rejection as follows, where each χ^2 has $n - 1$ DF:

$$\omega: \qquad \sum (X_i - \bar{x})^2 > \sigma_0^2 \chi_\alpha^2$$

to test $H_0(\sigma^2 \leqslant \sigma_0^2)$ against $H_a(\sigma^2 > \sigma_0^2)$, and

$$\omega: \qquad \sum (X_i - \bar{x})^2 < \sigma_0^2 \chi_{1-\alpha/2}^2 \quad \text{or} \quad > \sigma_0^2 \chi_{\alpha/2}^2$$

to test $H_0(\sigma^2 = \sigma_0^2)$ against $H_a(\sigma^2 \neq \sigma_0^2)$, and

$$\omega: \qquad \sum (X_i - \bar{x})^2 < \sigma_0^2 \chi_{1-\alpha}^2$$

to test $H_0(\sigma^2 \geqslant \sigma_0^2)$ against $H_a(\sigma^2 < \sigma_0^2)$.

To illustrate, suppose that n is chosen as 26, α as 0.10, and σ_0^2 as 12 for all cases to be considered. It then is easily verified that

$$\chi_{\alpha/2}^2 = 37.652, \quad \chi_{1-\alpha/2}^2 = 14.611, \quad \chi_\alpha^2 = 34.382, \quad \text{and} \quad \chi_{1-\alpha}^2 = 16.473$$

Therefore one has the following specific regions of rejection:

(a) ω: $\sum (X_i - \bar{x})^2 > 12(34.382) = 412.58$,   with $\alpha \leqslant$ value chosen

(b) ω: $\sum (X_i - \bar{x})^2 < 175.33$ or > 451.82,   with $\alpha \leqslant$ value chosen

(c) ω: $\sum (X_i - \bar{x})^2 < 197.68$,   with $\alpha \leqslant$ value chosen

If a random sample of size $n = 26$ has been drawn from a particular $N(\mu, \sigma^2) = 425.61$ when (a) is the test situation, then H_0 is rejected, because $\sum (X_i - \bar{x})^2$ is in ω_+. In each of the other two situations, the stated H_0 would be accepted.

PROBLEMS

1. A random sample of size $n = 21$ has produced $\sum (X_i - \bar{x})^2 = 27.3816$. Test $H_0(\sigma^2 \leqslant 1)$ against $H_a(\sigma^2 > 1)$ with $\alpha = 0.05$.

2. Do Problem 1 with a confidence interval.

3. If $\sum (X_i - \bar{x})^2 = 48.50$ from a random sample of size $n = 18$, test $H_0(\sigma^2 \geqslant 3)$ against $H_a(\sigma^2 < 3)$ with $\alpha \leqslant 0.10$.

4. Given the following practice data, test $H_0(\sigma^2 = 4.2)$ against $H_a(\sigma^2 \neq 4.2)$ with $\alpha = 0.05$.

   X_i: 3.71, 11.61, 5.06, 8.88, 4.63, 12.11, 7.59, 9.27, 8.56, 5.91, and 8.32

5. In Student's famous paper "The probable error of a mean," *Biometrika* 6: 1, 1908, the following data are analyzed:

   X: +1.2, +2.4, +1.3, +1.3, 0, +1.0, +1.8, +0.8, +4.6, and +1.4

   Test $H_0(\sigma^2 \leqslant 1.3)$ against $H_a(\sigma^2 > 1.3)$, using $\alpha \leqslant 0.10$. What assumptions must you make about these X's?

REVIEW PROBLEMS

1. If 25 red marbles, 40 blue marbles, and 35 white marbles are in an urn and well mixed, what is the probability that one marble drawn at random will be blue? What is the probability that it will be blue if it somehow is known that it is not white?

2. Suppose there are five different keys on a key ring and it takes a specific two of them to open a certain lock. What is the probability that a pair of keys picked at random will open the lock?

3. Some chemicals tend to induce the development of resistance to them among certain organisms after repeated administrations. It has been reported (*Salt Dig.* 16: June, 1964) that the chemical phenothiazine, used to kill stomach worms in cattle and sheep, does not induce such resistance. How would you conduct an experiment on sheep to test that hypothesis? What statistical tools would you employ?

4. It has been claimed that whitewashing the roofs of poultry houses in hot areas and in the summertime will reduce the temperatures in those houses from 8 to 10 degrees Fahrenheit. How would you set up an experiment to test that hypothesis, and what statistical tools would you use?

5. One often hears it said that good insulation will cut the heat bills enough to more than pay for the cost of insulation, say in a state such as Nebraska. How would you obtain data to test that general hypothesis? Would you have to make the statement more specific?

6. What binomial frequency distribution is created by tossing 10 unbiassed dice simultaneously and many times, if one records only the number of 5's and 6's after each such toss? What are the μ and σ^2 for this distribution?

7. What normal probability function would you use to compute $\sum\limits_{i=0}^{2} b(X; n, p)$ for the situation of Problem 6?

8. Suppose that a coin is so biassed that $\Pr\{\text{Heads}\} = 0.6$. Use a normal distribution to determine the probability that on a designated set of 25 tosses the fraction $X/25$ of Heads will exceed 0.60.

9. Referring to Problem 8, suppose you did not know that $\Pr\{\text{Heads}\} = p_H$, but obtained 16 heads on 25 tosses. What is the CI_{90} on p_H? What is the GLB_{90} on p_H?

10. Suppose that a random sample of size $n = 30$ has produced $\bar{x} = 52.7$ and $s^2 = 835.68$. What is the LUB_{90} on σ^2 if the sample came from some $N(\mu, \sigma^2)$ population?

11. Given the following practice data,

$$X: \quad -0.3, \ 1.5, \ 6.8, \ 0.3, \ 2.4, \ 3.1, \ 0.1, \ 4.3, \ 2.6, \ 3.4,$$

$$-0.2, \ 5.3, \ 2.3, \ 3.5, \ 1.9, \ 2.8, \ \text{and} \ 2.1,$$

test $H_0(\mu = 2)$ against $H_a(\mu > 2)$. What is the difference between this test and $H_0(\mu \leqslant 2)$ versus $H_a(\mu > 2)$? Can each be done with a confidence interval?

12. Suppose that an experimenter is going to conduct a paired-comparisons experiment and wishes to be able to detect a two-bushel difference in average yield between two varieties of wheat raised side by side on paired plots. If this experimenter has had enough experience with such data to feel confident that the standard deviation, s, will be about four bushels, and if he chooses $\alpha = 0.10$, how large a sample of pairs of plots would you suggest he take?

13. Suppose there are twelve tennis players in a clubhouse, six being women and six being men. If three of the women and two of the men cannot return a high lob, this fact being unknown to anyone but the individual, what is the probability that a mixed foursome (a man and a woman on each team) chosen at random will consist of four who cannot return a high lob?

14. Do Problem 11 by the G test.

15. How would you change just two of the numbers in Problem 11 so as to decrease s^2 and cause the least change in computations? How would you so change two numbers as to increase s^2 with the least change in computations?

16. Suppose that, when 300 baby turtles hatch in the sands along a certain tropical river, each independently has a probability of 0.5 of reaching the river safely. What is the probability that 30 or more arrive safely? What is the probability that none arrive safely?

17. Suppose that 35 out of 200 cans of fish sent to a certain grocery are contaminated with the deadly bacillus *Clostridium botulinum*. If the contaminated cans are mixed randomly among the uncontaminated and you purchase 5 cans, what is the probability that you get at least one contaminated can?

Chapter 4

Sampling Two Normal Populations, $N(\mu_1,\ \sigma_1^2)$ and $N(\mu_2,\ \sigma_2^2)$

4.1 INTRODUCTION

An experimenter may wish to study two varieties, treatments, or methods with respect to just one numerical measurement, such as yield of grain or net cash income, to learn whether those two varieties, treatments, or methods are substantially different with respect to a particular measurement. The experimenter knows that two treatments, say, are not likely to be identical with respect to *any* measurement and that they can be substantially different with respect to one measurement while essentially equal with respect to another measurement. Furthermore, it is well known that two experimental units given the same treatment will not give identical responses to a given treatment, and it is well known that the internal variations among units treated alike may differ from one treatment to another. Hence, the experimenter is seeking to use samples to detect important differences in *levels* of response to two apparently different treatments, or to detect differences in *uniformity* of response to two apparently different treatments, or to detect both level and uniformity differences. In terms of statistical concepts, it is said that, if the measurement being made conforms to some normal distribution within the same population of measurements, the experimenter is studying differences between population means (μ_1 and μ_2), differences between population variances (σ_1^2 and σ_2^2), or both. Furthermore, such studies will be made by means of relatively small randomized samples.

164

The questions raised in the preceding paragraph are of economic importance in many instances. For example, if the general level of yield of one variety of sorghum is higher than that of another variety, the grower may realize considerable economic advantage from planting the higher-yielding variety. However, the higher-yielding variety might yield more erratically from field to field, or from time to time, and thus be economically less dependable than the lower-yielding variety. This fact should become evident through a comparison of the sampling variances of the yields of the two varieties. A final decision on the merits of the two varieties as regards yielding ability would depend upon a weighting of the levels of yield and on the uniformities of yield from the two varieties over some representative area or over time.

Some of the important ways in which two normal populations could differ are illustrated by Figure 4.11. In (A) two varieties are considered to be equally uniform in yield from one area to another, but variety 1 yields at a lower level than variety 2, so $\mu_1 < \mu_2$, but $\sigma_1^2 = \sigma_2^2$. In (B) the two varieties are considered to be at the same general level of yield, but variety 2 is notably more erratic and therefore less dependable than variety 1 with regard to yield from one area to another or from one time to another within the same general environment; therefore, $\mu_1 = \mu_2$, but $\sigma_1^2 < \sigma_2^2$. In (C) is a situation in which variety 1 is more uniform in yield than variety 2 and also yields at a lower level; therefore, $\mu_1 < \mu_2$ and $\sigma_1^2 < \sigma_2^2$.

PROBLEMS

1. Make up two sets of data presumably from $N_1(\mu_1, \sigma_1^2)$ and $N_2(\mu_2, \sigma_2^2)$ and such that it *seems* reasonable that $\mu_1 > \mu_2$ but $\sigma_1^2 = \sigma_2^2$.

2. Describe four experimental studies which would have as their aims tests of the hypothesis that $\mu_1 = \mu_2$. Do likewise for the hypothesis that $\mu_1 \geqslant \mu_2$. What would seem to be logical alternative hypotheses for these tests?

3. It seems obvious that in any true-life study with natural populations, as contrasted with theoretical populations, the hypothesis that $\mu_1 = \mu_2$ never would be exactly true. Does this mean it is foolish to test $H_0(\mu_1 = \mu_2)$? Defend your point of view.

4. Does the following statement seem logical to you? Any test of $H_0(\mu_1 = \mu_2)$ must depend somehow on the sizes of σ_1^2 and σ_2^2, but a test of $H_0(\sigma_1^2 = \sigma_2^2)$ should not depend on the sizes of μ_1 and μ_2. Defend your answer.

5. Which of the following statements do you believe to be true about normal sampling?
   (a) If, unknown to the experimenter, $\mu_1 - \mu_2 = 0.4$, it will be more difficult to detect that $H_0(\mu_1 = \mu_2)$ is false than if $\mu_1 - \mu_2 = 2.3$, no matter what normal populations are being sampled.
   (b) If, unknown to the experimenter, $\sigma_1^2/\sigma_2^2 = 1.4$, it will be more difficult to detect that $H_0(\sigma_1^2 = \sigma_2^2)$ is false than if $\sigma_1^2/\sigma_2^2 = 3.8$, no matter what normal populations are being sampled.
   (c) Statement (a) would be true only if it were given that $\sigma_1^2 = \sigma_2^2$.

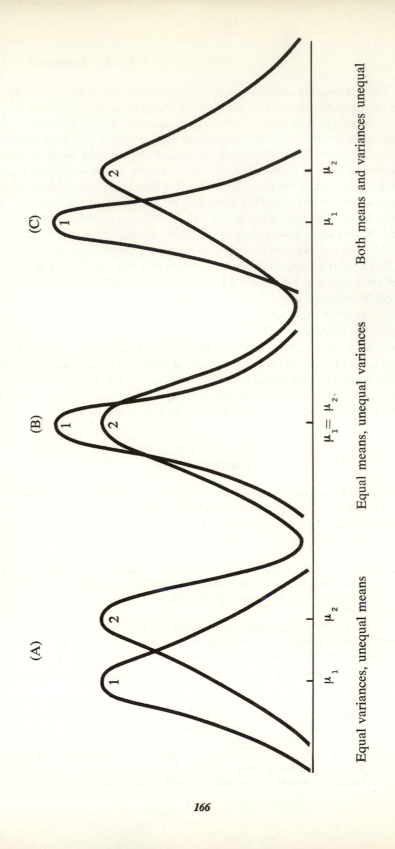

(A) Equal variances, unequal means

(B) Equal means, unequal variances

(C) Both means and variances unequal

4.2 TESTING THE HYPOTHESIS $H_0(\sigma_1^2 = \sigma_2^2)$ WHEN THE POPULATIONS ARE NORMAL BUT NOTHING IS ASSUMED ABOUT μ_1 AND μ_2

To determine whether it is reasonable to believe that two normal populations have the same variance, the hypothesis $H_0(\sigma_1^2 = \sigma_2^2)$ will be tested with one of the following alternatives: $\sigma_1^2 < \sigma_2^2$, $\sigma_1^2 \neq \sigma_2^2$, or $\sigma_1^2 > \sigma_2^2$. The choice of the most logical alternative hypothesis helps define the region of rejection in such a way as to give this test the greatest possible power under the circumstances.

Statistical analysis has shown that the ratio $F(n_1 - 1, n_2 - 1) = s_1^2/s_2^2$ of two independent and unbiassed estimates of σ_1^2 and σ_2^2, respectively, has what is called an F distribution only if $\sigma_1^2 = \sigma_2^2$ so that s_1^2 and s_2^2 are independent sample estimates of the same population variance. The mathematical formula for the frequency distribution curve of $F(n_1 - 1, n_2 - 1)$ is given in Equation 4.21, so that the mathematically inclined person can plot the curve for any chosen sizes of samples, n_1 and n_2, corresponding to the estimates s_1^2 and s_2^2, respectively. The relative frequency of occurrence of any sample F will be designated by $\phi(F)$. Its formula is:

$$(4.21) \qquad \phi(F) = \frac{\nu_1^{\nu_1/2} \cdot \nu_2^{\nu_2/2} \cdot F^{(\nu_1 - 2)/2}}{\beta(\nu_1/2, \nu_2/2)(\nu_1 F + \nu_2)^{(\nu_1 + \nu_2)/2}}$$

where $\nu_1 = n_1 - 1$, $\nu_2 = n_2 - 1$, and where $\beta(\nu_1/2, \nu_2/2)$ is a constant, called a beta function, which can be evaluated by mean of tables. The important features to note about this equation are that the ratio $F(\nu_1, \nu_2) = s_1^2/s_2^2$ *does* have a known sampling distribution function, $\phi(F)$, and that this distribution function does not involve any unknown parameters, for the $\nu_i = n_i - 1$ are known.

To illustrate Formula 4.21, suppose that independent random samples of sizes 5 and 11, respectively, are going to be drawn from the same $N(\mu, \sigma^2)$ population and that the $F(4, 10) = s_1^2/s_2^2$ will be computed. Then, $\nu_1 = 4$, $\nu_2 = 10$, and $\beta(2, 5) = (1! \, 4!)/6! = 1/30$ in this case. Therefore, the formula becomes

$$\phi[F(4, 10)] = \frac{4^2 \cdot 10^5 \cdot F}{(1/30)(4F + 10)^7} = \frac{48,000,000F}{(4F + 10)^7}$$

Using logarithms, one can obtain the following frequency distribution table for F(4, 10):

Figure 4.11.   Schematic illustration of ways normal populations can be different. (A) $\mu_1 < \mu_2$, $\sigma_1^2 = \sigma_2^2$; (B) $\mu_1 = \mu_2$, $\sigma_1^2 < \sigma_2^2$; (C) $\mu_1 < \mu_2$, $\sigma_1^2 < \sigma_2^2$.

F:	0	0.05	0.10	0.15	0.20	0.30	0.35	0.39	0.40
$\phi(F)$:	0	0.21	0.36	0.48	0.56	0.65	0.67	0.68	0.68

F:	0.42	0.50	0.60	0.80	1.00	1.20	1.40	1.60	1.80
$\phi(F)$:	0.68	0.67	0.64	0.55	0.46	0.37	0.30	0.24	0.19

F:	2.00	2.20	2.40	2.60	2.80	3.00
$\phi(F)$:	0.16	0.13	0.10	0.08	0.07	0.06

The graph of the F (4, 10) distribution is shown in Figure 4.21.

It should be noted again that the F distribution of Formula 4.21 does not involve any unknown parameters. As soon as the numbers of degrees of freedom, ν_1 and ν_2, are determined, the distribution is determined *regardless of the μ and σ^2 in the population from which the samples are to be drawn.*

Table XII provides an outline of the cumulative sampling distribution of $F(\nu_1, \nu_2)$ for a number of combinations (ν_1, ν_2). It can be shown statistically that the true mean of $F(\nu_1, \nu_2)$ is $\mu_F = \nu_2/(\nu_2 - 2)$, which is always greater than unity. The modal value of $\phi(F)$ occurs at $F = (\nu_1\nu_2 - 2\nu_2)/(\nu_1\nu_2 + 2\nu_1)$, which is 5/12 in the example in Figure 4.21. Thus the high point of any F curve is always to the left of $F = 1$ and also to the left of $F = \mu_F$. This information is helpful in sketching F distributions and in graphing regions of rejection. It also points out the asymmetry (skewness) of any F distribution.

The sampling distribution of $F(\nu_1, \nu_2)$ being known and not involving any unknown parameters, one can test hypotheses regarding the variances of two normal populations. The function $F(\nu_1, \nu_2)$ has a more general definition, which will be given later, but for now we define the F statistic by

(4.22) $$F(\nu_1, \nu_2) = s_1^2/s_2^2$$

where s_1^2 and s_2^2 are unbiassed independent estimates of the parameter σ^2 in $N(\mu, \sigma^2)$, with ν_1 and ν_2 degrees of freedom, respectively.

If the s_1^2 and s_2^2 are estimates from two normal populations with variances σ_1^2 and σ_2^2, one can test the hypothesis $H_0(\sigma_1^2 = \sigma_2^2)$, *nothing being said about* μ_1 and μ_2. As usual, the best region of rejection to use will depend upon the alternative hypothesis used. If the alternative is $H_a(\sigma_1^2 > \sigma_2^2)$, then the best region is one at the right-hand end of the $F(\nu_1, \nu_2)$ distribution. This is a reasonable region because, if σ_1^2 truly is larger than σ_2^2, then s_1^2 will tend to be larger than s_2^2, so that $F(\nu_1, \nu_2)$ will tend to be larger than would be expected from sampling variation alone.

For example, suppose that the α has been chosen as 0.10 and that a sample of size $n = 25$ is to be taken from each population. We wish to test $H_0(\sigma_1^2 = \sigma_2^2)$ against $H_a(\sigma_1^2 > \sigma_2^2)$. Table XII shows that to make the Pr{observed F(24, 24) $\geqslant F_0$} equal to 0.10 one takes F_0 at 1.70; therefore, the region of rejection of size $\alpha = 0.10$ is

$$\omega: \quad F(24, 24) \geqslant 1.70$$

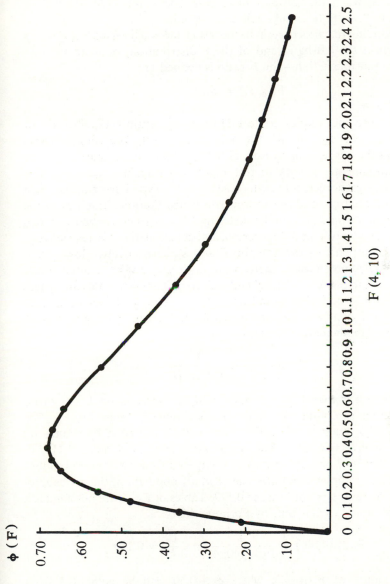

Figure 4.21. Frequency distribution of $F(4, 10)$. Here $\mu_F = \nu_2/(\nu_2 - 2) = 5/4$, modal F at $F = (\nu_1\nu_2 - 2\nu_2)/(\nu_1\nu_2 + 2\nu_1) = 5/12$.

Note, however, that the F ratio will be computed from $F(24, 24) = s_1^2/s_2^2$, regardless of the sizes of these sampling variances. The s_1^2 is computed from the sample designated in advance of the sampling as being taken from $N(\mu_1, \sigma_1^2)$ and, similarly, for s_2^2 as being from $N(\mu_2, \sigma_2^2)$. If s_1^2 turns out to be smaller than s_2^2 when the samples have been taken, the $F(24, 24)$ will be obviously < 1.70, so $H_0(\sigma_1^2 = \sigma_2^2)$ will be accepted.

Corresponding remarks pertain to the test $H_0(\sigma_1^2 = \sigma_2^2)$ versus $H_a(\sigma_1^2 < \sigma_2^2)$, but ω is then at the left-hand end of the F distribution, or—and this obviously is the sensible action—the F ratio is defined as

$$F(\nu_2, \nu_1) = s_2^2/s_1^2$$

and H_a is $\sigma_2^2 > \sigma_1^2$.

If it is more meaningful to test $H_0(\sigma_1^2 \leqslant \sigma_2^2)$ against $H_a(\sigma_1^2 > \sigma_2^2)$ or $H_0(\sigma_1^2 \geqslant \sigma_2^2)$ against $H_a(\sigma_1^2 < \sigma_2^2)$, the only change in the preceding remarks is to note that the α is less than or equal to that chosen in advance.

If an experimenter wishes to test $H_0(\sigma_1^2 = \sigma_2^2)$ against $H_a(\sigma_1^2 \neq \sigma_2^2)$, a two-tail test of significance is in order, the risk of a Type I error being taken equally from the extremes of the appropriate F distribution. Graphically, the region of rejection would be as in the sketch (p. 171), in general, where ν_1 and ν_2 stand for the DF involved in the numerator and denominator of F, respectively, and would correspond to the DF for s_1^2 and s_2^2, respectively. However, F tables are double-entry tables, there being both a ν_1 and a ν_2 to consider, and hence these tables are moderately difficult to prepare. They also are space-consuming, so it is desirable to cut down the amount of tables needed. It turns out that this can be done very simply for the test of $\sigma_1^2 = \sigma_2^2$ because it has been shown mathematically that

(4.23) $$F_{1-\alpha}(\nu_1, \nu_2) \equiv \frac{1}{F_\alpha(\nu_2, \nu_1)}$$

where $F_{1-\alpha}(\nu_1, \nu_2)$ is that $F(\nu_1, \nu_2)$ which will be exceeded on $1 - \alpha$ of all possible random sampling $F(\nu_1, \nu_2)$'s. Similar remarks hold for F_α. For example, $F_{0.975}(4, 40)$ is the F ratio which will be exceeded by chance by 97.5% of all sample $F(4, 40)$'s. The actual value of $F_{0.975}(4, 40)$ is 0.119, so one can say that if s_1^2 and s_2^2 were to be computed from two future random and independent samples from any one $N(\mu, \sigma^2)$ population, the probability is 0.975 that the ratio s_1^2/s_2^2 will exceed 0.119. Tables of $F_{0.975}$ are not common for the reason noted earlier but, by Formula 4.23,

$$F_{0.975}(4, 40) = \frac{1}{F_{0.025}(40, 4)} = \frac{1}{8.41} = 0.119$$

In general, values of $F_\alpha(\nu_1, \nu_2)$, where $\alpha > 0.50$, can be computed from Formula 4.23, provided the $F_{1-\alpha}(\nu_2, \nu_1)$ is obtainable from existing tables, such as Table XII. It will be found, however, that the computation of this formula, easy though it is, can be avoided in most practical situations.

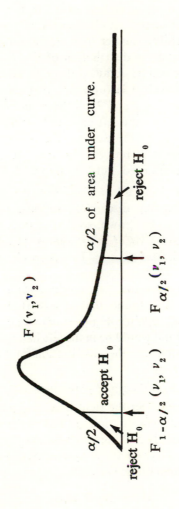

With Formula 4.23 in mind, it is simple to devise two-tail F tests which actually use only readily available right-hand tails of F distributions. The reasoning is as follows. In a normal two-tail test of $H_0(\sigma_1^2 = \sigma_2^2)$ versus $H_a(\sigma_1^2 \neq \sigma_2^2)$, the ratio $F(\nu_1, \nu_2) = s_1^2/s_2^2$ would be used with s_1^2 from population $N(\mu_1, \sigma_1^2)$ and *always in the numerator* of F. Otherwise, the degrees of freedom for F would not be in the order ν_1, ν_2, as stated. The left-hand half of the two-tail region of rejection is of size $\alpha/2$ and is occupied by those $\alpha/2$ $F(\nu_1, \nu_2)$'s produced when s_1^2 is considerably smaller than s_2^2, but all of those $F(\nu_1, \nu_2)$'s in the extreme left-hand $\alpha/2$ of the distribution of $F(\nu_1, \nu_2)$ correspond exactly to the $\alpha/2$ $F(\nu_2, \nu_1)$'s which can be obtained through Equation 4.23. Hence if, when testing $H_0(\sigma_1^2 = \sigma_2^2)$ against $H_a(\sigma_1^2 \neq \sigma_2^2)$, one always divides the larger s_i^2 by the smaller s_i^2, where $i = 1$ and 2, all those samples which would have produced $F(\nu_1, \nu_2)$'s in the extreme left-hand tail of the $F(\nu_1, \nu_2)$ distribution will now produce $F(\nu_2, \nu_1)$'s in the extreme right-hand tail of the $F(\nu_2, \nu_1)$ distribution. Thus, the region of rejection for this two-tail test is as follows, where *two* F distributions are used and $F = $ larger $s_i^2 \div$ smaller s_i^2.

(4.24) ω: $F(\nu_1, \nu_2) > F_{\alpha/2}(\nu_1, \nu_2)$ and $F(\nu_2, \nu_1) > F_{\alpha/2}(\nu_2, \nu_1)$

To illustrate the foregoing discussion, suppose that samples of sizes $n_1 = 10$ and $n_2 = 16$ are to be drawn, so that $\nu_1 = 9$ and $\nu_2 = 15$. Choose $\alpha = 0.10$. The rule for testing $H_0(\sigma_1^2 = \sigma_2^2)$ against $H_a(\sigma_1^2 \neq \sigma_2^2)$ is to use the 5% right-hand tail of $F(15, 9)$ if $s_1^2 < s_2^2$. This is specifically shown in Figure 4.22.

Now suppose that, after the two random samples are drawn from $N(\mu_1, \sigma_1^2)$ and $N(\mu_2, \sigma_2^2)$, it is found that $s_1^2 = 8.31$ and $s_2^2 = 27.58$, when we are testing $H_0(\sigma_1^2 = \sigma_2^2)$ against $H_a(\sigma_1^2 \neq \sigma_2^2)$. Referring to Figure 4.22, the $F(9, 15)$ would be 0.30 and would be in the left-hand portion of the original two-tail region of rejection on the distribution of $F(9, 15)$. However, if we compute the F ratio from

$$F = \text{(larger } s^2)/\text{(smaller } s^2)$$

then $F(15, 9) = 3.32$, which is in the right-hand 5% portion of the $F(15, 9)$ region of rejection and is, therefore, in region 3 of the figure. Thus, the use of this definition of F is simply making a two-tail test by using the right-hand tails of *two* distributions, $F(\nu_1, \nu_2)$ and $F(\nu_2, \nu_1)$, instead of a left-hand and a right-hand tail of *one* distribution, $F(\nu_1, \nu_2)$.

PROBLEMS

1. Suppose two lots of beef cattle under two apparently different diets produced the following data on average daily gains over a stated period of time:

Lot 1	*Lot 2*
$n_1 = 12$, mean $= \bar{x}_1 = 2.50$	$n_2 = 10$, mean $= \bar{x}_2 = 2.01$
variance $= s_1^2 = 0.1034$	variance $= s_2^2 = 0.0311$

Is $H_0(\sigma_1^2 = \sigma_2^2)$ an acceptable hypothesis over the alternative hypothesis $H_a(\sigma_1^2 > \sigma_2^2)$? What if the alternative were $H_a(\sigma_1^2 \neq \sigma_2^2)$?

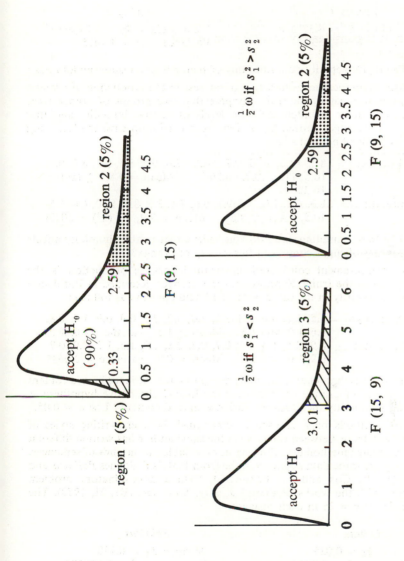

Figure 4.22.   Illustration of the two-tail F test of $H_0(\sigma_1^2 = \sigma_2^2)$ versus $H_a(\sigma_1^2 = \sigma_2^2)$ by the rule $F = (\text{larger } s^2)/(\text{smaller } s^2)$, $\alpha = 0.10$, and sample sizes are 10 and 16, respectively, from populations 1 and 2. Region 1 is replaced by region 3, if $s_1^2 < s_2^2$. Actual test if tables are available and $\alpha = 0.10$.

2. Suppose that two large fields of two different varieties of alfalfa have been randomly sampled for hay yields by harvesting 15 quarter-acre plots taken at random from each field. Given the following results of this sampling, test $H_0(\sigma_1^2 = \sigma_2^2)$ against $H_a(\sigma_1^2 \neq \sigma_2^2)$, using $\alpha = 0.10$, and draw appropriate conclusions.

Variety 1	*Variety 2*
Mean yield $= \bar{x}_1 = 4.3 T/$acre	Mean yield $= \bar{x}_2 = 5.2 T/$acre
Variance $= s_1^2 = 1.7530$	Variance $= s_2^2 = 1.4475$

How would you actually do a sampling of such fields to insure randomness?

3. One of the numerical measurements of interest in the production of oranges is the percent sugar in the fruit. Suppose that two groups of orange trees were grown under definitely different levels of relative humidity and that thereafter 15 oranges chosen at random from each crop gave the following results in terms of percent sugar:

High Humidity: 8.1, 10.0, 10.0, 9.7, 11.2, 12.0, 9.5, 8.5, 9.1, 8.6, 9.8, 10.5, 11.0, 10.2, and 9.0   Mean $= 9.8$, $\sum (x^2) = 16.22$

Low Humidity: 8.3, 6.5, 7.0, 7.5, 9.1, 6.6, 7.4, 8.5, 8.3, 10.0, 6.0, 5.5, 10.5, 9.4, and 8.6   Mean $= 7.9$, $\sum (x^2) = 30.24$

In view of these sampling data, do you believe that relative humidity affects the *uniformity* of sugar content in this variety of orange?

4. Another measurement considered important in orange production is the percent acid in the fruits. Suppose that the oranges described in Problem 3 (but not necessarily in the same order) had acid contents as follows:

High Humidity: 1.5, 1.1, 0.6, 0.8, 1.2, 2.0, 0.7, 2.5, 0.9, 0.9, 1.4, 0.8, 1.6, 1.7, and 1.5   Mean $= 1.3$,   variance $= 0.2846$

Low Humidity: 0.9, 0.5, 1.3, 1.1, 0.7, 0.8, 0.8, 1.0, 1.3, 1.2, 0.9, 0.7, 0.9, 1.0, and 0.5   Mean $= 0.9$,   variance $= 0.0635$

Is the hypothesis that relative humidity does not affect variance in acid content of this variety of orange acceptable, if the logical alternative hypothesis is that higher humidity increases the variance in acid content? Use $\alpha = 0.05$.

5. Statistical methods may be used to distinguish between writing styles of different writers or between times when the same author has written different works. One such method uses the lengths of syllables at the ends of sentences. Following are some data supposed to be from Plato's dialogues *Politicus* and *Critias* (D. R. Cox and L. Brandwood, "On a discriminatory problem connected with the works of Plato," *J. Roy. Stat. Soc.* (B): 21, 1959). The sample size is $n = 25$ in each instance.

Critias	*Politicus*
Mean $= \bar{x}_C = 0.035$	Mean $= \bar{x}_P = 0.130$
Variance $= s_C^2 = 0.00380$	Variance $= s_P^2 = 0.000397$

Is the hypothesis that Plato's writing style did not change with respect to variance in syllable length between the writing of those two dialogues an acceptable hypothesis in view of these sampling data? Choose your own region of rejection.

6. J. A. Beerbower in *In Search of the Past* (Prentice-Hall, Englewood Cliffs, N.J., 1960, p. 70) gives the following length measurements in millimeters from two random samples of brachiopods:

Sample A: 17.9, 18.4, 14.6, 16.9, 17.5, 18.3, 13.6, 14.4, 13.5, 11.4, 11.5, 7.8, 7.6, 7.5, 11.4, 8.7, 6.3, 8.7 $\sum (X_A) = 226.0$, $\sum (x_A^2) = 293.9844$

Sample B: 16.1, 15.8, 17.3, 15.9, 13.2, 15.9, 14.7, 14.8, 13.2, 9.1, 8.8, 10.0, 8.2, 6.6, 6.9, 6.2 $\sum (X_B) = 192.7$, $\sum (x_B^2) = 233.5394$

If this length can be considered a decisive factor, do you conclude that the two populations sampled have the same variance or not? Use a two-tail F test, because there is no basis for a one-directional alternative hypothesis.

7. Suppose that samples of two types of asphalt had the following percentage yields of asphaltene:

Texas: 12.3, 10.8, 13.0, 14.1, 12.6, 9.9, 10.7, 10.9, 11.6, 11.5, 12.5, and 12.0

Mexico: 15.8, 12.9, 14.6, 14.3, 15.1, 13.7, 13.4, 14.6, 15.0, 14.7, 13.4, and 13.0

Assuming proper normal sampling, test $H_0(\sigma_T^2 = \sigma_M^2)$ against $H_a(\sigma_T^2 \neq \sigma_M^2)$, and draw appropriate conclusions. Then change H_a to $\sigma_T^2 < \sigma_M^2$, and do likewise.

8. Suppose that some samples of the percentage yield of resins in a certain Texas asphalt were taken in two different series of experiments with the following results:

Series 1:   20.2, 21.8, 20.7, 20.9, 21.1, 21.9, 22.3, 21.6, 22.1, and 21.4
Series 2:   22.4, 21.9, 22.3, 22.5, 21.8, 22.4, 22.0, 21.6, 22.1, and 21.3

Test $H_0(\sigma_1^2 = \sigma_2^2)$ against $H_a(\sigma_1^2 \neq \sigma_2^2)$. Also test $H_0(\sigma_1^2 \leq \sigma_2^2)$ against $H_a(\sigma_1^2 > \sigma_2^2)$.

9. Use Formula 4.21 to plot the sampling distribution curve for the $F(\nu_1, \nu_2)$ needed for the first part of Problem 7. You are given that $\beta(11/2, 11/2) = 0.0000794$.

10. Make a sketch showing the specific region of rejection for the two-tail test of $H_0(\sigma_1^2 = \sigma_2^2)$ versus $H_a(\sigma_1^2 \neq \sigma_2^2)$ when $\alpha = 0.10$, $\nu_1 = 8$, and $\nu_2 = 20$.

11. Use Formula 4.21 to plot the sampling distribution curve for the $F(\nu_1, \nu_2)$ needed to do the first part of Problem 8, omitting the last two numbers in series 2.

12. Do Problem 7 for the hypothesis $H_0(\sigma_T^2 \geq \sigma_M^2)$ versus $H_a(\sigma_T^2 < \sigma_M^2)$.

4.3   TESTING THE HYPOTHESIS $H_0[(\mu_1 = \mu_2) \mid (\sigma_1^2 = \sigma_2^2)]$

One of the purposes of an experiment may be to decide whether the general levels of measurement in $N(\mu_1, \sigma_1^2)$ and $N(\mu_2, \sigma_2^2)$ are the same in the sense that $\mu_1 = \mu_2$. In this section we shall discuss making such a test on the assumption that $\sigma_1^2 = \sigma_2^2$. The manner in which one may become willing to assume that $\sigma_1^2 = \sigma_2^2$ is not of concern in this section. It should be noted, as a warning, that if one does perform a prior test of $H_0(\sigma_1^2 = \sigma_2^2)$, as described in Section 4.2, and then tests $H_0[(\mu_1 = \mu_2) \mid (\sigma_1^2 = \sigma_2^2)]$, one must not think of probabilities of Type I and Type II errors for the two tests together. From the point of view of the present section, it is *known* that $\sigma_1^2 = \sigma_2^2$ when one tests $H_0[(\mu_1 = \mu_2) \mid (\sigma_1^2 = \sigma_2^2)]$ or some variation thereof.

It can be shown that the most powerful test of the hypothesis $H_0[(\mu_1 = \mu_2) \mid (\sigma_1^2 = \sigma_2^2)]$, which is the hypothesis that the means are equal given that the variances are equal, is obtained from a t test, when the measurement, X, is normally distributed. However, the t used here is somewhat different from that used before in its appearance but not in its fundamental nature. There is one fundamental problem to solve, namely the estimation of the σ^2 when one has two random samples that might be from populations with different means.

On the assumption that the population variances are equal one could obtain an estimate of that common variance from either sample or by some acceptable means of obtaining a combined estimate from both samples, but in any event it is best to use all the information available in both samples, if one wishes to make the most powerful test. Obviously, precautions must be taken to insure that any real difference between the true means of the two populations being sampled shall not distort the estimate obtained for the common variance, σ^2. This sort of distortion is simply avoided by calculating deviations, $X_i - \bar{x}$, *within each sample separately*. This will produce sums of squares, which will be designated as $\sum(x_1^2)$ and $\sum(x_2^2)$ from the first and second samples, respectively. Each sum of squares will reflect only variation internal to its sample and will not reflect any difference which may exist between μ_1 and μ_2. The specific way in which these two sums of squares are to be used to obtain the best available estimate of the variance common to the two populations is shown by

(4.31)
$$s^2 = \frac{\sum(x_1^2) + \sum(x_2^2)}{n_1 + n_2 - 2}$$

This is an estimator of the variance, σ^2, which is assumed to be the same for each population. To illustrate the use of this formula, consider the following example:

Sample 1

$n_1 = 25, \quad \sum(x_1^2) = 136, \quad$ with 24 DF

Sample 2

$n_2 = 30, \quad \sum(x_2^2) = 205, \quad$ with 29 DF

$$s^2 = \frac{136 + 205}{25 + 30 - 2} = \frac{341}{53} = 6.43, \quad \text{with 53 DF}$$

Thus the estimate of the common population variance for the two populations from which samples 1 and 2 were taken is 6.43.

It was learned in Section 3.2 that the variance of a sample mean, $\bar{x}$, is σ^2/n and that, therefore, an estimate of that variance is obtained from s^2/n, but what is the variance of the difference between two means, $\bar{x}_1 - \bar{x}_2$? As mentioned in Chapter 2, it is a fact that the variance of such a difference for two *independent* samples is the sum of the separate variances for $\bar{x}_1$ and $\bar{x}_2$. For samples taken from populations with the same variance, the true variance of $\bar{x}_1 - \bar{x}_2$ is

(4.32) $$\sigma_{\bar{x}_1 - \bar{x}_2}^2 = \sigma^2/n_1 + \sigma^2/n_2 = \sigma^2(1/n_1 + 1/n_2)$$

which will be estimated by replacing σ^2, which is unknown, with its unbiassed estimator, s^2. After some obvious simplifications, a single formula for the estimated variance of the difference between the means of two random samples from populations with the same variance can be written as follows:

(4.33) $$s_{\bar{x}_1 - \bar{x}_2}^2 = \frac{\sum (x_1^2) + \sum (x_2^2)}{n_1 + n_2 - 2} \left(\frac{n_1 + n_2}{n_1 n_2} \right)$$

The t distribution employed earlier was the ratio of the quantity $(\bar{x} - \mu)$ to its standard deviation, $s_{\bar{x}}$. By analogy, consider the ratio

(4.34) $$\frac{(\bar{x}_1 - \bar{x}_2) - (\mu_1 - \mu_2)}{s_{\bar{x}_1 - \bar{x}_2}}$$

where the denominator is given by Formula 4.33 after the square root has been taken. It can be shown by statistical theory (beyond the scope of this book) that the ratio in that formula has a t distribution with $n_1 + n_2 - 2$ DF, if the two samples are independent random samples from normal populations with the same variance. Therefore, it is valid and useful to write

(4.35) $$t = \frac{(\bar{x}_1 - \bar{x}_2) - (\mu_1 - \mu_2)}{\sqrt{\dfrac{\sum (x_1^2) + \sum (x_2^2)}{n_1 + n_2 - 2} \left(\dfrac{n_1 + n_2}{n_1 n_2} \right)}}, \qquad \text{with } (n_1 + n_2 - 2) \text{ DF}$$

As emphasized earlier, a t distribution with ν DF is the same as any other t distribution with that same number of degrees of freedom. It makes no difference if one t distribution arose in connection with a study of chimpanzees and the other in connection with studies of jet propulsion: the number of degrees of freedom and the fact that the sampling distribution involved is a t distribution are all that matters. Therefore, one can use Formula 4.35 to set central or noncentral confidence intervals on the parameter $\mu_1 - \mu_2$ or can test H_0's about this difference in the same manner as that shown earlier. The following data are used to illustrate these points:

	From population 1		From population 2

X_1 X_2

X_1		X_2	
14.3	$n_1 = 10$	12.3	$n_2 = 12$
10.0	$\bar{x}_1 = 13.29$	9.4	$\bar{x}_2 = 10.76$
11.1	$\sum (X_1^2) = 1805.650$	8.6	$\sum (X_2^2) = 1415.7600$
12.6	$(\sum X_1)^2/n_1 = 1766.241$	13.7	$(\sum X_2)^2/n_2 = 1391.0533$
17.5	$\sum (x_1^2) = 39.4090$	10.8	$\sum (x_2^2) = 24.7067$
15.2		11.2	
12.6		11.5	
12.8		12.0	
13.7		9.9	
13.1		10.2	
$132.9 = \sum (X_1)$		10.8	
		8.8	
		$129.2 = \sum (X_2)$	

It is assumed that the experimenter has become satisfied that $\sigma_1^2 = \sigma_2^2 = \sigma^2$, so one computes the pooled estimate of σ^2 from

$$s^2 = \frac{39.4090 + 24.7067}{20} = 3.205785$$

hence $s_{\bar{x}_1 - \bar{x}_2} = \sqrt{3.2058(\frac{1}{10} + \frac{1}{12})} = 0.767$. The central $\mathrm{CI}_{1-\alpha}$ on $\mu_1 - \mu_2$ is, by analogy with previous CI's on μ,

(4.36) $(\bar{x}_1 - \bar{x}_2) - s_{\bar{x}_1 - \bar{x}_2} t_\alpha < \mu_1 - \mu_2 < (\bar{x}_1 - \bar{x}_2) + s_{\bar{x}_1 - \bar{x}_2} t_\alpha$

For this illustration one obtains the following central 90% confidence interval on $\mu_1 - \mu_2$:

$$\mathrm{CI}_{90}: \qquad 1.21 < \mu_1 - \mu_2 < 3.85$$

The GLB_{90} on $\mu_1 - \mu_2$ is computed from $\mathrm{GLB}_{90} = (\bar{x}_1 - \bar{x}_2) - s_{\bar{x}_1 - \bar{x}_2} t_{0.20}$ $= 1.52$ and from $\mathrm{LUB}_{90} = (\bar{x}_1 - \bar{x}_2) + s_{\bar{x}_1 - \bar{x}_2} t_{20} = 3.54$. One can draw appropriate conclusions from these various limits according to the purposes of an experiment. One also can test one of several hypotheses from the appropriate one of these limits.

As would be expected, one also can use Formula 4.35 directly, to test hypotheses about $\mu_1 - \mu_2$. For example, to test $H_0[(\mu_1 = \mu_1) \mid (\sigma_1^2 = \sigma_2^2 = \sigma^2)]$ against $H_a[(\mu_1 \neq \mu_2) \mid (\sigma_1^2 = \sigma_2^2 = \sigma^2)]$, one chooses, say, $\alpha = 0.10$, obtains ω of $|t| > 1.72$, and computes

$$t = \frac{|13.29 - 10.76| - 0}{0.767} = 3.30, \quad \text{with 20 DF}$$

Therefore H_0 is rejected quite decisively. Alternatively, one could test $H_0[(\mu_1 \geq \mu_2) \mid (\sigma_1^2 = \sigma_2^2 = \sigma^2)]$ against $H_a[(\mu_1 < \mu_2) \mid (\sigma_1^2 = \sigma_2^2 = \sigma^2)]$ with $\alpha \leq 0.10$. The region of rejection, ω, now is $t < 1.32$, and the observed t is as before, namely $t = 3.30$, which is not less than 1.32. Therefore H_0 is accepted with $\alpha \leq 0.10$.

Other t tests, analogous to those illustrated in Chapter 3, also could have been run, if the experiment seemed to require one of them *before the data were obtained.*

The most difficult computation in the t test of H_0 is that of determining the standard deviation in its denominator. This difficulty can be removed almost entirely (naturally, at some loss of power) by using the G test. The G test uses the sample range, R, to estimate the standard deviation, as noted earlier, but we now have two sample ranges and, therefore, use their average. With two samples of equal sizes the formula for this G becomes

(4.37)
$$G = \frac{\bar{x}_1 - \bar{x}_2 - (\mu_1 - \mu_2)}{\text{mean } R}$$

where the mean R is $(R_1 + R_2)/2$. Table X gives an outline of a portion of the sampling distribution of this two-sample G and is sufficient for many purposes. This G test can be used only with samples of the same size and $n = 20$ or less.

To illustrate the two-sample G test, suppose that the last two members of the sample from population 2, in the example given above, are deleted to attain equality of sample size at $n = 10$. It then is found that $\bar{x}_1 = 13.29$, $\bar{x}_2 = 10.96$, $R_1 = 17.5 - 10.0 = 7.5$, and $R_2 = 5.1$, and so $\bar{R} = (7.5 + 5.1)/2 = 6.3$. Therefore, $G = 0.370$ if $\mu_1 = \mu_2$ in Formula 4.36. With $n = 10$, Table X indicates that with any $\alpha \geqslant 0.020$ the hypotheses $H_0[(\mu_1 = \mu_2) \mid (\sigma_1^2 = \sigma_2^2 = \sigma^2)]$ would be rejected if the alternative hypothesis is that $\mu_1 \neq \mu_2$. If desirable in a given situation, one could test any of the hypotheses discussed earlier in connection with the t test, or could set central or noncentral limits on $\mu_1 - \mu_2$. The comments made in Chapter 3 where the one-sample G distribution (Table IX) was discussed would have counterparts here. For example, optimum confidence limits are obtained with the t distribution rather than with the G distribution, but the loss may be unimportant compared with savings in computation.

PROBLEMS

1. Referring to Problem 1, Section 4.2, and assuming that the population variances are equal, test $H_0(\mu_1 = \mu_2)$ against the alternative $H_a(\mu_1 > \mu_2)$. Against the alternative $H_a(\mu_1 \neq \mu_2)$. Use the t test and draw appropriate conclusions.

2. Do as in Problem 1, this section, for Problem 2, Section 4.2.

3. Do as in Problem 1, this section, for Problem 3, Section 4.2.

4. Do as in Problem 1, this section, for Problem 4, Section 4.2.

5. Do as in Problem 1, this section, for Problem 5, Section 4.2.

6. Do Problem 3, Section 4.2, by the G test.

7. Do Problem 4, Section 4.2, by the G test.

8. Do as in Problem 1, this section, for Problem 6, Section 4.2.

9. Use the data of Problem 6, Section 4.2, without the last two numbers (6.3 and 8.7) of the larger sample, to test $H_0[(\mu_A = \mu_B) \mid (\sigma_A^2 = \sigma_B^2)]$ against the two-directional alternative that the means are unequal, using the G test.

10. Referring to Problem 7, Section 4.2, test $H_0[(\mu_T = \mu_M) \mid (\sigma_T^2 = \sigma_M^2)]$ against $H_a[(\mu_T \neq \mu_M) \mid (\sigma_T^2 = \sigma_M^2)]$, and draw appropriate conclusions.

11. Do Problem 7, Section 4.2, by the G test.

12. Referring to Problem 8, Section 4.2, test $H_0[(\mu_1 = \mu_2) \mid (\sigma_1^2 = \sigma_2^2)]$ versus $H_a[(\mu_1 < \mu_2) \mid (\sigma_1^2 = \sigma_2^2)]$, and draw appropriate conclusions.

13. Change the data of Problem 8, Section 4.2, so that the series averages are *not* changed but the difference between $\bar{x}_1$ and $\bar{x}_2$ now causes rejection of $H_0[(\mu_1 = \mu_2) \mid (\sigma_1^2 = \sigma_2^2)]$ versus $H_a[(\mu_1 \neq \mu_2) \mid (\sigma_1^2 = \sigma_2^2)]$ with $\alpha = 0.01$.

14. Do Problem 10, this section, with H_a as $\mu_1 > \mu_2$.

15. Sketch the distribution curve for the t appropriate for Problem 10, this section, and show the specific region of rejection.

16. Given the following practice data:

$$X_1: \quad 3.5, \ -1.6, \ 0, \ 2.1, \ 1.9, \ 0.7, \ 2.4, \ 1.2, \ \text{and} \ -0.2$$
$$X_2: \quad 4.2, \ 3.1, \ -0.3, \ 5.6, \ 2.5, \ 2.9, \ 3.6, \ 3.9, \ 4.7, \ \text{and} \ 1.7$$

test $H_0[(\mu_1 \leqslant \mu_2) \mid (\sigma_1^2 = \sigma_2^2 = \sigma^2)]$ against $H_a[(\mu_1 > \mu_2) \mid (\sigma_1^2 = \sigma_2^2 = \sigma^2)]$ by a confidence interval and also by a t test. Use $\alpha = 0.05$, and comment on these two ways of testing this H_0.

17. Do Problem 16 using the G distribution, after omitting the last X_2.

18. Plot the G's of Table X for $n = 15$ against the α, and interpolate linearly for the G, with $\alpha = 0.025$. Could you "safely" extrapolate to determine the G for $\alpha = 0.20$ when $n = 15$?

4.4 TESTING THE HYPOTHESIS $H_0[(\mu_1 = \mu_2) \mid (\sigma_1^2 \neq \sigma_2^2)]$

Actually, the t test and the G test, used when the population variances are believed to be equal, are thought to tolerate considerable inequality between the two population variances without appreciable change in the probabilities of errors of Type I and II. Hence, unless the inequality between σ_1^2 and σ_2^2 appears to be quite marked, the t test or the G test probably should be used, because they are the most powerful tests available when their assumptions are strictly satisfied. There also is the fact that exact and undisputed tests appropriate to the situation in which the population variances are unequal and in which one wishes to test $H_0(\mu_1 = \mu_2)$, $H_0(\mu_1 \leqslant \mu_2)$, or $H_0(\mu_1 \leqslant \mu_2)$ are not available.

W. G. Cochran and Gertrude Cox (*Experimental Designs*, Wiley,

New York, 1957) suggest the following approximate t test of $H_0[(\mu_1 = \mu_2) \mid (\sigma_1^2 \neq \sigma_2^2)]$:

Step 1. Compute $\bar{d} = \bar{x}_1 - \bar{x}_2$, $\quad s_{\bar{d}} = \sqrt{\dfrac{\sum (x_1^2)}{n_1(n_1 - 1)} + \dfrac{\sum (x_2^2)}{n_2(n_2 - 1)}} =$

$\sqrt{s_{\bar{x}_1}^2 + s_{\bar{x}_2}^2}$; and then compute $t' = \bar{d}/s_{\bar{d}}$, which does not have a t distribution.

Step 2. Compute $t'_\alpha = \dfrac{w_1 t_{1\alpha} + w_2 t_{2\alpha}}{w_1 + w_2}$, where $w_i = \dfrac{\sum (x_i^2)}{n_i(n_i - 1)} = s_{\bar{x}_i}^2$, and $t_{i\alpha} =$ tabular t at the α-level of significance for $(n_i - 1)$ DF.

Step 3. If $t' \geqslant t'_\alpha$, reject H_0 and conclude that the population means are unequal.

To illustrate these steps, suppose that on two random samples of sizes $n_1 = 10$ and $n_2 = 15$ drawn under two different treatments it turned out that $\bar{x}_1 = 12$, $\bar{x}_2 = 7$, $\sum (x_1^2)/10(9) = 1.32 = s_{\bar{x}_1}^2 = w_1$, and $\sum (x_2^2)/15(14) = 4.68 = s_{\bar{x}_2}^2 = w_2$. Then, according to the instructions given above, the following step-by-step computations are obtained:

Step 1. $\bar{d} = 12 - 7 = 5$, $s_{\bar{d}} = \sqrt{1.32 + 4.68} = 2.45$, and $t' = 5/2.45$ $= 2.04$

Step 2. $w_1 = 1.32$ and $w_2 = 4.68$; so with $t_{1\alpha} = t_{1,\,0.05} = 2.262$ and $t_{2\alpha} = t_{2,\,0.05} = 2.145$

Assuming a 5% region of rejection, we have

$$t'_{0.05} = \frac{1.32(2.262) + 4.68(2.145)}{6} = 2.17$$

Step 3. Because t' is not $\geqslant t'_{0.05}$, H_0 is tentatively accepted (one notes that t' is quite close to the size of $t'_{0.05}$; hence the word "tentative.")

Cochran and Cox state that their approximate t' test probably is a little conservative with respect to the rejection of true hypotheses; that is, it probably is true that $\alpha \leqslant 0.05$ in the example given above.

When either of the two chief assumptions underlying the t and G tests (namely, normality and equal variances) is not likely to be satisfied in a given experimental situation, it may be well to consider using one of the non-parametric tests which are available. Such tests do not assume either normality or equality of variances. Some of these tests will be considered in Chapter 5.

PROBLEMS

1. Test $H_0[(\mu_1 = \mu_2) \mid (\sigma_1^2 \neq \sigma_2^2)]$ for the situation of Problem 1, Section 4.2.
2. Do as in Problem 1, this section, for Problem 2, Section 4.2.
3. Do as in Problem 1, this section, for Problem 3, Section 4.2.
4. Do as in Problem 1, this section, for Problem 4, Section 4.2.
5. Do as in Problem 1, this section, for Problem 5, Section 4.2.

REVIEW PROBLEMS

1. Suppose that Blakemore strawberry seeds are being studied with regard to percent germination after each of two different treatments of the seeds, namely mechanical scarification and such scarification plus application of 0.10 milligrams of Gibrel. Given that on germination of 150 seeds from each treatment after 21 days under standard germination conditions Treatment 1 showed 15.3% germination and Treatment 2 showed 21.2% germination, does the addition of 0.10 milligrams of Gibrel increase seed germination in this variety under the conditions studied or not?

2. Referring to Problem 1, what would your decision have been if n had been 75 and the percentages germinating had been the same?

3. It has been conjectured that strawberry seeds taken from different ends of the same berry differ in potential germination. Suppose that a random sample of 200 seeds from the basal ends of Blakemore strawberries and 200 seeds from the distal ends of strawberries of that same variety grown in the same plots gave the following results: basal end, 6.5% germination, and distal end, 3.5% germination. Is the conjecture stated above acceptable in the face of this evidence? Would it be if the latter percent germination were 5.0 instead of 3.5?

4. Referring to Problem 3, suppose that, when 0.10 milligrams of Gibrel have been added to the seed treatment, the following results are obtained on another 200 Blakemore seeds from each end of the berry: basal end, 10.0% germination, and distal end, 9.0% germination. Is this sufficient evidence to warrant the conclusion that the Gibrel removes any deficiency in germination that the seeds from the distal end of the berry might have? Use the set of data in Problem 3.

5. If 20 individual plots of Meimi winter barley had $\bar{x}_M = 50.6$ and $s_M = 3.7$ and 20 individual plots of Kenbar winter barley had $\bar{x}_K = 42.2$ and $s_K = 4.5$, is the hypothesis $H_0(\mu_M = \mu_K \mid \sigma_M^2 = \sigma_K^2)$ acceptable over the alternative $\mu_M > \mu_K$? Use $\alpha = 0.05$.

6. Take for Problem 5, this section, $R_M = 12.0$ and $R_K = 10.6$. Use the G test to answer the questions asked.

7. The chemical NCL 2,4-D has been used to protect potatoes from the scab, *Streptomyces scabies*. If with 300 potatoes selected at random from untreated areas and 300 from treated areas 8% of the treated potatoes had scab whereas 10% of those from untreated areas had scab, test the hypothesis, that this treatment is ineffective, against the alternative, that it does *some* good.

8. Some children retain a desire to eat foreign matter such as dirt, sand, etc., for an abnormally long time. This abnormal appetite is called pica. Layman *et al.* (*Psychol. Rev.* 13: 249–57, 1963) report on a study of this matter. Some children with pica also have psychiatric symptoms. There is some reason to believe that the area in the United States is a factor in the incidence of pica. Given the following data obtained by Layman *et al.*, test the hypothesis of no association between the region and incidence of pica and the psychiatric symptoms of the sort sampled.

Region	Pica	Psychiatric	Normal	Total
Southeast	56	7	25	88
Other	56	23	22	101
Total	112	30	47	189

9. An article by D. L. Lineham and L. D. Leet (*Bull. Seismol. Soc. Am.* 32: 11, 1942) reports the occurrence of 101 earthquakes in the northeastern United States and eastern Canada. If these occurrences are classified by season, one obtains the following numbers by season: spring, 27; summer, 27; fall, 18; winter, 29. Do you conclude that the occurrence of earthquakes varies by season, or not?

10. Controlled studies have been run on the response of sharks to human perspiration in tanks of seawater. A. L. Tester reports essentially the following results (among others) in *Pacific Sci.* 17: 156, 1963:

Kind of shark	Response:			
	Strong repulsion	Mild repulsion	Neutral	Total
Blacktip	16	26	6	48
Others	8	20	15	43
Total	24	46	21	91

Test for no association between response and kind of shark. Draw appropriate conclusions.

11. Referring to Problem 10, compute the CI_{90} on the true percentage of blacktips which would be strongly repulsed by human perspiration in seawater. What assumptions are you making?

12. Referring to Problem 10, test the hypothesis that $\leqslant 25\%$ of blacktip sharks are strongly repelled by human perspiration in seawater against the alternative that more than 25% are so repelled. Use $\alpha = 0.10$.

13. Some humans are highly sensitive to certain tuberculin skin tests. G. C. Klein and R. A. Patnode report on a study of serum protein changes in humans showing a positive tuberculin skin test (*Proc. Soc. Exptl. Biol. Med.* 113: 627–29, 1963). The following results were obtained for alpha-1 globulin before and after the skin test on 12 persons:

Person no.:	1	2	3	4	5	6	7	8	9	10	11	12
Before	0.16	0.27	0.22	0.33	0.27	0.35	0.30	0.28	0.30	0.29	0.30	0.22
After	0.29	0.36	0.31	0.33	0.26	0.36	0.38	0.34	0.42	0.24	0.33	0.33

Test the hypothesis that there is no change in alpha-1 globulin against the alternative that it is increased by the skin test.

14. Referring to Problem 13, estimate the true average difference, After minus Before, for the humans represented by this sample. Use $\alpha = 0.10$.

15. J. A. Mackintosh reports a study of reversal learning in the octopus in *Quart. J. Exptl. Psychol.* 14: 1962. By means of rewards of sardines when an octopus attacked a vertically placed 10×2 centimer rectangle, the subjects were trained until they attacked the vertical rectangle consistently within 20 seconds. Thereafter the subjects were trained to distinguish between the vertical and the horizontal position of the rectangle by use of a 5-volt shock when they incorrectly attacked the horizontal rectangle (long dimension sideways). This is called a negative response. After considerable overtraining on the vertical rectangle with rewards for correctly attacking it (positive responses), the positive and negative definitions were reversed. Following are some data on the average numbers of positive and negative responses per octopus the first day after the reversal training:

Positive: 9.2, 5.6, 5.9, 5.9, 5.2, 9.0, 8.3, 8.0, 8.0, 6.0, and 8.0
Negative: 4.5, 6.0, 7.2, 5.9, 5.6, 8.5, 6.7, 8.0, 8.5, 9.0, and 8.0

Although it does not fit the author's study, test the hypothesis that the true average numbers of positive and negative responses are equal against the alternative that the average number of positive responses is the greater. Assume $\sigma_P^2 = \sigma_N^2$. Use $\alpha = 0.10$.

16. Suppose that an entomologist is going to estimate the percentage of corn plants in a large field which are infested with corn borers. If he wishes to use $\alpha = 0.05$, how large a sample should he take to be sure the CI_{95} is no more than 10 units in length?

17. In some banks safety deposit boxes are opened with two keys. If a key ring contains 5 A-type keys and 6 B-type keys, what is the probability that an A-type and a B-type key chosen at random will open the lock?

18. Use the t distribution and the data of Problem 13 to compute a GLB_{90} on the change in alpha-1 globulin resulting from that skin test. Draw appropriate conclusions.

19. How would you sample the customers coming to a shopping center in order to ask a question of civic importance on which they later will vote?

20. Plot the frequency distribution of t with 10 DF. What are the mean and variance for the corresponding population?

21. Compare $\Pr\{t > 1.5\}$ for a t with 10 DF with $\Pr\{\lambda > 1.5\}$ for the $N(0, 1)$ distribution. What do you conclude?

22. If two baseball teams in the same tournament have probabilities 0.25 and 0.35, respectively, of winning that tournament, what is the probability that one of these two teams will win it? If they have those same probabilities but are in separate and independent tournaments, what is the probability that *both* win their tournaments?

23. Suppose that two manufacturing plants are producing camping stoves which are supposed to be identical and must meet certain specific standards or be declared defective. Suppose that random samples from the two production lines gave the following results:

| | *Stove was:* | | |
	Satisfactory	*Defective*	*Sum*
Plant 1	85	5	90
Plant 2	102	8	110
Sum	187	13	200

The production manager wants to know whether these plants are operating equally efficiently. Formulate an appropriate statistical hypothesis, test it, and answer his question.

Chapter 5

Sampling Populations with Unspecified Distributions

5.1 INTRODUCTION

It may be unreasonable in certain situations to believe that the measurements to be taken will belong to any known frequency distribution, such as the normal. Even though most of the tests previously discussed herein are thought to be relatively unharmed by moderate amounts of nonnormality in the populations being sampled, there still is both theoretical and practical need for statistical concepts and methods which do not assume normality or any other specific frequency distribution. Surprisingly enough, there are some quite powerful statistical tests that may be made, even when practically nothing is assumed about the population or populations to be sampled. Some of these tests limit the records actually used to mere presence or absence of something or to plus and minus signs of differences, with no quantitative measurement at all. Others are based on ranks of numbers in ordered arrays. Tests of this sort are called *nonparametric* (or, alternatively, distribution-free) tests, because they do not assume a type of distribution with one or more characteristic parameters.

The one parameter which is used in some nonparametric tests is the median, because it is true that, for *any* sort of distribution of measurements, the probability that a random observation will exceed the median is one half (1/2). In general, the median retains whatever desirable features it has as a measure of level, regardless of the frequency distribution of the statistical population involved.

Quite a few of the nonparametric tests are based upon ordered arrays of sample observations. It is recalled that the term "ordered array" is used to describe a sequence of numbers presented in order of their sizes. For example, the numbers 2, 17, 11, 6, 7, 10, 5, 15, 4, and 8 do *not* form an ordered array but the same numbers written as 2, 4, 5, 6, 7, 8, 10, 11, 15, and 17 do constitute an ordered array. If the largest number in an ordered array is given the rank 1, the next largest is given the rank 2, and so on, until the smallest number is given the rank *n*, attention is thereby shifted to the ranks of the numbers rather than to their actual sizes. If, in this example, the even numbers are compared with the odd numbers with respect to rank in a combined rank ordering, one obtains:

Ranks of evens: 10, 9,   7,   5, 4,
Ranks of odds: 8,   6,   3, 2, 1

If possession of low rank numbers indicates superiority in some useful sense, then in this same sense the odd numbers outrank the even numbers in this example. Statisticians have devised some interesting and useful nonparametric tests based on the use of ranks of sampling numbers in place of their actual sizes. These nonparametric tests make virtually no assumption regarding the frequency distribution of the population sampled.

It should be emphasized at the outset of this discussion of nonparametric procedures that the term "nonparametric" indicates that the hypotheses to be tested usually will have to be stated in a somewhat different form from those used so far, because there may be no describable parameters to be put into the H_0. If one were to claim to be testing $H_0(\mu = \mu_0)$, for example, this obviously would imply a parametric test instead of a nonparametric test, because the symbol μ could not be defined without some specification of the population's form. The median is an exception because of its universal definition, as noted earlier.

The experimenter is accustomed to using the mean to describe the general level of yield, gain, damage, price, income, quality, or whatever is being measured in a particular study. Probably this habit results from the fact that many types of measurement which are of interest in scientific research are approximately normally distributed. For the same reason either the standard deviation or the variance is used to measure the dispersion, or variability, of measurements about their own mean. If a population is decidedly nonnormal in form, or if its distribution type is unknown, there is no logical reason to insist that the mean and variance are the best parameters for describing the level and dispersion, respectively. It might be more reasonable, for example, to use the median as an indication of general level of measurement and deviations from the median as a description of the dispersion of the measurements in the population.

This chapter will be limited to only a few illustrative nonparametric tests among the many which have been devised by statisticians. The only assumption that may be made about the frequency distributions of the population being sampled will be that their cumulative distributions are continuous, which for our purposes means that the cumulative frequency curves have no breaks, or gaps, in them. The nonparametric tests presented in this chapter were selected to show the methods used in such tests and to cover the two sorts of test of hypothesis which already have been studied in earlier chapters, namely tests for differences in level (or location) and tests for differences in dispersion.

Most nonparametric tests are sensitive either to differences in general level of measurement or to both these differences and differences in dispersion. Surprisingly little on nonparametric tests of dispersion alone appears to have been published, presumably because the chief demand was thought to be for tests of level. This actually is unfortunate, because tests regarding means (level) based on assumed normality are more robust (less sensitive to nonnormality) than are tests on variances.

5.2 THE MEDIAN TEST FOR TWO SAMPLES

If two random samples from the same population are arrayed in a combined rank ordering, each member of each sample may be classified as being below, at, or above the median of the combined array. If this is done and the results summarized as

	Below md	*Above* md
Sample 1	n_{11}	n_{12}
Sample 2	n_{21}	n_{22}

then the resulting contingency table will exhibit the features, previously discussed, of two random samples from the same binomial population. If the two samples are from populations with different levels of measurement, there will be an association between the vertical and the horizontal classifications in this 2×2 table. As in Chapter 2, the chi-square test is used to decide whether the hypothesis that the two samples come from the same population should be accepted.

To illustrate this test, consider the following example, in which two samples are supposed to have come from two populations which may or may not differ in general level of measurement.

X_1:   17, 6, 1, 8, 0, 12, 26, 15, 16, 3, 22, 35, 5, 20, 32, 50, 11, 31, 40, and 28, $n_1 = 20$

X_2:   68, 13, 2, 10, 25, 61, 43, 45, 30, 27, 36, 55, 4, 7, 18, 19, 23, 41, and 52, $n_2 = 19$

The combined array is as follows, the X_1's being in boldface:

0, **1**, 2, **3**, 4, **5**, **6**, 7, **8**, 10, **11**, **12**, 13, **15**, **16**, **17**, 18, 19, **20**, **22**, 23, 25, **26**, 27, **28**, 30, **31**, **32**, **35**, 36, **40**, 41, 43, 45, **50**, 52, 55, 61, and 68

The median of the combined array is the twentieth number in the array, so md = 22. Therefore, the following 2 × 2 table can be compiled:

	Below md	*At or above* md	*Total*
X_1's	12 (9.3)	8 (10.7)	20
X_2's	7 (9.7)	12 (9.3)	19
Total	19	20	39

The theoretical number of the upper left-hand cell is $20(19)/39 = 9.3$ to one decimal, on the hypothesis of no association between population and level. The other theoretical numbers are as shown in parentheses. Therefore, $X^2 = (2.7)^2[2/9.3 + 1/10.7 + 1/9.7] = 3.00$, with 1 D. If $\alpha = 0.05$, it is concluded that the two populations probably are at the same general level. If α had been chosen, in advance, as 0.10, then it would have been concluded that the X_2's were from a population which was at a generally higher level of measurement than population 1.

PROBLEMS

1. Given the following practice data, perform the median test for equality of level:

   X_1:   8.6, 1.2, 4.6, 2.2, 7.3, 4.5, 6.0, 4.1, 5.4, 5.9, 7.2, 9.2, 2.8, 5.4, 8.0, 2.5, 3.5, 3.4, 6.5, and 5.6

   X_2:   8.0, 4.6, 6.6, 9.4, 11.0, 8.8, 8.2, 6.4, 2.6, 4.5, 9.1, 7.3, 2.8, 8.6, 6.8, 6.0, 9.4, 8.0, 6.7, 5.8, 8.7, 5.9, 8.0, 7.4, 4.9, 9.1, and 7.8

2. Suppose that the following numbers represent numbers of insects of a certain species surviving after two separate sprays were tested. The number given represents the number of survivors among 100 insects in individual cages sprayed by one of the insecticides:

   Spray 1:   15, 5, 10, 0, 1, 3, 11, 3, 8, 12, 8, 0, 4, 9, 5, 7, 1, 13, 2, 0, 27, 5, 8, and 7

   Spray 2:   14, 11, 5, 28, 16, 4, 9, 0, 5, 5, 4, 11, 10, 7, 9, 9, 18, 13, and 1

   Do you consider these sprays equally effective or not?

3. The data of Problem 3, Section 4.2, were previously analyzed on the assumption of normal sampling. Make no such assumption, and use the median test to decide whether the percent sugar level is affected by the difference in humidity studied in that problem.

4. Do as in Problem 3, this section, for the data of Problem 4, Section 4.2.

5. Decide by means of the median test whether sample A and sample B of Problem 6, Section 4.2, were drawn from populations of brachiopods with the same general level of length.

6. Decide by means of the median test whether the asphaltene levels were equal in the populations sampled in Problem 7, Section 4.2.

5.3 THE WILCOXON-MANN-WHITNEY TEST (WMW)

Another nonparametric test that can be used to test for level (or location) differences between two populations might be called the Wilcoxon-Mann-Whitney (WMW) test after the three main contributors to its development: F. Wilcoxon, H. B. Mann and D. R. Whitney. A. M. Mood and others have shown that, if the WMW test is used in a situation in which the *t* test is valid, the power of the WMW test as compared with that of *t* test is about 95% for large samples. Empirical evidence from actual sampling experience under controlled laboratory conditions verifies the fact that the WMW test is quite powerful even with relatively small samples, say with $n_1 = n_2 \geqslant 8$. However, this and other nonparameteric tests do not pinpoint the population differences in normal populations as well as the *t* test does.

The WMW test normally (and originally) is a one-tail test with the hypothesis $H_0[F(X_1) \equiv G(X_2)]$ versus $H_a[F(X_1) > G(X_2)]$ for all points along the X scale of measurement, where F and G are the cumulative distribution functions for X_1 and X_2, respectively. Graphically, the situation is as shown in Figure 5.31. It is obvious that when H_a is true the situation illustrated in this figure could have many specific forms. It also is obvious that if the cumulative distribution functions for X_1 and X_2 have the relationship $F(X_1) > G(X_2)$ for most of the range of the X's, then H_0 usually should be rejected. Hence, if H_0 is rejected, one assumes that in a useful sense the X_1 level of measurement exceeds the X_2 level of measurement. The WMW test is based upon the general fact that, if the level of size of the X_1's is higher than the level of size of the X_2's, then, if one draws random samples of sizes n_1 and n_2 from the X_1 and X_2 populations respectively, the X_1's in the combined array of X_1's and X_2's should tend to outrank the X_2's.

Specifically, one forms the ordered array for the combined samples of X_1's and X_2's and computes the following variate:

(5.31)
$$U = n_1 n_2 + \frac{n_1(n_1 + 1)}{2} - T$$

where T is the sum of the ranks of the X_1's in the combined array and n_1 is the number of X_1's in that sample, provided the alternative to $H_0[F(X_1) = G(X_2)]$ is $H_a[F(X_1) > G(X_2)]$ for all X_1's and X_2's. There is an obvious change in the definition of the variate U if the F and G are reversed in H_a. The rank order in the combined array of X_1's and X_2's is such that the largest X_i is given rank 1, the second largest is given rank 2, etc. In case of ties, the tied X's are each given the mean of the tied ranks. For example, if the two samples are

$$X_1: \quad 14, 5, 11, 19, 7, \text{ and } 12$$
$$X_2: \quad 9, 13, 24, 14, \text{ and } 14$$

the combined array and the ranks are then

> Array: 24, **19**, **14**, 14, 14, 13, **12**, **11**, 9, 7, **5**
> Rank: 1 **2** **4** 4 4 6 7 8 **9** **10** 11

The X_1's and their ranks are in boldface. Because $n_1 = 6$, $n_2 = 5$, and $T = 42$, one obtains from Formula 5.31:

$$U = 6(5) + \frac{6(7)}{2} - 42 = 9$$

This is a sampling variable, so the question is, What is the sampling distribution of U and how does one pick a region of rejection for the stated H_0 and H_a of size α? This certainly should be a familiar question by now.

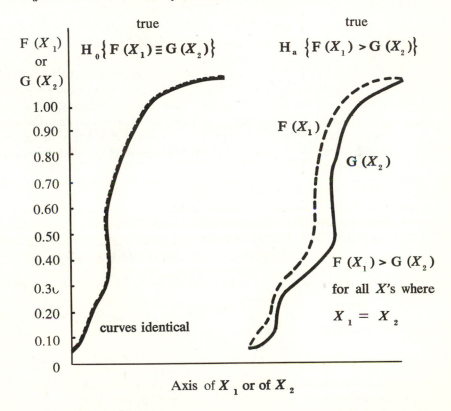

Figure 5.31. Schematic illustration of hypotheses involved in Wilcoxon-Mann-Whitney test. Graphs are cumulative frequency graphs under H_0 and H_a.

It can be shown that the variate, U, has an approximately normal frequency distribution about a true mean

(5.32) $\mu_U = n_1 n_2 / 2$

and has a true variance

(5.33) $\sigma_U^2 = n_1 n_2 (n_1 + n_2 + 1)/12$

if the n_1 and n_2 are at least 8 each. Hence, the sampling variate,

(5.34) $\lambda = \dfrac{U - (n_1 n_2/2)}{\sqrt{(n_1 n_2)(n_1 + n_2 + 1)/12}}$

essentially has an N(0, 1) frequency distribution, and we can test H_0 in the usual way with the aid of the cumulative standard normal distribution tables.

The 5% region of rejection, ω, for the one-tail U test is found in the usual way to be $\lambda > +1.645$, regardless of sample sizes, as long as they are not too small.

If it is logical to do so, one also can make a two-tail U test by using the two tails of the normal distribution. In that event the 5% region of rejection is $|\lambda| > 1.96$.

To illustrate the WMW test, consider the three cases of Table 5.31, in which the two samples have been put in rank order within each separate sample of each case and then put into a combined rank ordering of the two samples within each case. For case 1 of Table 5.31 it is found that the sum of the ranks of the X_1's in the combined rank order is $T = 105.5$; hence, the following results can be obtained for the WMW test of H_0(level of X_1 = level of X_2) against $H_a(H_0$ untrue):

$U = 10(10) + 10(11)/2 - T$

$U = 155 - 105.5 = 49.5$,   for these samples

$\mu_U = 10(10)/2 = 50$,   the true mean of U

$\sigma_U = \sqrt{10(10)(10 + 10 + 1)/12} = 13.23$,   the true variance of U for any case in which $n_1 = n_2 = 10$

Hence, if $\alpha = 0.05$, then $|\lambda| = |49.5 - 50|/13.23 = 0.038$, so H_0 is readily accepted.

When the WMW test is applied to the other two cases, one obtains the following regarding Table 5.31:

Case 2	*Case 3*
$T = 103$	$T = 67$
$U = 155 - 103 = 52$	$U = 155 - 67 = 88$
$\mu_U = 50$ again	$\mu_U = 50$ again
$\sigma_U = 13.23$ again	$\sigma_U = 13.23$ again
$|\lambda| = 2/13.23 = 0.15$	$|\lambda| = 38/13.23 = 2.87$
H_0 readily accepted at 5% level	H_0 rejected decisively at 5% level

Certain points regarding these analyses should be noted. (a) In cases 1 and 2 the X_1's occupied both ends of the combined array and thus averaged out at the same level as the X_2's. In case 2 the median X_1 apparently was considerably larger than the median X_2, but the greater dispersion of the

X_1's obscured any difference in level which might exist. In case 3 the difference between the medians was relatively much greater than in cases 1 and 2, but the X_1's also no longer occupied both ends of the combined array; that is, their variance was less.

TABLE 5.31. SOME ILLUSTRATIVE DATA WITH VARYING
DIFFERENCES BETWEEN MEDIANS

Case 1a		Case 2a		Case 3a	
X_1	X_2	X_1	X_2	X_1	X_2
13.4	12.9	15.3	9.5	19.4	10.6
10.4	11.1	14.6	9.0	13.0	6.2
9.4	9.8	13.0	8.2	12.2	5.4
9.3	9.4	10.9	8.0	11.8	5.4
7.6	7.3	7.9	7.6	10.2	4.0
7.0	7.2	7.4	4.5	8.2	3.8
5.0	4.0	2.8	4.2	7.4	3.8
3.9	3.6	1.1	3.6	6.6	3.4
2.8	2.6	1.0	3.1	5.2	1.4
1.4	1.6	0.6	2.5	4.2	1.0
md = 7.30	md = 7.25	md = 7.65	md = 6.05	md = 9.20	md = 3.90

Case 1b		Case 2b		Case 3b	
X_1 and X_2 combined		X_1 and X_2 combined		X_1 and X_2 combined	
13.4	7.2*	15.3	7.4	19.4	5.4*
12.9*	7.0	14.6	4.5*	13.0	5.4*
11.1*	5.0	13.0	4.2*	12.2	5.2
10.4	4.0*	10.9	3.6*	11.8	4.2
9.8*	3.9	9.5*	3.1*	10.6*	4.0*
9.4	3.6*	9.0*	2.8	10.2	3.8*
9.4*	2.8	8.2*	2.5*	8.2	3.8*
9.3	2.6*	8.0*	1.1	7.4	3.4*
7.6	1.6*	7.9	1.0	6.6	1.4*
7.3*	1.4	7.6*	0.6	6.2*	1.0*
md = 7.25		md = 7.50		md = 5.80	

Starred letters are X_2's.

PROBLEMS

1. Apply the WMW test for level to the data of Problem 3, Section 4.2. State the hypothesis tested and the conclusion drawn.
2. Do as in Problem 1, this section, for the data of Problem 4, Section 4.2.
3. Do as in Problem 1, this section, for the data of Problem 6, Section 4.2.

4. Make up two fictitious sets of X_1's and X_2's such that:
   (a) For the first set the WMW test will result in acceptance of the hypothesis that the levels of the X_1 and X_2 populations are equal.
   (b) For the second set the WMW test will cause the H_0 to be rejected with $\alpha = 0.05$ and a two-tail test.

5. With reference to Problem 4, keep the midranges of all sets of data the same but halve the range for part (a) and double the range for part (b). Comment on the effects of these changes, which apparently would not reflect a change in the level of measurement in the populations involved.

6. The following samples are from actual $N(5, 4)$ and $N(7, 4)$ populations respectively:

   X_1:   5.3, 6.5, 7.1, 3.3, 5.5, 2.2, 6.8, 4.9, 6.9, and 5.1
   X_2:   5.8, 3.6, 6.2, 7.0, 6.5, 7.1, 8.4, 8.1, 8.2, 5.1, 9.2, 5.0, 6.4, and 4.9

   Use the WMW test of H_0(level of X_1's = level of X_2's) against the alternative that the X_2's are from a population at a higher level than the X_1's. Then perform the t test and see whether there is a noticeable difference in conclusions. Use $\alpha = 0.10$.

7. Use the WMW test on Problem 1, Section 5.2.

8. Use the WMW test on Problem 2, Section 5.2.

9. The following two samples were drawn from $N(5, 4)$ and $N(7, 16)$ populations respectively. Use the WMW test on H_0(level of X_1's = level of X_2's) versus H_a(X_1's at lower level than X_2's). Use $\alpha = 0.10$.

   X_1:   4.5, 2.9, 5.9, 6.6, 2.1, 7.9, 6.9, 10.6, 2.6, 5.4, 5.5, 7.4, 3.8, 5.8, 7.0, and 3.2
   X_2:   3.8, 11.0, 7.4, 7.8, 7.0, 12.6, 2.6, 10.6, 6.6, 8.2, 10.6, 8.2, 8.2, 8.6, 3.8, 0.6, 10.6, and 4.2.

10. Referring to Problem 9, test $H_0(\sigma_1^2 = \sigma_2^2)$ against $H_a(\sigma_1^2 < \sigma_2^2)$. Then use the t test of $H_0[(\mu_1 = \mu_2) \mid (\sigma_1^2 \neq \sigma_2^2)]$ versus $H_a[(\mu_1 \neq \mu_2) \mid (\sigma_1^2 \neq \sigma_2^2)]$ with $\alpha = 0.10$. Discuss these results as compared with those from the use of WMW in Problem 9.

5.4 MOOD'S SQUARE RANK TEST FOR DISPERSION

Suppose that two samples, $X_{11}, \cdots, X_{1n_1}$ and $X_{21}, \cdots, X_{2n_2}$ have been drawn from two populations which are at the same general level of magnitude but have different dispersions, using the term "dispersion" quite generally. If these two samples are combined into one rank ordering, the sample from the less dispersed population will tend to occupy the middle ranks, while the numbers from the more dispersed population will tend to occupy the extremes of that combined rank ordering. Of course, this is only a general tendency, and chance variations will produce many exceptions. The average (and the median) rank of the two samples combined into one rank ordering will be $(n_1 + n_2 + 1)/2$, so, if r_i is the rank of the ith X_1, the differences, $r_i - (n_1 + n_2 + 1)/2$, will tend to be large if the X_1's are more dispersed than the X_2's, and vice versa. A. M. Mood (*Ann. Math. Stat.* 25: 514–22, 1954) has shown that if one sets

$$(5.41) \qquad W = \sum \{[r_i - (n_1 + n_2 + 1)/2]^2\}$$

where the summation is for $i = 1$ to n_1, then the true mean of W is

$$(5.42) \qquad \mu_W = n_1(n_1 + n_2 + 1)(n_1 + n_2 - 1)/12$$

where n_1 is the number of X_1's and the ranks of these X_1's are designated by the r_i. Furthermore, the true variance of the W is given by

$$(5.43) \qquad \sigma_W^2 = n_1 n_2(n_1 + n_2 + 1)(n_1 + n_2 + 2)(n_1 + n_2 - 2)/180$$

It also has been shown that the random variable

$$(5.44) \qquad \lambda = (W - \mu_W)/\sigma_W$$

is approximately distributed as $N(0, 1)$, the standard normal. For example, if $n_1 = n_2 = 10$, then $\lambda = (W - 332.5)/67.97$ is approximately $N(0, 1)$ with the W equal to $\sum_{i=1}^{10} [(r_1 - 10.5)^2]$. It is seen that, as with the WMW test, the problem of studying two populations of measurements nonparametrically has been attacked by finding a function of the ranks (namely, W) which can be referred to a standard normal distribution table. Thereafter, the tabular information available for the standard normal distributions can be used, as it was with the WMW U test.

The hypothesis tested by the Square Rank test is that the two populations which were sampled are equally dispersed, in whatever sense would fit the reasoning given above for expecting this test to reflect differences in dispersion. If there is no logical reason to believe, in advance of the sampling, that if H_0 is false a specified one of the two populations is more dispersed than the other, a two-tail test is in order. To determine the region of rejection, set

$$(W - \mu_W)/\sigma_W = \pm \lambda_\alpha$$

Similarly, if a one-tail test is in order, set $(W - \mu_W)/\sigma_W$ equal to $+\lambda_{2\alpha}$ or, separately, to $-\lambda_{2\alpha}$, whichever is appropriate to the situation at hand in a particular study. For example, if $\alpha = 0.10$, then $\lambda_\alpha = 1.645$ for a two-tail test and $\lambda_{2\alpha} = 1.282$ for a one-tail test.

To illustrate more fully this discussion, consider case 1 of Table 5.31. The combined rank ordering and the r_i for the X_1's are as follows:

Rank order: 13.4, 12.9*, 11.1*, 10.4, 9.8*, 9.4*, 9.4, 9.3, 7.6, 7.3*,
r_i for X_1's: 1   4   6.5 8   9

Rank order: 7.2*, 7.0, 5.0, 4.0*, 3.9, 3.6*, 2.8, 2.6*, 1.6*, 1.4
r_i for X_1's: 12   13   15   17   20

where the starred numbers are X_2's. The $(n_1 + n_2 + 1)/2 = 10.5$ is the median rank; therefore, $W = (-9.5)^2 + (-6.5)^2 + \cdots + (6.5)^2 + (9.5)^2 = 302.25$. Then $\mu_W = 10(21)(19)/12 = 332.50$, and the σ_W is calculated from

Formula 5.43 to be 67.97, so it is found that $\lambda = |\ 302.25 - 332.50\ |/67.97 = 0.46$. The standard normal table shows that such a λ would not fall in any reasonable region of rejection, because the probability that a sample standard normal variate will be larger than 0.46 is about 0.32. Hence it is concluded that there is no reason to doubt that the two populations sampled are about equally dispersed.

The region of rejection for a W test can be defined in terms of the size of W instead of in terms of the size of λ, if the same-sized samples are to be studied and if this would save time. For example, if $n_1 = n_2 = 10$, a two-tail region of rejection for W at the 10% level of significance is determined by setting $(W - 332.50)/67.97 = \pm 1.645$; hence, if the sample W lies in the region $220.7 < W < 444.3$, the hypothesis that the two populations are equally dispersed is accepted. Otherwise, it is rejected.

To determine the one-tail region of rejection for W at the 10% level, we set $(W - 332.50)/67.97$ equal to -1.282 or to $+1.282$, as the case may be, and obtain a ω of $W < 245.4$, or the right-hand region, a ω of $W > 419.6$.

If the levels of measurement of X_1 and X_2 are not the same, it is not clear how well any existing difference in dispersion between the two populations will be revealed by the Square Rank test for dispersion, because the difference in level of measurement will tend to put the X_1's, say, at the top of the combined array of the X_1's and X_2's. This conceivably might, in itself, cause W to average larger than it would if the levels of measurement were identical and only the dispersions were different.

In spite of the rather stringent H_0 set up for the WMW test during mathematical studies of its properties, this test appears not to be greatly affected by differences in dispersion in two populations. Similarly, the Square Rank test does not appear to be radically affected by different levels of measurement in two populations being studied with respect to dispersion. These points, and some others, are illustrated in Table 5.41 with $\alpha = 0.10$.

It is observed in this table that, if there is no difference between the two populations as far as levels are concerned but there is a real difference in dispersion (as measured by variance), the WMW test rejects the false hypothesis on about 10% of the samples taken. This illustrates the fact that the WMW test is not very sensitive to differences in variance and is therefore chiefly a test of level, or location. The Square Rank test for dispersion detects the known difference in variances about 63% of the time, if it is logical to use a one-tail test in the correct direction, but only about 46% of the time if a two-tail test is the logical one to use. Considering the small sample sizes, those observed powers are not at all unsatisfactory.

In the other columns of Table 5.41 the means are always unequal, one being 5 and the other being 7, which is quite a large percentage difference. It is noted that the WMW test is at least as much affected by relatively large variance as it is by unequal variances. The following tentative conclusions also seem to be justified by the data of this table:

(*a*) The power of the WMW test apparently does not vary greatly with difference in population varaince.

(*b*) The Square Rank test reflects actual differences in population variance reasonably well when the ratio is of the order of 4:1, but the power of this test may be influenced by differences among population means. For example, when the larger mean and the larger variance belonged to the same population, the power was noticeably higher than when the means were equal. Nevertheless, Mood's Square Rank test appears to be as good as any for testing equality of dispersion alone; in fact, a test of this sort seldom is mentioned in the literature at all.

TABLE 5.41. SOME EMPIRICALLY DERIVED POWERS OF INDICATED NONPARAMETRIC TESTS WITH TWO SAMPLES EACH OF SIZE $n = 10$ FROM NORMAL POPULATIONS WITH INDICATED PARAMETERS, WHERE $\alpha = 0.10$, EACH ESTIMATE OF POWER BASED ON 126 TO 321 SETS OF SAMPLES

	Populations sampled				
	$\mu_1 = 5$ $\mu_2 = 5$ $\sigma_1^2 = 4$ $\sigma_2^2 = 16$	$\mu_1 = 5$ $\mu_2 = 7$ $\sigma_1^2 = 16$ $\sigma_2^2 = 16$	$\mu_1 = 5$ $\mu_2 = 7$ $\sigma_1^2 = 16$ $\sigma_2^2 = 4$	$\mu_1 = 7$ $\mu_2 = 5$ $\sigma_1^2 = 16$ $\sigma_2^2 = 4$	$\mu_1 = 5$ $\mu_2 = 7$ $\sigma_1^2 = 4$ $\sigma_2^2 = 16$
Test used					
WMW	0.095	0.396	0.510	0.462	0.517
Sq. rk., 1	0.626	0.075	0.543	0.790	0.567
Sq. rk., 2	0.464	0.055	0.362	0.581	0.419

Sq. rk. 1 is a one-tail test, Sq. rk. 2 is a two-tail test.

The nonparametric tests suggested in this chapter are but three of the many which have been suggested. In fact, the subject of nonparametric statistics is big enough and important enough to justify a separate course by itself. Before leaving this subject, however, two other nonparametric tests for dispersion will be mentioned.

S. Siegel and J. W. Tukey (*J. Am. Stat. Assoc.* 55: 429, 1960) suggested a procedure which uses a combined rank order of the X_1's and X_2's but assigns ranks as follows, assuming the numbers are in increasing order of size from left to right:

Ranking:	X_2	X_1	X_1	X_2	$\cdots$	X_2	X_2	X_2	X_1
Rank no.:	1	4	5	8	$\cdots$	7	6	3	2

the middle rank being omitted, unless it is an even number. The ranks of the X_1's, say, as summed, and the WMW procedure is followed *in general*. Decisions made by the Siegel-Tukey test for dispersion may be quite definitely affected by the population levels of measurement. Table 1 of the Klotz reference in the next paragraph indicates that the Mood test for dispersion differences has greater efficiency than the Siegel-Tukey test for quite a variety of difference populations.

J. Klotz (*Ann. Math. Stat.* 33: 498, 1962) presents a nonparametric test for dispersion (or scale, as it also is called), which has asymptotic efficiency $= 1$ relative to the normal. He uses a statistic which is based on the cumulative normal, the combined rank ordering of the X_1 and X_2 measurements from the two samples, and on the sizes of samples. It is assumed that the medians of the X_1 and X_2 populations differ by a known amount, possibly zero. Klotz also provides tables which assist greatly in performing what he calls the Normal Scores test (n.s.), and which give a range of possible regions of rejection. These tables are reproduced in Tables XV and XVI. Their use will be illustrated by means of Table 5.31.

Case 1*b* of Table 5.31 is an ordered array of the combined X_1 and X_2 samples. Table 5.42 shows that array plus some Z_{N_i}'s and W_{N_i}'s defined as follows:

$$Z_{N_i} = 1 \text{ if the } i\text{th smallest } X_i \text{ (in our example, is an } X_2\text{)};$$
$$= 0 \text{ otherwise.}$$

W_{N_i} is the corresponding weight given in Table XVI. The hypothesis being tested essentially is

$$H_0(X_1 \text{ dispersion} = X_2 \text{ dispersion})$$

versus the alternative

$$H_a(X_1 \text{ dispersion} > X_2 \text{ dispersion}),$$

α being chosen as 0.05.

It is seen from Table 5.42 that H_0 will be accepted. If one uses the Mood test, one obtains:

$$W = 406.25, \qquad \text{when } \omega \text{ is } W > 419.6$$

Hence H_0 also is accepted by the Mood Square Rank test.

The F test, which is not robust with respect to departures from normality, gives the following results:

$$s_1^2 = 13.4405, \quad s_2^2 = 12.6536, \qquad \text{when } \omega \text{ is } F(9, 9) > 3.18$$

The sample F ratio is $F(9, 9) = 1.06$; therefore, H_0 is readily accepted. If the data of Table 5.42 were in fact normal data, so that the F test would be the best to use here, it could be noted that Klotz's Normal Scores test probably accepted H_0 more strongly than did Mood's Square Rank test. This result for small samples happens to be in accord with the known greater asymptotic efficiency of the Normal Scores test.

TABLE 5.42.   APPLICATION OF KLOTZ'S NORMAL SCORES TEST TO CASE 1*b* OF
TABLE 5.31 (SEE *Ann. Math. Stat.* 33: 498, 1962)

Ordered array[a] of X_1's and X_2's	Ranks,[a] i	Z_{N_i}	W_{N_i} (Table 3, of Klotz)	$Z_{N_i} W_{N_i}$
13.4	20	0	2.8241	0
12.9	**19**	1	1.7135	1.7135
11.1	**18**	1	1.1332	1.1332
10.4	17	0	0.7676	0
9.8	**16**	1	0.5076	0.5076
9.4	14.5	0	0.2529	0
9.4	**14.5**[b]	1	0.2529[b]	0.2529[b]
9.3	13	0	0.0918	0
7.6	12	0	0.0324	0
7.3	**11**	1	0.0036	0.0036
7.2	**10**	1	0.0036	0.0036
7.0	9	0	0.0324	0
5.0	8	0	0.0918	0
4.0	**7**	1	0.1855	0.1855
3.9	6	0	0.3203	0
3.6	**5**	1	0.5076	0.5076
2.8	4	0	0.7676	0
2.6	**3**	1	1.1332	1.1332
1.6	**2**	1	1.7135	1.7135
1.4	1	0	2.8241	0

Sum: 7.1542

The normal score (n.s.) is $\sum (Z_{N_i} W_{N_i}) = 7.1542$.
The region of rejection for $\alpha = 0.05$, N = 20, and m = 10 is n.s. > 10.864
from Table XIV under Probability of a larger S = 0.05; therefore H_0 is accepted.
[a] The X_1's and their ranks are given in boldface.
[b] There is a tie, so each X was given the average of the two ranks involved.
Also, linear interpolation was used in Klotz's Table 3 to get the W_{N_i} in each case.

PROBLEMS

1. Use the data of case 2, Table 5.31, to test for equality of dispersion of the X_1's and X_2's.

2. Do as in Problem 1 for the data in case 3 of Table 5.31.

3. Given the following simulated counts of flies on dairy cattle, test the hypothesis that they came from equally dispersed populations:

X_1:   13, 7, 5, 17, 4, 5, 10, 2, 9, 16, 3, 5
X_2:   17, 75, 23, 21, 24, 19, 43, 25, 35, 34, 17, 27

4. Use the data of Problem 3, Section 4.2, to test the hypothesis that these samples are from populations with equally dispersed measurements. Ignore the fact that in Section 4.2 normal distributions were assumed.

5. Test whether samples A and B of Problem 6, Section 4.2, came from unspecified populations with equal dispersions.

6. Use the data of Problem 4, Section 4.2, to test the hypothesis that these levels of humidity do not affect the dispersion of the percent acid measurements. Ignore the assumption of normality used in Section 4.2.

7. Given the following data for samples from two unspecified types of populations, use Mood's Square Rank test to decide whether the dispersions of those two populations are probably equal:

X_1:   3.1, 2.0, 4.5, 52.1, 26.8, 3.9, 10.4, 13.7, 0.7, 8.8, 40.6, and 1.5, $n_1 = 12$

X_2:   73.2, 30.7, 22.2, 18.5, 27.9, 60.4, 32.6, 20.5, 25.3, 28.3, and 19.6, $n_2 = 11$

8. Using the X_1's of Problem 7 and the following X_2's, test the same hypothesis as in Problem 7:

X_2:   0.7, 3.6, 86.5, 45.9, 2.0, 1.8, 1.6, 12.7, 9.7, 5.4, 23.8, 7.6, 5.4, and 0.4

9. You are given that the following three samples actually were from the following types of population:

X_1:   8, 19, 13, 1, 10, 0, 0, 3, 5, 25, 6, 14, 7, 2, and 4
X_2:   13, 12, 9, 8, 14, 0, 7, 9, 10, 8, 11, 6, 5, 13, 8, and 11
X_3:   28, 12, 7, 8, 5, 38, 25, 10, 14, 17, 8, 6, 10, and 8

The X_1's and X_2's are from populations with the same level of measurement, but the X_1 population is more dispersed than the X_2 population. The X_3's are from a population which has the same dispersion as the X_2's but is at a higher numerical level:
(a) Test the hypothesis that the X_1 and X_2 populations are equally dispersed, using the Square Rank test. Then use the F test, and draw appropriate conclusions.
(b) Do as in (a) for the X_1's and X_3's.
(c) Do as in (a) for the X_2's and X_3's.
Draw general conclusions over all three parts of this problem.

10. Referring to Problem 9, subtract 5 from each X_3 and then do as in part (c) of Problem 9. Compare this result, for when the levels are equal but the dispersions appear to be unequal, with the same test in Problem 9 for when both the levels and the dispersions appear to be unequal.

11. Do Problem 9 by the Siegel-Tukey test for dispersion, after reading the reference in the *Journal of the American Statistical Association*.

12. Do Problem 9 by Klotz's method.

REVIEW PROBLEMS

1. Suppose that a large tub contains millions of capsules, each containing a slip of paper on which is written one number from 1 to 10, inclusive. All numbers appear in the tub equally frequently. If a random sample of size $n = 20$ is

drawn and each number in each capsule is classed as > 2 or as $\leqslant 2$, what is the probability that

$$X^2 = \frac{(O_1 - 16)^2}{16} + \frac{(O_2 - 4)^2}{4}$$

will exceed 3.84 if O_1 is number of capsules in the sample which were > 2 and O_2 is number of capsules with numbers $\leqslant 2$? What if the sample size were increased to 200 and the theoretical numbers were changed to 160 and 40?

2. Referring to Problem 1, what effect would it have on your answers if attention were fixed on numbers $\leqslant 5$ and > 5, with corresponding changes in the theoretical numbers ($p = 1/2$) and in the meaning of the O_1? What if, unknown to the sampler, there was a considerable but equal excess of 5's and 10's? Of 5's only?

3. Suppose that the following pairs of measurements were taken during an experiment:

Pair no.:

	1	2	3	4	5	6	7	8	9
X_1:	36.1	42.7	26.6	29.0	32.2	38.8	27.4	34.7	27.5
X_2:	31.6	40.0	24.3	27.3	33.5	31.5	21.9	34.1	24.8

Use the t distribution to test $H_0(\mu = 0)$ against $H_a(\mu > 0)$, where μ is the true average difference, $X_1 - X_2$, normality of distribution can be assumed, and if $\sigma_1^2 = \sigma_2^2$.

4. Referring to Problem 3, change the X_2's in such a way as to increase the size of t considerably *without changing the average X_2*. Do the t test of the hypothesis in Problem 3, and draw appropriate conclusions.

5. Compute a CI_{90} on the true variance of $X_1 - X_2$, using the sample of Problem 3.

6. Use the data of Problem 3 to compute the greatest lower bound on the true variance of $X_1 - X_2$ with $\alpha = 0.10$.

7. Use the G distribution to do Problem 3.

8. Use the G distribution to compute a CI_{95} on the μ for Problem 3.

9. Suppose that a pair of dice is to be tossed 100 times and the sum on the two dice placed in one of the two following classes after each toss: "7 or 11" and "not 7 or 11." Suppose that the result 7 or 11 occurs on 32 of the 100 tosses. Test the hypothesis that the dice are unbiassed as regards this classification.

10. Referring to Problem 9, test $H_0(p \leqslant 2/9)$ against $H_a(p > 2/9)$ with $\alpha = 0.05$, where p is the true fraction of 7's and 11's.

11. The following random sample was drawn from an $N(\mu, \sigma^2)$ population:

X: -3.8, 1.0, 9.8, -0.6, -3.0, -1.0, 4.2, 1.4, 1.0, 7.8, 8.2, 5.4, 9.4, 13.0, and 2.2

Estimate σ^2 by a point estimate and then by an interval estimate, using $\alpha = 0.10$.

12. Use the data of Problem 11 to estimate μ by three different point estimators.

13. Use the data of Problem 11 to compute a greatest lower bound on μ, using $\alpha = 0.05$.

14. The following sample was drawn from a multinomial population as indicated:

Class:

	A	B	C	D	*Total*
Number:	62	22	24	4	112

Test $H_0(9A:3B:3C:1D)$ versus H_a(ratio not $9:3:3:1$), with $\alpha = 0.05$. Draw appropriate conclusions.

15. Referring to Problem 14, combine the A's and B's into one class and the C's and D's into another. Then test $H_0(p \geqslant 0.75)$ against $H_a(p < 0.75)$, where p is the true fraction which are A's and B's in the binomial population sampled. Use $\alpha = 0.10$. What do you conclude?

16. Suppose that a public-opinion poll taken on a random sample of voters produced 160 out of 300 in favor of building a certain dam in that area. What is the greatest lower bound on the percentage in the population sampled who favor this dam, if you use a confidence coefficient of 0.95? What does this tell you about opinion regarding this dam?

17. One of the measurements which is important to the study of the strength of structural concrete in terms of breaking load on test beams is the cement factor in sacks of cement per cubic yard of mixed concrete. Suppose on a random sample of 20 batches the cement factors varied from 5.80 to 7.53 with an arithmetic mean of 6.05. Use the G distribution to place a CI_{90} on the true average cement factor for the job so sampled.

18. Use the Klotz Normal Scores test to answer the questions in Problem 9, Section 5.4.

19. Use the data of Problem 3, Section 5.4, to test for equality of dispersion by Klotz's Normal Scores test and also by the F test. Draw appropriate conclusions.

20. Use the Klotz Normal Scores test to determine whether the samples of Problem 6, Section 5.3, probably came from equally dispersed populations. Choose $\alpha = 0.10$.

21. Use Klotz's Normal Scores test on Problem 9, Section 5.3, to see whether it detects the known difference in dispersion with $\alpha = 0.10$.

Chapter 6

Linear Regression and Correlation

6.1 INTRODUCTION

Foregoing discussions have visualized sampling situations in which but one numerical measurement is taken on each sampling unit in any particular study. For example, weights of animals might be measured, or the pH of each of a number of soil samples or the wheat yields of plots of land, and so on. In some statistical studies, however, it is advantageous to consider two types of numerical measurement simultaneously, because they appear to be related to each other in some interesting way. For example, the mean monthly temperatures recorded at Topeka, Kansas, for the first seven months of the calendar year have been found, over a long period of time, to be as follows, in degrees Fahrenheit:

	Jan.	Feb.	Mar.	Apr.	May	June	July
Temperature	38.0	41.7	54.0	66.0	74.4	83.8	88.7

In graphic form, on a temperature–time rectangular coördinate system, these data give the impression that the average monthly temperatures are linearly related to the months considered in their usual order. This is shown in Figure 6.11.

If, in the immediately preceding discussion, the month to which each temperature pertains were to be ignored, these temperatures would be just seven numbers which could have been recorded in the following random order: 54.0, 66.0, 88.7, 41.7, 74.4, 38.0, 83.8. Their mean is 63.8 and their variance is 341.04. It should be clear from the figure that the variance about the slanted line is much less than the variance about the horizontal line (341.04) through the mean temperature. Hence, it is apparent that adding to the study some information about the second variable, time, reduced enormously the amount of unexplained temperature variation, which appears to be in the randomly listed temperatures when time is ignored. It also is obvious, in general, that when two measurements are to be studied simultaneously, there is the additional problem of the relationship between these two measurements and how it should be described and studied by means of sampling data. In the figure it appears that time and temperature are linearly related, because the free-hand straight line drawn into that figure seems to fit the trend of temperature with time quite well.

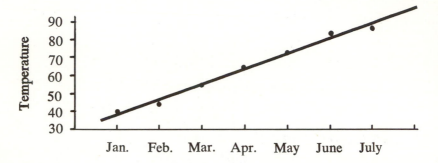

Figure 6.11. Linear relationship between two measurements, one subject to errors of measurement.

An important general feature of studying two numerical measurements simultaneously is the role played by sampling variation, or error. In elementary algebra variables X and Y are related by a strict formula, for example, the linear equation $Y = 3X - 6$. All pairs of values (X, Y) which are such that Y is equal to 6 less than 3 times X are said to satisfy this equation. The pair (3, 3) does satisfy this equation, but the pair (3, 3.001) does not. Graphically, all points which satisfy the equation $Y = 3X - 6$ are *on* the straight line shown in Figure 6.12. In mathematical discussions of an equation such as $Y = 3X - 6$ one does not talk about points (X_i, Y_i) which *almost* satisfy this equation, nor about how well a group of several points follows a straight line. In statistical analysis we almost always talk about and study groups of points which do not generally satisfy a mathematical equation but only come close to doing so.

In some experiments it is useful to measure pairs of variables, such as the age of a plant and its height, and to study these measurements together. It is obvious that, in a strict sense, there is no known functional relationship between age (X) and height (Y). Moreover, if there were, its form would be partially obscured by errors of measurement, by biological variations which occur from plant to plant, and by the fact that no experimenter ever has *all* the plants of a given sort available for measurement. However, it is reasonable

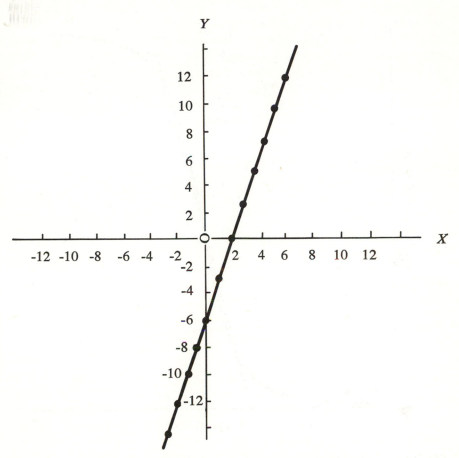

Figure 6.12. Graph of $Y = 3X - 6$, a linear equation.

to assume that for a well-defined sort of plant there is some basic mathematical relationship between the *average height* of such plants at a given age and that age itself. Thus, for some suitable age interval it may be reasonable to assume that

(6.11) $$\mu_{Y_i} = \alpha + \beta X_i$$

where μ_{Y_i} is the true average Y for age X_i and α and β are unknown parameters. Equation 6.11 represents a straight line through the Y mean points for $X = 1, 2, \cdots, i, \cdots, n.$

Equation 6.11 and the accompanying concepts and methods often are very useful in situations which theoretically involve a nonlinear relationship between Y and X. This point is illustrated in Figure 6.13, which simulates some kind of a growth curve. Even though the true equation of the growth

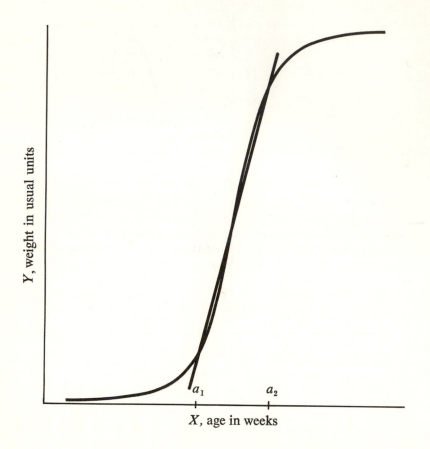

Figure 6.13. Hypothetical growth curve to illustrate an essentially linear section between $X = a_1$ and $X = a_2$.

curve hypothesized in this figure were quite complex and definitely nonlinear over its entire possible range, an assumption of linearity between ages a_1 and a_2 would produce greater simplicity and make a well-developed theory of regression available in exchange for a negligible loss of mathematical rigor.

Although it might be reasonable to assume the relation represented by equation 6.11, it should be recognized that the age and height of a single plant will not exactly satisfy this equation. Recognition of this is given statistically by writing the following equation for the *j*th plant measured in the *i*th age class:

(6.12)
$$Y_{ij} = \alpha + \beta_i + \epsilon_{ij}$$

where α and β are as before and ϵ_{ij} is a random variable with true mean equal to 0, so that the true average Y_{ij} is $\alpha + \beta X_i$, as in Equation 6.11. In non-mathematical terms, we do not want a mathematical description of the relationship between the two measurements which would produce a line that passed through *all*, or necessarily *any*, of the sample points, because such sample points include errors of observation. Yet we do suppose that the errors of observation average out, so that the true means of the *Y*'s for the various *X*'s do lie on a straight line. Equation 6.12 is called a *mathematical model* of a given experimental situation. When one becomes familiar with the use of mathematical models, they provide a concise and specific description of an experimental situation. They also lead the way to the use of valuable mathematical techniques.

In the background of any study of sample pairs of numerical measurements there always is a population of pairs of measurements from which the sample was taken. In practice, the information we have about that population is contained in the sample, but in a statistics course it is helpful to consider some relatively small populations for illustrative purposes and to draw samples from these illustrative populations. To this end, Table 6.11

TABLE 6.11.   PAIRS OF 16-WEEK AND 28-WEEK WEIGHTS (IN POUNDS) OF BRONZE TURKEYS RAISED AT MANHATTAN, KANSAS, ON THE KANSAS STATE UNIVERSITY POULTRY FARM

X	Y	X	Y	X	Y	X	Y	X	Y	X	Y	X	Y
4.9	13.3	5.4	14.6	5.2	13.4	5.4	14.0	4.6	13.0	4.7	12.7	4.8	12.9
4.9	12.4	5.0	12.6	5.1	12.5	5.2	13.1	5.3	13.5	5.4	13.6	4.7	14.3
4.9	13.8	5.1	13.7	5.2	13.2	4.6	14.0	4.7	14.3	4.8	14.1	4.9	13.6
5.0	14.0	5.1	13.6	5.2	13.5	5.3	13.5	6.2	13.5	6.5	14.8	6.4	14.3
6.5	13.5	6.4	14.4	6.5	13.0	5.5	13.5	6.1	15.3	5.5	13.0	6.0	14.3
6.5	13.8	6.5	13.3	5.5	14.3	6.2	14.4	6.1	13.4	6.3	13.9	6.5	13.7
6.4	14.0	6.4	14.4	6.5	16.4	5.9	14.4	6.5	14.9	5.9	14.8	5.5	14.6
5.5	13.1	5.6	13.2	5.7	12.8	5.8	13.5	5.9	13.5	6.0	13.6	6.1	13.7
6.2	14.0	6.3	14.0	6.4	14.0	6.5	14.1	5.5	12.5	5.6	13.3	5.7	13.2
5.8	13.9	5.9	13.8	6.0	13.8	6.1	15.0	6.2	14.7	6.3	15.2	6.4	15.1
6.1	13.6	6.7	13.8	6.8	13.7	6.9	13.7	7.0	14.5	7.1	14.2	7.2	14.2
7.3	14.3	7.4	14.3	6.6	14.3	6.7	14.4	6.8	14.4	6.9	14.4	7.0	14.5
7.1	14.5	7.2	14.5	7.3	14.5	7.1	14.7	7.2	13.3	6.7	15.5	7.0	15.9
7.4	14.7	7.3	14.7	6.6	14.1	6.6	14.4	7.1	15.3	7.1	14.9	7.0	15.6
7.4	14.0	7.0	15.0	7.2	15.5	7.2	15.2	6.8	15.3	7.3	15.4	7.1	13.9
7.0	14.7	6.9	14.8	6.6	15.5	7.0	14.7	6.8	15.1	7.1	13.2	7.3	14.0
7.2	14.9	6.7	14.6	6.7	14.8	6.8	15.0	7.3	12.8	7.3	14.3	7.3	13.6
7.0	13.5	7.0	15.0	6.8	13.9	7.4	14.1	6.9	15.0	7.2	13.3	7.3	15.3

TABLE 6.11 (*cont.*)

X	Y	X	Y	X	Y	X	Y	X	Y	X	Y	X	Y
6.6	14.0	6.6	14.8	7.4	14.1	7.3	14.0	6.0	14.0	7.0	14.1	6.8	14.2
7.4	15.6	7.3	16.3	7.0	15.8	6.6	14.7	6.8	13.9	7.0	13.4	7.2	14.8
7.4	14.9	7.5	14.7	7.6	14.7	7.7	13.7	7.8	14.7	7.9	14.8	8.0	15.7
8.1	15.1	8.2	15.1	8.3	15.7	8.4	15.7	8.5	15.8	7.5	14.5	8.2	15.1
8.3	15.5	7.8	15.3	7.9	16.6	8.3	17.1	8.3	15.3	7.5	15.4	7.6	14.7
8.5	14.5	8.5	15.0	7.5	14.8	8.4	16.0	7.5	15.6	7.8	16.1	7.8	15.5
7.7	15.9	7.8	16.0	8.3	13.4	8.2	14.9	8.1	14.4	8.2	14.0	8.3	14.5
8.2	13.5	7.5	16.0	8.0	15.0	7.5	15.5	7.7	15.8	7.5	14.4	7.6	15.4
8.0	16.7	7.5	14.3	8.0	16.4	8.1	16.7	8.5	15.1	7.6	14.6	8.5	15.2
7.8	14.3	8.1	15.2	7.6	17.0	7.9	15.2	8.1	14.2	7.5	13.8	8.5	15.0
7.9	15.9	8.1	14.4	8.4	15.0	8.2	15.6	8.4	14.8	7.8	13.7	8.2	15.0
7.6	13.3	7.6	14.2	8.1	14.1	8.0	13.5	8.1	15.2	8.2	15.3	7.5	15.5
7.9	15.8	7.7	16.3	7.8	17.0	7.8	13.5	8.0	15.6	8.3	16.2	8.4	14.8
8.4	14.4	8.0	13.2	8.5	16.9	8.0	13.7	8.2	15.5	8.3	15.0	8.2	15.7
8.0	13.6	8.0	14.3	8.4	15.0	8.5	15.1	8.2	15.4	8.0	14.9	8.1	15.0
8.5	15.2	7.8	14.0	7.6	15.2	7.6	14.1	8.5	15.5	7.7	14.3	7.5	14.6
8.1	14.3	8.1	14.4	8.0	13.8	8.2	13.8	7.6	14.9	8.2	15.3	8.1	15.3
7.5	14.1	8.5	15.3	8.1	15.4	7.5	15.0	8.0	15.0	7.8	14.0	8.5	16.0
7.9	15.5	8.1	16.5	8.5	16.0	7.5	13.9	7.5	14.3	7.5	14.0	7.6	14.0
7.8	14.0	8.8	14.2	9.0	15.5	8.9	15.0	8.8	14.4	9.0	15.5	9.5	17.2
9.4	16.0	9.0	15.8	9.1	16.2	8.7	16.3	9.4	16.9	9.4	16.0	9.0	15.1
8.7	16.3	9.2	15.7	9.1	15.2	9.2	16.4	9.4	16.5	8.6	15.2	8.7	15.7
9.0	15.9	8.9	14.6	9.0	16.3	9.0	16.1	8.6	16.4	9.2	14.3	8.6	14.1
9.2	15.1	8.6	13.9	8.6	15.0	8.7	16.2	9.0	16.1	9.1	15.2	9.2	15.1
9.2	14.0	9.0	14.4	9.0	15.5	8.6	14.4	8.6	15.0	8.7	15.2	9.1	16.5
8.8	15.5	8.8	14.5	9.1	15.3	8.6	15.9	8.6	15.1	8.9	15.2	9.2	15.5
8.6	14.6	8.6	15.3	9.2	15.3	9.0	15.6	9.1	15.4	8.7	17.0	8.8	14.8
9.0	15.5	9.2	15.8	9.0	15.5	9.0	15.5	8.6	14.1	8.7	15.6	9.1	16.2
8.8	15.1	8.6	14.9	8.7	14.9	8.7	14.7	8.8	14.8	8.9	14.8	9.0	14.9
9.1	14.6	9.2	15.8	9.3	15.8	9.4	15.9	8.6	16.0	8.7	16.0	8.8	16.1
8.9	16.6	9.0	16.7	9.1	16.7	9.2	16.8	9.3	16.9	9.4	17.0	8.8	17.2
9.3	17.6	8.6	14.5	9.0	14.9	8.8	14.2	8.9	15.0	9.0	15.0	9.1	14.8
9.3	14.5	8.9	15.1	8.6	17.4	10.1	16.7	9.8	15.4	9.5	14.8	9.6	15.0
9.8	15.2	9.8	16.0	9.6	15.5	9.8	15.2	9.5	17.0	9.5	17.8	10.4	16.7
8.9	15.8	10.5	17.1	9.8	16.4	9.5	15.5	9.6	16.0	9.7	16.2	9.8	16.2
9.9	15.8	10.0	16.4	10.1	16.5	9.5	15.7	10.2	16.8	10.3	16.9	10.4	15.9
9.5	14.8	9.7	15.6	9.9	14.5	10.1	15.8	10.3	14.9	10.3	15.3	9.6	14.4
10.5	17.5												

presents a two-measurement (or bivariate) population of actual weights of Bronze turkeys taken at 16 weeks of age and again on the same turkeys at 28 weeks of age. The letter *X* stands for the 16-week weight; *Y*, for the 28-week weight. When one is considering the *Y* measurement as the one of chief importance, but wishes to use the *X* measurement to predict *Y* or to reduce the apparent variation in *Y*, the *X*'s will be considered to be fixed numbers chosen in advance and not subject to sampling error. This point of view is accomplished by rounding the 16-week weights in Table 6.11 to the nearest pound, as in Figure 6.14. Later, in the discussion of linear correlation between two equally important random variables, Table 6.11 will be used as is, for this was the point of view when those data were taken.

The bivariate population of Table 6.11 possesses several characteristics which are of statistical interest and importance. These features are exhibited by Figure 6.14, for which each 16-week weight of a turkey is used to the nearest pound. The following are learned from this figure.

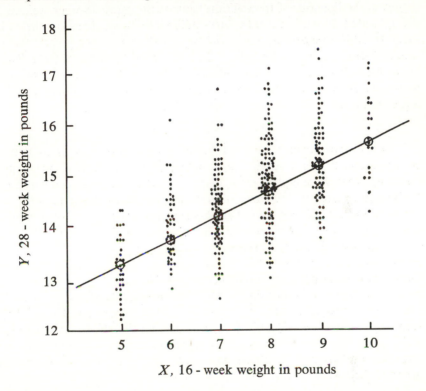

Figure 6.14. Plotting of data in population of Table 6.11, grouped at weights at 16 weeks so X is not subject to error.

(*a*) There is a general upward trend of the 28-week weights, as the 16-week weights increase; that is, a turkey which weighs more than another turkey at 16 weeks of age generally will also outweigh the smaller turkey at 28 weeks of age.

(*b*) Within each weight class at 16 weeks of age there is a frequency distribution of the corresponding 28-week weights, and this distribution is relatively symmetrical about the true mean 28-week weight (μ_{Y_i}) for the given 16-week weight (X_i).

(c) The means of the 28-week weights for the six 16-week weights shown lie perfectly upon a straight line with slope $\beta = 1/2$; hence, on the average, a turkey which outweighs another by one pound at 16 weeks of age will outweigh that turkey by only one-half pound at 28 weeks of age.

The six mean points being known to be on the line and the slope of the straight line known, the equation of the line is easily established. It also is of interest to write a formula for the 28-week weight of the jth turkey within the ith 16-week weight shown, as suggested by Formula 6.12. This formula clearly expresses the linearity of the relation between the mean 28-week weights for the indicated 16-week weights, but—unlike the usual linear mathematical formula—this equation makes allowance for the fact that for each 16-week weight there is a whole frequency distribution of 28-week weights. The ϵ_{ij} in the formula is the amount by which the 28-week weight of the jth turkey in the ith 16-week weight class fails to satisfy exactly the equation of the regression line:

$$\mu_{Y_i} = \alpha + \beta(X_i - \mu_X)$$

In this introductory study of linear regression it is assumed that the X measurement is not subject to sampling error. In practice, one is more concerned that the sampling error of X, if not zero, be small compared with the sampling error of Y. These turkey data, which are being used for convenience and practicality, do not strictly meet this assumption, so the student is asked to assume herein that the X's are not random variables.

In almost any study based upon sampling information the population parameter, β, is unknown, as is the exact location of the true regression line. Only n pair of sample measurements will be available for making decisions about the linear relationship between the measurements X and Y. For example, a random sample of 30 pairs of observations (X, Y) was drawn from the population of Table 6.11, with the results shown numerically in Table 6.12. Any decision regarding linearity of trend and the estimation of any desired characteristic of the true trend line, such as its slope, must be accomplished with the information in this sample.

TABLE 6.12.   A RANDOM SAMPLE OF $n = 30$ PAIRS (X, Y) FROM TABLE 6.11

X	Y	X	Y	X	Y	X	Y
4.8	12.9	7.2	13.3	7.9	15.9	8.8	14.4
6.5	14.8	7.0	15.0	8.0	14.9	9.2	15.7
6.4	14.4	6.9	14.7	8.1	15.0	9.0	15.9
5.5	13.5	6.8	15.1	8.0	13.8	8.6	14.4
6.1	13.4	7.2	13.2	7.6	14.9	9.1	15.3
6.0	13.6	7.5	14.3	7.5	14.1	9.0	16.6
7.4	14.3	8.5	15.1	7.5	13.9	9.2	16.8
7.0	14.5	8.5	15.2				

If all the observed pairs of weights shown in Table 6.11 satisfied a linear equation perfectly, then all the points of Figure 6.14 would lie perfectly on a straight line and all the (X, Y) pairs would satisfy perfectly a straight-line equation. Such, obviously, is not the case for either this table or this figure, because errors of weighing, and biological variations in general, prevent such perfect agreement between sample and population. The regression problem is complicated by the fact that the population line through the mean points designated as (μ_{Y_i}, X_i) must be estimated by means of sample data. One must determine:

(*a*) The probable general relationship between X and Y, such as whether it is linear, quadratic, etc.

(*b*) The best sampling estimates of the parameters in the equation $Y = f(X)$ for the regression line in the population of (X, Y) pairs.

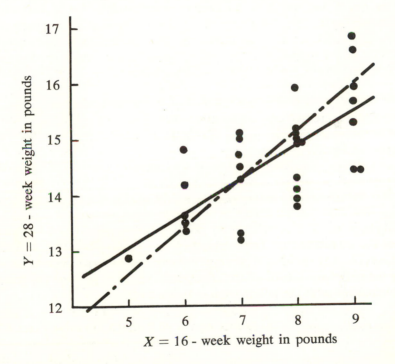

Figure 6.15.   Random sample of 30 pairs of observations from Table 6.11 and recorded in Table 6.12. Free-hand line (——— · ———) and least-squares line (———) drawn in for illustration of linear curve fitting.

Assuming that a set of sample observations on (X, Y) pairs does fit some linear relationship between X and Y quite well, how should a specific equation of the form $Y = A + BX$ be determined so that it can be defended as the best fitting straight line for this purpose? Obviously, the answer to this question depends to some extent upon the definition of the word "best." One definition, and the one most frequently employed, can be illustrated by means of the lines drawn into the scatter diagram of Figure 6.15. Some points lie above either line, and some lie below, at distances whose magnitudes can be measured by the lengths of lines drawn vertically from the points to whichever line is being considered. In a useful sense the fit achieved by any line, drawn to fit the trend of a scatter diagram, by showing how one measurement changes sizes in relation to another measurement, should be measured in terms of the collective amounts by which the line misses the points of the scatter diagram. In terms of vertical deviations of points from a line, which line of this figure fits those points the better?

It will facilitate the discussion to introduce some symbolism before presenting the specific methods to be used in determining the equation of the regression line, which is universally recommended. For a given X_i, let the corresponding value of Y be called Y_i if it is observed in the sample with X_i, but if a value for Y is calculated with $X = X_i$ in a regression equation, this calculated Y will be designated by $\hat{Y}_i$, called " Y hat." Also, let the general linear equation relating X and $\hat{Y}$ be written in the form:

$$(6.13) \qquad \hat{Y}_i = a + b(X_i - \bar{x})$$

where a and b are two constants which must be determined from the sample data in order to yield a specific regression equation for a specific scatter diagram. As stated earlier, the a and b will be calculated in terms of the collective amounts by which the line of equation 6.13 fails to pass through all the points of the scatter diagram. The a and b also are considered sample estimates of the corresponding population parameters α and β in

$$(6.14) \qquad \mu_{Y_i} = \alpha + \beta(X_i - \mu_X)$$

where μ_{Y_i} is the true population mean for all Y_i corresponding to $X = X_i$ and and μ_X is true mean of all fixed X's chosen for this experiment. The α is a constant, and the β is the slope of the population linear regression line through the mean points (X_i, μ_{Y_i}). For the turkey illustration of Table 6.11, β is 1/2, the μ_{Y_i} are the distances vertically to the circled mean points, and the μ_X is the mean of 5, 6, 7, 8, 9, and 10 (that is, $\mu_X = 7.5$).

It has been found best to measure the scatter of the (X, Y) points about the regression line obtained from sample data by the magnitude of $\sum_1^n (Y_i - \hat{Y}_i)^2$, because this quantity reflects the amount of variation about the proposed linear trend line, which is, therefore, that part of the total variation among the observed Y's about their own mean that cannot be associated with the linear relationship between Y and X. This quantity also is the logical basis of measurement of the variance of the sample points from the trend line to be obtained from the sample data.

As a result of this sort of reasoning the best fitting linear trend line has been chosen as that line for which the $\sum (Y - \hat{Y})^2$ has the least possible size, that is, is minimized. This action makes the standard deviation about the linear trend line as small as it can be made with any straight line. The mathematical process for achieving this goal produces formulas for the *a* and the *b* of Formula 6.13. When these values for *a* and *b* are substituted into Formula 6.13, the least-squares equation for the regression line is obtained. In other words, by this least-squares procedure the variability of the observed *Y*'s in the sample has been as fully explained statistically as is possible with a linear trend line.

The formulas for *a* and *b* obtained by the method of least squares are as follows:

$$(6.15) \qquad a = \bar{y}, \qquad b = \frac{\sum[(X_i - \bar{x})(Y_i - \bar{y})]}{\sum[(X_i - \bar{x})^2]} = \frac{\sum(x_i y_i)}{\sum[(x_i)^2]} = \frac{\sum(xy)}{\sum(x^2)},$$

for brevity, where the capital *X*'s and *Y*'s and the small *x*'s and *y*'s have their usual meanings. The term $\sum(x_i y_i)$, which the student may not have encountered before, is

$$(X_1 - \bar{x})(Y_1 - \bar{y}) + (X_2 - \bar{x})(Y_2 - \bar{y}) + \ldots + (X_n - \bar{x})(Y_n - \bar{y})$$

which is the sum of the products of corresponding deviations from their means for all (X_i, Y_i) observations in a sample of size *n*.

For the data of Table 6.12, $a = \bar{y} = \sum(Y)/n = 439.0/30 = 14.63$, the slope of the least-squares line is $b = \sum(xy)/\sum[(x)^2] = 23.0200/37.912 = 0.6072$, and $\bar{x} = \sum(X)/n = 226.8/30 = 7.56$. Therefore, the least-squares regression equation from Formula 6.13 becomes:

$$(6.16) \qquad\qquad \hat{Y} = 0.6072X + 10.04$$

after simplification. This equation represents a straight line which passes among the 30 sample points of the scatter diagram of Figure 6.15 in such a way that the variance about the straight line is the least it can be made with any straight line.

The slope of the sample regression line of Equation 6.16 is $b = 0.6072$, whereas it is known that for this example the true regression line has a slope $\beta = 1/2$ exactly. In practice, the β will not be known, so that *b* will be used as an estimate of β. When the *X*'s are not subject to error of measurement, this *b* is an unbiassed estimator of the β.

In view of the fact that an equation such as Equation 6.16 is a sampling estimate of one such as Equation 6.14, the $\hat{Y}$ of Equation 6.16 is called the *estimated average Y for the given X* which was substituted into Equation 6.16 to give that $\hat{Y}$; that is, $\hat{Y}_i$ is an estimate of μ_{Y_i}. For example, if *X* is taken as 5 in Equation 6.16, it is found that $\hat{Y} = 0.6072(5) + 10.04 = 13.1$. This is the estimated average 28-week weight of turkeys which weighed five pounds at 16 weeks of age. Reference to Figure 6.14 shows that this estimate is somewhat low, because with this known population we can find out that the true average 28-week weight of turkeys which weighed five pounds at 16 weeks of age is 13.5 pounds. It is expected that a sample estimate will be subject to error, so this only illustrates the sampling error made in this particular case. It will be learned from a subsequent discussion that greater accuracy in estimating a μ_{Y_i} is expected when the X_i is close to the mean X of the population under study. There often are more data near the mean, but

TABLE 6.13.   ILLUSTRATION OF SOME FEATURES OF THE METHOD OF LEAST SQUARES, DATA FROM TABLE 6.12

		Least-squares line $\hat{Y} = 0.6072X + 10.04$			Free-hand straight line $\hat{Y}_j = 0.88X + 7.92$		
X (1)	Y (2)	$\hat{Y}$ (3)	$Y - \hat{Y}$ (4)	$(Y - \hat{Y})^2$ (5)	$\hat{Y}_j$ (6)	$Y - \hat{Y}_j$ (7)	$(Y - \hat{Y}_j)^2$ (8)
4.8	12.9	12.95	−0.05	0.0025	12.14	+0.76	0.5776
6.5	14.8	13.99	+0.81	0.6561	13.64	+1.16	1.3456
6.4	14.4	13.93	+0.47	0.2209	13.55	+0.85	0.7225
5.5	13.5	13.38	+0.12	0.0144	12.76	+0.74	0.5476
6.1	13.4	13.74	−0.34	0.1156	13.29	+0.11	0.0121
6.0	13.6	13.68	−0.08	0.0064	13.20	+0.40	0.1600
7.4	14.3	14.53	−0.23	0.0529	14.43	−0.13	0.0169
7.0	14.5	14.29	+0.21	0.0441	14.08	+0.42	0.1764
7.2	13.3	14.41	−1.11	1.2321	14.26	−0.96	0.9216
7.0	15.0	14.29	+0.71	0.5041	14.08	+0.92	0.8464
6.9	14.7	14.23	+0.47	0.2209	13.99	+0.71	0.5041
6.8	15.1	14.17	+0.93	0.8649	13.90	+1.20	1.4400
7.2	13.3	14.41	−1.11	1.2321	14.26	−0.96	0.9216
7.5	14.3	14.59	−0.29	0.0841	14.52	−0.22	0.0484
8.5	15.1	15.20	−0.19	0.0361	15.40	−0.30	0.0900
8.5	15.2	15.20	0	0	15.40	−0.20	0.0400
7.9	15.9	14.84	+1.06	1.1236	14.87	+1.03	1.0609
8.0	14.9	14.90	0	0	14.96	−0.06	0.0036
8.1	15.0	14.96	+0.04	0.0016	15.05	−0.05	0.0025
8.0	13.8	14.90	−1.10	1.2100	14.96	−1.16	1.3456
7.6	14.9	14.65	+0.25	0.0625	14.61	+0.29	0.0841
7.5	14.1	14.59	−0.49	0.2401	14.52	−0.42	0.1764
7.5	13.9	14.59	−0.69	0.4761	14.52	−0.62	0.3844
8.8	14.4	15.38	−0.98	0.9604	15.66	−1.26	1.5876
9.2	15.7	15.63	+0.07	0.0049	16.02	−0.32	0.1024
9.0	15.9	15.50	+0.40	0.1600	15.84	+0.06	0.0036
8.6	14.4	15.26	−0.86	0.7396	15.49	−1.09	1.1881
9.1	15.3	15.57	−0.27	0.0729	15.93	−0.63	0.3969
9.0	16.6	15.50	+1.10	1.2100	15.84	+0.76	0.5776
9.2	16.8	15.63	+1.17	1.3689	16.02	+0.78	0.6084
			Sum:	12.9178		Sum:	15.8926
				$= \Sigma (Y - \hat{Y})^2$			$= \Sigma (Y - \hat{Y}_j)^2$

it also is true that errors in estimating β may cause the ends of the regression line used to estimate μ_{Y_i} to be swung relatively far from their true positions, and thus the estimates made from the ends of the line to be subject to greater errors. This heuristic conclusion will be justified more carefully later.

As previously stated, the method described herein for obtaining the equation of the straight line which best fits an apparent linear trend in the least-squares sense of "best" is called the *method of least squares*, because it minimizes the sum of the squares of the vertical deviations of the observed points from the proposed trend line and thereby minimizes the *residual variance* about the trend line. Table 6.13 was prepared to illustrate specifically the meaning of this minimization. Columns 6, 7, and 8 were obtained from the equation given over the right-hand side of that table. This equation represents a straight line which appears to the eye to fit the trend in the scatter diagram about as well as any straight line one could draw by eye.

It is noted that the total of the fifth column of Table 6.13 is less than that of the eighth column obtained without the method of least squares. This always will be true as long as the straight line used to compute $\hat{Y}_j$ is not obtained by the method of least squares. This is an illustration of the statement that the method of least squares makes the standard deviation (or the variance, if preferred) of the Y's from the trend line a minimum for any straight line. This feature of the least-squares line is a strong argument for its wide use in practice.

PROBLEMS

1. Draw a random sample of 12 pairs from Table 6.11, obtain the scatter diagram and the least-squares line, and then compute $Y_t - \hat{Y}_t$ for each X_t in your sample. Round the X's to the nearest pound after the sample is drawn.

2. Given the following practice data, compute the least-squares linear regression equation for estimating $\mu_Y = \alpha + \beta(X - \mu_X)$:

X:	-1	1	2	4	8	10	11
Y:	53	44	46	37	20	5	5

3. Make a scatter diagram for each of the following two sets of data, and then answer the questions below:

Set A	X:	1	2	3	4	5	6	7	8	9
	Y:	41	28	30	19	31	13	15	10	10

Set B	X:	1	2	3	4	5	6	7	8	9
	Y:	12	17	18	25	30	33	42	47	50

(*a*) With which set would the slope be negative?
(*b*) With which set would you be happiest, under the assumption that the population regression has the form $\mu_Y = \alpha + \beta(X - \mu_X)$?
(*c*) With which set would you expect the least residual variance about the sample regression line?
(*d*) With which set would you expect the estimate of β to be the more reliable, assuming μ_Y does equal $\alpha + \beta(X - \mu_X)$?

4. Verify the computations on the last line of Table 6.13.

5. Draw a random sample of 10 pair from Table 6.11, make a scatter diagram and draw into that figure a free-hand line which seems to you to fit the trend of the points as well as any straight line could fit it. Then compute and plot the least squares line for your data and plot it on the scatter diagram to see how well you judged the best fitting line.

6. Make a scatter diagram for Problem 1, and try to estimate the true regression coefficient, β, from that scatter diagram. Compare it with the known value of 0.5000, but try to ignore this knowledge when making your estimate, because you have only a sample set of points rather than the population, so the best fitting line for your graph may not have the slope 1/2.

7. A study of largemouth black bass in Reelfoot Lake, Tennessee (*J. Tenn. Acad. Sci.* 37: 1, 1961) reports the following average lengths and weights of fish in 10 age groups (in inches and ounces):

Length: 9.25 11.08 12.04 13.25 14.73 16.83 18.23 20.25 20.58 22.00

Weight: 7.00 12.66 16.36 25.00 32.30 47.67 61.10 60.50 74.66 96.33

Make a scatter diagram with Weight on the vertical axis and Length on the horizontal axis. Discuss the relationship which seems to exist between length and weight for the fish represented by this sample. Also plot log weight against length, and discuss the effect of this transformation.

8. Write down a mathematical model for the true (population) relationship between length and average weight at a given length, along the lines of Equation 6.14, and define the symbols used. Then do the same for individual weights, W_{ij}, and discuss the differences between these models for Problem 7.

9. Compute $\hat{W}$, weight, for fish with $L = 30$ inches from the population of Problem 7, using the method of least squares. Of what is this $\hat{W}$ an estimate?

10. Do Problem 8 for length and average log weight.

11. Do Problem 9 with log weights instead of weights.

12. Make up a set of 20 pairs of numbers, (X_i, Y_i), which are such that:
    (a) The scatter diagram suggests a linear relationship between X and Y, but the points are not all on a line.
    (b) The trend of the points is from the upper left corner of the graph downward to the lower right section of the graph. What sign would you think the β in the corresponding population should have? Would you think it impossible for a sample scatter diagram, such as you have constructed to come from a population like that in Table 6.11, ignoring the actual sizes of the numbers and their meanings there?

13. Compute the equation for $\hat{Y}$ for set B of Problem 3, plot it on the scatter diagram, and state what information this specific equation gives.

14. Given that a certain least-squares regression line turns out to have the equation $Y = 16.2 + 5.1X$ on the range from $X = 1$ to $X = 10$, what is the estimated average increase in Y when X is increased by two units? How is that figure related to the slope of the regression line? What is the significance of the 16.2 in the regression equation? Are there situations in which such a constant is meaningful and other situations in which it is not? Explain.

15. Given the following hypothetical sketch of the graph of a least-squares regression equation and the scales of measurement for it, obtain the regression equation graphically as accurately as possible.

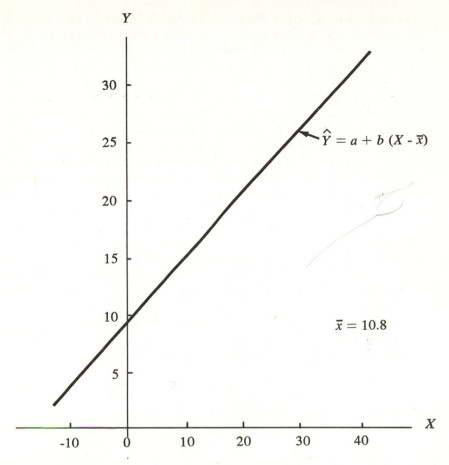

16. Do Problem 15 both with and without use of the $\bar{x}$ given on that sketch.
17. What is the $\bar{y}$ for the data of Problem 15, as nearly as you can tell graphically? What is the estimated average Y when $X = 0$? Can you tell from the sketch of Problem 15 how accurate the estimate of Y when $X = 0$ is? If not, what other information of a graphic nature would you need?

6.2 MEASUREMENT OF THE VARIATION ABOUT A LEAST-SQUARES TREND LINE

If measurements are taken on only one normally distributed variable Y, the variability (or dispersion) of the Y_i in a sample should be measured by means of the variance (or the standard deviation) about the mean of the Y_i. The population variance can be estimated by means of the unbiassed estimator $s_Y^2 = \Sigma(Y - \bar{y})^2/(n - 1)$, because this is an efficient and unbiassed estimator of σ_Y^2. The variation measured by σ_Y^2 and estimated by s_Y^2 usually is considered what is called sampling error. However, if for each Y_i there is an associated X_i and if the X_i and corresponding Y_i are linearly related in some definable and useful sense, not all of the apparent variability exhibited by a samples of Y's need be assigned to mere sampling error. Part of it can be accounted for in terms of the variability of the associated X's. For example, if, on the average, Y increases five units for each unit increase in X, the Y_i associated with $X_i = 10$ is expected to be about 15 units larger than the Y_j associated with $X_j = 7$; hence, some of the observed difference between a Y associated with an $X = 10$ and a Y associated with an $X = 7$ can be accounted for in terms of X-differences, and need not, therefore, be called sampling error.

Graphically, the preceding remarks imply that, if some Y and X measurements can be considered linearly related, the variance of the Y's should be calculated from the regression of Y on X rather than from the horizontal line $Y = \bar{y}$, which entirely ignores the X measurement. Algebraically, this means that the quantity $\sum(Y - \hat{Y})^2$ should be employed in the calculation of the standard deviation of Y, rather than the quantity $\sum(Y - \bar{y})^2$, which is used when Y is not associated with X. As will be shown later, the divisor needed in the calculation of this variance, or standard deviation, about the regression line will be $n - 2$ rather than $n - 1$.

The reason for the divisor of $n - 2$ cannot be given conclusively here, but it can be rationalized as follows. Suppose that a random sample of five observations on X and Y simultaneously were as follows:

$$X:\quad 1 \quad 2 \quad 3 \quad 4 \quad 5, \quad \bar{x} = 3$$
$$Y:\quad 5 \quad 4 \quad 6 \quad 8 \quad 7, \quad \bar{y} = 6$$

It is readily determined that $\hat{Y} = 0.80X + 3.6$; hence, the following table can be constructed for illustrative purposes:

X:	1	2	3	4	5
Y:	5	4	6	8	7
$\hat{Y}$:	4.4	5.2	6.0	$\hat{Y}_4$	$\hat{Y}_5$
$(Y_i - \hat{Y}_i)$:	0.6	-1.2	0	?	?

What are the deviations from the trend line for $X = 4$ and $X = 5$, respectively? The fact that $\sum(Y_i - \hat{Y}_i) = 0$ will be found to account for one of those deviations, and the fact that the sample line has a slope of $b = 0.80$ from this sample will account for the other deviation from the trend line. This leaves but 3 deviations from that trend line which could be considered chance deviations; hence, we shall say that $\sum(Y_i - \hat{Y}_i)^2$ has only $5 - 2 = 3 = n - 2$DF, when we are estimating variance about the trend line in the population and must estimate the two constants, α and β.

In the example given above let the unknown deviations, $Y_4 - \hat{Y}_4$ and $Y_5 - \hat{Y}_5$, be denoted by v and w, respectively. It follows that

$$\sum(Y_i - \hat{Y}_i) = 0.6 + (-1.2) + 0 + v + w = 0$$

which easily is reduced to the linear two-variable equation $v + w = 0.6$.

The slope of any straight line can be computed by determining the amount by which Y changes for any chosen change in X and then by taking the ratio of the former to the latter. For example if it is determined by measurement that on the interval $X = 1$ to $X = 5$ the height of the trend line above the horizontal axis increases from 10 to 30, the slope of that line is $(30 - 10)/(5 - 1) = 5$. It then is said that Y increases along the straight line 5 units for each unit increase in X. Thus, the slope is 5.

For the illustrative example being considered, the slope is, therefore, $(\hat{Y}_5 - \hat{Y}_4)/(X_5 - X_4)$, so $(\hat{Y}_5 - \hat{Y}_4)/1 = 0.80$. To transform this equation into one which involves the v and w, consider the following two equations:

$$Y_5 - Y_4 = Y_5 - Y_4, \quad \text{an identity}$$

$$\hat{Y}_5 - \hat{Y}_4 = 0.80$$

When the left and right members of the second equation are subtracted from the corresponding members of the identity, a second linear equation in v and w is obtained, namely $v - w = 1.8$. When the two linear equations in v and w,

$$v - w = 1.8$$
$$v + w = 0.6$$

are solved simultaneously, it is learned that $v = 1.2$ and $w = -0.6$. Hence, two deviations from the linear trend line have been computed from the knowledge that the sum of the deviations from that trend line always will be zero and from the known slope of this sample straight line. For this reason, it will be said that the $\sum (Y_i - \hat{Y}_i)^2$ has $n - 2$ degrees of freedom when the variance about the trend line is being estimated, even though the preceding demonstration only shows there are not more than $n - 2$ *DF*.

With the preceding discussions as background, the formula for the estimate of the standard deviation $\sigma_{y \cdot x}$ of the Y's in the population about their trend line, $\mu_Y = \alpha + \beta(X - \mu_X)$, becomes

(6.22) $$s_{y \cdot x} = \sqrt{\sum (Y_i - \hat{Y}_i)^2/(n - 2)}$$

for which the symbol $s_{y \cdot x}$ is read "*s* sub *y* dot *x*." For the data used as illustration in this section, $\sum (Y_i - \hat{Y}_i)^2 = 3.60$; hence, $s_{y \cdot x} = \sqrt{3.60/3} = 1.10$. This is a measure of the variation among the Y measurements which remains unexplained even after full account is taken of the linear trend of Y with X. If this trend is ignored and the X's are left entirely out of consideration, then $s_Y = \sqrt{10/4} = 1.58$, so the estimated standard deviation of the Y's has been reduced $100(0.48)/1.58 = 30.4\%$ by taking into account the linear relation between X and Y. Such success in accounting for part of the variation among the Y's clearly is important in statistical analyses, because the only occasions for statistical analyses arise as a result of the variability among measurements supposedly taken under reasonably homogeneous conditions.

The standard deviation, $s_{y \cdot x}$, about the linear trend line is specifically useful in certain applications of linear trend analysis, two of which will be considered now. As is always true of any sample straight line, the regression coefficient, b, estimates the true average change in the Y measurements for each unit change in the X measurement; that is, b estimates the β in $\mu_Y = \alpha + \beta(X - \mu_X)$. Its accuracy as such a measurement is of interest, and its accuracy will be measured by its standard deviation. The standard deviation of b is shown in books on mathematical statistics to be

$$(6.23) \qquad s_b = s_{y \cdot x} / \sqrt{\sum (x^2)}$$

With the data of Table 6.12, $\sum (Y - \hat{Y})^2 = 12.9178$, $\sum (x^2) = 37.9120$, and $n = 30$, so $s_{y \cdot x} = \sqrt{12.9178/28} = 0.679$. Therefore, $s_b = 0.679/\sqrt{37.9120} = 0.110$.

It also has been shown mathematically that the ratio

$$(6.24) \qquad t = (b - \beta)s_b$$

where β is the true regression coefficient which is estimated by b follows the same t distribution as that summarized in Table VII with $n - 2$ DF. Therefore, tests of hypotheses and confidence intervals regarding the parameter β can be derived from the t distribution as before.

For the sample turkey data of Table 6.12, the CI_{95} on β is obtained from

$$-2.05 \leqslant (0.6072 - \beta)/0.110 \leqslant +2.05$$

After the usual sort of simplification this becomes: $0.38 \leqslant \beta \leqslant 0.83$, so it is concluded with 95% confidence that the slope of the true linear regression line for the population of Table 6.11 lies between 0.38 and 0.83, inclusive. A more useful statement might be that it is concluded that turkeys which are 1 pound heavier than others at 16 weeks of age will, on the average, be 0.38 to 0.83 of a pound heavier at 28 weeks of age. That is, the lighter turkeys partially catch up with the heavier turkeys during that period of time, but they remain 0.38 to 0.83 of a pound lighter at 28 weeks of age for each pound they are lighter at 16 weeks of age. Naturally, these conclusions only pertain to the type of turkey in the population of Table 6.11.

Another application of linear trend analysis which makes use of $s_{y \cdot x}$ is one in which the average Y is to be estimated for some unobserved value of X. Suppose we are interested in estimating the average 28-week weight of turkeys which weigh 9.5 pounds at 16 weeks of age. If X is set equal to 9.5 in Formula 6.11, it is found that $\hat{Y} = 0.6072(9.5) + 10.04 = 15.8$ pounds at 28 weeks of age. How reliable is this estimate? A look at the scatter diagram leaves only the general impression that this estimate should be fairly reliable, but a more specific measure of reliability is needed. The standard deviation of $\hat{Y}_i$ is given by the formula

$$(6.25) \qquad s_{\hat{Y}_i} = s_{y \cdot x} \sqrt{1/n + (X_i - \bar{x})^2 / \sum (x^2)}$$

where this X_i is the value used to compute the $\hat{Y}$ from Equation 6.11. As explained earlier, this estimate of standard deviation has $n - 2$ DF, because the $s_{y \cdot x}$ has that many degrees of freedom. For the data being used in this example, it is learned that $s_{\hat{Y}} = 0.679\sqrt{1/30 + (9.5 - 7.56)^2/37.9120} = 0.679(0.364) = 0.247$, with 28 DF.

This sort of standard deviation applies when the X's have been chosen in advance and are not subject to errors of measurement. In this circumstance, the b is an unbiassed estimator of the parameter β. Under these circumstances, Formula 6.25 can be usefully rationalized, in lieu of a more rigorous demonstration of its validity. The $\hat{Y}_i$ for a particular $X = X_i$ is computed from $\hat{Y}_i = \bar{y} + (X_i - \bar{x})b = \bar{y} + x_i b$; hence, the variance of $\hat{Y}_i$ is obtained from the variance of a sum, $\bar{y} + x_i b$, in which the x_i is a fixed number for a given X_i. The variance of $\bar{y}$ is $s^2_{y \cdot x}/n$, because we assumed that the variance about the trend line is the same for all X's in the study, and $s^2_{y \cdot x}$ is the estimate of this common variance. The variance of the b is $s^2_{y \cdot x}/\sum (x^2)$, as noted earlier; and x_i is just a constant multiplier; hence, the variance of $x_i b$ is $x_i^2 s^2_{y \cdot x}/\sum (x^2)$. Now, *if* the variance of the sum, $\bar{y} + x_i b$, is just the sum of the variances of the two terms, it follows that $s^2_{\hat{Y}_i} = s^2_{y \cdot x_i}/n + x_i^2 s^2_{y \cdot x}/\sum (x^2) = s^2_{y \cdot x}(1/n + x_i^2/\sum (x^2))$, whose square root is just the formula given in Formula 6.25 for the standard deviation of Y for a given $X = X_i$. It is true that with fixed X's which are not subject to errors of measurement the variance of the sum used above is the sum of the variances of the terms added, but this will not be proved here. The reader will note, however, that this same type of theorem was used in Chapter 4 in computing the variance of the difference between two independent sample means, $\bar{x}_1$ and $\bar{x}_2$.

It also can be shown mathematically that the ratio

(6.26) $$t = (\hat{Y}_i - \mu_{Y_i})/s_{\hat{Y}_i}$$

where μ_{Y_i} is the true average Y for $X = X_i$, follows the t distribution discussed several times before and has $n - 2$ DF. Again, this knowledge makes it feasible to test hypotheses about μ_{Y_i} or to set confidence intervals on it.

If we wish to make an interval estimate which pertains to a single individual rather than to a group mean, we must take account of the greater variability among individuals than among means. For example, suppose that a study has been made of the relationship between the ages of Kansas females and their basal metabolism rates as expressed in calories per square meter of surface area per hour. It is supposed that the age interval chosen for study is such that a linear relationship exists between age and metabolism score and that the least-squares regression for predicting basal score from age has been obtained from a random sample. Suppose, also, that the equipment needed to determine this basal rate is not available in a certain area and a Kansas woman aged 25 wishes an estimate of her basal rate just as a matter of interest. The best point estimate we can make is the estimated average rate for women her age, but if an interval estimate is preferable here, account must be taken of the fact that with just one individual variations from person to person will not average out and more allowance must be made for individual variation.

Suppose Y_{ij} is the Y value to be obtained on the next observation to be taken after a random sample of size n is drawn, and one wishes to place useful limits on the Y_{ij} without actually drawing it, or suppose it turns out to be impossible, or not feasible, actually to observe the Y_{ij}, which stands for the jth random member of the population with $X = X_i$. Let $\hat{Y}_i$ be the estimated Y value for $X = X_i$. This Y_{ij} and the $\hat{Y}_i$ are independent random variables, so

$$\sigma^2_{Y_{ij} - \hat{Y}_i} = \sigma^2_{y.x}\left(1 + 1/n + \frac{(X_i - \bar{x})^2}{\sum (x^2)}\right)$$

from previous considerations and theorems. This variance will be estimated by

$$s^2_{Y_{ij} - \hat{Y}_i} = s^2_{y.x}\left(1 + 1/n + \frac{x_i^2}{\sum (x^2)}\right)$$

The ratio

$$\frac{Y_{ij} - \hat{Y}_i}{s_{Y_{ij} - \hat{Y}_i}}$$

has a t distribution with $n - 2$ DF. The corresponding confidence interval on Y_{ij}, the true Y value for the future observation, is obtained from the following probability statement:

$$\Pr\{\hat{Y}_i - t_\alpha s_{Y_{ij} - \hat{Y}_i} \leqslant Y_{ij} \leqslant \hat{Y}_i + t_\alpha s_{Y_{ij} - \hat{Y}_i}\} = 1 - \alpha$$

hence, one says that the following is a $1 - \alpha$ confidence interval on Y_{ij}:

(6.27) $\text{CI}_{1-\alpha}$: $\hat{Y}_i - t_\alpha s_{Y_{ij} - \hat{Y}_i} \leqslant Y_{ij} \leqslant Y_i + t_\alpha s_{Y_{ij} - \hat{Y}_i}$

To illustrate the preceding discussion specifically, suppose you are about to buy a turkey which weighs 6.5 pounds at 16 weeks of age and you are going to raise it until it is 28 weeks of age. What is the 95% confidence interval on this particular turkey's 28-weeks weight, assuming only that the sample data from the population of Table 6.11 are appropriate for computing this confidence interval? It was learned in the discussion of Table 6.12 that $\hat{Y} = 0.6072X + 10.04$ pounds is the least-squares equation for estimating the average Y from a given X. If $X = 6.5$ pounds, it is found that $\hat{Y} = 13.99$ pounds. Also, $s_{y.x} = 0.679$ of a pound, with 28 DF. Furthermore, for $X = 6.5$ it turns out that $s_{Y_{ij} = \hat{Y}_i} = 0.700$ of a pound. Therefore, the CI_{95} on the 28-week weight of this particular turkey which weighed 6.5 pounds at 16 weeks of age is $12.6 \leqslant Y_{ij} \leqslant 15.4$ pounds. Notice that the situation just considered clearly is one in which the confidence interval for an individual turkey is required. You do not have a group of turkeys such that the fast gainers can offset the slow and thereby give an average result at 28 weeks of age; you have just one turkey and must allow for the fact that individuals vary more than groups.

If one wishes only to test $H_0(\beta = 0)$ versus $H_a(\beta \neq 0)$, this test can be done more easily by comparing the reduction in $\sum (y^2)$ attained by using linear regression with the remaining sum of squares about this trend line than by using Formula 6.24. In symbols, one compares $(\sum xy)^2/\sum(x^2)$ with $\sum (y^2) - (\sum xy)^2/\sum (x^2)$ by means of the F distribution. The sum of squares of deviations from the linear trend line $\hat{Y} = \bar{y} + bx$ is

$$\sum (Y - \hat{Y})^2 = \sum (Y - \bar{y} - bx)^2 = \sum (y - bx)^2$$

$$= \sum (y^2 - 2bxy + x^2b^2) = \sum (y^2) - 2b \sum (xy) + b^2 \sum (x^2)$$

$$= \sum (y^2) - 2 \frac{\sum (xy)}{\sum (x^2)} \cdot \sum (xy) + \frac{(\sum xy)^2}{(\sum x^2)^2} \cdot \sum (x^2)$$

$$= \sum (y^2) - 2 \frac{[\sum (xy)]^2}{\sum (x^2)} + \frac{(\sum xy)^2}{\sum (x^2)}$$

Hence:

(6.28) $$\sum (Y - \hat{Y})^2 = \sum (y^2) - \frac{(\sum xy)^2}{\sum (x^2)}$$

Formula 6.28 indicates that the success of a linear trend analysis is measurable in terms of the size of $(\sum xy)^2/\sum (x^2)$ relative to the size of $\sum (y^2)$ or, if preferable, relative to the size of the "unexplained" variation $\sum (y^2) - (\sum xy)^2/\sum (x^2)$, which is called the *residual sum of squares about the trend line*. This comparison is best made by means of the ratio

$$\frac{\text{Reduction in } \sum (y^2) \text{ assignable to linear regression on } X}{\text{Residual } \sum (Y - \hat{Y})^2 \text{ remaining about regression line}}$$

$$= \frac{(\sum xy)^2/(\sum x^2)}{\sum (y^2) - (\sum xy)^2/\sum (x^2)}$$

Obviously, this ratio is relatively very small if $(\sum xy)^2/\sum (x^2)$ is very small compared with the residual variation about $\hat{Y} = \bar{y} + bx$ and is relatively very large if $(\sum xy)^2/\sum (x^2)$ is almost equal to $\sum (y^2)$. This ratio can have any size from 0 to $+\infty$, but cannot be negative. As a matter of fact, it can be shown statistically that if the ϵ_{ij} in the statistical model $Y_{ij} = \alpha + \beta(X_i - \mu_x) + \epsilon_{ij}$ are normally and independently distributed with mean $= 0$ and variance $= \sigma_{y.x}^2$, denoted by $NID(0, \sigma_{y.x}^2)$, then the ratio above is closely related to the $F(1, n - 2)$ variate. Specifically,

(6.29) $$F(1, n - 2) \quad \frac{(\sum xy)^2/\sum (x^2)}{\sum (Y - \hat{Y})^2/(n - 2)} = \frac{(\sum xy)^2/\sum (x^2)}{\sum (y^2) - (\sum xy)^2/\sum x^2}$$

It also is interesting to note that the F of this equation is just the square of the t of Equation 6.24 if $\beta = 0$. Unless the b or the s_b and $s_{y.x}$ or both are wanted for some other purpose, Equation 6.29 is usually the more convenient way to test $H_0(\beta = 0)$ against $H_a(\beta \neq 0)$. If H_a is $\beta > 0$ or $\beta < 0$, then Equation 6.24 should be used after a one-tail region of rejection has been defined.

PROBLEMS

1. Draw a random sample of size $n = 16$ from the population of Table 6.11, round the X's to the nearest pound, and then compute s_Y, $s_{y.x}$, $s_{\hat{Y}_i}$, and $s_{\hat{Y}_{ij} - \hat{y}}$. Describe the sort of variation each standard deviation measures.

2. Do the sampling required in Problem 1; then compute and interpret the central CI_{90} on the parameter, β.

3. Do the sampling required in Problem 1; then compute and interpret the central CI_{90} on μ_{Y_i} for $i = 3$. Do likewise for Y_{ij}.

4. Do the sampling required for Problem 1; then fit a straight line to the scatter diagram by eye and by the method of least squares. Compare and discuss the $\sum (Y_i - \hat{Y}_i)^2$ and $\sum(Y_j - \hat{Y}_j)^2$, where $\hat{Y}_i$ is the least-squares estimate of the average Y when $X = X_i$.

5. Given the following data on the relationship between the rate of planting spring oats, in pounds per acre, and the average yields, in bushels per acre, construct a scatter diagram, discuss linearity of trend as judged from the scatter diagram, and then fit a least-squares line to these data:

Rate:	24	48	72	96	120
Yields:	47.0	51.0	54.4	53.8	54.1

6. Using the data of Problem 2, Section 6.1, compute and interpret $s_{y.x}$.

7. Using the data of Problem 2, Section 6.1, obtain the CI_{90} on β. On μ_{Y_i} when $X = 5$.

8. Using the data of Problem 7, Section 6.1, obtain and interpret the CI_{95} on the weight of the next bass caught which is 15 inches long.

9. With the data of Problem 7, Section 6.1, compute and interpret the CI_{90} on β.

10. Compute the estimate $s_{\hat{Y}}^2$ for $X = 10$ and the data of Problem 7, Section 6.1.

11. Use the data of Problem 5 to test $H_0(\beta = 0.10)$ against $H_a(\beta < 0.10)$ with $\alpha = 0.10$.

12. Use the data of Problem 7, Section 6.1, to compute the GLB_{90} on the β for the population sampled.

13. Using the data of Problem 2, Section 6.1, compute and interpret the LUB_{95} on β. Also compute and interpret the LUB_{95} on μ_{Y_i} when $X_i = 5$.

6.3 THE PRODUCT-MOMENT COEFFICIENT OF LINEAR CORRELATION

It is not always desirable to obtain an equation for a linear relationship between two statistical measurements, as was done under the topic of regression. It may be preferable to describe the relationship as linear and then use a standard unitless measure of the strength or usefulness of this linear relationship. This may be the purpose in computing a correlation coefficient. This is somewhat in contrast to the reasons for computing regression equations and regression coefficients. Regression equations provide a means of predicting one measurement from samples of another, or for accounting for the variation in one variable in terms of values of the other, or for estimating the average change in one variable in terms of changes in the other measurement.

The correlation coefficient may be used simply as an index of the degree to which two measurements are linearly related, or it may be used to estimate a corresponding population parameter for a bivariate population. In the latter case it is necessary to have as the source of the samples taken a bivariate population in which both X and Y are subject to normal sampling error. It also is not important which measurement is called X and which is called Y. In case the correlation coefficient is to be used solely as an index of the extent to which two measurements of interest are linearly related, no assumptions regarding normality or sampling error are needed.

It already has been pointed out that the the variance of observed sample Y's about the least-squares regression line, $\hat{Y} = \bar{y} + bx$, depends upon the size of $\sum (Y - \bar{y} - bx)^2$, because this is $\sum (Y - \hat{Y})^2$. Hence

$$\sum (Y - \hat{Y})^2 = \sum (y^2) - 2b \sum (xy) + b^2(x^2)$$

$$= \sum (y^2) - 2 \frac{\sum (xy)}{\sum (x^2)} \cdot \sum (xy) + \left(\frac{\sum (xy)}{\sum (x^2)} \right)^2 \sum (x^2)$$

which, as shown earlier, is conveniently written

(6.31)
$$\sum (Y - \hat{Y})^2 = \sum (y^2) - \frac{[\sum (xy)]^2}{\sum (x^2)}$$

Therefore, it is obvious that the observed variability of the Y's about the linear trend line will be large or small according to the size of $[\sum (xy)]^2/\sum (x^2)$ compared with the size of $\sum (y^2)$. If the quantity $[\sum (xy)]^2/\sum (x^2)$ is multiplied by $\sum (y^2)/\sum (y^2)$, which is equal to 1, it follows that Formula 6.31 can be written in the form:

$$\sum (Y - \hat{Y})^2 = \sum (y^2)\left(1 - \frac{(\sum xy)^2}{\sum (x^2) \sum (y^2)} \right)$$

Clearly, the quantity

(6.32)
$$\frac{[\sum (xy)]^2}{\sum (x^2) \sum (y^2)}$$

has the following features, regardless of any assumptions about the nature of the numerical measurements X and Y.

(*a*) Its size cannot be less than zero nor more than 1, because it is composed of squares of real numbers and, if it exceeded 1, the sum of squares in Formula 6.31 would be negative, which is absurd for real numbers.

(b) If it is near zero, there is about as much scatter of the sample points about the linear regression line as there is about the horizontal line $\hat{Y} = \bar{y}$; hence, there is virtually no linear trend of Y with X.

(c) If it is nearly 1 in size, there is very little scatter of the sample points about the linear regression line; hence the straight line fits the trend of the data very well.

(d) As its size varies from 0 to 1, for different samples and situations, the scatter of the sample points about the least-squares trend line varies from a completely trendless "shotgun" pattern to a perfect fit to the linear trend line.

(e) It is unitless, so the features noted in (a) to (d) are true, regardless of the natures of X and Y or their units of measure.

(f) In its present form, it will not distinguish between regressions which have positive slope and those with negative slope, but this can be remedied by taking the square root and using the positive square roots of the numerator and denominator. The quantity $\sum (xy)$ has the same sign as the slope of the regression line; hence, it follows that the quantity

$$(6.33) \qquad r = \frac{\sum (xy)}{\sqrt{\sum (x^2) \sum (y^2)}}$$

is a unitless number within the range $-1 \leqslant r \leqslant +1$, which measures the direction and strength of the observed linear regression of a measurement Y on another measurement X, or vice versa. This number, r, generally is called the *product-moment coefficient of linear correlation* between X and Y.

If the numbers involved in X and Y are sampling numbers, the r obviously will have a sampling distribution. If the (X, Y) pairs are samples from what is called a *normal bivariate population*, the formula for their joint frequency distribution will include a quantity, to be designated by ρ; which is called the population correlation coefficient. The r then will be an estimate of this ρ. In this circumstance it may be useful to test a hypothesis about ρ or to compute a confidence interval on it. Obviously, we now are no longer thinking of the quantity 6.33 as merely an index. In a nonmathematical course of the sort for which this text is intended it is not possible really to clarify the term "normal bivariate population." Interested readers are referred to almost any textbook on mathematical statistics.

If the population correlation, ρ, actually is zero, its sample estimates, r_i, will not all be zero but will have a distribution that is approximately normal in form. It also has been shown that the now familiar t test can be used to test $H_0(\rho = 0)$ against an appropriate alternative hypothesis. The following function of the sample r is a t variate with $n - 2$ DF; thus,

$$(6.34) \qquad t = \frac{r - 0}{\sqrt{\dfrac{1 - r^2}{n - 2}}} = \frac{r\sqrt{n - 2}}{\sqrt{1 - r^2}} = r\sqrt{\frac{n - 2}{1 - r^2}}, \qquad \text{with } n - 2 \text{ DF}$$

As was seen in earlier discussions of tests of significance, H_0 will be rejected whenever the size of a sample t becomes so great that it is unreasonable, according to some predetermined standard, to believe that this sample t was the product of sampling variation alone. The student can verify that the t obtained from Formula 6.34 is algebraically identical with that previously used to test $H_0(\beta = 0)$.

It is more difficult to place a confidence interval on the population correlation, ρ, than on β, because the sample estimate, r, is far from normally distributed if the ρ is materially different from zero. The process of computing a confidence interval on ρ will be discussed somewhat heuristically by means of empirical data shown in Table 6.31 in the hope that this process will increase the reader's understanding of a procedure which cannot be developed mathematically in this book. First, it is noted that data such as those of Table 6.11 have been found by experience to satisfy reasonably well the requirement that the X and Y form a normal bivariate population with both variables subject to sampling error, so tests of significance and interval estimation are possible.

It was discovered by R. A. Fisher that, under the circumstances of Table 6.11, when the population correlation coefficient, ρ, is not zero, one should make use of the transformation:

$$(6.35) \quad z = \log_e \sqrt{(1 + r)/(1 - r)} = (2.30259/2) \log_{10} [(1 + r)/(1 - r)]$$
$$= (1.1513) \log_{10} [(1 + r)/(1 - r)]$$

because its sampling distribution is approximately normal in all important features, even when $\rho \neq 0$.

The data of Table 6.31 were obtained by drawing random samples of size $n = 12$ from Table 6.11, for which ρ is known to be $+0.749$. In practice this sort of information is not available, but here, as is frequently true in a statistics course, the student has access to information not available in practice, so that he can better understand the discussions of sampling phenomena which involve mathematical analysis beyond his training. The 200 sample r's and z's summarized in Table 6.31 have an observed frequency distribution shown in Figure 6.31.

The z graph of the figure merely illustrates the fact that the Fisher z transformation changes the nonnormal r distribution into a near-normal distribution, which then makes normal theory and tables applicable to some sampling problems involving r. In addition to showing this, Fisher also showed that the variance of z is given by

$$(6.36) \qquad \qquad \sigma_z^2 = 1/(n - 3)$$

a quantity which depends only on sample size. It turns out, then, that if $z\rho$ denotes the z corresponding to the parameter ρ, then the random variable

$$(6.37) \qquad \qquad y = (z - z\rho)\sqrt{(n - 3)}$$

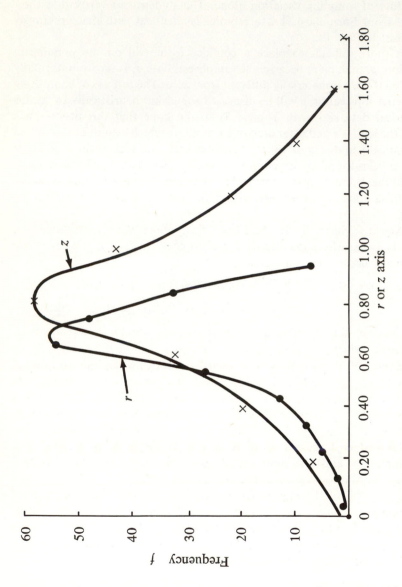

Figure 6.31.   Sampling frequency distribution of 200 sample r's and z's with $n = 12$, taken from Table 6.11.

is essentially a standard normal variate, so the usual standard normal tables are available for use in studies involving z and hence r. We can test hypotheses about $z\rho$, and hence about ρ, or we can set confidence intervals on $z\rho$ and derive therefrom the corresponding CI on ρ. For example, consider the

TABLE 6.31.   OBSERVED SAMPLING DISTRIBUTION OF r AND OF
$z = \log_e \sqrt{(1 + r)/(1 - r)}$ WHEN $n = 12$ AND $\rho = +0.749$
(TABLE 6.11 DATA)

r interval		f	z interval		f
0.890 to 1.000		7	1.70 to 1.89		1
0.790	0.889	33	1.50	1.69	3
0.690	0.789	49	1.30	1.49	10
0.590	0.689	55	1.10	1.29	22
0.490	0.589	27	0.90	1.09	44
0.390	0.489	13	0.70	0.89	59
0.290	0.389	8	0.50	0.69	33
0.190	0.289	5	0.30	0.49	20
0.090	0.189	2	0.10	0.29	7
−0.010	0.089	1	−0.10	0.09	1
	Total:	200		Total:	200

first sample drawn for Table 6.31. With $n = 12$, it was found that $r = +0.668$; therefore, by Formula 6.35, $z = 1.1513 \log_{10} [(1.668)/(0.332)] = 0.807$. The $\sigma_z^2 = 1/(12 - 3)$, so $\sigma_z = 0.333$, and $y = (0.807 - z\rho)/0.333$ is a member of a standard normal population, $N(0, 1)$. If a confidence coefficient of 0.95 has been chosen as appropriate for this interval estimate, the inequality

$$-1.96 \leqslant \frac{0.807 - z\rho}{0.333} \leqslant +1.96$$

requires $0.154 \leqslant z\rho \leqslant 1.460$, which then is the required CI_{95} on $z\rho$. The corresponding CI_{95} on ρ is obtained by solving Formula 6.35 for ρ, with ρ instead of r in that formula. Thus, $z_1 =$ lower limit on $z\rho = 0.154 = (1/2) \log_e [(1 + \rho_1)/(1 - \rho_1)]$ or $(1 + \rho_1)/(1 - \rho_1) = e^{0.308} = 1.36$; hence, $\rho_1 = 0.155$. In a similar manner, it is found that the upper confidence limit on ρ is $\rho_2 = 0.898$, so the final form of the CI_{95} on ρ is

$$0.155 \leqslant \rho \leqslant 0.898$$

In this case, it is known that this interval does, in fact, include the true population coefficient of linear correlation, $\rho = +0.749$. Actually, the interval obtained is so wide as to be of rather limited usefulness. If a narrower limit is desired, either a much larger sample must be taken or more risk of error by choosing a smaller confidence coefficient, $1 - \alpha$, or both. There are tables which facilitate the transformation from r to z or from z to r, so this arithmetic can be avoided (see R. A. Fisher and F. Yates, *Statistical Tables for Biological, Agricultural, and Medical Research*, Oliver and Boyd, Edinburgh, 1938, or a later edition.)

As another example for the discussion, consider some sampling data obtained by K. Finney and M. Barmore and reported in *Cereal Chem.* 25: 299, 1948. The sample produced a correlation coefficient of $r = 0.94$ between the protein content of the flour and the volume of the loaf of bread baked from that flour. This correlation came from a random sample of size $n = 30$. What information does this r provide? First of all, the mere fact that $r = 0.94$, when it could not numerically exceed 1.00, tells us that with this variety of wheat (Nebred) there is a strong linear relationship between the protein content of the flour and the volume of a loaf baked from that flour (assuming, of course, that the same formula, baking procedures, etc., are used). One would feel sure that the scatter diagram would reveal a close linear trend of Y (volume) with X (percent protein). In fact, this linear trend accounts for $(0.94)^2 = 0.8836 = 88.36\%$ of the variation in loaf volume among all 30 loaves, as shown by Formula 6.32. Although it seems highly unlikely in this case that the population coefficient of linear correlation would be zero, one can test $H_0(\rho = 0)$ against $H_a(\rho \neq 0)$ by the following t test:

$$t = \frac{0.94}{\sqrt{\dfrac{1 - 0.8836}{28}}} = \frac{0.94}{0.065} = 14.5, \qquad \text{with 28 DF}$$

Such a large t almost never occurs by chance, so it is concluded that $\rho \neq 0$. This conclusion can be checked in Table XXI. If there were any basis for testing $H_0(\rho = \rho_0)$, where $\rho_0 \neq 0$, this could be done, *but not by means of the t test given above.* Also, a $CI_{1-\alpha}$, a $GLB_{1-\alpha}$, or a $LUB_{1-\alpha}$ could be computed for ρ by using the z transformation.

Although Fisher's z transformation will normalize the sampling distribution of the correlation coefficient r quite effectively for moderate-sized samples, it is known that some nonnormality exists for small samples. Kendall and Stuart (*The Advanced Theory of Statistics*, Vol. 1, Griffin and Company, London, 1958) gave the following formulae for the true mean and variance of a random variable, which will be designated by $\zeta = z - z\rho$:

$$\mu_\zeta = \frac{\rho}{2(n - 1)} \left(1 + \frac{5 + \rho^2}{4(n - 1)} + \frac{11 + 2\rho^2 + 3\rho^4}{8(n - 1)^2} + \cdots \right)$$

(6.38) $$\sigma_\zeta^2 = \frac{1}{n - 1} \left(1 + \frac{4 - \rho^2}{2(n - 1)} + \frac{22 - 6\rho^2 - 3\rho^4}{6(n - 1)^2} + \cdots \right)$$

Kendall and Stuart point out that, if the n is large, $\mu_\zeta \cong 0$ and $\sigma_\zeta^2 \cong 1/(n - 3)$, as Fisher suggested. Then the quantity $(z - z_\rho)/(1/\sqrt{n - 3}) = \sqrt{n - 3}(z - z_\rho)$ has approximately the standard normal distribution.

Tables 6.32, 6.33, and 6.34 have been constructed to show how good an approximation the N(0, 1) distribution is for various combinations of ρ and n.

Tables 6.32 and 6.33, respectively, show the absolute amounts by which the true means and standard deviations of ζ differ from the normal approximation to which they correspond. However, the use suggested for the normal

TABLE 6.32.   VALUES OF μ_ζ OBTAINED BY USING THE KENDALL AND STUART FORMULA (NORMAL $\mu = 0$ EXACTLY)

	Sample size, n							
ρ	10	15	20	25	30	35	40	50
0.10	0.006	0.004	0.004	0.003	0.002	0.002	0.001	0.001
0.20	0.013	0.008	0.006	0.004	0.004	0.003	0.003	0.002
0.30	0.019	0.012	0.008	0.007	0.005	0.005	0.004	0.003
0.40	0.026	0.016	0.011	0.009	0.007	0.006	0.005	0.004
0.50	0.032	0.020	0.014	0.011	0.009	0.008	0.007	0.005
0.60	0.039	0.024	0.017	0.013	0.011	0.009	0.008	0.006
0.70	0.046	0.028	0.020	0.015	0.013	0.011	0.009	0.007
0.80	0.052	0.032	0.023	0.018	0.014	0.012	0.011	0.008
0.90	0.059	0.036	0.026	0.020	0.016	0.014	0.012	0.009

TABLE 6.33.   VALUES OF σ_ζ OBTAINED BY USING THE KENDALL-STUART FORMULA, WITH $\zeta = z - z_\rho$

	Sample size, n, and $1/\sqrt{n-3}$							
	10	15	20	25	30	35	40	50
	0.378	0.289	0.243	0.213	0.192	0.177	0.164	0.146
0.10	0.375	0.288	0.243	0.212	0.192	0.176	0.164	0.145
0.20	0.374	0.288	0.241	0.212	0.192	0.176	0.164	0.145
0.30	0.374	0.288	0.241	0.212	0.192	0.176	0.164	0.145
0.40	0.374	0.286	0.241	0.212	0.192	0.176	0.164	0.145
0.50	0.373	0.286	0.241	0.212	0.192	0.176	0.164	0.145
0.60	0.371	0.286	0.241	0.212	0.192	0.176	0.164	0.145
0.70	0.370	0.286	0.241	0.212	0.192	0.176	0.164	0.145
0.80	0.368	0.285	0.241	0.212	0.192	0.176	0.164	0.145
0.90	0.366	0.285	0.239	0.212	0.192	0.176	0.164	0.145

approximation is in the standard normal form, that is, a ratio of $z - z_\rho$ to its standard deviation. Hence, Table 6.34 was constructed to show how much of an error one probably makes when one uses the normal approximation in that way. This comparison is made for a number of combinations of ρ and n.

TABLE 6.34. COMPARISON OF THE TRUE DISTRIBUTION OF $\zeta = (z - z_\rho)/\sigma_\zeta$ WITH THE NORMAL APPROXIMATION SUGGESTED BY FISHER (SEE KENDALL AND STUART, p. 391)

When n = 10

ζ	Normal approx. $\dfrac{\zeta - 0}{1/\sqrt{7}}$	$\rho = 0.10,$ $\dfrac{\zeta - 0.006}{0.375}$	$\rho = 0.50,$ $\dfrac{\zeta - 0.032}{0.373}$	$\rho = 0.90,$ $\dfrac{\zeta - 0.059}{0.366}$
0.20	0.53	0.52	0.45	0.39
0.40	1.06	1.05	0.99	0.93
0.50	1.32	1.32	1.26	1.21
0.60	1.59	1.58	1.52	1.48
0.80	2.12	2.12	2.06	2.02

When n = 20

ζ	$\dfrac{\zeta - 0}{1/\sqrt{17}}$	$\rho = 0.10,$ $\dfrac{\zeta - 0.004}{0.243}$	$\rho = 0.50,$ $\dfrac{\zeta - 0.014}{0.241}$	$\rho = 0.90,$ $\dfrac{\zeta - 0.026}{0.239}$
0.20	0.82	0.81	0.77	0.73
0.40	1.65	1.63	1.60	1.56
0.50	2.06	2.04	2.02	1.98
0.60	2.47	2.45	2.43	2.40
0.80	3.30	3.28	3.26	3.24

When n = 30

ζ	$\dfrac{\zeta - 0}{1/\sqrt{27}}$	$\rho = 0.10,$ $\dfrac{\zeta - 0.002}{0.192}$	$\rho = 0.50,$ $\dfrac{\zeta - 0.009}{0.192}$	$\rho = 0.90,$ $\dfrac{\zeta - 0.016}{0.192}$
0.20	1.04	1.03	1.00	0.96
0.40	2.08	2.07	2.04	2.00
0.50	2.60	2.59	2.56	2.52
0.60	3.12	3.12	3.08	3.04
0.80	4.16	4.16	4.12	4.08

When n = 50

ζ	$\dfrac{\zeta - 0}{1/\sqrt{47}}$	$\rho = 0.10,$ $\dfrac{\zeta - 0.001}{0.145}$	$\rho = 0.50,$ $\dfrac{\zeta - 0.005}{0.145}$	$\rho = 0.90,$ $\dfrac{\zeta - 0.009}{0.145}$
0.20	1.37	1.37	1.34	1.32
0.40	2.74	2.75	2.72	2.70
0.50	3.43	3.44	3.41	3.39
0.60	4.11	4.13	4.10	4.08
0.80	5.48	5.51	5.48	5.46

R. A. Fisher "On the probable error of a coefficient of correlation deduced from a small sample" *Metron* 1: No. 4, 1, 1921.

In actual practice one does not know the size of the true correlation coefficient, ρ, but the information in Table 6.34 will serve as an indication of the possible errors to be made.

These three tables indicate the following points of interest in connection with Fisher's z transformation of the product-moment coefficient of linear correlation, r.

(*a*) The agreement between the normal approximation,

$$(\zeta - 0)/[1/\sqrt{(n - 3)}],$$

and the true distribution of $(\zeta - \mu_\zeta)/\sigma_\zeta$ is excellent, even when $n = 10$, unless the ρ is large, say $\geqslant 0.50$. However, if $n \geqslant 30$, the approximation still should be considered good for all ρ.

(*b*) The improvement in the normal approximation achieved by increasing n from 30 to 50 probably never will be worth while.

(*c*) Considering the fact that ρ is unknown in practice, one probably is not committing a serious error in keeping $n \geqslant 20$ and using Fisher's z transformation without any correction.

There are some circumstances under which it is desirable to test one or both of $H_0(\beta_1 = \beta_2)$ and $H_0(\rho_1 = \rho_2)$ against their respective alternatives. In earlier discussions we have insisted that the X_i's must be fixed numbers not subject to sampling error when discussing the regression of Y on X and have required that X and Y both be random variables with a bivariate distribution, when discussing r as being other than an index. The requirement of fixed X's can be, and is, relaxed for practical purposes, so in subsequent discussions this requirement will not be insisted upon.

To illustrate the circumstances in which $H_0(\beta_1 = \beta_2)$ might be a useful hypothesis, suppose that superior poultry husbandry could increase the amount by which a weight advantage at 16 weeks of age would be maintained more completely to 28 weeks of age. In the population considered earlier, a one-pound advantage at 16 weeks of age was reduced, on the average, to a half-pound advantage at 28 weeks of age. Thus, β was 1/2. It might be that the β could be increased by better management, better diets, or other methods. If so, turkeys raised under one procedure would have a different β from those raised under the other procedure, so a test of $H_0(\beta_1 = \beta_2)$ would be in order, with an appropriate alternative hypothesis.

With regard to $H_0(\rho_1 = \rho_2)$, the turkey research can be used again. For example, it might be of special interest to someone to know whether one method of raising turkeys produces a more consistent linear relationship between 16-week weight and 28-week weight than another method, so culling at 16 weeks of age could be done with greater confidence that the best turkeys had been saved. In a useful sense, the correlation coefficient would answer this question, because accuracy of prediction is directly related to the size of the correlation coefficient.

The statistical procedures for testing the equality of β's and, separately, of ρ's are as follows, in outline form.

For testing $H_0(\beta_1 = \beta_2)$:

(a) Pool the $\sum (Y_1 - \hat{Y}_1)^2$ and the $\sum (Y_2 - \hat{Y}_2)^2$ from the two independent random samples, pool their degrees of freedom, and then
calculate, using the simplest formulas for those sums of squares:

$$\text{Pooled } s_{y.x} = \sqrt{\frac{\sum (Y_1 - \hat{Y}_1)^2 + \sum (Y_2 - \hat{Y}_2)^2}{n_1 + n_2 - 4}}$$

(b) Compute $\sqrt{1/\sum (x_1^2) + 1/\sum (x_2^2)}$.
(c) Multiply the standard deviation from (a) by the result of (b), and
denote it as $s_{b_2 - b_1}$.
(d) Compute $t = (b_1 - b_2)/s_{b_1 - b_2}$, with $(n_1 + n_2 - 4)$ DF, and interpret
as usual.

For testing $H_0(\rho_1 = \rho_2)$:

(a) Transform r_1 and r_2 into z_1 and z_2, respectively, in the manner
illustrated earlier or by means of tables.
(b) Compute the standard deviation of the difference $z_1 - z_2$ by means of

$$\sigma_{z_1 - z_2} = \sqrt{1/(n_1 - 3) + 1/(n_2 - 3)}$$

(c) Calculate $y = (z_1 - z_2)/\sigma_{z_1 - z_2}$, and consider it as a standard normal
variate in making the decision to accept or to reject $H_0(\rho_1 = \rho_2)$
versus the appropriate alternative, H_a.

PROBLEMS

1. R. R. Reynolds, W. E. Bond, and B. P. Kirkland (*U.S. Dep. Agr. Bull.*: 861,
1944) published the following information on the relation between the cost
of hauling logs and the length of the haul in miles over high-grade gravel
roads:

Miles hauled:	1	2	3	4	5	6	7	8	9	10
Cost per 1000 cu. ft. ($):	0.35	0.44	0.53	0.62	0.71	0.81	0.90	0.99	1.08	1.17

Miles hauled:	11	12	13	14	15	16	17	18	19	20
Cost per 1000 cu. ft. ($):	1.26	1.36	1.45	1.54	1.63	1.72	1.82	1.90	2.00	2.09

Compute a linear correlation coefficient between length of haul and cost per
1000 cubic feet, and draw appropriate conclusions. Also compute and interpret the coefficient of linear regression of Y on X, where Y is the cost per
1000 cubic feet. For which situation were the assumptions probably best
satisfied, if one wished to make tests of significance or to compute confidence
intervals?

3. Construct a scatter diagram for the data of Problem 1, and discuss the assumption of a linear relation between X and Y.

4. Compute s_Y, $s_{y \cdot x}$, and s_b from the data of Problem 1. Then state what population standard deviation each estimates.

5. With the data of Problem 1 compute the CI_{90} on the true average increase in cost per 1000 cubic feet of logs for each additional mile hauled, and interpret that CI. Also compute the LUB_{90} on β.

6. Suppose that two random samples each of size $n = 15$ have produced $r_1 = 0.75$ and $r_2 = 0.65$. Test $H_0(\rho_1 = \rho_2)$ against its negation, and draw appropriate conclusions. Also compute the CI_{95} for each parameter, ρ_1 and ρ_2, and interpret each interval. Can these interpretations be related to the previous test of that H_0?

7. Draw a random sample of size $n = 25$ from Table 6.11, and test $H_0(\beta = 0)$ against its negation, using $\alpha = 0.10$. Make the same test, but against $H_a(\beta > 0)$. Also test $H_0(\rho = 0)$ against $H_a(\rho \neq 0)$.

8. Draw two separate random samples of sizes $n_1 = 25$ and $n_2 = 30$ from Table 6.11 and test $H_0(\rho_1 = \rho_2)$ against its negation, using $\alpha = 0.10$.

9. Make a scatter diagram for each sample of Problem 8, using the same set of coördinates but different symbols for the points, so that the two samples can be identified. Draw a free-hand line into each separate scatter diagram, and discuss their difference in slope in terms of $s_{b_1 - b_2}$.

10. Draw a random sample of size $n = 20$ from Table 6.11 and test $H_0(\rho = 0.500)$ against $H_a(\rho > 0.500)$, using the z transformation and $\alpha = 0.10$. Compute the CI_{90} on ρ and test $H_0(\rho = 0.500)$ against $H_a(\rho \neq 0.500)$.

11. Draw a random sample of size $n = 20$ from Table 6.11 and compute the least upper bound on ρ with a confidence coefficient of 0.90. What information does this give you?

12. Given the following random sample drawn from Table 6.11, compute the least upper bound on ρ and interpret it usefully in terms of the population sampled.

X:	5.2	7.1	9.5	9.2	8.6	5.3	8.6	9.5
Y:	13.2	14.9	17.8	15.8	13.9	13.5	14.5	17.2
X:	7.3	9.1	9.8	8.6	8.1	6.1	4.9	6.6
Y:	14.3	15.3	16.4	14.1	15.1	15.3	12.2	14.3

13. Use the sample of Problem 12 to estimate σ_y^2 and also $\sigma_{y \cdot x}^2$. Discuss the difference between them.

14. What percent of the $\sum (Y - \bar{y})^2$ for Problem 12 can one remove statistically by using the least-squares linear relation between Y and X?

15. Make up two bivariate samples each with $n = 15$ and such that you think the hypothesis $H_0(\rho_1 = \rho_2)$ would be rejected with $\alpha = 0.10$. Then test that H_0 with your data. *Note:* Keep r_1 and r_2 of the same sign.

16. Draw a random sample of size $n = 25$ pairs from Table 6.11 and test $H_0(\rho = 0.650)$ with $\alpha = 0.10$.

17. Make up two bivariate samples each with $n = 15$ and such that you think the $H_0(\beta_1 = \beta_2)$ would be rejected with $\alpha = 0.10$, keeping b_1 and b_2 of the same sign. Then test this H_0 with your data.

6.4   RANK CORRELATIONS

Sometimes it is either necessary or convenient to correlate the ranks of some X's with the ranks of their corresponding Y's. It may be that the X's and Y's are only ranks themselves, it may be that the normal bivariate assumption needed for the product-moment correlation, r, is unsatisfied, or it may be merely that it is economically feasible to use the rank type of correlation coefficient, because it is easier and less expensive to do so in several preliminary studies.

The practice of correlating ranks is both older and more extensive than is sometimes realized. Karl Pearson apparently was of the opinion that the idea of correlating ranks originated with Francis Galton during studies of inheritance. Sometimes C. Spearman is credited with doing much of the early work on rank-correlation methods, especially as applied to studies in psychology (*Am. J. Psych.* 15: 88, 1904). It is Spearman's coefficient, r_S, which will be discussed specifically here. The works of M. G. Kendall (*Rank Correlation Methods*, Griffin, 1955) and others recently have helped to increase the faith in, and the use of, ranks in statistical analysis. No attempt will be made here to study these matters exhaustively, because it is a small part of the whole area of nonparametric statistics, a course in itself.

The calculation of the Spearman, or rank-difference, coefficient of linear correlation, r_S, will be illustrated by means of the following pairs of ranks of students' grades in two college courses. Each pair gives the respective ranks of a student in statistics (X) and in mathematics of finance (Y). For example, the first student ranked second in his class in statistics on the final examination, but ranked fifth in the final examination in mathematics of finance.

Student No.:

	1	2	3	4	5	6	7	8	9	10	11	12	13	14	15	16
Statistics (X):	2	7	4	1	10	8	15	9	16	5	6	12	11	13	3	14
Finance (Y):	5	4	3	2	9	7	16	6	15	12	8	11	10	13	1	14
|Diff. in rank|:	3	3	1	1	1	1	1	3	1	7	2	1	1	0	2	0

It is seen from these data that there is a general but imperfect tendency of a student's grades to rank about the same in the two courses; that is, a student's rank in statistics has some relation to his grade in mathematics of finance. If this relationship is basically linear, it can be measured rather simply and satisfactorily by means of Spearman's rank-difference coefficient of linear correlation, r_S, given by the following formula:

(6.41)
$$r_S = 1 - \frac{6 \sum (d^2)}{n(n^2 - 1)}$$

where d is the difference between the X rank and the Y rank of a student and n is the number of pairs, (X, Y), that is, the number of students in the example. If all ranks for the X's agree exactly with the corresponding Y

rank, pair by pair, then the d's are all zero, and $r_S = 1$. If the ranks of the X's are $1, 2, 3, \cdots, n$, whereas the corresponding Y ranks are $n, (n - 1)$, $(n - 2), \cdots, 1$, it can be shown by numerical calculus (using Newton's Binomial Interpolation Formula, for example) that

$$\Sigma\,(d^2) = \frac{n(n^2 - 1)}{3}, \qquad \text{so that} \quad r_S = 1 - \frac{6\!\left(\dfrac{n(n^2 - 1)}{3}\right)}{n(n^2 - 1)} = -1$$

Thus, $-1 \leqslant r_S \leqslant +1$, as for the product-moment correlation coefficient, r.

For the data on grades in statistics and mathematics of finance, $d_1 = 2 - 5 = -3, d_2 = 7 - 4 = 3, \cdots, d_{16} = 14 - 14 = 0$, as shown in the preceding table, the signs being disregarded because the d's will be squared anyway. It then is found that $\Sigma\,(d^2) = 92$; hence, with $n = 16$, $r_S = 1 - 552/4080 = 1 - 0.135 = 0.865$.

If there are ties for any ranks, each X or Y tied is given the mean of the ranks for which there is a tie. For example, if three X's are tied for ranks 1, 2, and 3, each such X is considered to have rank 2, which is the mean of 1, 2, and 3.

As noted earlier it can be shown that r_S always has a size within the range $-1 \leqslant r_S \leqslant +1$. This fact can be verified in the example here by changing all the X ranks so they will be identical with the corresponding Y ranks and then by taking the X ranks exactly opposite to the Y ranks, that is, 1 with 16, 2 with 15, etc. This will give $r_S = +1$ and -1, respectively, when Formula 6.41 is applied.

An approximate test of significance for r_S can be made by computing its standard deviation, $\sigma_{r_S} = \sqrt{1/(n - 1)}$, where n is the number of *pairs* of observations in the sample, and then by considering $Y = r_S/\sigma_{r_S}$ a standard normal variate. For example, in the preceding study of the relation between grades in statistics and in mathematics of finance it was found, with $n = 16$, that $r_S = 0.865$ and $\sigma_{r_S} = \sqrt{1/(16 - 1)} = 0.258$, so $\lambda = 0.865/0.258 = 3.35$. The usual standard normal table, such as Table III, shows that a standard normal deviate would be that size, or larger, less than 1 time in 100 samples, so it is concluded that there is *some* linear correlation between X and Y.

Kendall urges the use of a different rank correlation coefficient, τ, because it is easier to determine its distribution and certain theoretical advantages over Spearman's r_S are associated with the tau. However, τ is somewhat more difficult to compute and is less commonly used in practice, so we shall only note its existence and refer the interested student to Kendall's book.

PROBLEMS

1. Compute r_S for the data of Problem 1, Section 6.3.
2. Compute the Spearman coefficient of linear correlation for the sample data of Table 6.12.

3. Make up two different sets of data for which $r_S = +1$. For which $r_S = -1$. For which $r_S = +0.50$.

4. For $r_S = 0.75$ with $n = 10$, test $H_0(\rho = 0)$, where ρ is the true correlation $\alpha = 0.10$ and H_a is the negation of H_0.

5. If $r_S = 0.50$, how large must n have been for this to be a significant correlation at the 5% level? At the 10% level?

6. Suppose two judges rank 10 cooked turkeys as follows with respect to appearance:

Turkey No.:

	1	2	3	4	5	6	7	8	9	10
Judge 1:	6	3	7	10	1	4	8	9	2	5
Judge 2:	4	1	7	8	2	5	9	10	3	6

Are these judges' rankings significantly correlated?

7. Illustrate with the data of Problem 6 that Spearman's rank-difference correlation coefficient is the same as the product-moment correlation performed on the ranks themselves.

8. Compute the r'_S for Problem 1, Section 6.3, by inspection.

9. Compute r_S for Problem 12, Section 6.3, and make an approximate test of $H_0(\rho = 0)$ versus $H_a(\rho \neq 0)$ with $\alpha = 0.05$.

10. Draw a random sample of size $n = 20$ from Table 6.11, and compute and compare r and r_S.

REVIEW PROBLEMS

1. An experiment on the effect of hydrostatic pressure on the sex ratio of the marine copepod *Tigriopus* by V. Vacquier, Jr (*Science*, 135: 724–725, 1962) produced the following results among others:

Pressure (atm):	1	450	500	550	600	650	700
Ratio (m/f):	5.5	4.0	3.0	2.2	0.57	0.03	0

Describe the relationship between these measurements statistically. Assuming this is a random sample of some describable population, compute and interpret a CI_{90} on a true linear regression coefficient closely related to this study.

2. The following data on the growth rate of *Neurospora crassa* grown in the presence of gases of differing molecular weights were obtained from an article by H. R. Schreiner, R. C. Gregoire, and J. A. Lawrie in the May 18, 1962, issue of *Science*, p. 654:

Gas (mol. wt.)$^{1/2}$:	He, 2.0	Ne, 5.2	N_2, 5.2	Ar, 6.3	Kr, 9.0	Xe, 11.0
Growth rate (mm/hr):	3.7	3.2	3.0	2.7	2.2	1.8

Compute a CI_{95} on the true rate of change of growth per unit change in the square root of the molecular weight, and interpret this interval.

3. It seems to be an accepted fact that conditioned responses in various mammals are affected by x irradiation. An article in the May 25, 1962, issue of *Science*, pp. 712–14, reports an experiment in which fish were used as the subjects.

The conditioned response was to electric light and the unconditioned response was to electric shock. Given the following data, decide whether (*a*) the mean frequencies of conditioned responses are affected by x irradiation and (*b*) the variances of these frequencies are affected by x irradiation.

Dosage (r)	*No. of fish*	*Mean*	*Stand. dev.*
0	14	77.2	8.8
7,200	12	76.7	10.2
10,100	32	66.8	11.6
18,400	10	51.6	18.0

4. The experiment partially described in Problem 3 produced the following data on the relationship between time (in units of 20 trials per day) and the percent of conditioned responses:

Time (20-day units):	1	2	3	4	5
No irrad., % CR:	32.0	40.5	55.6	60.0	70.0
10,100 r, % CR:	28.0	52.4	80.5	83.4	90.0

Test $H_0(\beta_{10,100r} = \beta_{or})$ versus $H_a(\beta_{10,100r} > \beta_{or})$. Also use $H_a(\beta$'s are not equal), and discuss the basic difference between these two tests.

5. The October 5, 1962, issue of *Science*, pp. 41–2, reports on an experiment on the uptake of strontium-85 by alfalfa, after the soil has been treated with this isotope. The data obtained are as follows:

Days growth after germination	*Uptake (%) per gram dried plant*
60 (1st crop)	1.65
88 (2nd crop)	1.35
116 (3rd crop)	1.29
144 (4th crop)	1.28
172 (5th crop)	1.20

Describe statistically the relationship between time from germination and uptake of strontium-85. Make and interpret all useful and pertinent statistical tests.

6. An article in the September 7, 1962, issue of *Science* presents evidence that grass bordering well-traveled highways contains amounts of tetraethyl lead, which may be a health hazard if eaten by cattle. The following data are abstracted from Figure 1 of that paper:

Dist. (ft) from highway:	5	10	50	100	200	500	750	1000
Ppm lead in grass ash:	700	630	250	100	68	42	16	25

The volume of traffic was about 20,000 cars per 24 hours. Start by making a scatter diagram of these data, and then make and interpret all desirable and pertinent statistical analyses.

7. A sampling study in the field of cereal chemistry produced the following product-moment linear correlation coefficients:

$$\text{Sample 1:} \quad n_1 = 44, \quad r_1 = -0.93$$
$$\text{Sample 2:} \quad n_2 = 44, \quad r_2 = -0.81$$

Test $H_0(\rho_1 = \rho_2)$ against its negation, and draw appropriate conclusions.

8. If $r_1 = -0.93$, as in Problem 7, could an $r_2 = -0.90$ ever cause rejection of the $H_0(\rho_1 = \rho_2)$? Defend your answer.

9. It has been stated that each of the ratios $(b - \beta)/s_b$ and $r/\sqrt{(1 - r^2)/(n - 2)}$ follows a t distribution with $n - 2$ DF under proper sampling conditions. Show that these two quantities are algebraically identical if $\beta = 0$.

10. Suppose that the following results were obtained from two samples involving different methods of some sort and that each sample was of size $n = 20$:

> Method 1: $r_1 = 0.40$, $H_0(\rho_1 = 0)$ is accepted with $\alpha = 0.05$
> Method 2: $r_2 = 0.60$, $H_0(\rho_2 = 0)$ is rejected with $\alpha = 0.05$

Yet $H_0(\rho_1 = \rho_2)$ is accepted readily with the same-sized region of rejection. Explain why such results are not contradictory. Also determine what size n must have to bring about rejection of all three hypotheses, if the correlations are left as they are now and α is kept at 0.05.

11. During a period of 17 days starting two months after the Russian nuclear tests in 1961, B. Kahn and C. P. Straub in Oregon conducted a study of iodine-131 found in the milk of cows on pasture and reported on it in the December 21, 1962, issue of *Science*, pp. 1334–5. The following data were taken from their graphs:

Date, December: 4   5   6   7   8   9   10 11 12 13 14 15 16 17 18
Av. picocurie/liter
(5 cows):   280 210 180 170 170 165 135 90 80 90 80 70 60 70 50

Describe the relationship between time (Date) and level of iodine-131 (average pc) as best you can by the method of least squares. What conclusions do you draw?

12. The following data are from the study of the previous problem, but for cesium-137. Make a scatter diagram and fit the best regression line by the method of least squares. Draw appropriate conclusions.

Date: 4   5   6   7   8   9   10   11   12   13   14   15   16   17   18
pc/liter: 30   40   40   40   50   60   60   70   70   90   70   80   80   70   90

13. Correlate the lengths and weights of the bass of Problem 7, Section 6.1, by means of the Spearman r_S.

14. Suppose that the assessed valuations of 25 lots in a certain section of a city are as follows for tax purposes (in dollars): 150, 210, 115, 350, 750, 125, 175, 200, 145, 230, 960, 180, 220, 105, 130, 300, 210, 375, 145, 160, 110, 200, 190, 1000, and 205. If you are assured that these valuations are typical of lots in the area involved,
    (a) Would you accept the assumption that the population distribution is normal?
    (b) What average do you recommend to describe the "typical" assessed valuation of lots there? Justify your choice.

15. Referring to Problem 14, omit the 750, 960, and 1000 dollar valuations, assume the remaining numbers are a random sample of size $n = 23$ from some $N(\mu, \sigma^2)$ population, and compute a GLB_{90} on μ. What information does this figure provide?

16. Suppose that you take a random sample of two dozen oranges from a large bin in a market and measure the circumference of each orange to the nearest

tenth of an inch, with the following results: 8.5, 9.3, 9.0, 8.1, 10.6, 9.4, 8.7, 8.5, 8.8, 9.2, 9.1, 8.4, 8.5, 8.7, 9.3, 8.6, 10.2, 9.5, 8.9, 8.6, 9.4, 8.7, 9.2, and 8.9. Obtain the CI_{90} on the true average circumference for all oranges in the bin, assuming a normal distribution and using the G distribution.

17. Referring to Problem 16, compute the median circumference.

18. Code the numbers in Problem 16 by subtracting 8.6, and then compute the GLB_{90} on the true average circumference in the bin.

19. Suppose that a random sample of 50 oranges from the bin of Problem 16 had 3 with scab on the skin. What is the LUB_{90} on the true percent scabby oranges in this large bin, assuming there are so many oranges in the bin that 50 is a small fraction thereof?

20. Suppose that the grades in all final examinations for a large group of students in freshman English are known to be normally distributed with a mean of 75. If it is known that 20% of these grades are in the interval 70 to 80, inclusive, what is the standard deviation, σ, of this population?

21. Suppose that 15 samples of concrete from a construction job had slump varying from 0.50 to 4.50 inches with a mean of 1.89 inches. If the true average slump for this job is supposed to be 1.75 inches or less, does this sample cause you to believe the job met the slump specification or not? Justify your answer statistically.

22. Suppose that in a certain voting population 55% of the registered voters actually favor candidate Brooks. What is the probability that a random sample of 100 from this population will produce less than 50 in favor of Brooks?

23. Plot the t distribution with 6 DF.

24. Refer to Table 6.34 and do the same computations for $n = 15$.

Chapter 7

Sampling More Than Two Normal Populations Simultaneously: Introductory Analysis of Variance

7.1 INTRODUCTION

When an experimenter draws two random and independent samples from two normal populations and tests $H_0[(\mu_1 = \mu_2) \mid (\sigma_1^2 = \sigma_2^2 = \sigma^2)]$ by means of the t test, he essentially asks whether it is reasonable to conclude that the two samples at hand came from identical normal populations. This same sort of question might be asked if three, four, $\cdots$, t samples were drawn from t populations and one wished to know whether those t populations are, in fact, identical. This situation is illustrated more specifically by asking whether t varieties which are believed to have the same variance also have the same mean yield. Tests of this hypothesis have been developed. The major such test to be considered in this chapter is an F test based on an *analysis of variance*, as devised by R. A. Fisher. In one sense the term "analysis of variance" is misleading, because one must assume that the population variances are equal before testing for equality of means by the analysis of variance, as is stated in $H_0[(\mu_1 = \mu_2 = \cdots = \mu_t) \mid (\sigma_1^2 = \sigma_2^2 = \cdots = \sigma_t^2 = \sigma^2)]$.

Although the equality of the variances is *assumed*, the experimenter may wish to do a preliminary analysis, to assure himself of the reasonableness of this assumption. It should be noted, however, that we are not proposing a joint testing of

$$H_0(\sigma_1^2 = \cdots = \sigma_t^2 = \sigma^2) \quad \text{and} \quad H_0(\mu_1 = \cdots = \mu_t \mid \sigma_1^2 = \cdots = \sigma_t^2 = \sigma^2).$$

The first test of $H_0(\sigma_1^2 = \cdots = \sigma_t^2 = \sigma^2)$ which we shall discuss (and probably the most rigorous such test) was developed by the British statistician M. S. Bartlett by utilizing the chi-square test (see *Supp. J. Roy. Stat. Soc.*, 4: 137, 1937). This test involves enough computation that, in practice, it often is replaced by some short-cut approximate test. This will be discussed after the more powerful Bartlett test is presented.

It will be convenient and better in accord with custom to use some different notation in the subsequent discussion. For example, the symbol n_i has been used to denote the sample size for group i, with $i = 1$ or 2; now we shall use instead r_i with $i = 1$ to t. The r probably comes from the word "replication" used frequently in connection with the analysis of variance; t comes from "treatment," a term broadly used to mean "variety," "method," "location," "economic stratum," etc. Other new notation will be introduced as needed. The grand mean, which has been denoted by $\overline{\overline{X}}$, now will be denoted by $x \ldots$ Correspondingly, the symbol $X..$ will denote the grand sum, so that $x.. = X../rt$ for a two-criteria classification.

The preceding remarks are pertinent to previous problems solved with the t distribution, but the analysis of variance is not limited to testing such hypotheses as $H_0[(\mu_1 = \mu_2 = \cdots = \mu_t) \mid (\text{equal variances})]$. As the name "analysis of variance" implies, the way will be opened for broad studies of those factors which cause observed numerical measurements to vary from one experimental unit to another, from one experiment to another, etc. It will be found useful to introduce deliberately several possible sources of variation, whose importance and whose interrelations can be studied by means of sampling data. This more general approach will become quite complex and will put considerable strain on the modest mathematical background assumed a prerequisite for reading this book. Hence, the analysis of variance will be introduced somewhat heuristically as an extension of t testing techniques and by using prior knowledge gained regarding the frequency distribution of the sample mean, $\bar{x}$. In this introductory chapter a test for the equality of the population variances also will be presented, and the student will learn the basic routine arithmetical procedures required in a one-classification analysis of variance.

7.2 TESTING THE EQUALITY OF MORE THAN TWO POPULATION VARIANCES

Let t be the number of groups of measurements taken, presumably one group from each of t populations, and let the number of measurements per group be r_i, where $i = 1$ to t. Also let s_i^2 be $\sum (x_i^2)/(r_i - 1)$, the usual unbiassed estimator of σ_i^2. A sampling variate, U, defined below as a function of the t sampling variances, s_i^2, has been shown to have, to a close approximation, a chi-square distribution with $t - 1$ DF. Thus, the test of

$$H_0[(\sigma_1^2 = \sigma_2^2 = \cdots = \sigma_t^2 = \sigma^2) \mid (\text{only normality})]$$

will make use of the chi-square tables with which the student already is familiar. As usual, it was necessary to construct a function of the sample data which has, at least to a satisfactory approximation, a known distribution *when* H_0 *is correct* and departs noticeably from this known distribution when H_0 is seriously false.

It is useful first to define a quantity λ', which is the product of ratios of the individual within-treatment variance estimators s_i^2 to the pooled estimate of σ^2 based on all t samples on the assumption that $\sigma_1^2 = \sigma_2^2 = \cdots = \sigma_t^2 = \sigma^2$. The specific form of λ' is

$$(7.21) \qquad \lambda' = \left(\frac{s_1^2}{s^2}\right)^{(r_1-1)/2} \times \left(\frac{s_2^2}{s^2}\right)^{(r_2-1)/2} \times \cdots \times \left(\frac{s_t^2}{s^2}\right)^{(r_t-1)/2}$$

where: $\qquad s^2 = \dfrac{\text{pooled } \sum (x_i^2)}{\text{pooled DF}} = \dfrac{\sum (x_1^2) + \cdots + \sum (x_t^2)}{r_1 + r_2 + \cdots + r^t - t}$

If the sample s_i^2's all happened to be equal, then λ' would be 1, but sampling error always would prevent this from being precisely true. If the s_i^2's are decidedly unequal, it is expected that the sampling distribution of λ' will reflect that situation. It turns out, however, to be better not to use the λ' directly but, rather, to use a function of it. This function involves logarithms to the base e and a "correction factor" before one obtains a distribution which conforms closely to the well-known chi-square distribution. Bartlett has shown that the variate U, defined as

$$(7.22) \qquad U = \frac{-2 \log_e \lambda'}{1 + \dfrac{1}{3(t-1)}\left(\displaystyle\sum_{i=1}^{t}\left(\frac{1}{r_i-1}\right) - \dfrac{1}{\displaystyle\sum_{i=1}^{t}(r_i-1)}\right)}$$

essentially is a chi-square with $t - 1$ DF. Hence, a test of

$$H_0[(\sigma_1^2 = \sigma_2^2 = \cdots = \sigma_t^2 = \sigma^2) \mid (\text{normality})]$$

versus H_a(some σ^2 are not equal to others) can be made in the usual way by selecting a region of rejection of size α and then computing the U from the sample data. This region of rejection is taken from the right-hand tail of the χ_{t-1}^2 distribution, because the U only can be made larger by inequalities among the σ_i^2.

To illustrate the use of the Bartlett test for homogeneity of variance, consider the following set of data pertaining to the breaking strengths of certain fabrics, as shown in Table 7.21. The original data have been coded by subtracting 15 pounds from each measurement of breaking strength, to simplify the calculations. Although the quantities in Formula 7.22 may look quite complex, the actual work of computing U can be so organized that it is not excessively laborious. This will be shown in another table after the test has first been carried out step by step.

TABLE 7.21. CODED BREAKING STRENGTHS (ORIGINAL − 15 POUNDS) OF SIX
FABRICS PLUS SOME COMPUTATIONS NEEDED FOR BARTLETT'S
TEST FOR HOMOGENEITY OF VARIANCE

	Breaking strengths, lb					
	1	2	3	4	5	6
	14.5	10.3	15.0	20.8	9.7	14.7
	16.0	13.9	11.6	17.6	10.3	12.9
	13.7	4.2	13.2	19.3	7.9	15.0
	14.1	10.1	9.9	12.5	10.6	14.5
	13.4	6.1	12.6	18.6	11.0	13.8
	13.9	16.4	12.0	15.1	8.3	12.8
	15.9	10.6	10.6	16.0	6.9	13.7
	14.0	4.0	8.5	13.7	9.8	14.3
	14.6	8.9	11.3	17.2	10.9	15.9
	13.8	11.3	14.0	16.8	11.1	14.6
Sums:	143.9	95.8	118.7	167.6	96.5	142.2
Means:	14.39	9.58	11.87	16.76	9.65	14.22
$\sum (x_i^2)$:	7.209	142.616	33.901	57.904	19.285	8.096
s_i^2:	0.8010	15.8462	3.7668	6.4338	2.1539	0.8996
DF	9	9	9	9	9	9

With all $r_i = 10$ in Table 7.21, all $(r_i − 1) = 9$. The pooled $\sum (x^2) =$
269.011, and the pooled DF $= 54$; therefore, $s^2 = 269.011/54 = 4.9817$ is
the pooled estimate of the common variance, σ^2, if $H_0(\sigma_1^2 = \cdots = \sigma_6^2 = \sigma^2)$
is true. Furthermore,

$$2 \log_e \lambda' = 2.3026(9)(\log_{10} 0.8010 + \log_{10} 15.8462 + \cdots + \log_{10} 0.8996)$$
$$- 54 \log_{10} 4.9817 = -29.199$$

to three decimals, the factor 2.3026 being used so the more common logarithms
to the base 10 may be employed. It follows, then, that $-2 \log_e \lambda' = +29.199$,
which is the numerator of U. The denominator is $1 + (1/15)(6/9 − 1/54) =$
1.0432; hence, $U = 29.199/1.0432 = 27.99$. This is taken to be a sampling
value of a chi-square with $t − 1 = 5$ DF. With any reasonable α, H_0 would
be rejected, and it would be concluded that the population variances corresponding to the six fabrics were *not* equal.

The process described above can be organized into convenient tabular
form, as shown in Table 7.22.

It appears possible from this table that, if fabric 2 were eliminated
temporarily, the remaining variances would be homogeneous, but the U
turns out to be much larger than the chi-square at the 5% level for 4 DF (as
the student can check, if he feels the need for more practice). It turns out with
additional study that one usefully can conclude the following about the sizes
of the six population variances for fabrics:

(7.23) $$\sigma_2^2 > (\sigma_3^2, \sigma_4^2, \sigma_5^2) > (\sigma_1^2, \sigma_6^2)$$

TABLE 7.22.   TEST OF $H_0(\sigma_1^2 = \cdots = \sigma_6^2 = \sigma^2)$ VERSUS H_a(SOME VARIANCES UNEQUAL), ILLUSTRATED FROM THE DATA OF TABLE 7.21

Sample no. (i)	$n_i - 1$	$\sum (x_i^2)$	s_i^2	$\log_{10} s_i^2$	$(n_i - 1) \log_{10} s_i^2$
1	9	7.209	0.8010	-0.09637	-0.86733
2	9	142.616	15.8462	1.19992	10.79928
3	9	33.901	3.7668	0.57597	5.18373
4	9	57.904	6.4338	0.80847	7.27623
5	9	19.285	2.1539	0.33323	2.99907
6	9	8.096	0.8996	-0.04595	-0.41355
Sums:	54	269.011			24.97743

Here $s^2 = 269.011/54 = 4.9817$, and $\log_{10} s^2 = 0.69738$, as before. It is also found that $\sum (n_i - 1) \log_{10} s^2 = 37.65852$ and $-2 \log_e \lambda' = -2.3026(24.97743 - 37.65852) = 29.199$, as before. With the denominator computed previously, $\chi^2 = 27.99$, with 5 DF, as before.

However, it should be pointed out that the picking-and-choosing process by which the decisions were reached has made it impossible to be clear about the α used in these decisions. But with α as conservative as 0.05, it seems unlikely that the useful information presented in Inequality 7.23 is far wrong.

Although the work required in making Bartlett's test for homogeneity of variance is not excessive, statistical analyses should be made as easy as possible, if only a small loss of power results. H. O. Hartley has presented a short-cut method which is quite widely used, because it is easier to use and is considered to be almost as powerful a test as Bartlett's under many circumstances. Hartley's test was published in 1950 in *Biometrika* 37: 308–312, under the title "The maximum F-ratio as a short-cut test for heterogeneity of variance."

The ease of Hartley's maximum-F test comes from two facts: (*a*) one needs only to compute the ratio

(7.24) $F_{max} = $ (largest s_i^2)/(smallest s_i^2)

and (*b*) tables are provided which give the regions of rejection one probably will need. Hence, the test is very simply made by computing F_{max} and then using Table XIV.

Strictly speaking, Hartley's maximum-F test of $H_0(\sigma_1^2 = \sigma_2^2 = \cdots = \sigma_t^2 = \sigma^2)$ versus H_a(some σ^2's are unequal) requires that all s_i^2's have the same number of degrees of freedom. Often they do not, so Hartley suggests that one use the average number of degrees of freedom as the ν in Table XIV.

To illustrate the preceding remarks, the following seven random samples are assumed to have been drawn from normal populations. The hypothesis

$H_0(\sigma_1^2 = \sigma_2^2 = \cdots = \sigma_t^2 = \sigma^2)$ is to be tested against H_a(some σ's are unequal).

X_1	X_2	X_3	X_4	X_5	X_6	X_7
13.0	8.6	11.2	9.2	13.0	5.0	2.9
−0.2	2.3	15.2	6.4	2.6	6.7	3.7
1.0	3.6	−3.2	7.2	−1.4	7.0	7.8
3.0	5.4	−2.0	3.2	8.2	5.0	3.2
3.0	9.2	−2.8	7.4	4.6	0.1	4.4
−0.6	2.6	11.6	6.8		−1.6	2.7
	3.9	12.8	3.0		−2.3	
		13.2				

	X_1	X_2	X_3	X_4	X_5	X_6	X_7
$\sum X$:	19.2	35.6	56.0	43.2	27.0	19.9	24.7
$\sum X^2$:	188.40	227.98	851.20	297.68	266.12	151.75	119.83
$(\sum X)^2/n$:	61.44	181.05	392.00	266.61	145.80	56.57	101.68
$\sum (x^2)$:	126.96	46.93	459.20	31.07	120.32	95.18	18.15
n_i:	6	7	8	7	5	7	6
s_i^2:	25.39	7.82	65.60	5.18	30.08	15.86	3.63

$$F_{\max} = (\text{largest } s^2)/(\text{smallest } s^2) = 65.60/3.63 = 18.07.$$

The average number of degrees of freedom in this example is $39/7 = 6$ to the nearest integer. There are 7 s_i^2's and hence Hartley's table, our Table XIV, is entered with $k = 7$ and $\nu = 6$. The region of rejection is $\omega: F_{\max} > 15.0$; therefore, $H_0(\sigma_1^2 = \sigma_2^2 = \cdots = \sigma_7^2 = \sigma^2)$ is rejected and H_a(some σ^2's are unequal) is accepted.

If Hartley's $F_{\max}$ test is used on the example previously worked by Bartlett's method, the results are:

$$F_{\max} = 15.85/0.8010 = 19.79, \qquad \text{with } k = 6, \nu = 9$$

The region of rejection for this case is $\omega: F_{\max} > 7.80$ with $\alpha = 0.05$; hence, $H_0(\sigma_1^2 = \cdots = \sigma_6^2 = \sigma^2)$ is rejected in favor of the alternative, H_a(some σ^2's are unequal). The H_0 appears to have been rejected with about the same confidence as with Bartlett's test.

PROBLEMS

1. Given the following practice data, test $H_0(\sigma_1^2 = \sigma_2^2 = \sigma_3^2 = \sigma^2)$ against H_a(some σ^2's are unequal) by Bartlett's method and by Hartley's method. Draw appropriate conclusions.

X_1:   1.7, 5.8, 4.0, 3.6, 0.7, 6.2, and 2.5
X_2:   4.3, 0.5, 7.6, 5.2, 9.9, 0.2, and 3.8
X_3:   12.6, 9.3, 11.5, 10.0, 14.6, 9.8, and 10.3

2. The following data are measures of nitrogen losses in soils over a 22-year period at Kansas State University under four different crop rotations (data furnished through the courtesy of Dr. J. A. Hobbs, Department of Agronomy):

Continuous small grains	*Altern. small grains, fallow*	*Small grain, manure, row crop*	*Small grain, peas, small grain, row crop*
0.012	0.011	0.019	0.006
0.019	0.018	0.026	0.020
0.028	0.033	0.008	0.028
0.017	0.030	0.032	0.012
0.017	0.029	0.011	0.009
	0.022	0.018	0.010
	0.029	0.031	0.005
		0.018	

Use Bartlett's test of $H_0(\sigma_1^2 = \cdots = \sigma_4^2 = \sigma^2)$ versus H_a(some σ^2's unequal), and draw appropriate conclusions.

3. Do Problem 2 by Hartley's F_{max} test.

4. The following data are from the same source as those in Problem 2 but are carbon losses for the same rotations, in order:

X_1:   0.22, 0.35, 0.38, 0.26, and 0.65
X_2:   0.21, 0.26, 0.41, 0.58, 0.55, 0.43, and 0.56
X_3:   0.48, 0.34, 0.36, 0.52, 0.44, 0.49, 0.65, and 0.60
X_4:   0.28, 0.29, 0.46, 0.27, 0.28, 0.36, and 0.27

Use Bartlett's test to test the hypothesis that the true variance in carbon losses is not dependent upon the rotation used versus the alternative hypothesis that H_0 is untrue in some respect.

5. Do Problem 4 by Hartley's F_{max} test.

7.3   A SIMPLE ANALYSIS OF VARIANCE ASSUMING NORMAL POPULATIONS AND HOMOGENEOUS VARIANCES

If t samples, each of the same size, r, are drawn from the same normal population, the pooled sum of squares, $\sum_{i=1}^{t} \sum_{j=1}^{r} (x_{ij}^2)$, from within samples, and the pooled DF $= t(r - 1)$ can be used to calculate an unbiassed estimate of the population variance, σ^2, as was done in Chapter 4.   This estimator is, as previously shown,

$$(7.31) \qquad s^2 = \frac{\text{pooled} \sum (x_j^2)}{\text{pooled DF}} = \frac{\sum (x_1^2) + \sum (x_2^2) + \cdots + \sum (x_t^2)}{t(r - 1)}$$

Use of this estimator is wholly analogous to the procedure for estimating the common variance, σ^2, when the t test is used to test $H_0[(\mu_1 = \mu_2) \mid (\sigma_1^2 = \sigma_2^2 = \sigma^2)]$ against a suitable alternative. Hence, one way to estimate σ^2 is to use an estimator based wholly on within-group variation. This estimator of Formula 7.31 is unaffected by differences in level of measurement from group to group.

It also is known that the variance of sample means drawn from the same normal population is but one rth of the variance in the population from which the means were drawn; hence, one can compute the variance of the t observed treatment means, $x_{1.}, \cdots, x_{t.}$, and obtain therefrom a second estimate of the population variance merely by multiplying the computed variance of the means by r. For samples known to have been drawn from the same normal population this process of obtaining a second unbiassed estimate of the population variance would appear to be little more than an academic exercise, because the two estimates must average to the same value in the long run, namely σ^2. However, knowing that the same variance can be estimated these two independent ways will provide a clue to the procedure used to decide whether the samples were *not*, in fact, probably drawn from the same normal population.

The general line of reasoning to be used will be illustrated with diagrams of possible sampling situations, some of which should lead to the decision to reject the hypothesis that the population means are equal, given that their variances are equal. To that end, consider the sampling situations, case 1 and case 2, illustrated in Figures 7.31 and 7.32, respectively.

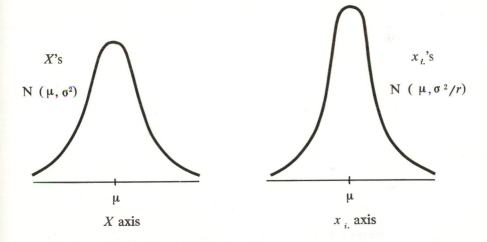

Figure 7.31.   Case 1: parent populations of X's are identical, so the population of means from samples of size r is $N(\mu, \sigma^2/r)$.

In case 1 the sample means, $x_{i.}$, have a dispersion described by the formula $\sigma^2_{x_{i.}} = \sigma^2/r$, where r is the sample size, but in case 2 the sample means will be more variable than this, because they tend to come from sections scattered along the scale of measurement. For example, the tth sample will tend to contain X's that are larger than those X's in the first sample, so $x_{1.}$ will tend to be smaller than $x_{t.}$. This built-in spread will cause the variance of these sample means to be greater than that of case 1. How much more dispersed the $x_i.$'s of case 2 will be than those of case 1 depends on how unequal the population means really are. In general, the situation of case 2 can be described as follows:

(7.32)   Variance of $x_i.$'s from case 2

$$= \sigma^2/r + \text{some positive quantity } K^2 \text{ depending on the } \mu\text{'s}$$
$$= \sigma^2/r + K^2$$

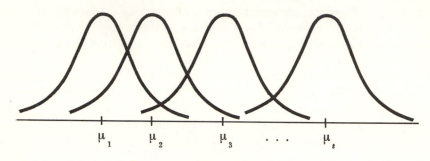

Population of X's

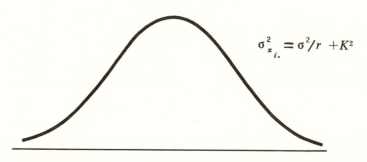

$$\sigma^2_{x_i.} = \sigma^2/r + K^2$$

Population of $x_i.$'s, one from each population of X's

Figure 7.32.   Case 2: parent populations of X's are equal, so variance of sample means is larger than σ^2/r by a positive amount K^2 which depends on how unequal the μ's are.

Therefore, if one assumed that $\mu_1 = \mu_2 = \cdots = \mu_t$ and estimated σ^2 by multiplying the variance of the observed sample means by r, this estimate actually would be an estimate of $\sigma^2 + r.K^2$, if case 2 were being sampled. On the average, then, the variance estimated from case 2 should be noticeably larger than the pooled estimate of σ^2, which is dependent upon the internal within-group variation and not at all upon the differences among the population means. It is this fact, in this simplest case, which makes it possible sometimes—depending on chance, on differences among the population means, and upon the power of the test—to detect that the hypothesis

$$H_0[(\mu_1 = \mu_2 = \cdots = \mu_t) \mid (\sigma_1^2 = \cdots = \sigma_t^2 = \sigma^2)]$$

should be rejected.

To illustrate the preceding discussion, consider the six random samples taken from the same normal population and summarized in Table 7.31.

TABLE 7.31.   SIX RANDOM SAMPLES FROM N(5, 4) EACH WITH $r = 10$, PLUS COMPUTATIONS

	1	2	3	4	5	6
	7.9	5.8	7.0	3.7	4.3	4.2
	5.6	3.2	5.7	2.8	9.6	6.2
	4.2	1.8	5.7	4.2	7.5	5.8
	7.2	5.1	4.8	2.4	3.7	6.1
	5.8	7.1	7.0	5.5	4.7	2.6
	7.3	3.8	0.6	1.6	5.0	5.8
	3.6	5.0	1.6	6.7	9.8	1.6
	3.0	5.1	2.6	6.6	2.3	6.8
	3.2	4.5	4.4	7.6	2.4	3.8
	2.4	5.5	3.8	2.0	4.1	2.0
Sums:	50.2	46.9	43.2	43.1	53.4	44.9
Mean:	5.02	4.69	4.32	4.31	5.34	4.49
$\sum (x^2)$:	36.136	19.529	42.876	42.189	66.424	32.969
s_i^2:	4.0151	2.1699	4.764	4.6877	7.3804	3.6632

Each sample is of size $r = 10$ and was known to be taken from N(5, 4). Starting with these samples, one can create samples from other normal populations with the same variance but different means simply by adding the same constant to each member of a given one of the samples. If different constants are added to each member of different samples, one produces samples from different normal populations. For example, if 5 be added to each member of sample 1, it becomes a sample from N(10, 4).

The $H_0[(\mu_1 = \cdots = \mu_6) \mid (\sigma_1^2 = \cdots = \sigma_6^2 = \sigma^2)]$ will be tested by comparing the two estimates of population variance described above, namely the pooled estimate produced by the within-group variability and the estimate obtained from the variance of the observed sample means. These two estimates are $s^2 = $ pooled estimate $= 4.4467$, by methods already described fully, and $s^{2'} = $ between-group estimate $= (1/5) \sum_1^6 (x_i. - x..)^2(10) = 1.705$.

If the $s^{2'}$ and the s^2, obtained respectively from the group-to-group and the within-group variations, are independent estimates of the same population variance, their ratio *in a predetermined order* is an F ratio. The fact that these two estimates *are* independent estimates of σ^2 can be argued two ways. One way is by common sense. One can see that as long as the sums of the samples stay the same—say at 50.2, 46.9, $\cdots$, 44.9, as in Table 7.31—the internal variance within each sample can be made as large or as small as you wish, and this will not change the external between-group variance at all, because the between-group sort of variance depends entirely upon the x_i's, which will not change as long as the sums of the samples stay the same. This fact suggests that variance within samples and variance between samples are two separate and independent concepts. The other way of arguing that the two estimates are independent estimates of σ^2 is by algebra. The total Sum of Squares of the deviations of all of the measurements in the t samples from their own grand mean, $x..$, can be shown to be the sum of two distinct and nonoverlapping quantities: the pooled Sum of Squares Within Samples and a quantity depending *only* upon the sample means and sample sizes. Specifically,

$$(7.33) \quad \sum_{i=1}^{6} \sum_{j=1}^{10} (X_{ij} - x..)^2 \equiv \sum_{i=1}^{6} \sum_{j=1}^{10} (X_{ij} - x_{i.})^2 + \sum_{i=1}^{6} r_i(x_{i.} - x..)^2$$

Total variation $\equiv$ within-sample variation +

between-sample variation

The estimate, s^2, comes wholly from the first term on the right-hand side, whereas the estimate $s^{2\prime}$ comes wholly from the second term on the right-hand side. Hence it is concluded that s^2 and $s^{2\prime}$ are two independent estimates of the same variance, if all samples are from the same $N(\mu, \sigma^2)$ population. If the samples are drawn from the same normal population, these two estimates are of the same population variance and their ratio in a predetermined order can be shown to be an F ratio. The algebraic identity seems to provide a rationale for the term "analysis of variance."

Before the analysis of variance for Table 7.31 is computed, Identity 7.33 will be illustrated from that table, as follows:

$$\sum_{i=1}^{6} \sum_{j=1}^{10} (X_{ij} - x..)^2$$

$$\equiv (7.9 - 4.695)^2 + (5.6 - 4.695)^2 + \cdots + (2.4 - 4.695)^2$$
$$+ (5.8 - 4.695)^2 + (3.2 - 4.695)^2 + \cdots + (5.5 - 4.695)^2$$
$$+ \cdot \quad \cdot \quad \cdot \quad \cdot \quad \cdot \quad \cdot \quad \cdot \quad \cdot \quad \cdot \quad \cdot \quad \cdot \quad \cdot \quad \cdot \quad \cdot$$
$$+ (4.2 - 4.695)^2 + (6.2 - 4.695)^2 + \cdots + (2.0 - 4.695)^2$$
$$= (+3.205)^2 + (+0.905)^2 + \cdots \text{finally} + (-2.695)^2$$
$$= 248.6485 = \text{the total Sum of Squares about } x..$$

$$\sum_{i=1}^{6} \sum_{j=1}^{10} (X_{ij} - x_{i.})^2 = (7.9 - 5.02)^2 + \cdots + (2.4 - 5.02)^2$$
$$\text{(from within sample 1)}$$
$$+ (5.8 - 4.69)^2 + \cdots + (5.5 - 4.69)^2$$
$$\text{(from within sample 2)}$$
$$+ \cdots + (4.2 - 4.49)^2 + \cdots + (2.0 - 4.49)^2$$
$$\text{(from within sample 6)}$$
$$= 240.123 = \text{Within-Samples Sum of Squares}$$

Because all $r_i = 10$,

$$\sum_{i=1}^{6} r_i(x_{i.} - x_{..})^2 = r \sum_{i=1}^{6} (x_{i.} - x_{..})^2$$
$$= 10[(5.02 - 4.695)^2 + \cdots + (4.49 - 4.695)^2]$$
$$= 10[(+0.325)^2 + \cdots + (-0.205)^2]$$
$$= 8.5255 = \text{Between-Samples Sum of Squares}$$

The computations performed above can be organized into a convenient form known as an analysis of variance table. In addition to the sums of squares involved in Identity 7.33 a column headed "Mean Square" is included. It contains the two independent estimates of σ^2 described earlier. On the assumption that the populations are identical, their ratio is an F. Each Mean Square is obtained by dividing the corresponding Sum of Squares by the degrees of freedom, DF. Table 7.32 shows this summary.

TABLE 7.32.   ANALYSIS OF VARIANCE FOR THE DATA OF TABLE 7.31

Source of variation	DF	Sum of Squares	Mean Square
Between samples	5	8.5255	1.7051
Within samples, pooled	54	240.1230	4.4467
Total about $x..$	59	248.6485	

The Between-Samples (or Different-Samples) Sum of Squares can be computed more easily than by obtaining the actual deviations of the Sample means from the grand mean, $x..$, because

$$\sum r_i(x_{i.} - x_{..})^2 \equiv \frac{(\sum X_{1j})^2}{r_1} + \cdots + \frac{(\sum X_{6j})^2}{r_6} - \frac{(\text{grand total})^2}{r_1 + \cdots + r_6}$$

as can be shown by changing the right-hand side to $r_1 x_{1.}^2 + \cdots + r_6 x_{1.}^2 - (r_1 + \cdots + r_6)x_{..}^2$ and using simple algebra. For the example given above, for which all r_i's are 10, one obtains

Between-Samples Sum of Squares

$$= \frac{(50.2)^2 + (46.9)^2 + \cdots + (44.9)^2}{10} - \frac{(281.7)^2}{60}$$

$$= (13311.07)/10 - 1322.5815 = 8.5255$$

as in Table 7.32. This table contains two independent estimates of the same σ^2, because all six samples are known, in this case, to have been drawn from the same normal population. The ratio of these two estimates, (Between-Samples Mean Square)/(Within-Samples Mean Square), in the predetermined order is an $F[(t-1), t(r-1)]$ in general and is $F(5, 54)$ for Table 7.32. It is found that for this table $F(5, 54) = 1.7051/4.4467 = 0.38$. According to Table XII, such as $F(5, 54)$ is quite small, so the H_0, that the population means are equal, is an acceptable hypothesis.

Now suppose that in Table 7.31 one unit is added to each member of sample 2, two units to each member of sample 3, $\cdots$, and finally 5 units to each member of sample 6. This is equivalent to having drawn those six samples from the six parent populations $N_1(5, 4)$, $N_2(6, 4)$, $N_3(7, 4)$, $N_4(8, 4)$, $N_5(9, 4)$, and $N_6(10, 4)$. The variance of each population still is $\sigma^2 = 4$, because coding by addition does not affect the deviations from the mean and hence does not affect the variance. How successful will an analysis of variance be in detecting these known differences among the populations from which the samples now have been taken?

The sampling data of Table 7.31 now will be altered as just described and the analysis of variance performed to anwer this question. When this arithmetic is done, the student will observe that, aside from rounding off errors, the Within-Samples Mean Square has not changed; only the Between-Samples Mean Square and, of course, the Total Sum of Squares, will have changed when those inequalities among the population means have been introduced. This is as it should be, because the population variances have not been changed (as noted before), but the population means have been moved farther apart; hence, only the estimate of population variance based upon the sample means, one from each population, will be larger, on the average.

The analysis of variance for Table 7.33 is shown in Table 7.34.

The computation of the Between-Samples Sum of Squares is accomplished most easily as follows:

$$\frac{(50.2)^2 + (56.9)^2 + \cdots + (94.9)^2}{10} - \frac{(431.7)^2}{60} = 176.426$$

where the 431.7 is the grand total of all 60 sample observations in these six samples. This sum of squares is precisely the same as $\sum_{i=1}^{6} r_i(x_{i.} - x..)^2$ with all $r_i = 10$ in this instance, and $x_{1.} = 5.02$, $x_{2.} = 5.69, \cdots, x_{6.} = 9.49$. The $x..$ is $431.7/60 = 7.195$, the grand mean of all 60 observations in this experiment. The Within-Samples Mean Square also could, with the r_i equal, be

TABLE 7.33.   SIX RANDOM SAMPLES, EACH OF SIZE $r = 10$, DRAWN FROM N(5, 4), N(6, 4), N(7, 4), N(8, 4), N(9, 4), AND N(10, 4), RESPECTIVELY

	1	2	3	4	5	6
	7.9	6.8	9.0	6.7	8.3	9.2
	5.6	4.2	7.7	5.8	13.6	11.2
	4.2	2.8	7.7	7.2	11.5	10.8
	7.2	6.1	6.8	5.4	7.7	11.1
	5.8	8.1	9.0	6.5	8.7	7.6
	7.3	4.8	2.6	4.6	9.0	10.8
	3.6	6.0	3.6	9.7	13.8	6.6
	3.0	6.1	4.6	9.6	6.3	11.8
	3.2	5.5	6.4	10.6	6.4	8.8
	2.4	6.5	5.8	5.0	8.1	7.0
Sum:	50.2	56.9	63.2	73.1	93.4	94.9
$x_{i.}$:	5.02	5.69	6.32	7.31	9.34	9.49
$\sum x_i^2$:	36.136	19.539	42.876	42.189	66.424	32.969
s_i^2:	4.0151	2.1699	4.7640	4.6877	7.3804	3.6632

obtained by computing the variance of the six sample means and multiplying this variance by 10, the sample size.

It is noted from Table XII that the $F(5, 54) = 7.94$ from Table 7.34 is so large that it would be in any sensible region of rejection, so

$$H_0[(\text{all } \mu\text{'s are equal}) \mid (\text{all } \sigma^2\text{'s are equal})]$$

is rejected. Thus, the excessively large variance among the sample means, which in turn was caused by having taken the six samples from populations with different means, has caused F to be so large that H_0 is rejected. In practice, when one does not know whether the population means are unequal, the evidence contained in the $F(\nu_1, \nu_2)$ obtained from such an analysis of variance is used as the basis for deciding to reject or to accept H_0 on the basis of a *reductio ad absurdum* line of reasoning.

When an F test has led to the rejection of such an H_0 as that tested in Table 7.34, one is led to believe that some of the population means are

TABLE 7.34.   ANALYSIS OF VARIANCE FOR THE DATA OF TABLE 7.33

Source of variation	DF	*Sum of Squares*	*Mean Squares*	H_0	F	*Decision*
Between samples	5	176.43	35.29	μ's equal	7.94	reject H_0
Within samples	54	240.12	4.447			
Total about $x..$	59	416.55				

unequal. If one is interested in the means themselves, there remains the question, Which population means are equal and which are unequal? This is the subject of the next section, and is discussed under the title of *multiple comparisons*.

However, before turning to the topic of multiple comparisons it is useful to consider the problems studied in Table 7.31 and 7.33 from the point of view of linear regression. The study of linear regression in Chapter 6 includes the matter of estimating a measurement, Y, from its linear relation to another measurement, X. We shall now take a similar point of view for X measurements in different samples which are to be studied by means of the analysis of variance. Initially this correspondence will seem almost trivial, but in more complex analyses of variance this approach will be found to be useful in the determination of the proper F test and in the interpretation of various sorts of analyses of variance.

In Table 7.31 all six samples came from the same normal population, so the identification of the sample adds nothing to our ability to predict the potential size of the jth member of the ith sample. Actually, the potential size of any X_{ij} is the same in this situation, regardless of which sample it is in, yet we know that each measurement is, in general, different from any other measurement—given sufficient accuracy of measurement—so we ascribe to each X_{ij} some measure of its individuality. Hence, in the situation in which all X_{ij}'s are from the same $N(\mu, \sigma^2)$ population, we describe the jth observation in the ith sample by the following formula, called the *statistical model* for this experiment:

(7.34) $$X_{ij} = \mu + \epsilon_{ij}$$

where the ϵ_{ij} are described as errors of measurement, so classified because we prefer to hold open the possibility that grouping the observations into samples might be associated with some average difference from sample to sample. The term *errors of measurement* is used to include actual errors of measurement plus any individuality that an experimental unit may have. For example, it is well known that plants of precisely the same genetic background are not identical with respect to almost any measurement one could take. If such plants were grown in different fields, the fields also might affect the measurement taken, so the subscript i could refer to fields and the subscript j to the jth plant taken from the ith field. Naturally, the piece of land in the ith field on which the jth plant actually grew would not be identical with a plot in another field on which a plant of the same genetic composition grew, so this sort of notation helps to designate where individual and group differences might occur.

With respect to Table 7.33, it is seen that identification of the sample in which a particular measurement appears *is* relevant to the ability to predict the size of X_{ij}, because some samples are from populations with larger means than those of others. Thus, if μ now stands for the grand average X over all populations represented by the samples taken, the equation for X_{ij} should include a quantity which differentiates between populations. Thus, we write

$$(7.35) \qquad\qquad X_{ij} = \mu + \tau_i + \epsilon_{ij}$$

where the τ_i measures the amount by which being from the ith population potentially adds to (τ is $+$), or subtracts from (τ is $-$), the basic average, μ. It is sensible and convenient to have the τ's add to zero, because this is the simplest way of indicating advantages and disadvantages associated with populations. Actually, for a fixed set of treatments, $\tau_i = \mu_{i.} - \mu$. We know from Table 7.33, from the way the populations were constructed, that $\mu = 7.5$, because the populations are represented equally in Table 7.33 and because $\mu_1 = 5, \mu_2 = 6, \mu_3 = 7, \mu_4 = 8, \mu_5 = 9$, and $\mu_6 = 10$, which have an average of 7.5. Also, the advantages and disadvantages (τ_i) associated with the six populations are $-2.5, -1.5, -0.5, +0.5, +1.5$, and $+2.5$, respectively. Outside the classroom these τ's usually will not be known and hence must be estimated and studied by means of sample information, but this illustrates what is meant by the μ's and the τ's.

To pursue the illustration in Table 7.33, we note that we could partially predict each member of each sample in that table, for we know the μ and we know the τ_i for each observation. We do not, however, know the ϵ_{ij}. Thus, we write a formula for the first observation in the sample 1 as follows:

$$X_{11} = \mu + \tau_1 + \epsilon_{11}$$
$$= 7.5 + (-2.5) + \epsilon_{11}$$
$$= 5 + \epsilon_{11}$$

The ϵ_{11} is estimated from the sample observation of $X_{11} = 7.9$ to be $+2.9$, but this is only an estimate. The next time a random sample of size $r = 10$ is taken from $N(5, 4)$, the first observation will undoubtedly be other than 7.9, and the estimate of ϵ_{11} will be other than $+2.9$.

As a second example of the meaning of Formula 7.35, consider the 8th observation in the 4th sample of Table 7.33. Before the sample was taken, one could predict, knowing as we do here that the sample was from $N(8, 4)$, that $X_{48} = 7.5 + (+0.5) + \epsilon_{48}$. The sample estimate of ϵ_{48} turned out to be $+1.6$; but this is not the ϵ_{48}, only an estimate of it.

More will be said on this general topic from time to time, to acquaint the student with this approach before the linear models generally used for the analysis of variance are studied in more detail in Chapter 8. It would be well for the student to practice writing down predictions (or models) for similar problems along the lines shown above. These models are similar to the regression models in Chapter 6.

PROBLEMS

1. Suppose that the following data are random samples from four normal populations which have the same variance, σ^2, but may or may not have the same means, μ_1, μ_2, μ_3, and μ_4:

	From N(μ_1, σ^2)	From N(μ_2, σ^2)	From N(μ_3, σ^2)	From N(μ_4, σ^2)
	12.2	4.9	8.0	4.6
	9.5	10.6	12.1	6.7
	11.6	7.0	5.7	5.0
	13.0	8.3	8.6	3.8
	10.1	5.5	7.2	8.2
	9.6	11.7	12.4	7.7
$\sum X$:	66.0	48.0	54.0	36.0
$\sum X^2$:	736.82	421.40	522.46	232.02
$x_{i.}$:	11.0	8.0	9.0	6.0
$x_{i.} - x_{..}$:	$+2.5$	-0.5	$+0.5$	-2.5

Grand total, 204.0; $x_{..}$, 8.5

Test $H_0[(\mu_1 = \mu_2 = \mu_3 = \mu_4) \mid (\sigma_1^2 = \cdots = \sigma_4^2 = \sigma^2)]$ against H_a(some μ's are unequal / equal variances). Use $\alpha = 0.10$.

2. Do Problem 1 by computing the Between-Samples Sum of Squares and the Within-Samples Sum of Squares directly from $\sum_1^4 [r_i(x_{i.} - x_{..})^2]$ and $\sum_1^4 \sum_1^{10} (X_{ij} - x_{i.})^2$, respectively.

3. Verify Identity 7.33 with the data of Problem 1.

4. If, for Problem 1, you are given that $\mu_1 = 10$, $\mu_2 = \mu_3 = 8$, and $\mu_4 = 5$, specifically identify the estimate of ϵ_{34} in the model $X_{ij} = \mu + \tau_i + \epsilon_{ij}$, where $i = 1$ to 4 and $j = 1$ to 6.

5. The following data were provided from soil tests at Kansas State University through the courtesy of Dr. J. A. Hobbs, Department of Agronomy. These numbers are nitrogen losses under different rotation plans during the period 1916–1938.

X_1:   0.048, 0.061, 0.042, 0.043, 0.047, 0.055, and 0.051

X_2:   0.036, 0.029, 0.037, 0.036, 0.029, 0.038, and 0.037

X_3:   0.048, 0.060, 0.057, 0.054, 0.056, 0.059, and 0.049

X_4:   0.040, 0.044, 0.033, 0.048, 0.037, 0.043, and 0.039

X_5:   0.006, 0.020, 0.028, 0.012, 0.009, 0.010, and 0.005

X_6:   0.019, 0.026, 0.008, 0.032, 0.011, 0.018, and 0.031

Test $H_0(\mu_1 = \mu_2 = \cdots = \mu_6 / \sigma_1^2 = \cdots \sigma_6^2 = \sigma^2)$ against the alternative that some means are unequal, and draw appropriate conclusions. Would it alter the F test if you multiplied each X_{ij} by 1000 to eliminate decimals?

6. Write down a model for the X_{ij} of Problem 5, fully defining all symbols.

7. The following data are for carbon losses in the same plots as in Problem 5. Do the same analyses as were required in Problem 5.

X_1:   0.57, 0.49, 0.46, 0.45, 0.48, 0.57, and 0.36
X_2:   0.52, 0.52, 0.73, 0.70, 0.59, 0.41, and 0.66
X_3:   0.66, 0.73, 0.59, 0.43, 0.16, 0.60, and 0.38
X_4:   0.42, 0.61, 0.45, 0.48, 0.29, 0.51, and 0.53
X_5:   0.28, 0.29, 0.46, 0.27, 0.28, 0.36, and 0.27
X_6:   0.48, 0.34, 0.36, 0.52, 0.44, 0.49, and 0.65

8. Write down the linear model for the X_{ij} of Problem 7, where $i = 1$ to 6 and $j = 1$ to 7. Then describe ϵ_{42} as fully as possible.

9. For the linear model of Problem 8 describe the τ_3 as fully as possible.

10. Referring to Problem 5, measurements of the nitrogen contents of the plots were made in 1916 before the different rotations were started. Given the following 1916 readings, perform the analysis of variance, and draw all useful conclusions.

X_1:   0.162, 0.182, 0.167, 0.170, 0.179, 0.172, and 0.169
X_2:   0.141, 0.138, 0.147, 0.157, 0.144, 0.142, and 0.145
X_3:   0.161, 0.182, 0.166, 0.166, 0.167, 0.180, and 0.162
X_4:   0.165, 0.172, 0.161, 0.168, 0.177, 0.175, and 0.173
X_5:   0.143, 0.158, 0.166, 0.143, 0.160, 0.150, and 0.150
X_6:   0.163, 0.166, 0.164, 0.174, 0.150, 0.160, and 0.176

7.4   MULTIPLE COMPARISONS FOR DETERMINING WHICH POPULATION MEANS ARE EQUAL AND WHICH ARE UNEQUAL

The question of which μ's are equal and which are unequal when t normal populations have been sampled, as in Section 7.3, has been answered from *some* point of view by a number of writers. Only two of those approaches will be considered in some detail here. The interested student can find information and reviews of the literature in this field in Duncan's article in the March 1955 issue of *Biometrics* and in the references he cites. This field is a very complex one for two reasons, given below.

(a) Various points of view can be taken about the importance of Type I errors relative to Type II errors and even about the definition of a Type I error rate. For example, when four treatments are being studied, one can ask about six two-mean, four three-mean, and one four-mean comparisons. Although some experimenters may be interested only in, say two-mean comparisons, others may be more interested in the experiment as a whole. It is easy to see how complicated these matters could get with, say, 10 treatments.

(b) It is not possible to discuss fully the powers of various procedures without assuming some differences among the μ's, and the μ's can be different in infinitely many ways. The Student-Newman-Keuls point of view was that protection against Type I errors in two-mean, three-mean, $\cdots$, t-mean comparisons should be kept at the same level, namely $100(1 - \alpha)\%$. Duncan has expressed the belief that this point of view causes an unwarranted loss of power to avoid Type II errors. This was his point of view when he introduced his New Multiple Range Test with its special protection levels based on degrees of freedom. The protection against Type I error decreases with p according to the formula $100(1 - \alpha)^{p-1}\%$.

R. A. Fisher combined an F test of

$$H_0[(\mu_1 = \mu_2 = \cdots = \mu_t) \mid (\sigma_1^2 = \sigma_2^2 = \cdots = \sigma_t^2 = \sigma^2)]$$

with follow-up α-level t tests, *provided* H_0 *were rejected*. Although the prior F test maintains $100(1 - \alpha)\%$ protection against Type I error on the t mean comparison, no further effort is made to maintain any specified level of protection against Type I error for p-mean comparisons when $p < t$, where p equals the number of treatments considered together.

The extreme in lack of protection against Type I error is the multiple-t test. This is a two-mean test of all possible pairs, μ_i versus μ_j, without a prior F test.

As has already been noted, there is a close inverse relationship between protection against Type I error and power to avoid Type II error. In general, with a given situation at hand, actions taken to increase protection against Type I error result in loss of power. Thus, an experimenter needs to be clear about the relative importances of Type I and Type II errors in his work and about the sorts of comparison he wishes to make best.

One of the simplest multiple-comparison procedures is the Fisher Least Significant Difference, so it will be discussed first. It is carried out as follows. If an analysis of variance leads to the decision to reject H_0[population means equal) | (variance equal)] at a predetermined level of significance, then use the t test on every possible pair of means, $x_{i\cdot}$ and $x_{j\cdot}$, with the same α level of rejection. The Error (or Within-Groups) Mean Square is taken as s^2 in the computation of $s_{x_{i\cdot} - x_{j\cdot}}$, so the standard deviation of the difference between two means stays the same for all two-mean comparisons. This makes it possible to compute a single significant difference against which each $x_{i\cdot} - x_{j\cdot}$ is measured for statistical significance. The formula for Fisher's *least significant difference* at the α level of significance is as follows:

$$(7.41) \qquad \mathrm{LSD}_\alpha = t_\alpha \sqrt{s^2\left(\frac{1}{r_i} + \frac{1}{r_j}\right)}$$

where s^2 is Error Mean Square, t_α is the α-level two-tail t for the Error degrees of freedom, and r_i and r_j are the sample sizes corresponding to $x_{i\cdot}$ and $x_{j\cdot}$, respectively. If $r_i = r_j = r$, one obtains

$$(7.42) \qquad \mathrm{LSD}_\alpha = t_\alpha \sqrt{2s^2/r}$$

It is convenient in practice to put the observed sample means into an ordered array, so that the LSD can be used directly in assessing the significance of each possible difference between two sample means. To illustrate the use of an LSD, consider the example of Table 7.34, in which an analysis of variance led to a significant F with $\alpha = 0.05$. The Error Mean Square was $s^2 = 4.4467$, so LSD $= 2.005\sqrt{4.4467(2/10)} \simeq 1.89$.

To complete the illustration of Fisher's LSD procedure, consider Table 7.41.

TABLE 7.41.   ORDERED ARRAY OF SAMPLE MEANS FROM TABLE 7.33 AND INDICATIONS OF SIGNIFICANT DIFFERENCES AMONG THE MEANS AT THE % LEVEL (*)

Sample number:	6	5	4	3	2	1
Mean $(x_{i.})$:	9.49	9.34	7.31	6.32	5.69	5.02

LSD* $= 1.89$. The $x_{i.}$'s lying above the same horizontal line are not significantly different; those over different lines are with $\alpha = 0.05$.

Among six sample means there are $6(6 - 1)/2 = 15$ possible two-mean comparisons. For each such pair there must be a decision to accept or to reject H_0, as shown in Table 7.42. (We shall not complicate the situation by

TABLE 7.42.   SUMMARY OF THE 15 POSSIBLE LSD COMPARISONS FOR TABLE 7.41, WITH $\alpha = 0.05$

Hypothesis	Decision	Correctness	Hypothesis	Decision	Correctness
$\mu_1 = \mu_2$	accept	wrong	$\mu_2 = \mu_6$	reject	right
$\mu_1 = \mu_3$	accept	wrong	$\mu_3 = \mu_4$	accept	wrong
$\mu_1 = \mu_4$	reject	right	$\mu_3 = \mu_5$	reject	right
$\mu_1 = \mu_5$	reject	right	$\mu_3 = \mu_6$	reject	right
$\mu_1 = \mu_6$	reject	right	$\mu_4 = \mu_5$	reject	right
$\mu_2 = \mu_3$	accept	wrong	$\mu_4 = \mu_6$	reject	right
$\mu_2 = \mu_4$	accept	wrong	$\mu_5 = \mu_6$	accept	wrong
$\mu_2 = \mu_5$	reject	right			

considering three decisions per pair, $\mu_i > \mu_j$, $\mu_i = \mu_j$, and $\mu_i < \mu_j$, because this generally seems unnecessarily complex in practice.) It is seen from Table 7.42 that, when all μ_i are unequal, then:

(*a*) Nine decisions out of 15 possible are right with respect to the inequality of population means. Hence, one could say heuristically that Fisher's $LSD_{0.05}$ had a power $= 9/15 = 0.60$ to detect the falsity of a hypothesis that two means are equal when, in fact, the means are unequal to the extent shown.

(*b*) Every one of the six incorrect decisions is caused by the failure of the $LSD_{0.05}$ test to detect a true difference as small as either 1 or 2 between corresponding population means, none of which exceeds 10.

If a 10% level of significance is chosen instead of a 5% level, it is logical to expect, on the average, that more true differences will be detected. The 10% $LSD_{0.10} = 1.58$; and the student can verify this value for the $LSD_{0.10}$ and the fact that only one more correct decision will be made in the example. Although it is obvious that increasing the probability of a Type I error from 0.05 to 0.10 will increase the power of the test to detect inequalities, it is equally obvious that this generally will increase the frequency with which one will falsely declare equal means to be unequal, so some sort of an appropriate compromise must be struck between these two kinds of error in any particular sampling situation. One of the difficulties with existing methods for making multiple comparisons is that no one is quite sure what the probabilities are for either Type I or Type II errors, although the extent of this uncertainty can be estimated.

A second procedure for making multiple comparisons among means of *t* groups of data is D. B. Duncan's New Multiple Range Test, or NMRT, in subsequent discussions. A full description and discussion of this method is given by Duncan in *Biometrics* 11: 1–42, 1955. The NMRT does not require a prior F test but does require that one obtain an unbiassed estimate of sampling variance appropriate to the situation being studied, so an analysis of variance often is run before applying the NMRT. As noted earlier, Duncan has introduced a special sort of protection against Type I errors, which depends upon the number of degrees of freedom for treatments, that is, upon the number of means being studied simultaneously in a subgroup. He also has handled the measurement of power somewhat differently, by using $p(p-1)/2$ power functions for a study of the power of this test when p means are involved. Strictly speaking even the test of $H_0(\mu_1 = \mu_2)$ versus $H_a(\mu_1 \neq \mu_2)$ is not a two-decision problem, because μ_1 can be unequal to μ_2 in two ways; thus, there are two inequalities and an equality, or *three* decisions possible. The Neyman-Pearson concept of power is a two-decision concept; hence, Duncan uses $p(p-1)/2$ power functions, one for each two-decision situation. This is not the place to go into the matter further, but the existence of several concepts of power may be related to some of the complexity which seems to exist in the field of multiple comparisons.

Another difference between Duncan's NMRT and the Fisher LSD is that the NMRT uses different measuring sticks for significance, depending on how many means are in the array, including the two extremes which are being judged for a significant difference. The Fisher LSD employs only one measure of a significant difference, namely the LSD_α.

To illustrate Duncan's NMRT, we again shall consider the data of Table 7.33, to which an F test and Fisher's $LSD_{0.05}$ already have been applied. The region of rejection again will be of size $\alpha = 0.05$, and the

Mean Square for Error will be $s^2 = 4.4467$, so $s_{\bar{x}} = \sqrt{4.4467/10} = 0.6668$, in view of the fact that each mean was obtained from 10 observations. Under Duncan's NMRT the measuring stick for a significant difference between two sample means at the 5% level is called an R_p^α and is obtained by multiplying $s_{\bar{x}}$ by certain numbers taken from tables supplied by Duncan and others. A condensed form of each of his 5% and 1% level tables is given is Table XIII. The Error DF are shown down the left-hand side of the table, and the number, p, of groups involved in a test is shown across the top of the table. When two adjacent means are tested for a significant difference, then $p = 2$; when the two means which are tested for a significant difference are the extremes of an array of three means, then $p = 3$; and so on, until $p = t$ for the test of the significance of the difference between the largest and smallest sample means from the whole experiment.

In the example now being considered there are six groups of data, so t is 6 and p will be 2, 3, 4, 5, and 6 in turn. Further, the s^2 has 54 DF. After simple linear interpolation in Table XIII it is found that:

	$p = 2$	$p = 3$	$p = 4$	$p = 5$	$p = 6$
5% q:	2.84	2.99	3.09	3.15	3.21
$R_p^{0.05}$:	1.89	1.99	2.06	2.10	2.14

The $R_2^{0.05} = 1.89$, which is Fisher's $LSD_{0.05}$, will be used to test the significance of differences between sample means which are adjacent to each other any place in the ordered array of those means, the $R_3^{0.05} = 1.99$ will be used when there is one mean between the two which are being studied for a significant difference, etc., until $R_6^{0.05} = 2.14$ is the difference between the extreme sample means in the ordered array of 6 means which will be considered significant at the 5% level. By using these measures of significance the following results are obtained for the data of Table 7.33, the same meaning being attached to the values underlined as before when Fisher's $LSD_{0.05}$ was applied to these same data:

Group number:	6	5	4	3	2	1
Mean, $\bar{x}_t$:	9.49	9.34	7.31	6.32	5.69	5.02

In this particular example the decisions made by the NMRT are identical with those made by Fisher's $LSD_{0.05}$ at the same level of significance, but such will not always occur, because the $LSD_{0.05}$, which is equal to $R_2^{0.05}$, is always identically equal to the smallest $R_p^{0.05}$. There obviously will be situations in which use of the $LSD_{0.05}$ will declare observed differences significant at the 5% level when those differences are not as large as the appropriate $R_p^{0.05}$. Thus, if Duncan's NMRT is protected in just the right way against Type I errors, Fisher's LSD is insufficiently protected against them, because it will declare more nonsignificant differences significant than will Duncan's NMRT, *if there are any equal population means.* Note, however, that Duncan's NMRT does not require a prior significant F and therefore will do testing for inequalities among μ's when the LSD_α has accepted equality; hence, it is not clear just how the protection under LSD_α differs from that under NMRT in the long run.

There is one restriction included in the NMRT that has not yet been mentioned. You are not to test for significance within subgroups whose extremes are not significantly different; hence, you start testing the extreme differences and work in toward the smaller subgroups. For example, it would be a violation of this rule if you were to test $x_{2.}$ against $x_{3.}$ in the example given above, because they are a subgroup of a group of three means whose extremes, $x_{4.}$ and $x_{2.}$, already have been judged not to be significantly different.

In view of the fact that nothing very definite has been done toward comparing the various multiple-comparison procedures *when some of the population means are unequal*, some empirical evidence on this matter has been obtained at Kansas State University from rather extensive sampling of populations with known differences between the means and all variances equal. This sampling was done with an electronic computer, because large numbers of samples of any specified size and from any specified normal populations can be drawn quite readily. Thereafter, any specified testing procedure can be applied, and one can obtain empirical, or Monte Carlo, estimates of the probabilities of Type I and Type II errors under various experimental conditions by means of sampling studies. Obviously, there is an endless variety of different sampling situations one could visualize, so these empirical studies have tried to simulate a wide range of possibilities of relative inequalities among the μ's and still keep the study as simple as possible.

The point of view regarding Type I errors and error rates taken in these studies is as follows:

(*a*) The experimenter wants to know which specific treatment (using this term very broadly) means are equal, on the average, and which are unequal, that is, which of the μ_i and μ_j are equal and which are unequal. If it is decided that $\mu_i \neq \mu_j$, the experimenter will assume that if $x_{j.} > x_{i.}$, then $\mu_j > \mu_i$.

(*b*) The most useful concept of a Type I error is that it occurs when the test concludes that $\mu_i \neq \mu_j$ when in fact $\mu_i = \mu_j$. It is immaterial whether $x_{i.}$ and $x_{j.}$ are separated by no other $x_{i.}$'s or by p other $x_{i.}$'s, although the measuring stick for $x_{i.} - x_{j.}$ might best depend on those circumstances, as it does in Duncan's NMRT procedure. Therefore, one measures protection against Type I error by the ratio:

$$(7.43) \quad \frac{100 \times (\text{no. of correct 2-mean decisions when } \mu_i = \mu_j)}{\text{total number of 2-mean decisions when } \mu_i = \mu_j} = \text{protection}$$

(*c*) The most useful concept of power here also involves only two-mean decisions, so power will be measured by

$$(7.44) \quad \frac{100 \times (\text{no. of correct decisions when } \mu_i \neq \mu_j)}{\text{total number of 2-mean decisions when } \mu_i \neq \mu_j} = \text{power}$$

Following are some illustrations of sampling situations which were studied this way, samples of size $n = 10$ being used in all instances.

Case 1.   Sampled $N(5, 4)$, $N(5, 4)$, $N(5, 4)$, $N(7, 4)$, and $N(7, 4)$ simultaneously. For brevity, this case is symbolized as $N(5, 5, 5, 7, 7; 4)$. This experiment simulates a sampling situation in which 10 decisions are to be made about the hypothesis, $H_0[\mu_i = \mu_j) \mid (\sigma_i^2 = \sigma_j^2)]$. We know that 4 of the 10 decisions should be decisions to accept H_0 and the other 6 should be decisions to reject it, and we know precisely which decisions are which. If 300 sets of means are obtained during a sampling, 3000 decisions can be made, of which 1200 should be decisions to accept H_0 and 1800 should be to reject it. Thus, after a sufficient number of sets of samples it is possible to obtain an estimate of the probabilities of Type I and Type II errors on a per decision basis as defined above.

Case 2.   Sampled $N(5, 4)$, $N(5, 4)$, $N(5.5, 4)$, $N(5.5, 4)$, $\cdots$, $N(7, 4)$, which is indicated briefly by $N(5, 5, 5.5, 5.5, 6, 6, 6.5, 6.5, 7, 7; 4)$. With 10 populations (as in this case) there are $10(10 - 1)/2 = 45$ possible decisions regarding equality of population means tested in pairs, for every set of samples taken. This sampling situation differs from case 1 by having finer gradation of differences between population means, but the range of differences between population means is the same. This should make it more difficult for any test to detect all the differences that actually do exist.

It is recognized that the 45 two-mean decisions made from one set of case 2 samples are not independent decisions, because one "wild" $x_{i.}$ in the set of 10 means will affect a number of decisions. Because it is hoped that the effects of this lack of independence will not distort the conclusions subsequently drawn, and because the task of making only one two-mean decision per set of ten samples would make the study impossibly laborious, it was decided to make the study as herein reported.

It was found to be much more difficult to perform the NMRT procedure on a digital computer than to perform the Fisher LSD test; hence, there are numerous gaps and shortages under the NMRT which, it is hoped, will be remedied later by additional work. Emphasis was placed on the LSD test because it is both the easiest and the most criticized of the two tests. Moreover, D. B. Duncan has recently published (*Ann. Math. Stat.* 32: 1013, 1961) a new approach to the multiple-comparison problem, which may mean a replacement of his NMRT procedure by another suggestion on his part.

The results of the Kansas State Monte Carlo studies are shown in Tables 7.43 and 7.44. It is important to remember that the evidence in these tables

TABLE 7.43.　RESULTS FROM A MONTE CARLO STUDY OF FISHER'S LSD METHOD OF MAKING MULTIPLE COMPARISONS FOR A TYPE I ERROR EXPERIMENT

Experimental situation	Correct decisions, % (numbers in parentheses are numbers of decisions)			
	When $\mu_i = \mu_j$		When $\mu_i \neq \mu_j$	
	$\alpha = 0.05$	$\alpha = 0.10$	$\alpha = 0.05$	$\alpha = 0.10$
N(5, 5, 5, 7, 7; 4)	(2,688) 96	(848) 90	(4,032) 52	(1,272) 69
,, ; 6)	(800) 96	(800) 90	(1,200) 39	(1,200) 53
,, ; 8)	(800) 95	(800) 91	(1,200) 26	(1,200) 37
,, ; 10)	(800) 96	(800) 92	(1,200) 19	(1,200) 30
,, ; 12)				
,, ; 14)				
,, ; 16)	(1,928) 97	(800) 93	(2,892) 13	(1,200) 17
N(5, 5, 5, 5, 5, 7, 7, 7, 7; 4)	(11,298) 95	(4,263) 89	(12,912) 57	(4,872) 71
,, ; 6)	(4,200) 96	(4,200) 90	(4,800) 38	(4,800) 53
,, ; 8)	(4,200) 96	(4,200) 92	(4,800) 27	(4,800) 39
,, ; 10)	(4,200) 97	(4,200) 93	(4,800) 20	(4,800) 31
,, ; 12)				
,, ; 14)				
,, ; 16)	(6,300) 97	(4,200) 93	(7,200) 12	(4,800) 21
N(5, 5, 5.5, 5.5, 6, 6, 6.5, 6.5, 7, 7; 4)	(1,500) 96		(12,000) 18	
,, ; 6)				
,, ; 8)				
,, ; 10)				
,, ; 12)				
,, ; 14)				
,, ; 16)	(1,370) 98		(10,960) 3	

TABLE 7.43 (*cont.*)

Experimental situation	Correct decisions, % (numbers in parentheses are numbers of decisions)			
	When $\mu_i = \mu_j$		When $\mu_i \neq \mu_j$	
	$\alpha = 0.05$	$\alpha = 0.10$	$\alpha = 0.05$	$\alpha = 0.10$
N(5, 5, 6, 6, 7, 7, 8, 8, 9, 9; 4)	94 (1,500)		54 (12,000)	
" ; 6)				
" ; 8)				
" ; 10)				
" ; 12)				
" ; 14)				
" ; 16)				
N(5, 5, 5, 5, 5.5, 5.5, 5.5, 6, 6, 6, 6.5, 6.5, 6.5, 7, 7, 7, 7; 4)	93 (500)		20 (4,000)	
" ; 6)	95 (4,500)	92 (3,000)	23 (16,000)	30 (10,000)
" ; 8)	96 (6,000)	92 (6,000)	13 (32,000)	21 (32,000)
" ; 10)	96 (6,000)	92 (6,000)	10 (32,000)	18 (32,000)
" ; 12)	97 (5,250)	93 (5,250)	7 (28,000)	15 (28,000)
" ; 14)	98 (6,000)	95 (6,000)	5 (32,000)	9 (32,000)
" ; 16)				
N(5, 6, 7, 8, 9; 4)	Not applicable	Not applicable	52 (9,030)	61 (2,000)
" ; 6)	"	"	41 (2,000)	51 (2,000)
" ; 8)	"	"	35 (2,000)	44 (2,000)
" ; 10)	"	"	25 (2,000)	34 (2,000)
" ; 12)	"	"	16 (6,510)	26 (2,000)
" ; 14)	"	"		
" ; 16)	"	"		

TABLE 7.43 (cont.)

Experimental situation	Correct decisions, % (numbers in parentheses are numbers of decisions)			
	When $\mu_i = \mu_j$		When $\mu_i \neq \mu_j$	
	$\alpha = 0.05$	$\alpha = 0.10$	$\alpha = 0.05$	$\alpha = 0.10$
N(5, 5, 7, 7, 9, 9, 11, 11, 13, 13; 4)	(1,500) 96		(12,000) 83	
,, ; 6)				
,, ; 8)				
,, ; 10)				
,, ; 12)				
,, ; 14)				
,, ; 16)				
N(5, 5, 5, 5, 5, 5, 5, 8, 8, 8, 8, 8, 8, 8, 8; 4)	(1,540) 96		(12,320) 53	
,, ; 6)	(9,000) 94	(9,000) 90	(10,000) 92	(10,000) 96
,, ; 8)	(17,550) 95	(17,550) 90	(19,500) 78	(19,500) 86
,, ; 10)	(13,500) 95	(13,500) 89	(15,000) 65	(15,000) 76
,, ; 12)	(17,640) 95	(17,640) 90	(19,600) 55	(19,600) 67
,, ; 14)	(16,380) 95	(16,380) 90	(18,200) 37	(18,200) 50
,, ; 16)				
N(5, 7, 9, 11, 13; 4)	Not applicable	Not applicable	(5,960) 77	(2,000) 88
,, ; 6)	,,	,,	(2,000) 77	(2,000) 82
,, ; 8)	,,	,,	(2,000) 70	(2,000) 76
,, ; 10)	,,	,,	(2,000) 68	(2,010) 73
,, ; 12)	,,	,,	(2,000) 50	(2,000) 63
,, ; 14)	,,	,,		
,, ; 16)	,,	,,		
N(5, 5.5, 6, 6.5, 7, 7.5, 8, 8.5, 9, 9.5; 4)	Not applicable	Not applicable	(16,920) 48	(8,010) 57
,, ; 6)	,,	,,	(9,000) 41	(9,000) 50
,, ; 8)	,,	,,	(9,000) 34	(9,000) 42
,, ; 10)	,,	,,	(9,000) 28	(9,000) 38
,, ; 12)	,,	,,	(18,090) 18	(9,000) 26
,, ; 14)	,,	,,		
,, ; 16)	,,	,,		

TABLE 7.44.   RESULTS FROM A MONTE CARLO STUDY OF DUNCAN'S NMRT FOR MAKING MULTIPLE COMPARISONS OF POPULATION MEANS

Experimental situation	Correct decisions, % (numbers in parentheses are numbers of decisions)	
	When $\mu_i = \mu_j$ $\alpha = 0.05$	When $\mu_i \neq \mu_j$ $\alpha = 0.05$
N(5, 5, 5, 7, 7; 4)	(1,840) 98	(2,760) 53
", ; 16)	(1,128) 92	(1,692) 17
N(5, ", 5, 5, 5, 5, 7, 7, 7, 7; 4)	(7,035) 98	(8,040) 49
; 16)	(2,100) 94	(2,400) 13
N(5, 6, 7, 8, ", 9; 4)	Not applicable	(7,030) 51
; 16)		(4,510) 18
N(5, ", 7, 9, 11, 13; 4)	Not applicable	(3,960) 74
; 16)		
N(5, 5, ", 5.5, 5.5, 6, 6, 6.5, 6.5, 7, 7; 4)	(1,500) 97	(12,000) 16
; 16)	(1,370) 97	(10,960) 5
N(5, 5, 6, 6, ", 7, 7, 8, 8, 9; 9; 4)	(1,500) 96	(12,000) 49
; 16)	(500) 95	(4,000) 18
N(5, 5.5, 6, ", 6.5, 7, 7.5, 8, 8.5, 9, 9.5; 4)	Not applicable	(8,910) 44
; 16)		(9,090) 15
N(5, 5, 5, 5, 5.5, 5.5, 6, 6, 6, 6, 6.5, 6.5, 6.5, 7, 7, 7, 7; 4)	(1,500) 98	(8,000) 15
; 16)		
N(5, 5, 7, 7, ", 9, 9, 11, 11, 13, 13; 4)	(1,500) 96	(12,000) 81
; 16)	(1,540) 97	(12,320) 48

does not prove that one method of making multiple comparisons is better than another, but the tables do give some interesting evidence regarding the comparative powers of these tests to detect true population differences between means under what could represent practical conditions. The tables also indicate the probable relative frequencies of Type I errors, the basis upon which Fisher's LSD always is criticized. More of this sort of empirical evidence is needed—and is currently being obtained—before any firm decisions can be made. However, it is believed that the following tentative conclusions can be drawn from these two tables.

(a) Over the range of sets of μ's studied, there is no support for the fear that the Fisher LSD test lacks protection against Type I errors. This conclusion is at variance with the literature on this subject except in so far as that literature is only concerned with cases in which the μ's all are equal. Equality of the μ's probably is not the general situation in experimental research.

(b) The power of the LSD test compares favorably with that of the NMRT over the range of sets of μ's investigated. This is not wholly unexpected, because Duncan's use of special protection levels was an attempt to strike a balance between protection against Type I error, believed to be inadequate with the LSD test, and sufficient power to detect real differences, believed to be maximum for the multiple-t test (which is just the LSD without the requirement of a prior significant F test).

(c) As expected, the power of any test depends on the actual differences which exist among the μ's.

(d) As also is expected, the power of any test depends on the size of the population variance.

PROBLEMS

1. Given the following practice data, take $\alpha = 0.05$, perform an analysis of variance, and apply the LSD and NMRT multiple-comparison procedures if justified thereafter.

Variety 1	Variety 2	Variety 3	Variety 4	Variety 5
3.8	5.5	8.0	4.1	6.1
5.0	4.8	5.9	3.6	7.0
4.5	6.0	7.5	5.1	5.8
4.1	5.0	6.6	4.4	8.0
4.3	5.8	7.0	5.0	6.2

2. Code the data of Problem 1 by subtracting 3.8 from each number, and then redo the analyses requested in that problem. Comment on the effects of such coding. What if each number were to be multiplied by 10, to eliminate decimals? What if you took the logarithm of each number to the base 10?

3. Make up a set of hypothetical data for five "varieties" with four observations per variety and such that the NMRT and LSD will lead to at least two different decisions with $\alpha = 0.10$?

4. Use the data of Problem 1, Section 7.2, to test $\mu_i = \mu_j$ for $i, j = 1, 2, 3$ but $i \neq j$, by the $LSD_{0.05}$ test.

5. Do Problem 4 by the NMRT with $\alpha = 0.05$.

6. Do Problem 4 for the data of Problem 4, Section 7.2, after omitting enough numbers to make $r = 5$ in all cases.

7. Do as in Problem 6 by the NMRT with $\alpha = 0.05$.

8. Apply the $LSD_{0.05}$ test to the data of Problem 1, Section 7.3.

9. Do Problem 8 by the NMRT with $\alpha = 0.05$.

10. Apply Fisher's $LSD_{0.10}$ to the data of Problem 5, Section 7.3, to test $H_0[(\mu_i = \mu_j) \mid (\sigma^2 \text{ are equal})]$ versus $H_a(\text{some } \mu\text{'s are unequal})$ for all i and j.

11. Do as in Problem 10, but use the NMRT instead of the LSD.

12. Do the $LSD_{0.10}$ test on the data of Problem 7, Section 7.3.

13. Do the NMRT procedure on the data of Problem 7, Section 7.3, with $\alpha = 0.10$.

7.5   THE SIMPLEST ANALYSIS OF VARIANCE WHEN THE NUMBERS PER TREATMENT ARE UNEQUAL

The basic theorem that the variance of sample means is one nth of the variance, σ^2, in the population sampled obviously becomes meaningless if the samples are of different sizes, because there is no common sample size to use in the theorem. However, the basic identity

$$(7.51) \qquad \sum_{i=1}^{t} \sum_{j=1}^{r_i} (X_{ij} - x..)^2 \equiv \sum_{i=1}^{t} \sum_{j=1}^{r_i} (X_{ij} - x_{i.})^2 + \sum_{i=1}^{t} [r_i(x_{i.} - x..)^2]$$

still holds with unequal sample sizes, r_i. Moreover, a very simple adjustment of the computational procedure for the Between-Groups Sum of Squares is all that one needs to obtain the analysis of variance with unequal sample sizes and to obtain simple between-group and within-group classifications.

The Within-Groups Sum of Squares and the Total Sum of Squares are obtained as with equal sample sizes. The Between-Groups Sum of Squares is got from the following formula:

$$\text{Between-Groups Sum of Squares} = \frac{(\text{Group 1 Sum})^2}{r_1} + \cdots$$
$$+ \frac{(\text{Group } t \text{ Sum})^2}{r_t} - \frac{(\text{Grand Total})^2}{\sum r_i}$$

when there are t groups of data with r_i observations in the ith group. Actually, this formula is precisely the last term on the right in Identity 7.51, as can be seen by expressing

$$\frac{(\text{Group } i \text{ Sum})^2}{r_i} \qquad \text{as} \qquad r_i x_{i.}^2$$

and

$$\frac{(\text{Grand Total})^2}{\sum (r_i)} \quad \text{as} \quad (r_1 + r_2 + \cdots + r_t)(x..^2)$$

To illustrate these computations, consider the data on the beam diameter of the antlers of mule deer from different localities in Colorado, shown in Table 7.51. Additional computations on this table produce

$$0.785^2 + 0.550^2 + \cdots + 0.805^2 + 0.590^2 = 14.550975$$

$$(19.125)^2/26 = 14.067909$$

TABLE 7.51.   BEAM MEASUREMENTS OF COLORADO MULE DEER WHICH ARE $1\frac{1}{3}$
YEARS OLD BUT FROM DIFFERENT AREAS

Area A	Area B	Area C	Area D
0.785	0.875	0.610	0.905
0.550	0.900	0.775	0.680
0.345	0.655	0.895	0.770
0.500	0.725	0.750	0.885
0.660	0.845	0.820	0.805
0.790	0.600	———	0.590
0.810	0.780	3.850	———
———	0.820		4.635
4.440	———		
	6.200		
$r_1 = 7$	$r_2 = 8$	$r_3 = 5$	$r_4 = 6$
$x_{i.}$: 0.634	0.775	0.770	0.772

Grand Total $\sum X = 19.125$, Grand Total $\sum (X^2) = 14.550975$

Supplied by courtesy of Jack Grieb, Colorado Game Research Center, Fort Collins, Colorado

Therefore,

$$\sum_{i=1}^{4} \sum_{j=1}^{r_i} (x_{ij}^2) = 0.483066 = \text{Total Sum of Squares about } x..$$

$$\text{Between-Areas Sums} = \frac{(4.440)^2}{7} + \frac{(6.200)^2}{8} + \cdots + \frac{(4.635)^2}{6} - 14.067909$$

$$= 0.098358$$

Hence the Within-Areas Sums is $0.483066 - 0.098358 = 0.384708$.

The analysis of variance table is shown in Table 7.52. This table shows the test of H_0(all $\mu_{i.}$ are equal|equal σ_i^2) versus H_a(some $\mu_{i.}$'s are unequal). The F test shows there is no reason to doubt H_0. It would be amazing if the true average beam diameters of deer in different areas were *precisely* equal, but a naturalist would be assured that any true difference which did exist probably was slight for those areas included in this study.

TABLE 7.52. ANALYSIS OF VARIANCE FOR DATA OF TABLE 7.51 WITH UNEQUAL NUMBERS PER GROUP OF MEASUREMENTS

Source of variation	DF	Sum of Squares	Mean Square	F	Decision
Different areas	3	0.098358	0.03279	1.87	Accept H$_0$
Deer, same area	22	0.384708	0.01749		
Total about x..	25	0.483066			

PROBLEMS

1. Compute the analysis of variance for the following data, assumed to meet the assumptions of the analysis of variance:

Treatment used on units:

1	2	3	4	5
3.8	2.7	3.5	4.0	3.2
4.1	4.1	2.5	4.5	3.7
4.0	3.6	4.2	4.2	4.2
3.7	3.6	3.7	3.7	4.0
3.0		2.9		3.6
		2.8		

2. Show for the data of Problem 1 that Identity 7.51 holds true.
3. Use the data of Problem 2, Section 7.2, to test $H_0[(\mu_1 = \cdots = \mu_4) \mid (\sigma_1^2 = \cdots = \sigma_4^2 = \sigma^2)]$ against H_a(some μ's are unequal) with $\alpha = 0.10$.
4. Use the data of Problem 4, Section 7.2, to do as in Problem 3, this section.
5. Omit from 0 to 4 numbers—at your choice—from each column in Table 7.31 and then do the analysis of variance with $\alpha = 0.10$.
6. Given the following practice data, compute the members of Identity 7.51 and then, after verifying the identity, do the analysis of variance, using those Sums of Squares:

Treatment:

A	B	C	D
12.2	6.7	10.7	4.3
8.6	10.2	9.3	7.2
10.9	5.8	9.7	5.0
9.5	6.2	8.5	5.6
9.8	8.5	7.4	6.2
11.0			4.9
10.6			

7. Make up a set of four groups of five numbers, each such that Fisher's LSD and Duncan's NMRT will produce at least one different decision.

7.6 MULTIPLE-COMPARISON PROCEDURES WHEN SAMPLE SIZES (r_i) ARE UNEQUAL

The Fisher LSD procedure and the unrestricted multiple-t test are not altered basically when the r_i's are unequal, because they were defined for the general case in the first place. However, the work involved usually will be greater, because more than one LSD probably will be required to make the desired decisions. This will depend upon how many of the r_i's are unequal and on how many of the tests of differences, $(x_{i.} - x_{j.})$, actually must be made before all the $t(t-1)/2$ possible pairwise decisions can be made. Common sense and good planning of these tests almost always will make it possible to reduce this maximum number substantially.

Duncan's NMRT probably would be very difficult to adjust exactly for unequal sample sizes, because he has constructed special tables which include his special protection levels against Type I errors. However, C. Y. Kramer (*Biometrics*, 12: 307, 1956) has given an approximation procedure which is relatively simple and quite logical. It consists of using R_p''s (instead of R_p's, as before), which are obtained by using

(7.61) $$s_{\bar{x}}' = \sqrt{(1/2)(1/r_i + 1/r_j)s^2}$$

instead of $s_{\bar{x}} = \sqrt{s^2/r}$, which was used when sample sizes were equal.

To illustrate the use of LSD and NMRT when the sample sizes are unequal, we shall use the analysis of variance and ordered array of means given by Kramer (as shown in Table 7.61).

When the observed sample means are put into an ordered array and Fisher's LSD procedure is applied (as explained fully below) the following table of results is obtained:

	Treatment:					
	F	*D*	*A*	*B*	*C*	*E*
$x_{i.}$:	458	498	521	528	564	630
r_i:	3	5	4	3	5	2

If the LSD technique were to be carried out for every possible test, eight different LSD's would be needed because of the different sample sizes. However, logical reasoning is sufficient to reduce this number, as will be shown. First, the hypothesis $H_0[(\mu_C = \mu_E) \mid (\text{equal } \rho_i^2)]$ is tested by means of $\text{LSD}_{0.05} = 2.120\sqrt{2397.0(1/5 + 1/2)} = 86.8$. Because $630 - 564 = 66$ is less than 86.8, that H_0 is accepted. To decide whether $\mu_B = \mu_E$ we compute $\text{LSD}_{0.05} = 2.120\sqrt{2397(1/3 + 1/2)}$, which is 94.7. The difference between the sample means for treatments B and E is $630 - 528 = 102$, which is larger than the 5% LSD of 94.7, so $H_0(\mu_B = \mu_E)$ is rejected. This latter decision leads to the rejection of the hypotheses $\mu_E = \mu_A$, $\mu_E = \mu_D$, and μ_E, because the differences between the corresponding x_i.'s are greater than when B was involved, and the r_i's are larger, which would make the $LSD_{0.05}$ smaller. To decide whether $\mu_C = \mu_D$ we compute $LSD_{0.05} = 2.120\sqrt{2397.0(1/5 + 1/5)} = 65.6$ and, because the corresponding difference between the means is 66.0, we reject the hypothesis that those two population means are equal. This result also makes it reasonable to accept the equality of the population means for treatments A and C, because the difference between their sample means is but 43.0 with sample sizes smaller than were used for computing $LSD_{0.05} = 65.5$. In a similar manner it is determined that the population means for treatments B and F probably are equal. One now can draw the horizontal lines shown in the table above and draw pairwise conclusions about any two population means. Thus, only three of the eight possible LSD's needed to be computed.

TABLE 7.61. AOV TO ILLUSTRATE USE OF FISHER'S LSD AND DUNCAN'S NMRT WHEN SAMPLE SIZES ARE UNEQUAL ($\alpha = 0.05$)

Source of variation	DF	Mean Square	F	Decision
Between treatments	5	9306.2	3.88	reject H_0
Within treatments	16	$2397.0 = s^2$		
Total about $x..$	21			

From Kramer, in *Biometrics* 12: 307, 1956.

As noted earlier, Kramer has given an approximate procedure for using Duncan's NMRT when the sample sizes are unequal. When his method is applied to the data of this illustration and Equation 7.61 is used, the end result differs from the decisions made with Fisher's $LSD_{0.05}$ in only one instance: the horizontal line below A, B, and C is extended to the left to include D. Thus Duncan's NMRT accepts the equality of μ_C and μ_D whereas Fisher's $LSD_{0.05}$ procedure rejects that hypothesis. In this situation, we do not know which method has made the correct decision, as we did when certain classroom examples were used and we knew the true populations being sampled, so one cannot say whether $LSD_{0.05}$ has lacked protection or NMRT has lacked power.

To apply Kramer's modification of Duncan's NMRT when the r_i's are unequal, one needs to compute several $s'_{\bar{x}}$ from Equation 7.61. In the present situation, $s^2 = 2397.0$ and the r_i's are 2, 3, 4, and 5. Suppose $r_i = 2$ and $r_j = 3$; then $s'_{\bar{x}} = \sqrt{\frac{1}{2}(\frac{1}{2} + \frac{1}{3})2397.0} = 998.75 = 31.6$. This standard error is appropriate for comparing the E mean with either the F or the B mean. The test of x_E. with x_F. involves an array of six means. The R_6 is $31.6(3.35) = 105.9$, which is less than $x_E. - x_F. = 172$; hence, $H_0[(\mu_E = \mu_F) \mid (\sigma_i^2$'s are equal)] is rejected in favor of $H_a(\mu_E \neq \mu_F)$. More specifically, it is concluded that $\mu_E > \mu_F$. In a similar way one computes: $R'_3 = 31.6(3.15) = 99.5$ and $x_{E.} - x_{B.} = 102$, hence $H_0[(\mu_E = \mu_B)|(\sigma_i^2 \text{ are equal})]$ also is rejected with $\alpha = 0.05$, and it is concluded that $\mu_E > \mu_B$ also.

Kramer's modification of Duncan's NMRT could be used in a similar manner to make other decisions about the true means involved in this study.

One point should be added about Duncan's NMRT for when the r_i's are unequal. According to his procedure *when the r_i's are equal*, if an array of p means is tested and found homogeneous as regards the population means, one does not make any tests *within* that p mean array. If the r_i's are unequal, what becomes of this rule? Kramer's modification is only an approximate test so, presumably, one would not err greatly in doing whatever testing within such an array one's judgment and the sizes of the r_i's dictated.

Because the unrestricted multiple-t gives precisely the same results as Fisher's LSD when the analysis of variance has produced a significant F (as it did in this example), there is no need to do the multiple-t procedure separately here.

PROBLEMS

1. Do the NMRT on the example of Tables 7.51 and 7.52.

2. Use the NMRT on Problem 1, Section 7.5.

3. Make up an example with four treatments and with unequal r_i's and such that Fisher's LSD could be used on it. Then use both Fisher's LSD and Duncan's NMRT to decide which population means are equal and which are unequal. Use $\alpha = 0.10$.

4. Use the $LSD_{0.05}$ procedure for unequal r_i's on the data of Problem 6, Section 7.5.

5. Use Kramer's procedure for the NMRT with unequal r_i's on the data of Problem 2, Section 7.2, with $\alpha = 0.10$.

6. Do as in Problem 4 for the data of Problem 4, Section 7.2.

7. Do as in Problem 5 for the data of Problem 4, Section 7.2.

7.7   EMPIRICAL STUDY OF F DISTRIBUTION, AND POWER OF THE F TEST

In view of the fact that the mathematical competence of the student in this course is not assumed to be high, it is useful to study the sampling distribution of F empirically, that is, from actual experience. The F to be used in this study will be the ratio of the Between-Groups Mean Square to the Within-Groups Mean Square when the hypothesis

$$H_0[(\mu_1 = \cdots = \mu_t) \mid (\sigma_1^2 = \cdots = \sigma_t^2 = \sigma^2)]$$

is exactly true. This situation was reproduced by drawing 325 sets consisting of five groups of 10 observations each from an N(5, 16) population. The Between-Groups and the Within-Groups Mean Squares were recorded for each such set, the former being designated by s_1^2 and the latter by s_2^2. Then $F(4, 45) = s_1^2/s_2^2$ is the statistic recorded and summarized in a frequency distribution with a total frequency equal to 325. The F's computed from these 325 sets of samples under two circumstances are summarized in Table 7.71. One circumstance is that just described, with H_0 exactly true, and the other is that in which H_0 is false, because the data were so changed that the samples in each set of five actually came from three N(5, 16) populations and two N(7, 16) populations. This situation was achieved by adding 2 units to each member of two of the five samples in a set. This does not change the variance but does increase the mean by two units.

TABLE 7.71.   OBSERVED FREQUENCY DISTRIBUTION OF F(4, 45) FROM 325 SAMPLES, WHEN H_0 IS TRUE BECAUSE ALL SAMPLES WERE DRAWN FROM N(5, 16), AND WHEN H_0 IS FALSE BECAUSE THREE SAMPLES OF EACH SET OF FIVE WERE DRAWN FROM N(5, 16) AND TWO FROM N(7, 16) ($n = 10$ FOR ALL SAMPLES TAKEN)

The H_0 is true				The H_0 is false, as noted			
F interval	f	R.C.F. %	1 − R.C.F. %	F′ interval	f	R.C.F. %	1 − R.C.F. %
≥ 4.00	3	100	0	≥ 6.00	2	100	0
3.00 to 3.99	8	99	1	5.00 to 5.99	7	99	1
2.50 2.99	10	97	3	4.50 4.99	6	97	3
2.10 2.49	15	94	6	4.00 4.49	5	95	5
1.80 2.09	18	89	11	3.60 3.99	14	94	6
1.50 1.79	34	83	17	3.20 3.59	15	90	10
1.20 1.49	35	73	27	2.80 3.19	22	85	15
0.90 1.19	43	62	38	2.40 2.79	26	78	22
0.60 0.89	59	49	51	2.00 2.39	32	70	30
0.30 0.59	57	31	69	1.60 1.99	37	60	40
0 0.29	43	13	87	1.20 1.59	43	49	51
	325			0.80 1.19	56	36	64
				0.40 0.79	46	18	82
				0 0.39	14	4	96
					325		

True mean F(4, 45) = 45/43 = 1.05   Observed mean F′(4, 45) = 1.92 when
Observed mean F(4, 45) = 1.11 H_0 is false

R.C.F. = relative cumulative frequency.

Figure 7.71 illustrates the concept of the power of the F test by showing the relative cumulative frequency distribution when H_0 is true and when it is false as a result of the alternations just described. The figure shows some important facts which are contained also in the table but may be more easily seen graphically. If H_0 is true, it is found that the 5% region of rejection is

$F(4, 45) \geq 2.60$, approximately. The table gives $F_{0.05}(4, 45) = 2.58$, which is in very close agreement with the graphic result. It is seen, further, that if H_0 is false, as indicated on the right-hand side of the table, the corresponding

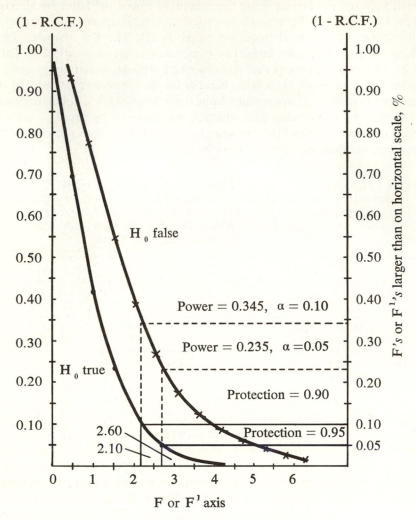

Figure 7.71.   Cumulative curves for Table 7.71: when H_0 is true, samples are from $N(5, 5, 5, 5, 5; 16)$; when H_0 is false, samples are from $N(5, 5, 5, 7, 7; 16)$.

cumulative frequency graph of the figure has about 23.5% of its area to the right of $F(4, 45) = 2.58$; hence, we say that the power of this F test in this situation is approximately 0.235, because that is the fraction of all experiments under the given conditions which would result in this false H_0 being rejected when $\alpha = 0.05$, according to Figure 7.71.

If a 10% region of rejection is used, tabular $F_{0.10}(4, 45)$ is 2.08. Figure 7.71 now approximates the power at 0.345.

The frequency distributions of Table 7.71 are given graphically in Figure 7.72 to show the general form of the F distribution and the effect of a false H_0.

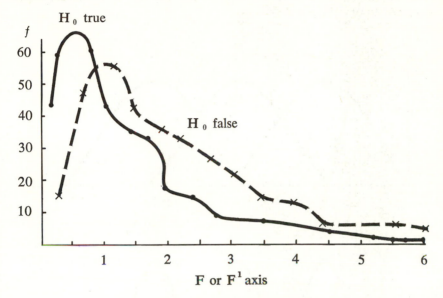

Figure 7.72. Observed distributions summarized in Table 7.71: the approximate F(4, 45) distribution is shown by the solid line (————) the effect of a false H_0 by the broken line (—x—).

The relatively low power of the F test in the preceding illustration comes to a considerable degree from the large population variance. It is entirely logical that the greater the amount of variability among the individuals in a population the more easily would differences among populations be masked. That is, it is difficult to decide whether the general level of measurement is different in two or more statistical populations, if there is great inconsistency of measurement within each population. This is shown visually in Figure 7.73, in which three populations have means that differ by 3 to 6 units in both graphs, but in the first graph the populations have approximately four times the variance of the populations in the second. It is obvious from these figures that the populations of (A) overlap so much that it would be difficult to tell which of those populations produced a certain random sample, unless the sample sizes were quite large. In (B), however, there is much less overlapping of the population distribution, so here it would be much easier to decide which population produced a certain sample. For example, in the graphs $\mu = 5$, the single random observation $X = 8$ is almost certain to have come from the middle population of that graph. In view of the fact that the three populations of (A) and the three of (B) in Figure 7.73 have exactly the same spread among population means, it is clear that detection of differences among populations depend heavily upon the variances of the population involved (say in an experiment), as well as upon the actual differences among the μ's.

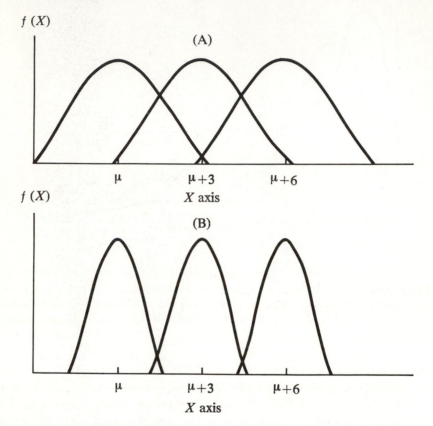

Figure 7.73. The effect of decreasing the population variance (by good design and execution of an experiment, for example) on the power of a statistical test to detect inequalities among μ_i's.

Table 7.72 was prepared to show how reducing the population variance by good planning of an experiment, care in the conduct of the experiment, etc., can benefit the statistical analyses to be made from research data by increasing the power of the appropriate tests to detect existing population differences. The table also shows how either a relaxation or a tightening of the level of significance demanded affects the power of the F test to detect real differences among population means.

TABLE 7.72.   CALCULATED THEORETICAL POWERS (BY TANG'S TABLES AND PROCEDURE) OF THE F TEST FOR SIX LEVELS OF SIGNIFICANCE AND FOUR SIZES OF POPULATION VARIANCES WITHIN EACH LEVEL OF SIGNIFICANCE

α, region of rejection	σ^2, population variance	Power of F test	α, region of rejection	σ^2, population variance	Power of F test
0.20	5	0.89	0.02	5	0.56
	8	0.74		8	0.33
	10	0.66		10	0.25
	16	0.51		16	0.14
0.10	5	0.80	0.01	5	0.45
	8	0.60		8	0.24
	10	0.51		10	0.18
	16	0.36		16	0.09
0.05	5	0.70	0.001	5	0.22
	8	0.47		8	0.08
	10	0.38		10	0.05
	16	0.25		16	0.02

All samples are of size $n = 10$ and are drawn from N(5, σ^2), N(5, σ^2), N(5, σ^2), N(7, σ^2), and N(7, σ^2) to produce F(4, 45)'s. $H_0(\mu$'s are equal | variances are equal) is false and should be rejected.

The reward in terms of increased power to be obtained from the use of every possible legitimate means to reduce population variance is obvious from Table 7.72. It also is obvious that, if one uses a 0.1% level of significance, one might as well accept H_0 without further consideration, unless the population variance is very low or the sample sizes very large (or both).

7.8   USE OF THE STUDENTIZED RANGE TO PERFORM A SIMPLE ONE-WAY ANALYSIS OF VARIANCE

Many times the experimental data that are available for statistical analysis are so costly to obtain that it is preferable to use the best and most powerful statistical analyses on the available data. However, there are situations in which it is justifiable to use a quicker and cheaper analysis, so a method of testing $H_0[(\mu_1 = \cdots \mu_t) \mid (\sigma_1^2 = \cdots \sigma_t^2 = \sigma^2)]$ has been developed in which the range is used as the measure of variability, instead of the standard deviation. With the aid of tables, the computations with the range are quite easy.

P. B. Patnaik (*Biometrika* 37: 78, 1950) has shown that the sampling statistic,

(7.81)
$$q = \frac{W_t c \sqrt{r}}{\bar{w}_{\text{tr}}}$$

has approximately the distribution of the studentized range (Table XVIII) with parameters t and ν if:

W_t = the range of the Treatment means, $x_{1.}, x_{2.}, \cdots, x_{t.}$
$\bar{w}_{tr}$ = the mean of the Treatment ranges: $w_1, \cdots, w_t$
r = the number of observations per Treatment
$c = d_r(1 + 1/4\nu + 1/32\nu^2 - 5/128\nu^3)$
t = the number of Treatments
$k = V/d_r^2$
$\nu = 1/(-2 + 2\sqrt{1 + 2k})$
d_r = the true mean of w/σ found in Table XIX
$V = 1/t$, the variance of w/σ found in Table XIX

Hence, one can compute q from Equation 7.81, choose a size α for the region of rejection as 0.01, 0.05, or 0.10 (because these are available in tables) and then see whether this q falls within the region of rejection.

For an illustration of this analysis of variance consider the following set of practice data, in which nine observations were made under each of six treatments:

		Treatment No.:				
1	2	3	4	5	6	
3	11	10	1	18	4	
−2	5	6	12	12	11	
7	8	13	3	15	0	
5	7	11	7	10	7	
1	7	5	4	7	3	
4	14	8	6	13	6	
0	4	6	10	13	14	
9	10	17	5	9	5	
0	6	5	6	11	13	
$x_{t.}$: 3	8	9	6	12	7	$W_t = 9$
w_t: 11	10	12	11	11	14	$\bar{w}_{tr} = 11.5$

From Table XIX, $d_9 = 2.97003$ and

$$V = (1/t)V_9 = \tfrac{1}{6}(0.65262) = 0.10877,$$

and so

$$k = 0.10877/(2.97003)^2 = 0.012331$$

and

$$\nu = 1/(-2 + 2\sqrt{1.024662}) = 40.783.$$

With these results it is determined that

$$c = 2.97003[1 + 1/4(40.783) + 1/32(40.783)^2 - 5/128(40.783)^3] = 2.9883.$$

The average treatment range is $\bar{w}_{tr} = 11.5$, and the range of the treatment means is $W_6 = 9$; therefore, by Formula 7.81,

$$q = \frac{9(2.9883)\sqrt{9}}{11.5} = \frac{80.68}{11.5} = 7.02$$

According to Table XVIII, with $\alpha = 0.05$ the upper 5% region of rejection for $t = 6$ and $\nu = 41$ is

$$\omega: \qquad q \geqslant 4.23$$

so $H_0[(\mu_1 = \cdots = \mu_6) \mid (\sigma_1^2 = \cdots = \sigma_6^2 = \sigma^2)]$ is rejected in favor of the alternative hypothesis, that some of the μ's are not equal to others. This also would have been the decision had α been shown as 0.01, for $q_{0.01} = 5.11$ when $t = 6$ and $\nu = 41$.

The same example now will be worked by the regular one-way analysis of variance, to show the difference in amount of work and the similarity of conclusions.

The Total Sum of Squares is

$$\sum_i^6 \sum_j^9 (X_{ij} - x..)^2 = \sum\sum (X_{ij}^2) - \left(\frac{\sum\sum X_{ij})^2}{rt}\right) = 4125 - \frac{(405)^2}{54} = 1087.5$$

The Between-Treatments Sum of Squares is

$$r \sum_{i=1}^t (x_{i.} - x..)^2 = \frac{27^2 + 72^2 + \cdots + 63^2}{9} - \frac{(405)^2}{54} = 409.5$$

Therefore, the Within-Treatments Sum of Squares is $1087.5 - 409.5 = 678.0$, and the analysis of variance table is as follows:

Source of variation	DF	Sum of Squares	Mean Square	F(5, 48)
Between-Treatments	5	409.5	81.90	5.80
Within-Treatments	48	678.0	14.12	
Total about $x..$:	53	1087.5		

If α is chosen 0.05, as for the range test, the region of rejection, ω for testing $H_0[(\mu_1 = \cdots = \mu_6) \mid (\sigma_1^2 = \cdots = \sigma_6^2 = \sigma^2)]$ against H_a(some μ's are unequal) is $F_{0.05}(5, 48) \geqslant 2.41$, according to Table XII. The observed $F(5, 48) = 5.80$, is larger than $F_{0.05}(5, 48)$; hence, H_0 certainly would be rejected by this F test.

In general, the range analysis of variance and the regular analysis of variance agree very well regarding H_0. In this simple example, with small integers as data, the difference in time and labor is not great, but with the usual sort of decimals and three-digit to five-digit numbers, Patnaik's range analysis of variance would be much the easier test to perform.

Although no multiple-comparison procedures following Patnaik's test appear to have been developed, it seems logical that some useful information could be derived by using the G test on $H_0(\mu_i = \mu_j)$ versus $H_a(\mu_i \neq \mu_j)$, provided $H_0[(\mu_1 = \cdots = \mu_t) \mid (\sigma_1^2 = \cdots = \sigma_t^2 = \sigma^2)]$ had been rejected. Obviously, those who criticize Fisher's LSD test also would criticize this range LSD test for the same reasons.

PROBLEMS

1. Given the following practice data, do the analysis of variance by Patnaik's range test and draw appropriate conclusions:

		Treatment No.:		
1	2	3	4	5
28.7	30.6	47.8	27.2	52.1
20.5	25.2	33.6	36.5	37.8
32.9	18.3	40.5	38.1	44.2
25.0	28.8	37.0	22.6	47.0
19.2	20.6	41.1	30.3	36.6
21.1	20.1	35.3	29.8	42.2

2. Do Problem 1, Section 7.4, by Patnaik's range analysis.

3. Do Problem 7, Section 7.3, by Patnaik's procedure.

4. Do Problem 10, Section 7.3, by Patnaik's range procedure.

5. Do Problem 1, Section 7.3, by Patnaik's range analysis of variance.

6. The following samples of size $r = 10$ were drawn from the populations indicated. Perform Patnaik's range analysis of variance of $H_0[(\mu_1 = \cdots = \mu_6) \mid (\sigma_1^2 = \cdots = \sigma_6^2 = \sigma^2)]$, ignoring the truly unequal σ^2's. Then apply the G test of $H_0(\mu_i = \mu_j)$ versus $H_a(\mu_i \neq \mu_j)$, where $i, j = 1$ to 6 to see how well these tests detect the true differences shown.

$N(5, 4)$	$N(6, 4)$	$N(7, 4)$	$N(1, 16)$	$N(9, 16)$	$N(11, 16)$
6.0	5.4	7.3	5.0	12.1	6.6
6.8	1.6	10.8	13.0	15.4	6.2
5.3	6.0	6.0	5.0	17.8	5.4
5.5	1.0	7.7	2.6	8.6	9.0
5.4	2.8	5.6	4.6	7.4	5.8
2.4	4.9	5.9	13.8	2.2	8.6
6.6	5.5	6.2	5.4	8.2	18.2
6.7	5.1	7.1	9.0	11.4	15.0
3.8	3.9	8.7	15.2	5.4	17.4
4.5	5.1	10.4	6.2	10.5	11.8

7. The amount of protein-bound iodine (PBI) in human blood is used to measure the basal metabolism rate of humans. Given the following hypothetical data

		Group No.:		
	I	II	III	IV
	5.3	7.2	7.0	7.6
	6.0	6.9	5.4	7.0
	4.9	5.3	5.8	7.9
	5.4	6.7	6.3	6.8
	4.5	6.6	5.4	7.5
	4.5	7.5	5.5	7.6
Sum:	30.6	40.2	35.4	44.4

for an investigation of possible differences in PBI among four groups of people, test $H_0[(\mu_1. = \cdots = \mu_4) \mid$ (equal variances)] against H_a(some $\mu_i.$'s are different), assuming that for the jth sample under the ith group

$$X_{ij} = \mu + \tau_i + \epsilon_{ij}, \qquad \text{where } i = 1 \text{ to } 4 \text{ and } j = 1 \text{ to } 6$$

with the usual assumptions for Model I (fixed effects). Use $\alpha = 0.05$.

8. Without changing the sums or sample sizes in Problem 7, alter the data so that there is not a significant Group Mean Square even with $\alpha = 0.10$.

9. The following four random samples were drawn from normal populations with the same variance:

Sample No.:			
1	2	3	4
5.5	6.6	5.9	7.3
5.5	8.4	2.2	6.1
4.3	5.5	5.7	8.3
1.4	8.9	6.8	10.2
3.3	8.3	6.1	4.7
9.2	8.4	7.7	4.5
5.8	9.9	2.0	4.5

Use Patnaik's range analysis of variance to test $H_0[(\mu_1 = \cdots = \mu_4) \mid (\sigma_1^2 = \cdots = \sigma_4^2 = \sigma^2)]$ against its negation.

7.9   ANALYSIS OF VARIANCE FOR TWO-WAY CLASSIFICATIONS OF EXPERIMENTAL UNITS

Suppose that an engineer wishes to compare the strengths of concrete beams made with different types of cement and with different aggregates. The types of cement could include the products of different companies, different air-entrainment additives, etc. The aggregates should involve a range of sizes of gravel and different sources from which the gravel was obtained, such as from different rivers. Suppose that there are to be t types of cement and r aggregates. It also will be supposed at first (although it is unrealistic) that only one concrete beam is made from each combination of a type of cement with a kind of aggregate, a total of tr beams. This will simplify the introduction of new parts in the analysis of variance.

The strength of a randomly selected beam from this study could depend on some, or all, of the following four sources of variation in beam strength: (1) the type of cement used, (2) the kind of aggregate used with this cement, (3) an interaction of some sort between cement and aggregate, and (4) a random error typical of the beam that happened to be made from a specific combination of cement and aggregate. We shall disregard the third source temporarily and thus simplify the problem. In terms of a statistical model, one can write a formula for the strength of a randomly chosen beam made with Cement i and using Aggregate j, as follows:

(7.91)
$$X_{ij} = \mu + \tau_i + \beta_j + \epsilon_{ij}$$

where

X_{ij} = breaking load of the beam made with Cement i and Aggregate j

μ = the grand average breaking load for all conceivable such beams made with any of these specific cements combined with any of these specific aggregates

τ_i = the effect on average breaking load of using Cement i as compared with the grand average, μ. In fact, $\mu_i = \mu_{i.} = \mu$, where $\mu_{i.}$ = true mean for Treatment i. For example, if the average advantage of using Cement 1 is 50 pounds above the grand average, then $\tau_1 = 50$.

β_j = the average effect of using Aggregate j relative to the grand average, $\mu_{.j} - \mu$ for fixed Aggregates

ϵ_{ij} = the random error represented in the particular beam made from the combination of Cement i and Aggregate j

Obviously, this statistical model assumes that the Cement, Aggregate, and error effects on beam strength are independent, linear, and additive. It thus assumes that all that an X_{ij} contains, beyond $\mu + \tau_i + \beta_j$, is a normal random error ϵ_{ij}. In some circumstances there will be what is called *inter-action*, so a different model will be needed.

In terms of an analysis of variance, the following outline of one would be appropriate and also is what one would consider reasonable:

Source of variation	DF
Different Cements	$t - 1$
Different Aggregates	$r - 1$
Error (Remainder)	$(r - 1)(t - 1)$
Total about $x..$	$rt - 1$

It is noted that there is an Error (Remainder) source of variation with $(t - 1)(r - 1)$ DF, which appears to be what is left over after the known sources, Cements and Aggregates, have been accounted for. As a matter of fact, in accordance with the idea used in Identity 7.33 earlier, it can be shown that the following identity holds for the present experimental situation:

(7.92)
$$\sum_{i=1}^{t} \sum_{j=1}^{r} (X_{ij} - x..)^2 \equiv \sum_{i=1}^{t} \sum_{j=1}^{r} [(X_{ij} - x_{i.} - x_{.j} + x..)^2]$$

$$+ r \sum_{i=1}^{t} [(x_{i.} - x..)^2] + t \sum_{j=1}^{r} [(x_{.j} - x..)^2]$$

where $x_{i.}$ is the sample mean for Cement i, $x_{.j}$ is the sample mean for Aggregate j, and $x_{..}$ is the grand mean of samples. The second and third terms on the right-hand side of this identity measure, respectively, the net effects of Cements and Aggregates over the whole experiment. The first term on the right measures something else, which also is independent of the Cement and Aggregate effects and is additive to them in the determination of the total variation of the strengths of the tr sample beams about their grand average strength. In the present experimental plan and model we have no choice but to consider this first term as an Error source of variation, and use its corresponding Mean Square as our estimate of σ^2, but this source of variation *could* be something other than just sampling error—for example, a tendency of some cements to work better with certain aggregates than with others—that is, an *interaction* between Cement and Aggregate. If this seems reasonable, the study must be planned so this additional source of variation can be studied. This matter will be illustrated later.

TABLE 7.91.   HYPOTHETICAL EXAMPLE OF A TWO-WAY CLASSIFICATION OF EXPERIMENTAL DATA, ASSUMING NO INTERACTION AND THE MODEL $X_{ij} = \mu + \tau_i + \beta_j + \epsilon_{ij}$

	Cement No.							
Aggregate	1	2	3	4	5	*Total*	*Mean*	$x_{.j} - x_{..}$
A	10	14	6	22	13	65	13	0
B	12	9	8	20	11	60	12	−1
C	8	10	4	18	10	50	10	−3
D	16	15	10	28	16	85	17	+4
Cem. sum:	46	48	28	88	50	260		
Cem. mean:	11.5	12.0	7.0	22.0	12.5		$13.0 = x_{..}$	
$x_{i.} - x_{..}$:	−1.5	−1.0	−6.0	+9.0	−0.5			

TABLE 7.92.   ANALYSIS OF VARIANCE SUMMARIZING THE COMPUTATIONS FROM TABLE 7.91 (MODEL: $X_{ij} = \mu + \tau_i + \beta_j + \epsilon_{ij}$; FIXED EFFECTS)

Source of variation	DF	*Sum of Squares*	*Mean Square*	F *ratio*	*Decision*
Cements	4	482	120.5	51.65	Some $\tau_i \neq 0$
Aggregates	3	130	43.33	18.57	Some $\beta_j \neq 0$
Error (Remainder)	12	28	2.333		
Total about $x_{..}$:	19	640			

The following computations can be made from Table 7.91 and used in the analysis of variance table shown in Table 7.92:

$$\sum_{i=1}^{5} \sum_{j=1}^{4} (X_{ij} - x..)^2 = \text{Total SS} - \frac{(GT)^2}{rt}$$

$$= 4020 - \frac{(260)^2}{20} = 640 = \text{Total Sum of Squares}$$

$$\sum_{i=1}^{5} [(X_{i.} - x..)^2] = (-1.5)^2 + (-1)^2 + (-6)^2 + (9)^2 + (-0.5)^2$$

$$= 120.50$$

Hence,

$$r. \sum_{i=1}^{5} (x_{i.} - x..)^2 = 4(120.50) = 482.0 = \text{Cement Sum of Squares}$$

$$\sum_{j=1}^{4} (x._{j} - x..)^2 = (0)^2 + (-1)^2 + (-3)^2 + (4)^2 = 26$$

$$5(26) = 130 = \text{Aggregate Sum of Squares}$$

$$\sum_{i=1}^{5} \sum_{j=1}^{4} (X_{ij} - x_{i.} - x._{j} + x..)^2$$

$$= (10 - 11.5 - 13 + 13)^2 + (14 - 12 - 13 + 13)^2 + \cdots$$

$$+ (16 - 12.5 - 17 + 13)^2$$

$$= 28.00 = \text{Error Sum of Squares}$$

These computations demonstrate the Identity 7.92, but it is worth pointing out here, before the analysis of variance table is given, that the same results can be obtained routinely as follows:

$$\text{Cement Sum of Squares} = \frac{(46)^2 + (48)^2 + (28)^2 + (88)^2 + (50)^2}{4} - \frac{(260)^2}{20}$$

$$= 482.0$$

$$\text{Aggregates Ss} = \frac{(65)^2 + (60)^2 + (50)^2 + (85)^2}{5} - \frac{(260)^2}{20} = 130$$

Error Ss = Total Ss − Cements Ss − Aggregates Ss, wherein the symbol Ss obviously designates the final corrected Sum of Squares which will appear in the analysis of variance.

When these results are put into a convenient tabular form, Table 7.92 is obtained.

It is informative to study the Error Sum of Squares of Table 7.92 in some detail. The algebraic expression used to compute it can be rewritten in the following way:

(7.93) $X_{ij} - x_{i.} - x._{j} + x.. \equiv X_{ij} - [x.. + (x_{i.} - x..) - (x._{j} - x..)]$

In this form, it can be seen that the observed X_{ij} is being compared (by subtraction) with the best estimate one could make for a concrete beam made with Cement i and Aggregate j, because account has been taken of the worth or poorness of Cement i (and of the Aggregate j), on the average, both relative to the grand average, $x\ldots$ One might wonder why one needs an estimate of the strength of a beam made with Cement i and Aggregate j, but it must be remembered that the observation given, X_{ij}, is known to include some sampling error, and an estimate of its magnitude is wished. The best estimate of the average effect of using Cement i is given by $x_{i.} - x..$, and similarly for the average effect of Aggregate j; therefore, the best estimate of the average *combined* effects of Cement i and Aggregate j is obtained from $(x_{i.} - x..) + (x_{.j} - x..)$. It follows, then, that the best estimate of what Cement i and Aggregate j should produce together would be got by adding $(x_{i.} - x..) + (x_{.j} - x..)$ to the grand average, $x..$, and this is precisely what is done in Identity 7.93 for comparison with the observed X_{ij}.

As mentioned earlier, it has been assumed so far in this section that the "errors," $(X_{ij} - x_{i.} - x_{.j} + x..)$, will be random errors of measurement. This may not be true, because it may be that Treatment effects may be related to Block effects, using the terms "Treatment" and "Block" generally —to include Cement and Aggregate, for example. The effect of one type of cement on the strength of concrete beams may depend upon the aggregate used with it. If so, this is called an interaction effect, and Cements and Aggregates are said to interact with each other. If this occurs, the first member on the right-hand side of Identity 7.92 will be larger than it would be if only random errors were producing it.

If it is believed that the random variable X_{ij} is not well expressed by $\mu + \tau_i + \beta_j + \epsilon_{ij}$ because there is an *extra* effect from combining the ith Treatment with the jth Block, then the model

$$(7.94) \qquad X_{ijk} = \mu + \tau_i + \beta_j + (\tau\beta)_{ij} + \epsilon_{ijk}$$

may be in order, where the $(\tau\beta)_{ij}$ is intended to measure the additional effect (though possibly negative), beyond and added to τ_i and β_j, of combining the ith Treatment and the jth Block. For a fixed set of Treatments and Blocks the $(\tau\beta)_{ij}$ can be expressed in terms of the true means for the $(i-j)$th cell, the ith Treatment, the jth Block, and the μ. If $\mu_{ij.}$ denotes the true mean when the ith Treatment is combined with the jth Block, then $\mu_{ij.} - \mu$ is the difference between the mean of that $(i-j)$th cell and the grand mean, but this difference obviously *is* affected by the ith Treatments' overall advantage or disadvantage and, similarly, for the jth Block. This difference, $\mu_{ij.} - \mu$, is *not* affected by the differences between units within the $(i-j)$th cell. Hence, to measure the $(\tau\beta)_{ij}$ effect we must subtract from $\mu_{ij.} - \mu$ the Treatment and Block effects; thus.

$$(7.95) \qquad \mu_{ij.} - \mu - (\mu_{i..} - \mu) - (\mu_{.j.} - \mu) \equiv \mu_{ij.} - \mu_{i..} - \mu_{.j.} + \mu$$

The reader will observe that this identity is wholly analogous to one term of Identity 7.92, which is expressed in terms of estimators of the parameters in Identity 7.95.

To summarize Model 7.94:

$$\tau_i = \mu_{i..} - \mu, \qquad \beta_j = \mu_{.j.} - \mu, \qquad \text{and} \qquad (\tau\beta)_{ij} = \mu_{ij.} - \mu_{i..} - \mu_{.j.} + \mu$$

for the fixed-effects model in which specific Treatment and Blocks are envisaged.

In the model of Equation 7.91 and Table 7.91 it is not possible to measure any interaction, if it is occurring, because whatever interaction effect there might be is inseparably mixed with the random error. To obtain an estimate of true Error it is necessary to have two or more observations from each combination of Cement and Aggregate (or of Treatment and Block, in general) and to use Model 7.94. Table 7.93 presents hypothetical data for a

TABLE 7.93. HYPOTHETICAL FIXED-EFFECTS STRENGTH-OF-CONCRETE EXPERIMENT WITH PROVISION FOR STUDY OF THE INTERACTION BETWEEN CEMENT AND AGGREGATE

MODEL: $X_{ijk} = \mu + \tau_i + \beta_j + (\tau\beta)_{ij} + \epsilon_{ijk}$

Aggregate		Cement					Aggregate	
		1	2	3	4	5	Total	Mean
A		10, 11, 13	10, 14, 14	9, 6, 7	25, 22, 20	14, 13, 15		
	Sum:	34	38	22	67	42	203	$13.53 = x_{.1}$
B		10, 12, 15	12, 9, 11	4, 8, 11	15, 20, 19	17, 11, 14		
	Sum:	37	32	23	54	42	188	$12.53 = x_{.2}$
C		10, 8, 10	8, 10, 9	7, 4, 7	21, 18, 22	8, 10, 13		
	Sum:	28	27	18	61	31	165	$11.00 = x_{.3}$
D		19, 16, 15	17, 15, 16	6, 10, 12	35, 28, 25	19, 16, 14		
	Sum:	50	48	28	88	49	263	$17.53 = x_{.4}$
	Cem. sum:	149	145	91	270	164	819	
	Cem. mean:	12.49	12.08	7.58	22.50	13.67		$13.65 = x_{..}$
		$x_{1.}$	$x_{2.}$	$x_{3.}$	$x_{4.}$	$x_{5.}$		

Cement–Aggregate study with three beams supposedly made from each combination of Cement and Aggregate.

It is seen in Table 7.94 that the cements do not compare in exactly the same way with all four aggregates. For example, Cement 2 has a sum with Aggregate A which is 4 units larger than Cement 1's sum with Aggregate A, whereas the sum for Cement 2 is 5 units *less* than the sum with Cement 1 when Aggregate B is used. Obviously, some or all of this variation could be mere sampling variation. One purpose of the analysis of variance to be run on these data is to separate the random variation called sampling error from the nonsampling error, such as might be caused by an interaction between Cements and Aggregates.

TABLE 7.94.   CEMENT–AGGREGATE SUMS FROM TABLE 7.93 ($q = 3$ PER CELL)

Aggregate	Cement					Aggregate	
	1	2	3	4	5	Total	Mean
A	34	38	22	67	42	203	13.53
B	37	32	23	54	42	188	12.53
C	28	27	18	61	31	165	11.00
D	50	48	28	88	49	263	17.53
Cem. sum:	149	145	91	270	164	819	
Cem. mean:	12.42	12.08	7.58	22.50	13.67		13.65

Table 7.94 is a summary table from Table 7.93 and is needed to compute and to understand the Cement × Aggregate interaction.

The analysis of variance for Table 7.93 and 7.94 is shown in Table 7.95. Its one new computational feature is the Sum of Squares for the Cement × Aggregate interaction. This is computed as follows:

Cement × Aggregate Ss

$$= \frac{(34)^2 + (38)^2 + \cdots + (49)^2}{3} - \frac{(819)^2}{60} - \text{Cements Ss} - \text{Aggregates Ss}$$

$$= 104.6334$$

or, more specifically,

Cement × Aggregate Ss $= 1884.3167 - 1429.2333 - 350.4500 = 104.6334$

Basically, the analysis of variance in Table 7.95 follows the identity

$$\sum_{i=1}^{5} \sum_{j=1}^{4} \sum_{k=1}^{3} (X_{ijk} - x\ldots)^2 \equiv \sum_i \sum_j \sum_k (X_{ijk} - x_{ij.})^2 + rq \sum_i (x_{i..} - x\ldots)^2$$

$$+ tq \sum_i (x_{.j.} - x\ldots)^2 + q \cdot \sum_i \sum_j (x_{ij.} - x_{i..} - x_{.j.} + x\ldots)^2$$

One could work out the proper Sums of Squares, as was done earlier.

TABLE 7.95.   ANALYSIS OF VARIANCE FOR TABLES 7.93 AND 7.94

Source of variation	DF	Sum of Squares	Mean Square	F
Cements	4	1429.2333	357.3	60.73
Aggregates	3	350.4500	116.7	19.85
Cement × Aggregate	12	104.6334	8.719	1.48
Samples same cements and aggregates	40	235.3333	5.883	
Total about $x\ldots$	59	2119.6500		

There are three hypotheses to be tested by means of the analysis of variance in Table 7.95. These and their corresponding regions of rejection with $\alpha = 0.05$ are as follows:

(a) $H_{01}[\mu_{1..} = \mu_{2..} = \cdots = \mu_{5..}) \mid$ (all σ_{ij}^2 are equal)] versus H_a(some $\mu_{i..}$ are unequal); or, referring to the model, which is

$$X_{ijk} = \mu + \tau_i + \beta_j + (\tau\beta)_{ij} + \epsilon_{ijk}$$

$H_0[$(all $\tau_i = 0) \mid$ (all σ_{ij}^2 equal)] versus H_a(some $\tau_i \neq 0$):

$$\omega_1: \qquad F_{0.05}(4, 40) > 2.61$$

(b) $H_{02}[$(all $\mu_{.j.}$ are equal) $\mid$ (all σ_{ij}^2 are equal)] versus H_a(some $\mu_{.j.}$ are unequal), or $H_0[$(all $\beta_j = 0) \mid (\sigma_{ij}^2$ equal)] versus H_a(some $\beta_j \neq 0$):

$$\omega_2: \qquad F_{0.05}(3, 40) > 2.84$$

(c) $H_{03}[(\mu_{ij.} = \mu_{i..} + \mu_{.j.} - \mu) \mid (\sigma_{ij}^2$ are equal)] versus negation of H_0, or $H_0[$(all $(\tau\beta)_{ij} = 0) \mid$ (all σ_{ij}^2 are equal)] versus its negation:

$$\omega_3: \qquad F_{0.05}(12, 40) > 2.00$$

It is recalled that we are dealing only with the fixed-effects model (Model I) in this chapter. This is why the $\sigma_{ij}^2 =$ within-cell variance is assumed constant with all H_0's.

Because the H_{03} may be a bit startling to the student, it will be discussed in some detail. It is recalled from the discussion pertaining to Identity 7.95 that the true interaction effect is measured by

$$\mu_{ij.} - \mu_{i..} - \mu_{.j.} + \mu \equiv \mu_{ij.} - (\mu_{i..} + \mu_{.j.} - \mu)$$

Here it is logical, *if there is no interaction between Treatments and Blocks*, that $\mu_{ij.} = \mu_{i..} + \mu_{.j.} - \mu$, so that the true interaction is zero. The F test here assumes that some effect does *not* exist, and if the H_0 is rejected, it is upon the basis of a *reductio ad absurdum* line of reasoning. Thus we test for interaction by assuming that there is none, so that $\mu_{ij.}$, the true cell mean, does, in fact, exactly equal the sum, $\mu_{i..} + \mu_{.j.} - \mu$.

Careful thought must be given to the choice of the correct denominator for any F test used in connection with an analysis of variance. This will be discussed rather fully later, when a better foundation has been laid for such a discussion, and for the present we shall use the Samples Mean Square as the denominator for all three F tests and only remark here that this is the correct procedure for a so-called fixed-effects (Model I) experiment.

It is instructive to account for the 40 DF, shown for "Samples same cements and aggregates" in Table 7.95, directly from the set-up of the experiment rather than merely as the remaining DF after the others have been determined. In Table 7.93 there are three measurements in each combination of a type of cement and a kind of aggregate. The sum of squares of deviations of these three in each cell from their own mean has 2 DF, and there are 20 such cells in the table; moreover, 2(20) = 40, the Samples DF. If all 20 of these sums of squares within each cell are added together, the sum is the 235.3333 given in Table 7.95 as the Sum of Squares for "Samples same cements and aggregates"; thus this is a pooled sum of squares, such as we have used a number of times previously. This variation obviously is produced solely by the within-cell sort of variation that logically is unexplained random variation.

It should be clear from Table 7.95 that the hypothesis, that the true average strengths of these cements, averaged over these four aggregates equally, are equal, should be rejected. A similar conclusion is drawn regarding the aggregates in view of an $F(3, 40) = 19.85$ which is much greater than the $F_{0.05}(3, 40) = 2.84$. However, the $F(12, 40)$ for testing for any interaction between cements and aggregates is 1.49 and would not be significant with even $\alpha = 0.10$; so it is concluded that these cements and aggregates do *not* interact; that is, the comparisons of these cements do not depend importantly upon which of these four aggregates one uses.

If desirable, one also could now apply one of the previously studied multiple-comparison procedures to the cement means and, separately, to the aggregate means, to see where the specific differences among these cements and among these aggregates are.

Finally, an example will be considered in which there *is* an interaction between cements and aggregates. Actually, this example was constructed from the data in Table 7.93 by interchanging the data for Cements 3 and 4 under Aggregate A and also under Aggregate D. This left the Total, Error, and Aggregate Sums of Squares unchanged, but Table 7.94 is replaced with Table 7.96. The specific hypotheses to be tested are as noted earlier for Table 7.95.

TABLE 7.96.   CEMENT-AGGREGATE SUMS FOR REVISED TABLE 7.93
NEEDED TO SHOW A CEMENT × AGGREGATE INTERACTION
(MODEL AS FOR TABLE 7.93)

Aggregate	Cement					Aggregate sum
	1	2	3	4	5	
A	34	38	67	22	42	203
B	37	32	23	54	42	188
C	28	27	18	61	31	165
D	50	48	88	28	49	263
Cem. sum:	149	145	196	165	164	819

The complete analysis of variance for these revised cement data is shown in Table 7.97, where again it is assumed that the correct denominator for each F test is the Samples Mean Square, because Model I is assumed.

It is seen in this table that the Mean Square for what is called the Cement × Aggregate interaction is so much larger than that for Samples within the same Cement–Aggregate combination, that there is no doubt that these are two different sources of variation; that is, there truly is interaction.

TABLE 7.97. ANALYSIS OF VARIANCE FOR DATA SUMMARIZED IN TABLE 7.96 (MODEL I)

Source of variation	DF	Sum of Squares	Mean Square	F
Cements	4	134.2333	33.56	5.70
Aggregates	3	350.4500	116.8	19.85
Cement × Aggregate	12	1399.6334	116.6	19.82
Samples same cements and aggregates	40	235.3333	5.883	
Total about x...	59	2119.6500		

After it has been decided that there definitely is an interaction, it is useful to construct a table of Cement–Aggregate means and analyze differences between means for statistical significance within the same Cement, and also within the same Aggregate. This will be done with the aid of Table 7.98.

TABLE 7.98. CEMENT–AGGREGATE MEANS FROM EXPERIMENTS OF TABLE 7.96, WHICH HAS BEEN SHOWN, IN TABLE 7.97, TO HAVE AN INTERACTION

Aggregate	Cement					Probable ranking of the cements
	1	2	3	4	5	
A	11.3	12.7 * 22.3 * 7.3 * 14.0				3 > 1, 2, 4, 5; 5 > 4
B	12.3	10.7 7.7 * 18.0 * 14.0				4 > 1, 2, 3, 5; 5 > 3
C	9.3	9.0 6.0 * 20.3 * 10.3				4 > 1, 2, 3, 5; 5 > 3
D	16.7	16.0 * 29.3 * 9.3 * 16.3				3 > 1, 2, 4, 5; 5 > 4

LSD* for rows or for columns = $2.021 \sqrt{5.883(2/3)} = 4.0$.

The changes in degree and direction of significant differences among Cements from Aggregate-to-Aggregate reveal the Cement × Aggregate interaction. It is not possible to recommend one of these cements over the other four without saying which aggregate is to be used. It is possible, however, to say that either Cement 3 or Cement 4 will be best to use with one of these four aggregates, but each also can be the poorest. Hence, only two cements would have to be stocked, if the aggregate might be any one of the four studied.

If the situation justifies the loss of some power to detect a false hypothesis in exchange for a faster and less expensive analysis, one can use Hartley's range analysis of variance for two-way analyses of variance (*Biometrika* 37: 271–280, 1950). This analysis makes use of the distribution of the studentized range, as does Patnaik's one-way range analysis of variance, described earlier. It is recalled that the studentized range (q) is a ratio of the range of independent normal measurements to an independent estimate of the standard deviation of the population of these measurements.

In developing such a test as Patnaik's or Hartley's it is necessary to define a ratio, q, which has the distribution of the studentized range. In the present case this involves an estimate of σ based on the range, plus some tables to give the proper scale factors and the number of degrees of freedom. The latter corresponds to the Error DF in a regular analysis of variance but is smaller. This fact is one reason for some loss of power, because the lower the number of DF, the lower the power, in general. The mathematical statistics required to justify Hartley's test is given in his paper, previously cited. We shall confine ourselves to an outline of the test procedure followed by an illustration of the actual test, leaving the interested reader to read Hartley's article for further information, if he wishes.

Hartley's range analysis of variance for testing

$$H_0[(\mu_1 = \cdots = \mu_t) \mid (\sigma_1^2 = \cdots = \sigma_t^2 = \sigma^2)]$$

versus H_a(some μ's are unequal) is performed as follows, when there are t Treatments and r Blocks in the experiment, the Treatments being fixed.

Step 1. Form a table of differences between individual measurements and their own Treatment mean.

Step 2. Compute the ranges of those differences for each Block, w_j, where $j = 1$ to r.

Step 3. Compute an estimate of σ from

(7.96)
$$s_w = \sum_1^r (w_j)/rc$$

where:

$$\sum (w_j) = \text{sum of the Treatment ranges within Block}$$
$$r = \text{number of Blocks}$$
$$c = \text{a scale factor from Table XX for the } r \text{ and } t \text{ of the experiment}$$

This s_w is an estimate of the same σ, as is the $\sqrt{\text{Error Mean Square}}$ but has fewer degrees of freedom.

Step 4. Compute $\bar{w}_{tr}$, the range of the Treatment means

Step 5. Compute the studentized range from

(7.97)
$$q = \frac{\bar{w}_{tr}\sqrt{r}}{s_w}$$

Step 6. Look up in Table XX the equivalent DF, ν, corresponding to the scale factor c obtained in Step 3.

Step 7. After choosing α and defining the region of rejection, ω, as $q \geqslant q_\alpha$ for the studentized range, compare with the sample q from Equation 7.97, and make the appropriate decision about H_0 and H_a.

This step-by-step procedure is illustrated by means of the following data:

			Treatment No.:			
Block	1	2	3	4	5	
I	18.6	27.5	13.6	14.9	15.0	
II	11.4	25.0	9.6	11.2	13.8	
III	25.7	33.6	16.5	18.1	20.2	
IV	20.1	28.3	14.1	15.6	18.2	
V	26.3	30.2	17.2	19.4	23.8	
VI	10.7	21.4	8.7	10.6	14.0	
Mean:	18.8	27.7	13.3	15.0	17.5	$\bar{w}_{tr} = 14.4$

Table 7.99 was constructed by subtracting the Treatment means from the numbers in the column above them and obtaining differences between individual measurements under a given Treatment and their own mean. For example, $18.6 - 18.8 = -0.2$ in the upper left-hand corner of the table.

TABLE 7.99. DIFFERENCES BETWEEN INDIVIDUAL MEASUREMENTS WITHIN TREATMENTS AND THEIR OWN MEANS FOR HARTLEY'S RANGE ANALYSIS OF VARIANCE

	Treatment					Treatment range w_j
Block	1	2	3	4	5	
I	−0.2	−0.2	0.3	−0.1	−2.5	2.8
II	−7.4	−2.7	−3.7	−3.8	−3.7	4.7
III	6.9	5.9	3.2	3.1	2.7	4.2
IV	1.3	0.6	0.8	0.6	0.7	0.7
V	7.5	2.5	3.9	4.4	6.3	5.0
VI	−8.1	−6.3	−4.6	−4.4	−3.5	4.6
						$22.0 = \sum_1^r w_j$

$c = 2.15$ (Table XX, with $t = 5$ and $r = 6$). $s_w = 22.0/6(2.15) = 1.71$.
$$\bar{w}_{tr} = 14.4.$$

With the preceding computations available, it is found from Equation 7.97 that $q = 14.4\sqrt{6}/1.71 = 20.6$. The equivalent DF for $c = 2.15$ (or for $t = 5$ and $r = 6$) is found in Table XX to be $v = 18.2$. This number of degrees of freedom represents a slight loss of DF for estimating σ^2, namely a $20 - 18.2 = 1.8$ loss, and hence some loss of power.

By Table XVIII of the studentized range, q, the 5% region of rejection, ω for $r = 6$ and $v = 18.2$ (interpolated linearly) is $q > 4.49$; therefore, the sample $q = 20.6$ causes H_0 to be rejected decisively. It is concluded that some or all of the Treatment means ($\mu_{i.}$) are unequal. It next would be possible and probably useful to make multiple comparisons by means of the G test.

PROBLEMS

1. Given the following practice data, compute the regular analysis of variance, and draw all appropriate conclusions, making the assumption that the Samples Mean Square is the proper denominator for all F tests.

Treatment No.:

Breed	1	2	3	4	*Breed total*
1	3.8, 4.0	4.2, 4.3	4.0, 4.3	3.6, 3.5	31.7
2	4.7, 4.5	4.3, 4.6	4.8, 5.2	4.3, 4.4	36.8
3	5.1, 4.8	4.7, 4.8	5.4, 5.6	5.2, 5.0	40.6
4	4.3, 4.8	3.9, 4.2	4.0, 4.1	4.3, 3.8	33.4
5	4.1, 4.3	4.4, 4.4	3.9, 4.0	3.7, 4.0	32.8
6	3.9, 4.2	4.0, 4.6	4.1, 3.8	4.4, 4.7	33.7
Trt.	52.5	52.4	53.2	50.9	209.0

Total $Ss = 10.6592$, Breeds $Ss = 6.8017$, Treatments $Ss = 0.2342$.

2. Alter Problem 1 so as to increase the Samples Sum of Squares, but do not change either the Treatment or Breeds Sum of Squares.

3. Alter Problem 1 so that the Treatment × Breed interaction is reduced but the Treatment Sum of Squares is unchanged.

4. Alter Problem 1 so that all Sums of Squares except Total and Samples are changed.

5. Do Problem 1 by Hartley's range analysis of variance on the *sums* of the cells, as though those were the original data.

6. Make up a problem with $t = 3$, $r = 5$, and $q = 2$ such that there is a Treatment × Block interaction *without* a reversal of Treatment ranks from Block to Block.

7. Write down the statistical model for Problem 1, assuming fixed effects. Where in your model, definitions, and assumptions is homogeneity of variance covered?

8. Suppose that a study has been made of the effects of well-defined levels of exercise on the blood cholesterol of male humans in four age groups with the following results in the usual units:

Age group	Low		Level of exercise Medium		High		Age sum
20 to 29	190	175	160	190	155	170	
	210	180	155	170	150	160	
	170		165		155		
							2555
30 to 39	200	185	170	165	175	155	
	210	190	190	170	160	180	
	175		180		165		
							2670
40 to 49	220	250	180	185	200	185	
	210	190	195	215	170	175	
	200		220		190		
							2985
50 to 59	230	250	225	210	180	220	
	245	220	200	195	200	230	
	215		225		190		
							3235
Level sum:	4115		3765		3565		11,445

Write down the appropriate statistical model for this study, and do a complete analysis of these data, using $\alpha = 0.10$, assuming normality as needed, and assuming homogeneity of variance. Given: Total Ss = 37,791.25, Age Ss = 19,024.58, and $(11,445)^2/60 = 2,183,133,75$.

9. Do the analysis of variance of Problem 8, after coding the data by subtracting 150 from each X_{ijk}.

10. Draw one number at random from each cell of Problem 8, and thereafter do an analysis of variance by Hartley's range procedure, letting Level of Exercise correspond to Treatment and letting Age Group be Block. Use $\alpha = 0.10$ again.

REVIEW PROBLEMS

1. Salt is considered important in diets designed to put weight on meat animals. Suppose that in a certain experiment one group of 15 pigs was fed a standard diet without added salt and another group of 15 entirely comparable pigs was fed the same diet plus salt *ad libitum*. The results of this experiment being as given below, test $H_0[(\mu_S = \mu_{NS}) \mid (\sigma_S^2 = \sigma_{NS}^2)]$ versus its negation. Also put a CI_{90} on $\mu_S - \mu_{NS}$, and discuss it in relation to the previous test of H_0.

	Hypothetical experimental results	
	Standard diet	*Salt-ad-libitum diet*
$\bar{x}$:	0.70 lb/day	1.70 lb/day
s:	0.25 lb/day	0.35 lb/day
R:	1.10 lb/day	1.15 lb/day
r:	15	15

2. Referring to Problem 1, change the H_a to $\mu_S > \mu_{NS}$ and do as directed for that problem.

3. Salt mixed with an oilmeal sometimes is used to decrease the danger to cattle of the presence of poisonous weeds in their pastures. One theory is that it is chiefly a lack of adequate salt that causes the cattle to eat the poisonous weeds, and even the weed killers, which they ordinarily would shun. Suppose that a large range area infested with poisonous weeds is fenced into two entirely comparable pastures and 500 beef cattle graze on each half. One group has access to all the salt it wants by means of the oilmeal mixture. The other has none of this mixture nor any additional salt in any other form. Given the following results of this test, decide whether the salt-oilmeal mixture helps prevent illness or death or both from poisonous weeds, assuming all illnesses and deaths were shown medically to be due to poisonous weeds:

	Not sick	*Sick but lived*	*Died*	*Total*
Extra salt	440	50	10	500
No extra salt	295	180	25	500

4. It was thought for some time that no relationship existed between right and left acuity dominance and sight-seeing dominance in the eyes of humans. An article in the September 1, 1961, issue of *Science* (H. F. Crovitz, "Differential acuity of the two eyes and the problem of ocular dominances," *Science* 134: 614, 1961) presents the following data which seem to raise doubts about the previous concepts on this matter:

Acuity dominance	*Right-sighting dominance*	*Left-sighting dominance*
None	66	21
Right	76	23
Left	80	53
	222	97

The subjects in this sample were 319 college students. Assuming that the data were so taken as to represent a random sample from a describable population, do you agree that there is no relationship between acuity dominance and sighting dominance?

5. Suppose that there are 500 crows roosting in a grove containing equally many oak and elm trees and no other species of tree. It is determined with binoculars that there are 300 male crows and 200 female crows in the flock. Furthermore, 200 of the males are in oak trees whereas 150 females are in the elm trees. Is this evidence sufficient to justify the conclusion that there is a sex factor in the choice between oaks and elms for roosting sites of crows?

6. Assuming that the data of Problem 5 are valid sampling data for this purpose, do the following.
   (a) Test the hypothesis that male crows prefer to roost in oak trees "two to one."
   (b) Compute a 90% confidence interval on the true percent of all male crows represented by these data who prefer to roost in oak trees.

7. A person wishes to make a study of diameters of elm trees and of the incidence of serious disease in two relatively small stands of timber. In a valid manner this person selects 25 elm trees at random from each of the two stands and measures each tree's diameter at a height level with the top of his shoulders. At the same time he professionally classifies each of those 25 trees and the

five elms nearest to it (radially) as either seriously diseased or not. Thus, 150 trees are so classified in each stand of timber. Suppose that the results of this study are as follows:

Stand	n	Mean diameter (inches)	Std. dev.	Stand	Seriously diseased	Not seriously diseased
South	25	18.5	4.1	South	18	132
North	25	20.2	3.6	North	23	127

(a) Test the general hypothesis that the average diameter of elm tree is the same in the two stands, against a reasonable alternative.

(b) Test $H_0(\sigma_S^2 = \sigma_N^2)$ versus its negation, where S = South.

(c) Is the incidence of serious disease different in the two stands?

(d) Criticize the sampling procedure.

8. Suppose that a sociologist wishes to determine by sampling what effect a recent world event has had on adult opinion regarding a current tax proposal. It is possible that age level, property ownership, income level, and political party (plus other factors which will be ignored here) could influence a respondent's answers. How would you draw a random sample of 500 in a city of 50,000 adults? What hypotheses would you plan to test, and how would you propose to test them?

9. Suppose that a test criterion, ζ (such as X^2, t, or F), has the following true sampling distribution when H_0 is true, when H_{a1} is true and H_0 is tested; also when H_{a2} is true but H_0 is tested, respectively:

(a) Specifically state the region of rejection for H_0 when $\alpha = 0.10$.

(b) Determine the power of this ζ test against H_{a1} for $\alpha = 0.10$.

(c) How much gain in power against H_{a2} would it produce to change from an $\alpha = 0.05$ to an $\alpha = 0.15$? Rationalize this gain, and discuss the choice of the α in experimental research.

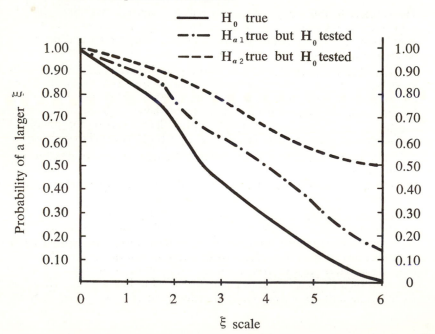

10. There are some disagreements among scholars regarding authorship and time of composition of certain outstanding pieces of writing such as the *Federalist Papers*, Plato's *Dialogues*, etc. Some statistical studies of these matters require sampling of the writings in question. Suppose you wished to draw a random sample of the last five syllables of sentences from certain specific copies of the *Federalist Papers*. How would you do this sampling?

11. Suppose that a jumping contest is held with samples of 10 of each of two species of frog. Each frog makes three jumps, and his distances are averaged to give one figure for each frog. Suppose the following results (in tenths of inches) were obtained. Decide statistically whether the true average length of jump is the same for these two species, after assuring yourself that the assumption $\sigma_1^2 = \sigma_2^2$ is a reasonable one to make:

Species 1:   10.7, 15.6, 15.2, 12.9, 11.2, 12.1, 14.3, 12.5, 10.0, and 13.7
Species 2:   16.3, 12.5, 13.7, 13.9, 11.2, 10.8, 14.3, 13.6, 15.3, and 12.9

12. Turn to Chapter 1 and count the number of words in the first sentence in each of the first new paragraphs of the first ten pages. Do the same for Chapters 2, 3, 4, 6, and 7. Test the hypothesis that there is not a chapter difference in average length of sentence in terms of numbers of words, assuming that the process used will give a proper sampling for such a test. Then criticize this method of sampling.

13. Do the same as in Problem 12, but count the number of letters in each sentence instead of the number of words. Should the final results of Problems 12 and 13 be the same, aside from minor sampling errors?

14. Do the same as in the previous two problems, but count the number of adjectives in the sentences instead of the number of words or number of letters. Should the final decision here be the same as for Problem 12? For problem 13?

15. Given the following hypothetical data, test $H_0[(\mu_1 = \mu_2 = \cdots = \mu_4) \mid (\sigma_1^2 = \cdots = \sigma_4^2 = \sigma^2)]$.

	Treatment		
1	2	3	4
25.2	30.3	21.9	28.5
20.0	24.6	24.4	30.1
18.6	19.1	18.9	26.7
23.2	28.7	22.6	23.3

	1	2	3	4	
Sum:	87.0	102.7	87.8	108.6	Grand total: 386.1
Mean:	21.75	25.68	21.95	27.15	
$\sum X^2$:	1919.24	2711.75	1942.94	2974.04	

16. Apply Duncan's NMRT to the data of Problem 1, to test whether the population means are equal. Draw appropriate conclusions.

17. Estimate the common variance of the groups of data of Problem 15 by:
(a) Multiplying the computed variance of the Treatment means by 4.
(b) Using the pooled Within-Groups Sums of Squares and the pooled DF. What distribution does the ratio of such estimates have?

18. With the data of Problem 15 verify the addition theorem that the Total Sum of Squares about the grand mean, $x..$, is the sum of the Between-Treatments Sum of Squares and the Within-Treatments Sum of Squares.

19. Code the data of Problem 15 by subtracting 20 from each number, and then do the analysis of variance.

20. Make up a problem which has Treatment Means $x_1. = 3.5$, $x_2. = 4.7$, $x_3. = 1.4$, $x_4. = 5.0$ from six samples per treatment and so that $F(3, 20)$ is significant with $\alpha = 0.05$. Then change your data so that $F(3, 20)$ is non-significant with $\alpha = 0.10$.

21. Given the following data and calculations, make a complete analysis of variance plus all useful multiple comparisons.

Total Ss = 2081.50

$$\frac{(360)^2 + \cdots + (360)^2}{8} = 90,212.50$$

Grand total $\sum (X)$:   1890

$(1890)^2/40 = 89,302.50$

Treatment

0_1	0_2	M_0	M_1	M_2
37	55	48	56	50
53	60	44	50	38
46	53	43	58	35
41	49	42	63	45
50	42	32	48	46
38	44	36	60	53
48	48	40	46	46
47	49	45	59	47
360	400	330	440	360

22. Do Problem 21 after coding the data by subtracting 45 from each of those 40 numbers. Can you use the Total Ss = 2081.50 given in Problem 21 ?

23. Given the following analysis of variance and Variety means from a hypothetical experiment, use Duncan's NMRT and Fisher's LSD, each with $\alpha = 0.05$, to determine which population means probably are equal and which are unequal. Draw appropriate conclusions.

Source of variation	DF	Sample mean square
Variety of tulip	4	8606.4
Plants same variety	40	1911.7
Total about $x..$	44	

Variety:	3	1	5	2	4
Mean:	52.6	75.8	90.1	102.4	135.6

24. Given the following sketch of the $F(5, 20)$ distribution, mark off the regions of rejection for (*a*) one-tail test with $\alpha = 0.10$, (*b*) two-tail test with $\alpha = 0.10$, and (*c*) one-tail test with $\alpha = 0.01$.

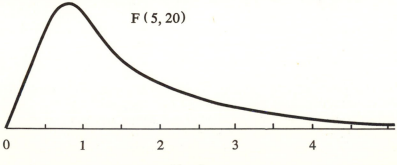

F (5, 20)

F axis

25. Do Problem 21 by Patnaik's method.

26. Referring to Problem 24, would the peak of the curve move to the left, to the right, or stay where it is, for $F(5, 100)$? For $F(20, 20)$? For $F(3, 20)$ For $F(2, 20)$?

27. Which of the following sampling quantities have a t distribution, which have a $N(0, 1)$ distribution, and which have some other distribution?
    (a) $(b - \beta)/\sigma_b$
    (b) $(b - \beta)/s_b$
    (c) $(\hat{Y}_i - \mu_{\hat{Y}_i})/s_{\hat{Y}_i}$
    (d) r^2

    (e) $\Sigma (X)/n$
    (f) $\dfrac{(r - \rho)\sqrt{n - 2}}{\sqrt{1 - r^2}}$

    (g) $\dfrac{r\sqrt{n - 2}}{\sqrt{1 - r^2}}$, for $\rho = 0$
    (h) $\Sigma (xy)/\Sigma (x^2)$

28. Given the following data and calculations, compute and interpret the central 90% confidence interval on β if the Y_{ij} are normally distributed with mean $= \alpha + \beta X_i$ and variance $= \sigma_{yx}^2$ for all i:

X:	4.5	5.0	5.5	6.0	6.5	7.0	7.5	8.0	8.5	9.0	9.5
Y:	14.0	13.4	13.2	15.1	14.9	15.6	15.8	15.0	16.0	16.7	17.0

    $\Sigma (X) = 77.0$, $\quad \Sigma (x^2) = 27.50$, $\quad \Sigma (XY) = 1185.50$, $\quad \Sigma (Y) = 166.7$,
    $\Sigma (y^2) = 15.45$, $\quad (\Sigma xy)^2/\Sigma (x^2) = 12.58$, $\quad \Sigma (xy)/\Sigma (x^2) = 0.676$,
    $\Sigma (X) \cdot \Sigma (Y) = 12835.9$

29. Referring to the data of Problem 28, compute and interpret the 90% greatest lower bound on the true linear regression coefficient, β.

30. Given the data of Problem 28, compute and interpret a central CI_{90} on the Y for the next random sample drawn from that population at $X = 7.5$.

31. Given the following sample from a multinomial population, test $H_0(9A : 3B; 3C; 1D)$ versus its negation. Use $\alpha = 0.20$, and draw appropriate conclusions:

	A	B	C	D	Sum
Observed:	40	26	19	11	96

32. Make up a set of 18 pair of observations presumably from a normal bivariate population and such that the product-moment coefficient of linear correlation is between 0.5 and 0.7. Also make a scatter diagram showing that the assumption of linearity is reasonable.

Chapter 8

Models and Expected Mean Squares for the Analysis of Variance for Completely Randomized and Randomized Complete Block Designs

8.1 INTRODUCTION

Now that the student has acquired a working acquaintance with the methodology of simple analysis of variance, it is time to become more objective and precise about the assumptions made and the hypotheses being tested during an analysis of variance. This aim can be accomplished by describing the *statistical model* for each of several types of experiments and by deriving the *expected Mean Squares* for them. The expected Mean Squares are needed to indicate and justify the F tests for an analysis of variance. Often, with the more complex models the determination of the proper F test is far from obvious.

The student now should be sufficiently aware of the problems and procedures of experimental statistics to accept and appreciate the following relevant facts.

(*a*) The experimental situations in which statistical concepts and procedures are needed are those in which numerical measurements are used to derive new information.

(*b*) The general circumstances under which some measurements are to be taken must be described mathematically, so that the assumptions and type of population involved will be specifically stated, because statistical analysis is a mathematical operation and all such operations are based upon definitions, postulates, and assumptions.

(*c*) There is random error in all those measurements which are the end result of the experiment, so that all decisions are subject to error.

It is reasonable and true that the statistical model must take proper account of all these foregoing facts.

The other general point to keep in mind is that an analysis of variance leads to sample Mean Squares, which inevitably have sampling distributions. These distributions involve the now-familiar chi-square distribution plus what is called the expected Mean Square. This is the long-run average value of a sample Mean Square. For example, if an experiment involves seven measurements under each of five Treatments, and if one imagines this same experiment to be repeated many times, there will be that many Treatment Mean Squares from these sampling experiments. The average of all these sample Mean Squares is, essentially, the expected Treatment Mean Square. Considerable attention will be given in this chapter to the determination of expected Mean Squares for various models and the corresponding analyses of variance.

At the outset of an experiment it is important to be clear about the points of view being taken concerning the several sources of variation described in an analysis of variance table. Whether those sources of variation have been introduced deliberately or are inherent in the sampling situation, they must be handled in such a way that valid tests of significance can be made by appropriate statistical procedures. To illustrate, suppose that an agronomist wishes to study the yielding potentials of five specific varieties of sorghum. Naturally, he must plant more than one plot of each variety in order to obtain an estimate of the sampling variance against which he must measure observed differences in yield. It will be assumed that there should be six plots planted of each variety in this test. Hence, the minimum number of sources of variation will be two: one called Between Varieties the other called Within Varieties.

The plots upon which this experiment will be planted surely must be considered a sample of the environment in which these varieties of sorghum will be raised, for, if not, there would be no point in conducting this experiment on these plots. It is well known, however, that the plots are not identical with respect to any characteristic which could affect the yields of the sorghum varieties. It also is well known that these plot-to-plot differences within the same variety are relatively minor and unpredictable in any practical sense. Furthermore, the plot-to-plot differences probably will change from year to year, so, all told, it seems logical to call the plot-to-plot variations within the same variety *random variations*. Usually we shall assume that such variations are normally and independently distributed about a mean of zero and with a variance of σ^2, regardless of the variety involved. That is, we shall assume homogeneity of variance in addition to normality of distribution and independence of these random errors for any one experiment. This is denoted symbolically by $NID(0, \sigma^2)$.

Besides recognizing the existence of an essentially random sampling error the experimenter must decide on the point of view he is taking regarding the varieties he wishes to study. Some varieties are of interest in themselves—perhaps as possible new varieties for farmers to plant in a given area. Other varieties are only of interest in so far as they are representative of a *class* of varieties. The experimenter needs to ask himself which point of view he is taking in his experiment.

To summarize the foregoing, three questions must be asked and answered satisfactorily in advance of the actual conduct of the experiment:

(*a*) Are the Treatments to be used in this experiment considered to be representative of some larger class of Treatments—such as combine sorghums, or grain sorghums of some general type—or is one only interested in the levels of effects of just those particular Treatments included in our experiment? If the former best describes the attitude, the Treatment variation is said to constitute a *random source of variation*, because no interest is taken in these specific Treatments except as they produce variations in, say, yields. If, however, the experimenter only wishes to decide whether certain varieties will, on the average yield the same amounts of grain, then Varieties is said to be a *fixed source of variation*, because one thinks in terms of fixed population parameters associated with these specific varieties.

(*b*) Has the experiment been so designed that the two sources of variation, Between-Treatments and Within-Treatments, are additive (that is, independent) parts of the Total Variation about the grand mean, $x..$? It is assumed that this is true when one writes a linear statistical model in which the symbols for the Between-Treatment and the Within-Treatment effects are merely added together, along with terms for the grand mean and the errors of measurement.

(*c*) Is it reasonable to believe that the measurements within each Treatment potentially are $N(\mu, \sigma^2)$ variates? This assumption often is taken for granted, because the normal does so often fit sampling situations well; but it should be given some thought at the start of any experiment.

As a prelude to writing down the statistical model for an experiment we shall first consider the concept of a *completely randomized experimental design*. Suppose that a sufficiently large area of land is laid out into the 30 equal-sized plots needed for an experiment with 6 plots of each of 5 varieties of sorghum, as in the experiment being considered in the preceding discussion. Suppose also that the name of one of the five varieties is written on each of 30 mixable objects representing the 30 plots to be used in this experiment in such a way that each variety name appears exactly six times. Thereafter these 30 objects are thoroughly mixed, drawn one at a time, and recorded in the 30 cells of a table, such as Table 8.11. This process of determining which variety is to be grown on which specific plots of the experiment makes it true that every possible arrangement of these 30 plots, with respect to the varieties on them, initially had the same chance to be the one used in the experiment. This is the essential characteristic of a completely randomized design.

In Table 8.11 the letter V stands for "variety" and the subscripts indicate the variety number (first subscript) and the plot number within the variety (second subscript). Thus, V_{54} stands for the 4th plot chosen to be planted with variety 5.

Under the conditions described for this fixed-effects experiment it seems logical and useful to assume that the yield for any predesignated plot will be the sum of two effects: one associated with the variety to be planted on that plot, the other associated with the unpredictable random individuality of that plot this particular year. This latter effect on yield really is a composite of elements in the micro-environments under which the plants will grow on that plot.

TABLE 8.11. PLANTING ARRANGEMENT FOR A COMPLETELY RANDOMIZED DESIGN WITH SIX PLOTS OF EACH OF FIVE VARIETIES OF SORGHUM, DETERMINED BY RANDOM DRAWS

V_{14}	V_{34}	V_{11}	V_{44}	V_{35}	V_{21}
V_{52}	V_{16}	V_{22}	V_{31}	V_{56}	V_{51}
V_{25}	V_{15}	V_{24}	V_{42}	V_{55}	V_{41}
V_{23}	V_{13}	V_{26}	V_{46}	V_{54}	V_{36}
V_{43}	V_{45}	V_{12}	V_{33}	V_{53}	V_{32}

The preceding verbal description of an experiment can be usefully summarized in the statistical model for the experiment. Actually, the process of writing down a description of an experiment by means of its model consists, essentially, in putting common sense and some specific and reasonable assumptions into a mathematical form for the sake of precision of description. These ideas can be illustrated by means of the experiment outlined in Table 8.11.

Suppose that variety 1 has a true average potential advantage in yielding ability which can be properly described by $+7$ bu./acre, as compared with the average of all five varieties in the study. This corresponds to the statement that variety 1 will, on the average, yield 7 bu./acre more than the average of all five varieties to be planted in this experiment, when they are grown under the conditions that will be maintained during this experiment. Suppose that the advantages ($+$'s) and the disadvantages ($-$'s) of the other four varieties can be measured as follows:

Variety No. i:	2	3	4	5
Variety's "advantage" (τ):	-3	0	$+2$	-6

It is noted that the "advantages" add to zero when variety 1 is included. This is just a sensible convenience which makes the arithmetic simpler.

Now, suppose that we somehow know the potential, but essentially random, "advantage" this year for each of the 30 plots, independent of the variety to be grown on each, and that these hypothetical "advantages" are as shown in Table 8.12. It is to be kept in mind that these hypothetical "advantages" are being used to illustrate true, though unknown, situations in actual experimental research. Each variety possibly does have a potential "advantage," or there would be no point to the experiment, and each plot *does* have a potential "advantage" which must be kept in mind when interpreting experimental data.

TABLE 8.12. HYPOTHETICAL POTENTIAL PLOT "ADVANTAGES" FOR THE EXPERIMENT OF TABLE 8.11, WITH NO RELATION TO THE VARIETIES LATER TO BE PLANTED ON THESE PLOTS DURING THE EXPERIMENT MINUS (PLOT NUMBER AND "ADVANTAGE")

1, +2	2, −4	3, +1	4, 0	5, −2	6, +3
7, +1	8, 0	9, +6	10, −4	11, −3	12, +7
13, −2	14, +2	15, +1	16, +5	17, 0	18, −2
19, +2	20, −1	21, −3	22, −4	23, +5	24, 0
25, +3	36, 0	27, −2	28, +1	29, +3	30, −7

If the general level of yield of these five varieties of sorghum considered as a group under the conditions sampled during this experiment potentially is $\mu = 95$ bu./acre, what is the most intelligent guess regarding the yield of the jth plot of variety i? To be specific, what is the best estimate of the yield that will be obtained from plot 1 in Table 8.12, it being remembered that it will be the fourth plot assigned to variety 1? Starting with the grand mean, $\mu = 95$, and then adding the "advantages" previously assigned the variety and plot involved, one would reason logically that the yield of plot 1 should be computed as

$$X_{14} = 95 + (+7) + (+2) = 104 \text{ bu./acre}$$

if it is valid—as we have supposed herein—to assume that the variety and random "advantages" are additive. A test for additivity will be described later, so that this assumption can be checked after an experiment has been run.

Similarly, the best "guess" we could make for the yield to be obtained from plot 22 would be computed as:

$$X_{46} = 95 + (+2) + (−4) = 93 \text{ bu./acre}$$

As previously noted, the 95 is the grand mean, μ, for all conceivable plots of these particular five varieties, the $+2$ is the average effect of variety 4 (to be designated as τ_4) expressed relative to the μ, and the $−4$ is the random error (to be called ϵ_{46}) associated with the 6th plot of variety 4 this year. It also should be noted that the ϵ_{ij} in Table 8.12 do *not* add to zero. Although the expected value of the ϵ_{ij} is zero for the jth plot of the ith variety, the particular plots used this year are only a random sample of plots representing this same general environment. The fact that $\sum (\epsilon_{ij}) \neq 0$ for these particular 30 plots this year is analogous to the fact that $\sum (X_i - \mu) \neq 0$ for a sample from $N(\mu, \sigma^2)$, whereas $\sum (X_i - \bar{x}) = 0$.

The term *expected value* will be used to denote the long-run average value of a variate, that is, the long-run average of a measurement whose specific value at any given time depends upon chance to some important degree. For example, when six unbiassed coins are to be tossed and the number of heads recorded after each set of tosses, a measurement $X = 0, 1, 2, 3, 4, 5,$ or 6 can be obtained. Over many such sets of tosses, the average number of heads, and the average size of X, will be very close to $\mu = 3$. As noted in Chapter 2, $\mu = np$ for this situation; hence, we say that the expected value of this variate X is 3. More briefly, we write $E(X) = 3$. Similarly, the variate X will have a variance, which could be computed from a large number of sets of tosses and shown to be $np(1 - p)$ for binomial sampling. In general, $\sigma_X^2 = E[(X - \mu)^2]$, because the variance is the long-run average squared deviation of a random variate X from its true mean, μ.

If a variate has a true mean of zero, as is logical for any random error, ϵ_{ij}, then its $\mu = 0$; therefore, $E(\epsilon_{ij}) = 0$. Furthermore, the true variance of such a variate is just the expected value of its square; that is, $E(\epsilon_{ij}) = \sigma^2$, because $E(\epsilon_{ij} - 0)^2 = E(\epsilon_{ij}^2) = \sigma^2$, from what has been said previously.

Another important point about expected values in which the random errors, ϵ_{ij}, are involved deserves mention here. If it is stated that two or more variates are independent with means each equal to zero, as is assumed for the ϵ_{ij}, it can be shown that the expected value of any product of two such variates is zero. This fact will not be proved here; it is simply stated as very useful information in the analyses to follow. For example, if the random errors of observation, the ϵ's, are uncorrelated for a particular experimental situation, then $E(\epsilon_{ij} \cdot \epsilon_{kl})$ is always 0, if the subscripts ij and kl are not identical. If they are identical, this expected value is just the variance, σ^2. To illustrate the usefulness of this property of uncorrelated variates, suppose one wishes to determine the expected value of the square of a sum (as will need to be done repeatedly in subsequent work), and one needs to determine $E(\epsilon_{i1} + \cdots + \epsilon_{ir})^2$. When the indicated squaring is done inside the parentheses, one obtains the following expression:

$$(\epsilon_{i1} + \cdots + \epsilon_{ir})^2 = (\epsilon_{i1}^2 + \cdots + \epsilon_{ir}^2) + 2(\epsilon_{i1}\epsilon_{i2} + \cdots + \epsilon_{i-1}\epsilon_r)$$

In view of the zero expected values of each of the crossproducts, $\epsilon_{ij}\epsilon_{kl}$, in the second parentheses, the expected value of each of those terms is zero; hence, $E[(\epsilon_{i1} + \cdots + \epsilon_{ir})^2] = E(\epsilon_{i1}^2 + \cdots + \epsilon_{ir}^2) = r \cdot \sigma^2$, if each ϵ_{ij}^2 has the same expected value, namely σ^2, as is assumed for most linear models.

To recapitulate the preceding symbolic discussion briefly: if the errors of measurement made on the jth plot of the ith treatment are uncorrelated with those on the kth plot of the lth treatment, this fact is denoted by the symbol, $E(\epsilon_{ij} \cdot \epsilon_{kl}) = 0$.

PROBLEMS

1. Construct a design similar to Table 8.11 for a completely randomized (CR) experiment with seven plots of each of eight soil treatments: $T_1, \cdots, T_8$.

2. With reference to Problem 1, make up a suitable set of treatment effects, τ_i, where $i = 1$ to 8, and a set of errors, ϵ_{ij}, for this problem. Then give the best guesses for the values of X_{25} and X_{63}, using the notation previously introduced.

3. Suppose you wish to compare the durabilities of four formulations of concrete by laying out strips of each concrete five times along a highway. It is decided that the 20 strips of space needed for this study shall be assigned to the specific concretes by a CR design. Lay out a specific CR design for this study and give the linear model involved.

4. With reference to Problem 3, what would the symbol ϵ_{23} mean? Would $\sum_{i=1}^{4} \sum_{j=1}^{5} \epsilon_{ij} = 0$? Would $E(\epsilon_{14}) = 0$?

5. With reference to Problem 3, write down a formula for X_{23} and define all symbols used.

8.2. FIXED AND RANDOM MODELS FOR COMPLETELY RANDOMIZED EXPERIMENTAL DESIGNS

Suppose that, in general, an experiment involves t specified Treatments, each appearing in the experiment r times in a completely randomized design, such as shown in Table 8.11. It was suggested earlier that it be assumed that the yield of plot ij is potentially the sum of three terms, namely, the true grand mean for the situation being sampled, the true potential effect of Treatment i on plot yield measured *from* μ, and a random error characteristic of the jth plot of the ith Treatment. These assumptions are embodied in the statistical model described by the following formula:

$$(8.21) \qquad X_{ij} = \mu + \tau_i + \epsilon_{ij}, \qquad \text{with } i = 1 \text{ to } t \quad \text{and} \quad j = 1 \text{ to } r$$

where τ_i is a constant, which measures how much above or below the grand average, μ, the average yield under Treatment i is expected to be in the long run (how much τ_i is + or −). The ϵ_{ij} measures the potential deviation of the jth plot of the ith Treatment from its true mean, $\mu_{i.} = \tau_i + \mu$. It usually is assumed that the ϵ_{ij} are normally and independently distributed with true mean = 0 and a variance, σ^2, or, symbolically, the ϵ_{ij} are assumed to be normally and independently distributed with mean zero and variance σ^2, NID(0, σ^2). The randomized sampling used in such experiments seems often to justify this assumption, and this is a necessary assumption for some of the desirable statistical analyses we wish to use.

The model of Formula 8.21 is shown symbolically and in some detail in Table 8.21. The determination of the treatment to be planted on each plot was made by means of a table of random numbers. Plot 1 of Treatment 1 was assigned the number 1, plot 2 of Treatment 1 was assigned the number 2, etc., until plot 6 of Treatment 5 was assigned the number 30. The plots of the diagram of Table 8.21 were assigned treatments in order, from left to right and starting at the upper left-hand corner. It happened that the first number drawn from the table of random numbers was 04; hence, plot 4 of Treatment 1 was assumed to have been planted in the upper left-hand corner, Table 8.21. Thus the indicated yield there is X_{14}.

TABLE 8.21.   OUTLINE FOR A COMPLETELY RANDOMIZED EXPERIMENTAL DESIGN WITH FIVE TREATMENTS AND SIX PLOTS PER TREATMENT

$$X_{14}=\mu+\tau_1+\epsilon_{14} \quad X_{32}=\mu+\tau_3+\epsilon_{32} \quad X_{25}=\mu+\tau_2+\epsilon_{25} \quad X_{23}=\mu+\tau_2+\epsilon_{23} \quad X_{43}=\mu+\tau_4+\epsilon_{43}$$
$$X_{34}=\mu+\tau_3+\epsilon_{34} \quad X_{16}=\mu+\tau_1+\epsilon_{16} \quad X_{15}=\mu+\tau_1+\epsilon_{15} \quad X_{13}=\mu+\tau_1+\epsilon_{13} \quad X_{45}=\mu+\tau_4+\epsilon_{45}$$
$$X_{11}=\mu+\tau_1+\epsilon_{11} \quad X_{22}=\mu+\tau_2+\epsilon_{22} \quad X_{24}=\mu+\tau_2+\epsilon_{24} \quad X_{26}=\mu+\tau_2+\epsilon_{26} \quad X_{12}=\mu+\tau_1+\epsilon_{12}$$
$$X_{44}=\mu+\tau_4+\epsilon_{44} \quad X_{31}=\mu+\tau_3+\epsilon_{31} \quad X_{42}=\mu+\tau_4+\epsilon_{42} \quad X_{46}=\mu+\tau_4+\epsilon_{46} \quad X_{33}=\mu+\tau_3+\epsilon_{33}$$
$$X_{35}=\mu+\tau_3+\epsilon_{35} \quad X_{56}=\mu+\tau_5+\epsilon_{56} \quad X_{55}=\mu+\tau_5+\epsilon_{55} \quad X_{54}=\mu+\tau_5+\epsilon_{54} \quad X_{53}=\mu+\tau_5+\epsilon_{53}$$
$$X_{21}=\mu+\tau_2+\epsilon_{21} \quad X_{51}=\mu+\tau_5+\epsilon_{51} \quad X_{41}=\mu+\tau_4+\epsilon_{41} \quad X_{36}=\mu+\tau_3+\epsilon_{36} \quad X_{32}=\mu+\tau_3+\epsilon_{32}$$

The potential treatment means for the design of Table 8.21 on these same plots are

Treatment	Mean
1	$x_{1.} = \mu + \tau_1 + \epsilon_{1.}$
2	$x_{2.} = \mu + \tau_2 + \epsilon_{2.}$
3	$x_{3.} = \mu + \tau_3 + \epsilon_{3.}$
4	$x_{4.} = \mu + \tau_4 + \epsilon_{4.}$
5	$x_{5.} = \mu + \tau_5 + \epsilon_{5.}$

where $x_{i.}$ = the mean of the sample X's for Treatment i and $\epsilon_{i.} = (\epsilon_{i1} + \cdots + \epsilon_{i6})/6$ = the average random error among the six randomly chosen plots of Treatment i. The grand mean of the X_{ij} would be the true mean of the $x_{i.}$'s, and would be $= \mu + \epsilon_{..}$, because the τ_i's are deviations from the grand mean and therefore add to zero. Note again that the mean of the X's obtained under the conditions of this particular experiment is *not* μ. However, before the experiment was started, the expected value of the mean $x_{..}$ would be μ. A similar distinction exists for the mean $x_{i.}$ of the ith Treatment. After the experiment is fixed and run, the average X for Treatment i is $x_{i.}$, but before the experiment is run, $E(x_{i.}) = \mu_{i.} = \mu + \tau_i$.

The decision that the population means for the Treatments are equal corresponds to the decision that all of the τ_i's are zero. Thus, the hypothesis expressed in $H_0[(\mu = \cdots = \mu_t) \mid (\sigma_1^2 = \cdots = \sigma_t^2 = \sigma^2)]$, versus an appropriate alternative, corresponds to $H_0[(\text{all } \tau_i = 0) \mid (\sigma_1^2 = \cdots = \sigma_t^2 = \sigma^2)]$ versus the same alternative. It is noted again that the X_{ij} are random variables because of the presence of the ϵ_{ij} in the statistical model for any X_{ij}.

It was stated in Chapter 7 that the Total Sum of Squares of the deviations of the X_{ij} from their own mean, $x_{..}$, can be subdivided into two independent parts by means of the following identity appropriate to an experiment with r units under each of t treatments:

$$(8.22) \quad \sum_{i=1}^{t} \sum_{j=1}^{r} (X_{ij} - x..)^2 \equiv \sum_{i=1}^{t} \sum_{j=1}^{r} [(X_{ij} - x_{i.}) + (x_{i.} - x..)]^2$$

$$\equiv \sum_i \sum_j (X_{ij} - x_{i.})^2 + r \sum_i (x_{i.} - x..)^2$$

because

$$\sum_i \sum_j [2(X_{ij} - x_{i.})(x_{i.} - x..)] = \sum_{i=1}^{t} [2(x_{i.} - x..) \sum_{j=1}^{r} (X_{ij} - x_{i.})] = 0$$

Identity 8.22 is the basis of the analysis of variance shown in Table 8.22.

TABLE 8.22.   SYMBOLIC ANALYSIS OF VARIANCE FOR A COMPLETELY
RANDOMIZED MODEL I EXPERIMENT

Source of variation	DF	Sample Sum of Squares	Mean Square
Between Treatments	$t - 1$	$r \sum (x_{i.} - x..)^2$	$\dfrac{r}{t-1} \sum (x_{i.} - x..)^2$
Within Treatments	$t(r - 1)$	$\sum_i \sum_j (X_{ij} - x_{i.})^2$	$\dfrac{1}{t(r-1)} \sum_i \sum_j (X_{ij} - x_{i.})^2$
Total about $x..$	$rt - 1$	$\sum \sum (X_{ij} - x..)^2$	

In brief, the total variation of the X_{ij} about their own mean has been analyzed into Between-Treatments and Within-Treatments components; hence the name *analysis of variance*. It also is noted that Total DF (equal to $tr - 1$ in this example) $\equiv$ Within-Treatments DF + Between-Treatments DF $\equiv$ $t(r - 1) + (t - 1)$.

It is important in the use and interpretation of an analysis of variance to know the long-run average, or expected value, of each sample Mean Square, because it can be proven that the sampling distribution of the ith Mean Square to be obtained from the normal sampling supposed herein is

$$(8.23) \qquad E\{Ms_i\}\chi^2_{\nu_i}/\nu_i$$

where Ms_i is a sample Mean Square and ν_i is the DF for this Ms.

The F ratio can be defined more generally than it was defined earlier, namely, as the ratio of two independent estimates of the same normal variance. Its more general definition is as follows, in terms of two independent sample chi-squares derived from normal populations with the same variance:

$$(8.24) \qquad F(\nu_1, \nu_2) = \frac{\chi^2_1/\nu_1}{\chi^2_2/\nu_2} = \frac{\nu_2 \chi^2_1}{\nu_1 \chi^2_2}$$

where $\nu_1 =$ DF for χ_1^2 and $\nu_2 =$ DF for χ_2^2, as usual. If the Between-Treatments and the Within-Treatments Mean Squares are estimating the same variance (as they would be if there were no Treatment effects so that all $\tau_i = 0$), the E{Ms}'s would be equal and the ratio of the sample Mean Squares would be an F ratio. Therefore, it is important to evaluate the expected Mean Squares so the proper F ratios can be established.

By using Formula 8.21, which is appropriate for the model of Table 8.22, it is found that

$$X_{ij} - x_{i.} = (\mu + \tau_i + \epsilon_{ij}) - (\mu + \tau_i + \epsilon_{i.})$$

$$= \mu + \tau_i + \epsilon_{ij} - \mu - \tau_i - \epsilon_{i.} = \epsilon_{ij} - \epsilon_{i.}$$

$$= \epsilon_{ij} - (\epsilon_{i1} + \epsilon_{i2} + \cdots + \epsilon_{i,j-1} + \epsilon_{ij} + \epsilon_{i,j+1} + \cdots + \epsilon_{ir})/r$$

$$= (r\epsilon_{ij} - \epsilon_{i1} - \epsilon_{i2} - \cdots - \epsilon_{ir})/r$$

(Note that ϵ_{ij} appears twice in the last expression.) Now it follows that

$$(X_{ij} - x_{i.})^2 = \frac{1}{r^2} (r\epsilon_{ij} - \epsilon_{i1} - \epsilon_{i2} - \cdots - \epsilon_{ij} - \cdots - \epsilon_{ir})^2$$

$$= \frac{1}{r^2} (r^2\epsilon_{ij}^2 + \epsilon_{i1}^{21} + \cdots + \epsilon_{ij}^2 + \cdots + \epsilon_{ir}^2) + \frac{1}{r^2} (-2r\epsilon_{ij}^2)$$

$$+ \frac{1}{r^2} (\text{cross products of independent } \epsilon\text{'s})$$

Therefore, with the use of the information, given earlier, regarding expected values of independent random variables it is found that

$$E\{(X_{ij} - x_{i.})^2\} = \frac{1}{r^2} (r^2\sigma^2 + r\sigma^2) + \frac{1}{r^2} (-2r\sigma^2) = \left(\frac{r-1}{r}\right)\sigma^2$$

The right-hand side of this equation does not involve the index i at all; hence, it holds for each of the t Treatments. It follows that the expected value of the sample Mean Square for Within Treatments is

$$E\left\{ \frac{1}{t(r-1)} \sum_{i=1}^{t} \sum^{r} (X_{ij} - x_{i.})^2 \right\} = \frac{1}{t(r-1)} \left[rt\left(\frac{r-1}{r}\right)\sigma^2 \right] = \sigma^2$$

and thus,

(8.25) $E\{\text{Within-Treatments Ms}\} = \sigma^2$

As a matter of fact, this must be true, or the assumptions of our completely randomized (CR) Model I would not be satisfied, namely, that the ϵ_{ij} are NID$(0, \sigma^2)$, regardless of i and j.

In view of the previous statements about the distribution of a sample Mean Square, it now is seen that the distribution of the Within-Treatments Mean Square is given by $\sigma^2 \chi_2^2 / t(r-1)$, because $\nu_2 = t(r-1)$.

The expected value of the Between-Treatments Mean Square is obtained in a similar manner. The Between-Treatments Mean Square is given by

$$\frac{r}{t-1} \sum_{i=1}^{t} [(x_{i.} - x..)^2]$$

so we need to evaluate $x_{i.} - x..$ in terms of Model 8.21. By direct substitution one has:

$$x_{i.} - x.. = \mu + \tau_i + \epsilon_{i.} - \mu - \epsilon.. = \tau_i + (\epsilon_{i.} - \epsilon..)$$

$$= \tau_i + [(\epsilon_{i1} + \epsilon_{i2} + \cdots + \epsilon_{ir})/r - (\epsilon_{11} + \cdots + \epsilon_{1r}$$
$$+ \epsilon_{21} + \cdots + \epsilon_{tr})/tr];$$

$$= \tau_i + \frac{1}{r}(\epsilon_{i1} + \epsilon_{i2} + \cdots + \epsilon_{ij} + \cdots + \epsilon_{ir})$$
$$- \frac{1}{rt}(\epsilon_{11} + \epsilon_{12} + \cdots + \epsilon_{ij} + \cdots + \epsilon_{tr});$$

$$= \tau_i + \frac{1}{tr}[t(\epsilon_{i1} + \epsilon_{i2} + \cdots + \epsilon_{ij} + \cdots + \epsilon_{ir}) - \epsilon_{11}$$
$$- \epsilon_{12} - \cdots - \epsilon_{i1} - \cdots - \epsilon_{ir} - \cdots - \epsilon_{tr}];$$

$$= \tau_i + \frac{1}{tr}[(t-1)(\epsilon_{i1} + \cdots + \epsilon_{ir}) - \epsilon_{11} - \cdots - \epsilon_{i-1,r}$$
$$- \epsilon_{i+1,r} - \cdots - \epsilon_{tr}]$$

Hence,

$$(x_{i.} - x..)^2 = \tau_i^2 + \frac{1}{t^2 r^2}[(t-1)^2(\epsilon_{i1}^2 + \epsilon_{i2}^2 + \cdots + \epsilon_{ir}^2) + \epsilon_{11}^2$$
$$+ \cdots + \epsilon_{i-1,r}^2 + \epsilon_{i+1,r}^2 + \cdots + \epsilon_{tr}^2]$$
$$+ 2\tau_i[(t-1)(\epsilon_{i1} + \cdots + \epsilon_{ir}) - \epsilon_{11} - \cdots$$
$$- \epsilon_{i-1,r} - \epsilon_{i+1,r} - \cdots - \epsilon_{tr}]/tr$$
$$+ \text{cross products } \epsilon_{ij}\epsilon_{kl} \quad \text{with} \quad ij \neq kl$$

Thus,

$$E\{(x_{i.} - x..)^2\} = \tau_i^2 + \frac{1}{t^2 r^2}[r(t-1)^2\sigma^2 + (tr-r)\sigma^2] + \text{zeros}$$

$$= \tau_i^2 + \frac{\sigma^2}{t^2 r}[(t-1)^2 + (t-1)]$$

$$= \tau_i^2 + \frac{t-1}{t^2 r}\sigma^2(t-1+1)$$

$$= \tau_i^2 + \left(\frac{t-1}{tr}\right)\sigma^2 \quad \text{for each } i$$

Therefore,

$$E\{\text{Treatment Mean Square}\} = \frac{r}{t-1} \sum_{i=1}^{t} (\tau_i^2) + \left(\frac{rt}{t-1}\right)\left(\frac{t-1}{tr}\right)\sigma^2; \quad \text{or,}$$

$$(8.26) \qquad E\{\text{Treatment Mean Square}\} = \sigma^2 + \frac{r}{t-1} \sum_{i=1}^{t} (\tau_i^2)$$

It follows from Equation 8.26 and the previous discussion that the sampling distribution of the Between-Treatment Mean Square is given by

$$\left(\sigma^2 + \frac{r}{t-1} \sum_{i=1}^{t} (\tau_i^2)\right) \chi_{t-1}^2 / (t-1)$$

In the event that all Treatments have the same true mean, so that all $\tau_i = 0$, the distribution of the Between-Treatments Mean Square becomes

$$\sigma^2 \chi_{t-1}^2 / (t-1)$$

Hence, the ratio of the Between-Treatments Mean Square to the Within-Treatments Mean Square is an $F[t-1, t(r-1)]$ distribution, because the σ^2's divide out of numerator and denominator. It is noted again that the population variances must be equal, or an F ratio is not obtained.

If these results are generalized to the extent that it is assumed that there are not necessarily equally many observations per treatment, one obtains the more general results shown in Table 8.23 for a completely randomized design.

TABLE 8.23.   ANALYSIS OF VARIANCE AND EXPECTED MEAN SQUARES
FOR COMPLETELY RANDOMIZED MODEL I DESIGN

Source of variation	DF	Sample Mean Square	Expected Mean Square
Different Treatments $t-1$		$\dfrac{1}{t-1} \sum_{1}^{t} r_i(x_{i.} - x..)^2$	$\sigma^2 + \dfrac{1}{t-1} \sum_{1}^{t} (r_i \tau_i^2)$
Error (within Treatment)	$\sum_{1}^{t} (r_i - 1)$	$\dfrac{1}{\sum_{1}^{t} (r_i - 1)} \sum_{1}^{t} \sum_{1}^{r_i} (X_{ij} - x_{i.})^2$	σ^2
Total about $x..$:	$\sum (r_i) - 1$		

It is apparent from this table that if the hypothesis $H_0[(\mu_1 = \cdots = \mu_t) \mid (\sigma_1^2 = \cdots = \sigma_t^2 = \sigma^2)]$ is true, the expected Treatment Mean Square is σ^2, as noted earlier, and the ratio of the Treatment and Error Mean Squares can be shown to be an F ratio. Demonstration of this fact is one of the important benefits to be derived from the process of deriving the expected Mean Squares for an analysis of variance. The alternative hypothesis, H_a, in this situation is that $\mu_i \neq \mu_j$ for some i and j or the equivalent statement, that some τ_i are not zero. If the observed $F[(t - 1), \sum (r_i - 1)]$ is in the chosen region of rejection, it is concluded that some of the τ_i are not zero and, hence, some of the μ_i are unequal to others.

Suppose, next, that the Treatments included in this experiment are properly regarded as a random sample of a whole class of similar Treatments. The jth observation under the ith Treatment still will depend upon μ, τ_i, and ϵ_{ij} but the assumptions relative to the τ_i will be altered. Specifically, the statistical model for a CR random-effects design, with all $r_i = r$ will be as follows:

(8.27) $X_{ij} = \mu + \tau_i + \epsilon_{ij},$ with $i = 1$ to t and $j = 1$ to r

where:

> μ = the grand average X_{ij} over all conceivable units of all Treatments represented by the random sample of t Treatments of this class
>
> τ_i = advantage ($+$) or disadvantage ($-$) of the ith Treatment relative to μ, and the τ_i are NID(0, σ_τ^2) variates
>
> ϵ_{ij} = the random error characteristic of the jth unit under the ith Treatment

We assume that $E(\mu) = \mu$, $E(\tau_i) = 0$, the ϵ_{ij} are NID(0, σ^2) for all i and j; therefore $E(\tau_i\epsilon_{ij}) = 0$, and $E(\tau_k\tau_l) = 0$ if $k \neq l$. Note that $\sum_t (\tau_i) \neq 0$ now, because only a sample of Treatments is drawn. Note also that these assumptions imply homogeneity of variance from Treatment to Treatment and that errors of observation are uncorrelated with each other and with the Treatments involved. This random-effects model is called Model II.

As before, the Treatment and Error Mean Squares are given algebraically by

$$\frac{r}{t - 1} \sum_{i=1}^{t} (x_{i.} - x_{..})^2 \quad \text{and} \quad \frac{1}{t(r - 1)} \sum_{i=1}^{t} \sum_{j=1}^{r} (X_{ij} - x_{i.})^2$$

respectively; hence, we need to express $(x_{i.} - x_{..})$ and $(X_{ij} - x_{i.})$ in terms of the model. This is done below.

Using the Model, (8.27), one obtains, successively,

$$x_{i.} = (1/r) \sum_{j=1}^{r} (X_{ij}) = (1/r) \sum_{j=1}^{r} (\mu + \tau_i + \epsilon_{ij}) = \mu + \tau_i + \epsilon_{i.}$$

where $\epsilon_{i.}$ = average ϵ_{ij} for the ith treatment and this sample of size r. Moreover,

$$x_{..} = (1/rt) \sum_{i=1}^{t} \sum_{j=1}^{r} (X_{ij}) = (1/rt) \sum_{i} \sum_{j} (\mu + \tau_i + \epsilon_{ij})$$

$$= \mu + (1/t) \sum_{i} (\tau_i) + \epsilon_{..}$$

Therefore,

$$x_{i.} - x_{..} = \tau_i - 1/t \sum_i (\tau_i) + (\epsilon_{i.} - \epsilon_{..})$$

$$= (1/t)[(t-1)\tau_i - \tau_1 - \cdots - \tau_{i-1} - \tau_{i+1} - \cdots - \tau_t]$$

$$- (1/rt)[(t-1)(\epsilon_{i1} + \cdots + \epsilon_{ir}) - \epsilon_{11} - \cdots$$

$$- \epsilon_{i-1,r} - \epsilon_{i+1,1} - \cdots - \epsilon_{rt}]$$

There are r ϵ's multiplied by $(t-1)$ and $r(t-1)$ *other* ϵ's. Therefore,

$$(x_{i.} - x_{..})^2 = (1/t^2)[(t-1)^2\tau^2_{-i} + \tau_1^2 + \cdots + \tau_{i-1}^2 + \tau_{i+1}^2 + \cdots + \tau_t^2]$$

$$+ (1/r^2t^2)[(t-1)^2(\epsilon_{i1}^2 + \cdots + \epsilon_{ir}^2) + \epsilon_{11}^2 + \cdots$$

$$+ \epsilon_{i-1,r}^2 + \epsilon_{i+1,1}^2 + \cdots + \epsilon_{rt}^2]$$

+ cross products of τ's and ϵ's, whose expected values are zero

Then,

$$E\{(x_{i.} - x_{..})^2\} = \frac{1}{t^2}[(t-1)^2\sigma_\tau^2 + (t-1)\sigma_\tau^2]$$

$$+ \frac{1}{r^2t^2}[r(t-1)^2\sigma^2 + r(t-1)\sigma^2] + 0$$

$$= \left(\frac{t-1}{t}\right)\sigma_\tau^2 + \left(\frac{t-1}{rt}\right)\sigma^2$$

after suitable simplification. But it has been shown that the

$$\text{Treatment Mean Square} = \frac{r}{t-1}\sum_i (x_{i.} - x_{..})^2$$

and the above result for $E[(x_{i.} - x_{..})^2]$ does not depend upon the index, i; hence,

(8.28) $$E(\text{Treatment Mean Square}) = \sigma^2 + r\sigma_\tau^2$$

for the random-effects **CR** model.

For the Within-Treatments (or Error) Mean Square,

$$X_{ij} - x_{i.} = \mu + \tau_i + \epsilon_{ij} - \mu - \tau_i - \epsilon_{i.} = \epsilon_{ij} - \epsilon_{i.}$$

Hence,

$$(X_{ij} - x_{i.})^2 = \frac{1}{r^2}[(r-1)^2\epsilon_{ij}^2 + \epsilon_{i1}^2 + \cdots + \epsilon_{i,j-1}^2 + \epsilon_{i,j+1}^2 + \cdots + \epsilon_{ir}^2]$$

+ cross products whose mathematical expectations are zero

After application of the processes already illustrated, it is found, as expected, that

$$\text{(8.29)} \qquad \text{E(Error Mean Square)} = \sigma^2$$

for the random-effects CR model experiment.

The results for both the fixed-effects and the random-effects models are summarized in Table 8.24 for completely randomized experiments.

TABLE 8.24. SUMMARY OF EXPECTED MEAN SQUARES FOR THE FIXED-EFFECTS AND THE RANDOM-EFFECTS COMPLETELY RANDOMIZED MODELS

Source of variation	DF	Expected Mean Squares	
		Fixed-effects	*Random-effects*
Treatments	$t - 1$	$\sigma^2 + \dfrac{r}{t - 1} \sum \tau_i^2$	$\sigma^2 + r\sigma_\tau^2$
Error (within Treatment)	$t(r - 1)$	σ^2	σ^2

It can now be deduced from Table 8.24 and previous discussion of the distributions of sample Mean Squares that the Model I and Model II Mean Squares and their sampling distributions for a CR design are as in Table 8.25. It is observed that if $H_0[(\mu_1 = \cdots = \mu_t) \mid (\sigma_1^2 = \cdots = \sigma_t^2 = \sigma^2)]$ is, in

TABLE 8.25. DISTRIBUTIONS OF MEAN SQUARES FOR COMPLETELY RANDOMIZED MODELS I AND II DESIGNS

Source	Model	Distribution
Between Treatments	Fixed-effects (I)	$[\sigma^2 + r/(t - 1) \sum (\tau_i^2)]\chi_{t-1}^2/(t - 1)$
Between Treatments	Random-effects (II)	$[\sigma^2 + r\sigma_\tau^2]\chi_{t-1}^2/(t - 1)$
Within Treatments	Fixed-effects (I)	$\sigma^2 \cdot \chi_{t(r-1)}^2/(t - 1)$
Within Treatments	Random-effects (II)	$\sigma^2 \cdot \chi_{t(r-1)}^2/t(r - 1)$

fact, true, the Between-Treatments sample Mean Square for a fixed-effects CR experiment has the following distribution:

$$\sigma^2 \chi_{t-1}^2/(t - 1)$$

so that the ratio

(Between-Treatments Mean Square)/(Within-Treatments Mean Square) has an $F[(t - 1), t(r - 1)]$ distribution or, put another way, in terms of the τ_i one can say that on the hypothesis H_0(all the $\tau_i = 0$) versus H_a(some

$\tau_i \neq 0$), $F[(t - 1), t(r - 1)] =$ (Treatment Mean Square)/(Error Mean Square), where Error = Within-Treatment in these experiments.

On the hypothesis $H_0(\sigma_\tau^2 = 0)$ versus $H_a(\sigma_\tau^2 \neq 0)$, an F ratio again is suitable as the test criterion.

PROBLEMS

1. Completely verify the expected Mean Squares of Table 8.24.

2. Describe fully an experiment in your own field, or in another, for which each of the models of Table 8.24 would be appropriate.

3. Suppose that a scientist wishes to study three specific dietary supplements used to feed out beef cattle which have been on pasture. The beef animals to be used in this experiment are fed independently and can be considered random sampling units. Write out a statistical model for this experiment, assuming 10 animals chosen at random for each supplement. Clearly define all symbols used.

4. Referring to Problem 3, derive the expected Diets Mean Square and state what the distribution of the sample Diets Mean Square is. Do likewise for the Within-Diets Mean Square.

5. Suppose that an agronomist wishes to study the level of yield of white corn varieties. He selects 5 white corn varieties at random and raises 6 plots of each variety in a completely randomized design. Write down the model and outline of the analysis of variance for this experiment, defining all symbols clearly.

6. Referring to Problem 5, give sufficient reasoning to show that the ratio (Between Varieties Mean Square)/(Within Varieties Mean Square) has an F distribution.

7. Make up and fully describe a fixed-effects CR design in your own field of interest or in another. Write down the model and outline of the analysis of variance for this experiment.

8. Describe the F test you would use in Problem 7, justify that ratio as an F, and state the hypothesis being tested.

8.3   FIXED-EFFECTS MODEL (MODEL I) FOR A RANDOMIZED COMPLETE BLOCK DESIGN

Suppose again that an experimenter is interested in studying t specific Treatments to learn which, if any, are better than others. He is not trying to represent a larger group of Treatments (such as high-roughage diets, lecture-type teaching methods, etc.) by a random sample from a whole class of such Treatments; he merely wishes to test the hypothesis that the population means of his particular Treatments are equal, against the alternative hypothesis, that some or all of these means are unequal. However, he now believes that he can reduce the basic sampling error in the populations involved by pregrouping the experimental units into more homogeneous subgroups, to be called Blocks. If the experimenter is dealing with plots of land, he may feel that he can group the plots available for the experiment into groups of t plots each, on the basis of soil fertility, for example. Each of the t Treatments will be assigned one plot within each Block, perhaps by means of a table of random numbers. If this sort of pregrouping of the plots into homogeneous Blocks is to be useful, it must be true that, *before any Treatments are applied*, plots within the same Block definitely are more alike than are the plots in different Blocks. Otherwise, there will be no reduction in sampling variance, and σ^2 will not be smaller than if the experimenter had not gone to the trouble of defining Blocks at all. Furthermore, the analysis of variance will have sacrificed some degrees of freedom, which could have been used more efficiently in the estimation of the error variance, σ^2.

The model for a randomized complete block (RCB) design certainly must include constants for measuring Block effects, but there is a question regarding the relationship between Treatment effects and Block effects. If the Treatment effects upon the measurement, X_{ij}, and the Block effects upon the same measurement, X_{ij}, are not in any way interrelated but merely add together to produce each X_{ij} (aside from the ever-present random sampling error, ϵ_{ij}), then the Block and Treatment effects are said to be *additive*. In this event, the appropriate model is

(8.31) $$X_{ij} = \mu + \tau_i + \beta_j + \epsilon_{ij}$$

where β_j is the advantage $(+)$ or disadvantage $(-)$ associated with being in Block j, relative to the grand average μ. However, it also may be that the Block and Treatment effects are interrelated. For example, the Blocks of an experiment might be based upon different soil types, and Treatments might be varieties of some sort. It is entirely reasonable in such circumstances that some varieties might do relatively better on one soil type than on another, so soil type and variety might thus be interrelated. If so, we say that soil type (Block) and variety (Treatment) are interacting and one needs to measure the Block × Treatment interaction. It then is necessary to write a model which takes account of this *interaction*. In this event, one might propose to write the following model for a randomized-blocks design when interaction exists between Treatments and Blocks:

$$X_{ij} = \mu + \tau_i + \beta_j + (\tau\beta)_{ij} + \epsilon_{ij}$$

if there is but one observation per Treatment and Block. However, the interaction effects between Treatments and Blocks measured by the $(\tau\beta)_{ij}$

cannot be separated from the Error effects, ϵ_{ij}, unless more than one observation is taken per Treatment and Block. When q observations are taken per Treatment and Block, we can write the following model:

(8.32) $$X_{ijk} = \mu + \tau_i + \beta_j + (\tau\beta)_{ij} + \epsilon_{ijk}$$

where:

X_{ijk} = the measurement for the kth sample within the jth Block and ith Treatment

μ = the grand average of all possible X_{ijk} under these specific Blocks and Treatments

τ_i = the advantage (τ is $+$) or disadvantage (τ is $-$), on the average over the Blocks used in this experiment, for the ith Treatment measured relative to μ, so that $\sum_i \tau_i = 0$

β_j = similarly, for Block effects

$(\tau\beta)_{ij}$ = the true average advantage ($+$) or disadvantage ($-$) of combining the ith Treatment and the jth Block measured relative to μ, so that $\sum_i (\tau\beta)_{ij} = \sum_j (\tau\beta)_{ij} = \sum_i \sum_j (\tau\beta)_{ij} = 0$; this interaction is in addition to Treatment and/or Block effects included in τ_i and/or β_j.

ϵ_{ijk} = the additive random advantage ($+$) or disadvantages ($-$) characteristic of the kth experimental unit in Block j and assigned to Treatment i, before Treatment i was applied; these Errors are assumed to be NID$(0, \sigma^2)$ for all i, j, k.

If the $(\tau\beta)_{ij} \neq 0$ for every combination of i and j, there is interaction, and Treatment and Block effects are said to be nonadditive. It is not always true that the experimenter can decide this matter without obtaining data and making an appropriate test. If he has one observation per Treatment and Block, he can test for nonadditivity by means of J. W. Tukey's test (see *Biometrics* 5: 232, 1949). No attempt will be made here to justify this test, but it will be illustrated by means of Tables 8.31 and 8.32. The basic data are presented in Table 8.31, along with necessary calculations, and the final decision regarding additivity is made as shown in Table 8.32. The analysis of variance required to single out and test the one degree of freedom associated with nonadditivity is presented in Table 8.32 by using the computations from Table 8.31.

The symbols used in Table 8.31 have their usual meanings except, perhaps, the p_j, which are obtained as follows, with $j = 1$ for illustration:

$$p_1 = 18(-14.17) + 13(-11.17) + 18(-7.17) + \cdots + 16(+20.83)$$

$$= +22.92$$

as shown in the upper right-hand corner of Table 8.31.

TABLE 8.31.   COUNTS OF HOUSEFLIES ON DAIRY CATTLE.

Block (day of count)	8 A.M.	10 A.M.	1 P.M.	3 P.M.	5 P.M.	7 P.M.	Sum	$x_{.j}$	$d_j = x_{.j} - x_{..}$	$p_j = \sum_i X_{ij} d_i$
				Hour of day X_{11}						
I	18	13	18	42	17	16	124	20.67	1.50	+22.92
II	5	7	25	17	75	30	159	26.50	7.33	+1,122.97
III	5	5	9	32	23	113	187	31.17	12.00	+2,438.21
IV	5	17	8	24	21	25	100	16.67	−2,50	+450.00
V	2	4	10	14	24	28	82	13.67	−5.50	+710.06
VI	3	5	14	23	19	19	83	13.83	−5.34	+11.81
VII	5	10	5	11	43	40	114	19.00	−0.17	+1,089.62
VIII	2	2	20	30	25	55	134	22.33	3.16	+1,247.22
IX	4	9	11	9	35	27	95	15.83	−3.34	+712.85
X	5	16	7	11	34	21	94	15.67	−3.50	+515.02
XI	2	3	10	16	17	60	108	18.00	−1.17	+1,313.64
XII	4	5	7	11	27	46	100	16.67	−2.50	+1,097.00
Sum:	60	96	144	240	360	480	1,380			10,831.32
$x_{i.}$:	5.0	8.0	12.0	20.0	30.0	40.0		$19.17 = x_{..}$		
$d_i = (x_{i.} - x_{..})$:	−14.17	−11.17	−7.17	+0.83	+10.83	+20.83				

$P = \sum (d_j p_j) = 27,723.9067.$ $\sum (d_j^2) = 306.0335,$ $\sum (d_i^2) = 928.8334.$

$P = \sum (d_j^2) = 27,723.9067.$

Sum of squares for nonadditivity $= P^2/(\sum d_i^2 \cdot \sum d_j^2) = 2703.97.$

It is concluded from the analysis of variance in Table 8.32 that the Day and the Hour effects interact and, therefore, there is nonadditivity. This means that Model 8.31 should not be used, because we cannot properly estimate the error variance in this circumstance. For example, an assumption that the ϵ_{ij} are NID(0, σ^2) in the model probably would not be valid, because independence or homogeneity of variance, or both, would not exist. In such a circumstance it would be advisable in the future to design the experiment so there would be more than one observation per Day and Hour. This would make it possible to estimate both the interaction effect and the magnitude of the sampling error within the same Block and Hour. This is done by Model 8.32.

TABLE 8.32.   ANALYSIS OF VARIANCE FOR TESTING
FOR NONADDITIVITY BY TUKEY'S METHOD

Source of variation	DF	Sum of Squares	Mean Squares
Treatments (hour of day)	5	11,146	2,229*
Blocks (days)	11	1,836	166.9 ns
Error + (Hour × Block)	55	10,130	
Nonadditivity:	(1)	(2,704)	2,704*
Remainder:	(54)	(8,426)	156.9

Method described in *Biometrics* 5: 232, 1949.

The preceding discussion of a test for nonadditivity and its implications, and also the meaning of the term interaction, can be illustrated specifically by means of the three hypothetical experiments shown in Table 8.33. These

TABLE 8.33.   HYPOTHETICAL RANDOMIZED COMPLETE BLOCK EXPERIMENTS
ILLUSTRATING CONCEPTS OF THE ERROR AND INTERACTION
EFFECTS AND THEIR COMBINATION

Block	Experiment A			Experiment B			Experiment C		
	I	II	III	I	II	III	I	II	III
1	5	7	11	5	7	11	5	7	11
2	7	9	13	6	9	12	12	9	6
3	4	6	10	5	5	10	6	8	12
4	12	14	18	13	14	23	24	15	11
5	0	2	6	2	3	5	4	4	4

three RCB experiments have been constructed in such a way that Experiment A has neither interaction nor error, Experiment B probably has only sampling error and no interaction, whereas Experiment C probably has some of both.

The analysis of variance for each experiment of Table 8.33 is as shown in Table 8.34.

In Experiment A of Table 8.33, Treatment II is two units larger than Treatment I and four units smaller than Treatment III, *in every block.* Associated with these identical linear relationships between Treatments from Block to Block is a zero Remainder Sum of Squares and Mean Square. Expressed another way, it is noted that the comparisons among Treatments I, II, and III stay exactly the same in a linear sense from Block to Block; there is not even random variation. Such a situation never exists in a real experiment.

In Experiment B, the comparisons among the Treatments from Block to Block are not identically the same but are close to the same, and the Remainder Mean Square, while not zero, is small. Presumably, this is simply a result of sampling error.

TABLE 8.34. ANALYSIS OF VARIANCE FOR DATA OF TABLE 8.33

Source of variation	DF	Mean Square, A	Mean Square, B	Mean Square, C
Between Treatments	2	46.67	49.26	3.80
Between Blocks	4	57.00	73.16	64.10
Remainder	8	0	2.518	17.05
Total about $x..$	14			

In Experiment C the comparisons among Treatments change radically, even to the extent of reversed order of sizes, from Block to Block, and the Remainder Mean Square is relatively much larger than in the other two experiments. This presumably is the consequence of both Error (which is always present in practice) and some true interaction between Treatments and Blocks. Thus it appears that the Remainder Source of Variation probably reflects changes in Treatment comparisons which occur from Block to Block. Hence it is reasonable to say that the less consistent the Treatment comparisons are from Block to Block, the larger the Remainder Sum of Squares tends to be, everything else remaining the same.

For simplicity, we shall start the discussion of expected Mean Squares for RCB designs with the case of no interaction between Treatments and Blocks, so that Model 8.31 applies. The ϵ_{ij} which will appear in subsequent discussions of this simplest RCB design will be assumed to be the result of random sampling error alone, rather than of a combination of this and an interaction effect. In later discussions, when more than one sample is taken per Treatment and Block, an Interaction Source of Variation will be added to the model and to the corresponding analysis of variance.

The following identity is useful in the derivation of the expected Mean Squares for the fixed-effects RCB model with but one observation per Treatment and Block:

$$(8.33) \quad \sum_{i=1}^{t} \sum_{j=1}^{r} (X_{ij} - x..)^2 \equiv \sum_i \sum_j (x_{i.} - x..)^2 + \sum_i \sum_j (x_{.j} - x..)^2$$

$$+ \sum_i \sum_j (X_{ij} - x_{i.} - x_{.j} + x..)^2$$

$$\equiv r \sum_i (x_{i.} - x..)^2 + t \sum_i (x_{.j} - x..)^2$$

$$+ \sum_i \sum_j (X_{ij} - x_{i.} - x_{.j} + x..)^2$$

That is,

$$\text{Total Ss} \equiv \text{Treatments Ss} + \text{Blocks Ss} + \text{Error Ss}$$

$$\text{Total DF} \equiv \text{Treatments DF} + \text{Blocks DF} + \text{Error DF}$$

$$tr - 1 \equiv (t - 1) \qquad\quad + (r - 1) \qquad + (t - 1)(r - 1)$$

TABLE 8.35.   OUTLINE OF A MODEL I (FIXED-EFFECTS) RANDOMIZED COMPLETE
BLOCK DESIGN OF AN EXPERIMENT IN WHICH ADDITIVITY
HOLDS TRUE, SO THERE IS NO INTERACTION

Block	Treatment 1	Treatment t	Block mean
1	$X_{11} = \mu + \tau_1 + \beta_1 + \epsilon_{11} \cdots$	$X_{t1} = \mu + \tau_t + \beta_1 + \epsilon_{t1}$	$x_{.1} = \mu + \beta_1 + \epsilon_{.1}$
2	$X_{12} = \mu + \tau_1 + \beta_2 + \epsilon_{12} \cdots$	$X_{t2} = \mu + \tau_t + \beta_2 + \epsilon_{t2}$	$x_{.2} = \mu + \beta_2 + \epsilon_{.2}$
.	.	.	.
.	.	.	.
r	$X_{1r} = \mu + \tau_1 + \beta_r + \epsilon_{1r} \cdots$	$X_{tr} = \mu + \tau_t + \beta_r + \epsilon_{tr}$	$x_{.r} = \mu + \beta_r + \epsilon_{.r}$

Treatment mean:

$$x_{1.} = \mu + \tau_1 + \epsilon_{1.} \qquad \cdots \qquad x_{t.} = \mu + \tau_t + \epsilon_{t.} \qquad\qquad x.. = \mu + \epsilon..$$

$$\sum_i \tau_i = \sum_i \beta_j = 0$$

To see the usefulness of Identity 8.33, consider Table 8.35, in which the experiment and the model have been fully outlined. The reader can verify that the identity is derived from

$$X_{ij} - x.. \equiv (X_{ij} - x_{i.} - x_{.j} + x..) + (x_{i.} - x..) + (x_{.j} - x..)$$

in a manner exactly analogous to that used with the CR design. The cross products vanish for the usual reasons.

The sample Mean Squares for Treatments, Blocks, and Error for Model 8.31 are, respectively,

$$(8.34) \quad \frac{r}{t - 1} \sum_{i=1}^{t} (x_{i.} - x..)^2, \qquad \frac{t}{r - 1} \sum_{j=1}^{r} (x_{.j} - x..)^2, \qquad \text{and}$$

$$\frac{1}{(r - 1)(t - 1)} \sum_{i=1}^{t} \sum_{j=1}^{r} (X_{ij} - x_{i.} - x_{.j} + x..)^2$$

Again it is of interest to derive the expected Mean Squares for these three sources of variation, because this procedure will clarify the assumptions made during an analysis of variance and will help specify the hypothesis being tested by an appropriate F test.

Following the methods used with the CR designs earlier, one obtains the following results by using Formula 8.31 and Table 8.35.

$$x_{i.} - x.. = \tau_i + (\epsilon_{i.} - \epsilon..)$$

and so

$$\sum_{i=1}^{t} (x_{i.} - x..)^2 = \sum_{i=1}^{t} (\tau_i^2) + 2 \sum_{i=1}^{t} [\tau_i(\epsilon_{i.} - \epsilon..)] + \sum_{i=1}^{t} (\epsilon_{i.} - \epsilon..)^2$$

But it is assumed that the random errors of observation, the ϵ_{ij}, are independent of the treatments; so the τ_i's and the ϵ's are uncorrelated, and each expected value of any of their cross products is zero. Hence, for the sake of simplicity, these cross products will be left out of the following expressions. Thus

$$\sum_{i=1}^{t} (x_{i.} - x..)^2 = \sum_{i} \left[(\tau_i^2) + \sum_{i} (\epsilon_{i.} - \epsilon..)^2 \right]$$

Because the τ's are constants, $E(\sum \tau_i^2) = \sum (\tau_i^2)$. For a particular value of the index i,

$$E(\epsilon_{i.} - \epsilon..)^2 = E \left[\frac{\epsilon_{i1} + \cdots + \epsilon_{ir}}{r} - \frac{\epsilon_{11} + \cdots + \epsilon_{rt}}{rt} \right]^2$$

or, after simplification,

$$= E \left[\frac{(t-1)(\epsilon_{i1} + \cdots + \epsilon_{ir}) - \text{other } (rt - r)\epsilon_{kl}\text{'s}}{rt} \right]^2,$$

$$\text{where } kl \neq i1, i2, \cdots, \text{ or } ir,$$

$$= \frac{1}{r^2 t^2} [(t-1)^2 r \sigma^2 + r(t-1)\sigma^2] = \frac{(t-1)\sigma^2}{rt}$$

Therefore, the expected Treatment Mean Square is the sum of such terms for $i = 1, i = 2, \cdots,$ and $i = t$, each multiplied by $r/(t-1)$. Thus,

$$E \left[\frac{r}{t-1} \sum_{i} (\epsilon_{i.} - \epsilon..)^2 \right] = \frac{rt}{t-1} \frac{t-1}{rt} \sigma^2 = \sigma^2.$$

When the $\frac{r}{t-1} \sum (\tau_i^2)$ obtained earlier is added, the expected value of the Treatment Mean Square is found to be:

$$(8.35) \qquad E(\text{Treatment Mean Square}) = \sigma^2 + \frac{r}{t-1} \sum (\tau_i^2)$$

for a Model I RCB design with no subsampling and no interaction between Blocks and Treatments. Actually, this is the same expected Mean Square for Treatments obtained earlier for a CR design. The basic difference between the two situations is that with a justifiable RCB design the sampling variance, σ^2, should be, and generally will be, smaller for the RCB design than for a CR design under the same circumstances, because the plots were grouped into more nearly homogeneous subgroups called Blocks. If the grouping of the sampling units into subgroups called Blocks does not cause σ^2 to be smaller than the corresponding CR design, the use of the RCB design has resulted in a useless loss of $r - 1$ DF, which could have strengthened the estimation of σ^2.

The expected value for the Blocks Mean Square is got in an entirely similar manner, because this Block effect also is assumed to be a fixed effect, and therefore the assumptions regarding the constants would be the same. Although the expected value of the Error Mean Square is obtained in a similar manner (and will turn out to be the same as before, namely, σ^2), its derivation will be outlined, because it is a bit more complex to derive.

We need first to obtain an expression for $(X_{ij} - x_{i.} - x_{.j} + x_{..})$. This expression is found, by straightforward substitution from Equation 8.31 and Table 8.35, to be $\mu + \tau_i + \beta_j + \epsilon_{ij} - \mu - \tau_i - \epsilon_{i.} - \mu - \beta_j - \epsilon_{.j} + \mu + \epsilon_{..}$; hence,

$$(X_{ij} - x_{i.} - x_{.j} + x_{..})^2$$

$$= \left[\epsilon_{ij} - \frac{\epsilon_{i1} + \cdots + \epsilon_{ir}}{r} - \frac{\epsilon_{1j} + \cdots + \epsilon_{tj}}{t} + \frac{\epsilon_{11} + \cdots + \epsilon_{rt}}{rt} \right]^2$$

$$= \frac{1}{r^2 t^2} [rt\epsilon_{ij} - t\epsilon_{i1} - \cdots - t\epsilon_{ij} - \cdots - t\epsilon_{ir} - r\epsilon_{1j} - \cdots$$

$$- r\epsilon_{ij} - \cdots - r\epsilon_{tj} + \epsilon_{11} + \cdots + \epsilon_{ij} + \cdots + \epsilon_{rt}]^2$$

Then, again using the statistical independence of the ϵ's, one finds, after some algebraic simplifications paralleling those used before, that

$$E[(X_{ij} - x_{i.} - x_{.j} + x_{..})^2] = \frac{\sigma^2}{rt} [(r - 1)(t - 1)]$$

for each of the rt combinations of i and j; hence, with a divisor of $(t-1)(r-1)$, it is found that:

$$(8.36) \quad E(\text{Error Mean Square}) = \left[\frac{\sigma^2}{rt} (r - 1)(t - 1) \right] \cdot \left[\frac{1}{(r - 1)(t - 1)} (rt) \right]$$

$$= \sigma^2$$

This result is identical with that obtained for the CR design. Again, the only difference between the CR and the RCB designs in the same situation is that a Blocks Sum of Squares has been taken out of the Total Sum of Squares about $x..$ in the hope that the sampling variance will be enough smaller to compensate for the $r - 1$ degrees of freedom lost from the estimate of the error variance, σ^2. If this generally is untrue for a given experimental situation, the RCB design is unjustified in that situation and should not be used.

The results of the preceding work on the RCB design under Model I are summarized in Table 8.36. It is seen from this table that on the hypothesis

TABLE 8.36. ANALYSIS OF VARIANCE AND EXPECTED MEAN SQUARES FOR A FIXED-EFFECTS RANDOMIZED COMPLETE BLOCK DESIGN FOR t TREATMENTS AND r BLOCKS, NO INTERACTION PRESENT

Source of variation	DF	Sampling Mean Square	Expected Mean Square
Treatments	$t - 1$	$\dfrac{r}{t - 1} \sum\limits_{i=1}^{t} (x_{i.} - x..)^2$	$\sigma^2 + \dfrac{r}{t - 1} \sum\limits_{i=1}^{t} (\tau_i^2)$
Blocks	$r - 1$	$\dfrac{t}{r - 1} \sum\limits_{j=1}^{r} (x_{.j} - x..)^2$	$\sigma^2 + \dfrac{t}{r - 1} \sum\limits_{j=1}^{r} (\beta_j^2)$
Error	$(r - 1)(t - 1)$	$\dfrac{1}{(r - 1)(t - 1)} \sum\limits_{i=1}^{t} \sum\limits_{j=1}^{r} (X_{ij} - x_{i.}$ $- x_{.j} + x..)^2$	σ^2

H_0(all $\tau_i = 0$) the expected Treatment Mean Square $= \sigma^2 =$ the expected Error Mean Square. Thus, these two Mean Squares are estimating the same variance, and they are independent estimates. It can be shown that their ratio is an F by the procedure illustrated earlier. A similar statement regarding the hypothesis that there are no Block differences, H_0(all $\beta_j = 0$), justifies the use of the F test in this model to determine whether there is a significant Block effect. These justifications of the F tests (nonmathematical though they are) in the analysis of variance were the chief reasons for deriving the expected Mean Squares in the analysis of variance table, Table 8.36.

PROBLEMS

1. Suppose that a drug company wishes to test the effects of three specific new drugs on the growth rate of white rats. They feel that there could be important differences between rats in different litters but that rats within the same litter should be very similar. Hence Blocks are defined as litters, and three rats within each of 15 litters are chosen at random as the experimental units within each Block. Thereafter each rat within each litter is randomly chosen to be given one of the three drugs in some appropriate way. Assuming litter (Block) differences do not interact with the drugs (Treatments), write down and fully define the statistical model for this fixed effects RCB design.

2. Referring to Problem 1, write out the analysis of variance and expected Mean Squares for this experiment.

3. Referring to Problem 2, describe the sampling distributions of the Treatment and Error Mean Squares, and show why the ratio (Between-Treatments Mean Square)/(Error Mean Square) is an F distribution. Also state specifically which F distribution it is.

4. Suppose that four alloys which could be used for making pipe for use underground are to be tested under eight soil conditions. Three sample pipes made from each alloy are to be tested under each soil condition. Write out the model and analysis of variance for this experiment.

5. Write down the expected Mean Squares as specifically as possible for Problem 4.

6. Make up your own hypothetical experiment for an RCB design involving four fixed Treatments and six fixed Blocks and such that the Error Mean Square is zero. Make a specific randomized plan for this experiment and do the appropriate analysis of variance.

7. Modify the data used in Problem 6 to produce a considerable interaction, that is, a large Error Mean Square. Do the analysis of variance for this new experiment.

8. Completely verify the expected Mean Square for Blocks in Table 8.36.

9. Completely verify the expected Error Mean Square in Table 8.36.

10. In what way was the fact that the Treatments were assumed to represent fixed effects used in deriving any of the Mean Squares in Table 8.36?

11. Write down the specific identity in sums of squares for the analysis of variance for Problems 1, 4, and 6.

12. Suppose that an $N(5, 7)$ population is to be sampled in such a way that Model 8.31 applies, with $t = 6$ and $r = 5$. What is the specific frequency distribution of the Error Mean Square? Is its graph symmetrical? Unimodal? Continuous?

8.4   RANDOM MODEL FOR A RANDOMIZED COMPLETE BLOCK DESIGN WITH r BLOCKS OF t TREATMENTS EACH (MODEL II)

The equation for this model looks the same as that for the RCB design considered earlier with fixed effects, but the assumptions and some of the end results are different. It is recalled that with a Model II design the Treatments and Blocks are considered to be random samples of some general classes of Treatments and of Blocks, respectively. It also will be assumed at first that the Treatment and Block effects are additive, that is, that there is no interaction between these two effects, so that the formula for the model can be written as follows:

$$(8.41) \qquad X_{ij} = \mu + \tau_i + \beta_j + \epsilon_{ij}$$

where:

X_{ij} = the observation under the ith Treatment and jth Block

τ_i = a random variate associated with Treatment effects and such that that the τ_i are NID(0, σ_τ^2) variates

β_j = variates which are NID(0, σ_β^2) and are independent of the τ_i and of the ϵ_{ij}

μ = the guard mean of all possible or conceivable X_{ij} under the conditions sampled

ϵ_{ij} = NID(0, σ^2) variates which are independent of the τ_i and of the β_j

In view of the previous assumptions of randomness and independence, the variance of a single observation is:

$$\sigma_{X_{ij}}^2 = E(X_{ij} - \mu)^2 = E(\mu + \tau_i + \beta_j + \epsilon_{ij} - \mu)^2$$

$$= E(\tau_i^2 + \beta_j^2 + \epsilon_{ij}^2 + \text{cross products})$$

Hence

(8.42) $$\sigma_{X_{ij}}^2 = \sigma_\tau^2 + \sigma_\beta^2 + \sigma^2$$

The right-hand side of Formula 8.42 merely states that the Total variance is the sum of three independent components: Treatments variance, Blocks variance, and Error variance. This emphasizes the fact that with the random-effects models emphasis is on the explanation of the sources of variation contributing to the Total variance rather than upon differences among population means, as with the fixed-effects models. In a random-effects model there is no reason why an experimenter should be interested in the true mean of the ith Treatment, because this ith Treatment is only the ith member of the sample of Treatments drawn for this study from a whole class of Treatments. If this point of view does not fit the experimenter's ideas, he should reconsider use of this model.

Reference is made once more to Table 8.35, but with one very important change. Because the t Treatments and the r Blocks in this model are only samples of corresponding classes of Treatments and Blocks, respectively, the sums of the τ_i and of the β_j in the rows and columns, respectively, of that table are *not* zero. Hence the following expressions are obtained for the Treatment and grand means:

$$x_{i.} = \mu + \tau_i + \frac{\beta_1 + \cdots + \beta_r}{r} + \epsilon_{i.}$$

$$x.. = \mu + \frac{\tau_1 + \cdots + \tau_t}{t} + \frac{\beta_1 + \cdots + \beta_r}{r} + \epsilon..$$

Therefore,

$$x_{i.} - x.. = \frac{\tau_1 + \cdots + \tau_{i-1} + (t-1)\tau_i + \tau_{i+1} + \cdots + \tau_t}{t} + (\epsilon_{i.} - \epsilon..)$$

It follows that

$$(x_{i.} - x..)^2 = \frac{1}{t^2} [\tau_1 + \cdots + \tau_{i-1} + (t-1)\tau_i + \tau_{i+1} + \cdots + \tau_t]^2$$

$$+ \frac{1}{r^2 t^2} [(t-1)(\epsilon_{i1} + \cdots + \epsilon_{ir}) - (\epsilon_{11} + \cdots$$

$$+ \epsilon_{i-1,r} + \epsilon_{i+1,r} + \cdots + \epsilon_{tr})]^2$$

+ cross products of τ's and ϵ's, which have expected value
zero

Then,

$$E(x_{i.} - x..)^2 = \frac{1}{t^2} [(t-1)^2 \sigma_\tau^2 + (t-1)\sigma_\tau^2] + \frac{1}{r^2 t^2} [(t-1)^2 r \sigma^2 + r(t-1)\sigma^2]$$

+ cross products with expected value zero

$$= \left(\frac{t-1}{t}\right)\sigma_\tau^2 + \left(\frac{t-1}{tr}\right)\sigma^2, \qquad \text{for every } i \text{ and } j$$

Therefore, the Expected Treatment Mean Square is

$$E\left\{ \frac{r}{t-1} \sum_{i=1}^{t} (x_{i.} - x..)^2 \right\} = \frac{r}{t-1} (t)\left(\frac{t-1}{t}\right)\sigma_\tau^2 + \frac{rt}{t-1} \left(\frac{t-1}{rt}\right)\sigma^2; \quad \text{or}$$

$$(8.43) \qquad\qquad E\{\text{Treatment Ms}\} = r\sigma_\tau^2 + \sigma^2$$

Table 8.41 shows the complete symbolic analysis of variance for the random model, Model II.

Assuming normality, as is necessary in situations to which the analysis of variance is applied, F tests can be employed to test the hypotheses

TABLE 8.41.   ANALYSIS OF VARIANCE AND EXPECTED MEAN SQUARES
FOR A RANDOM-EFFECTS (MODEL II) EXPERIMENT WITH A
RANDOMIZED COMPLETE BLOCK DESIGN, NO
INTERACTION PRESENT

Source of variation	DF	Sample Mean Square	Expected Mean Square
Between Treatments	$t-1$	$\frac{r}{t-1} \sum_{i=1}^{t} (x_{i.} - x..)^2$	$\sigma^2 + r\sigma_\tau^2$
Between Blocks	$r-1$	$\frac{t}{r-1} \sum_{j=1}^{t} (x_{.j} - x..)^2$	$\sigma^2 + t\sigma_\beta^2$
Error	$(t-1)(r-1)$	$\frac{1}{(r-1)(t-1)} \sum_{i=1}^{t} \sum_{j=1}^{r} (X_{ij} - x_{i.} - x_{.j} + x..)^2$	σ^2
Total about $x..$	$rt-1$		

$H_0(\sigma_\tau^2 = 0)$ and $H_0(\sigma_\beta^2 = 0)$ against their respective negations. For example, the sample $F[(t - 1), (t - 1)(r - 1)]$ is equal to (Treatment Ms)/(Error Ms), *if* the σ_τ^2 really is 0. This should be clear from the expected Mean Squares of Table 8.41.

PROBLEMS

1. Verify the expected Treatment Mean Square in Table 8.41.

2. What sort of experiment would you visualize in your own field of study (or one of your choice here) that would require a model such as is assumed in Table 8.41?

3. Verify the expected Error Mean Square of Table 8.41.

4. Write down the statistical distribution of the Blocks Mean Square for Table 8.41. Do the same for the Error Mean Square, and then justify an F test of $H_0(\sigma_\beta^2 = 0)$ from these distributions.

5. What is the statistical distribution of the quantity $[r/(t - 1)] \sum_i (x_{i.} - x_{..})^2$ in Table 8.41 if $H_0(\sigma_\tau^2 = 0)$ is false? What if $H_0(\sigma_\tau^2 = 0)$ is true?

6. Suppose that a poultry scientist selects 4 sires and 10 dams at random from a certain broiler breed and mates each sire to each dam over a suitable period of time so that the offspring can be designated by sire and dam. If 5 chicks are to be chosen at random from each sire-dam family, write down the model for a study of weight gains, using Sires as Treatments and Dams as Blocks. Fully define all symbols used. Also assume no Sire-Dam interaction.

7. Write down the outline of the analysis of variance for Problem 6 as fully as possible, including the expected Mean Squares.

8. Define all possible F tests for Problem 7, and show why each ratio is an F ratio under the hypothesis tested.

9. With reference to Problem 8, give the regions of rejection specifically, and draw sketches of each F distribution and region of rejection as specifically as possible.

10. Make up and fully describe an RCB Model II experiment which you can do, and justify it as properly being a Model II experiment. Also justify the Blocks as being homogeneous subgroups of the total number of experimental units in your experiment.

8.5 GENERALIZATION AND SUMMARY

The derivation of the expected Mean Squares for an RCB design with q samples per Treatment and Block requires, first, that one specify whether the effects, such as Treatments, Blocks, and Interaction, are regarded as fixed or as random. It now is possible to distinguish three principal situations:

(*a*) Both Treatments and Blocks are considered fixed; that is, neither is considered a sample from a larger universe; this is the *fixed-effects model*, Model I.

(2) Both Treatments and Blocks are considered random samples of their respective universes; this is a *random-effects model*, Model II.

(3) Either Treatment or Blocks is considered a fixed effect, and the other is considered a random effect; this is known as a *mixed-effects model*.

The models just described verbally need to be described more specifically as follows. For any model:

(8.51) $$X_{ijk} = \mu + \tau_i + \beta_j + (\tau\beta)_{ij} + \epsilon_{ijk}$$

where the specific assumptions for these symbols depend, as follows, upon the model assumed.

For a Fixed-effects Model, Model I:

μ = the grand average of all X_{ijk} conceivable for these specific Treatments and specific Blocks

τ_i = the true average effect of the ith Treatment relative to μ and with these specific Blocks; hence, $\sum_{i=1}^{t} (\tau_i) = 0$ and $E(\tau_i) = \tau_i$

β_j = the true average effect of the jth Block relative to the grand mean, μ, and with these t Treatments in each Block; hence, $\sum_{j=1}^{r} (\beta_j) = 0$ and $E(\beta_j) = \beta_j$

$(\tau\beta_{ij})$ = the true average effect of combining the ith Treatment with the jth Block relative to μ; hence,

$$\sum_{i=1}^{t} [(\tau\beta)_{ij}] = \sum_{j=1}^{r} [(\tau\beta)_{ij}] = \sum_{i=1}^{t} \sum_{j=1}^{r} [(\tau\beta)_{ij}] = 0$$

ϵ_{ijk} = the random error of observation associated with the kth observation within the ith Treatment and the jth Block; it is assumed that the ϵ_{ijk} are NID(0, σ^2) variates and that

$$E(\epsilon_{ij}\tau_i) = E(\epsilon_{i \cdot k}\beta_j) = 0$$

For the Random-Effects Model:

μ = the grand average of all conceivable X_{ijk} *under the conditions sampled by these Treatments and these Blocks combined*

τ_i = the potential, or average, effect of the ith sample Treatment relative to μ and under the conditions sampled by these Blocks; the τ_i are assumed to be NID(0, σ_τ^2) variates, which also are independent of the β_j and the ϵ_{ijk}

β_j = an N(0, σ_β^2) variate which measures the potential effect of this jth sample Block under the conditions sampled during this experiment; the β_j are assumed independent of each other and of the τ_i and the ϵ_{ijk}

$(\tau\beta)_{ij}$ = N(0, $\sigma_{\tau\beta}^2$) variate which measures the potential effect of combining the ith sample Treatment with the jth sample Block; the $(\tau\beta)_{ij}$ are assumed independent of each other, of the τ_i, of the β_j, and of the ϵ_{ijk}

ϵ_{ijk} = are NID(0, σ^2) variates which measure the error in the kth sample unit under the ith sample Treatment and in the jth Block; the ϵ_{ijk} are assumed independent of the τ_i, and of the β_j.

Mixed-effects Model with Treatments Fixed, Blocks Random:

μ = the grand average of all conceivable units with any combination of these particular Treatments with all Blocks sampled by these Blocks and under the conditions of this experiment

τ_i = as for the fixed-effects model but with the Blocks sampled

β_j = as for the random-effects model but in association with only these particular Treatments

$(\tau\beta)_{ij}$ = the true effect of combining this particular ith Treatment with the jth sample Block; it is assumed that $\sum_{i=1}^{t} (\tau\beta)_{ij} = 0$, because only these specific t Treatments are involved and, hence, for a given j there are no other $(\tau\beta)_{ij}$ than $(\tau\beta)_{ij}, \cdots, (\tau\beta)_{ij}$; but the r Blocks in this sort of experiment are only a sample of a whole population of similar Blocks, so $\sum_{j=1}^{r} (\tau\beta)_{ij} \neq 0$; because the Blocks are a random sample, the $(\tau\beta)_{ij}$ are considered to be NID$(0, \sigma_{\tau\beta}^2)$ variates

ϵ_{ijk} = are NID$(0, \sigma^2)$ variates which measure the sampling error in the kth sample taken under the ith Treatment within the jth sample Block. The ϵ_{ijk} are assumed independent of the Treatments and Blocks involved

The Expected Mean Squares are derived in the usual manner, by means of the following identity:

$$(8.52) \quad X_{ijk} - x\ldots \equiv (X_{ijk} - x_{ij.}) + (x_{ij.} - x_{i..} - x_{.j.} + x\ldots)$$
$$+ (x_{i..} - x\ldots) + (x_{.j.} - x\ldots)$$

As before, it can be shown that, all cross products adding to the zero over the usual summations, one obtains from this identity the following identity in the squares:

$$(8.53) \quad \sum_{i=1}^{t} \sum_{j=1}^{r} \sum_{k=1}^{q} (X_{ijk} - x\ldots)^2$$
$$\equiv \sum_i \sum_j \sum_k (X_{ijk} - x_{ij.})^2 + q \sum_i \sum_j (x_{ij.} - x_{i..} - x_{.j.} + x\ldots)^2$$
$$+ rq \sum_i (x_{i..} - x\ldots)^2 + tq \sum_j (x_{.j.} - x\ldots)^2$$

Here, as before, there is a corresponding partition of the Total degrees of freedom, as shown in each analysis of variance table.

It also is helpful to use an outline, such as Table 8.51, to direct the evaluation of the quantities in Identity 8.53 in terms of Mean Squares in the analysis of variance.

Table 8.52 then was obtained as the summary of the three models studied in this section for when there are q samples per Treatment and Block.

It has been said several times in previous discussions that the ratios of

TABLE 8.51.   DIAGRAM OF A MIXED-MODEL RANDOMIZED COMPLETE BLOCK DESIGN FOR t FIXED TREATMENTS AND r RANDOM BLOCKS, AND q SAMPLES PER TREATMENT AND BLOCK

Treatments (all)	Block 1	Block r (sample)	Treatment Means
1	$X_{111} = \mu + \tau_1 + \beta_1 + (\tau\beta)_{11} + \epsilon_{111}$ $\cdots$ $X_{11q} = \mu + \tau_1 + \beta_1 + (\tau\beta)_{11} + \epsilon_{11q}$	$X_{1r1} = \mu + \tau_1 + \beta_r + (\tau\beta)_{1r} + \epsilon_{1r1}$ $\cdots$ $X_{1rq} = \mu + \tau_1 + \beta_r + (\tau\beta)_{1r} + \epsilon_{1rq}$	$x_{1..} = \mu + \tau_1\,\beta_{.} + (\tau\beta)_{1.} + \epsilon_{1..}$
i	$X_{i11} = \mu + \tau_i + \beta_1 + (\tau\beta)_{i1} + \epsilon_{i11}$ $\cdots$ $X_{i1q} = \mu + \tau_i + \beta_1 + (\tau\beta)_{i1} + \epsilon_{i1q}$	$X_{ir1} = \mu + \tau_i + \beta_r + (\tau\beta)_{ir} + \epsilon_{ir1}$ $\cdots$ $X_{irq} = \mu + \tau_i + \beta_r + (\tau\beta)_{ir} + \epsilon_{irq}$	$x_{i..} = \mu + \tau_i + \beta_{.} + (\tau\beta)_{i.} + \epsilon_{i..}$
t	$X_{t11} = \mu + \tau_t + \beta_1 + (\tau\beta)_{t1} + \epsilon_{t11}$ $\cdots$ $X_{t1q} = \mu + \tau_t + \beta_1 + (\tau\beta)_{t1} + \epsilon_{t1q}$	$X_{tr1} = \mu + \tau_t + \beta_r + (\tau\beta)_{tr} + \epsilon_{tr1}$ $\cdots$ $X_{trq} = \mu + \tau_t + \beta_r + (\tau\beta)_{tr} + \epsilon_{trq}$	$x_{t..} = \mu + \tau_t + \beta_{.} + (\tau\beta)_{t.} + \epsilon_{t..}$
Block means:	$x_{.1.} = \mu + 0 + \beta_1 + 0 + \epsilon_{.1.}$	$\cdots x_{.r.} = \mu + 0 + \beta_r + 0 + \epsilon_{.r.}$	$x_{...} \neq \mu + 0 + \beta_{.} + 0 + \epsilon_{...}$

TABLE 8.52. SUMMARY OF ANALYSES OF VARIANCE FOR RANDOMIZED COMPLETE BLOCK DESIGNS WITH t TREATMENTS, r BLOCKS, AND q SAMPLES PER TREATMENT AND BLOCK; FIXED, RANDOM, AND MIXED MODELS SUMMARIZED AS STATED, TREATMENTS FIXED EXCEPT IN RANDOM MODEL

General model: $X_{tjk} = \mu + \tau_t + \beta_j + (\tau\beta)_{tj} + \epsilon_{tjk}$

Source of variation	DF	Sampling Mean Square	Expected Mean Square when effects are assumed to be:		
			Fixed	Random	Mixed, with Treatment fixed
Treatments	$t-1$	$\dfrac{rq}{t-1}\sum_{i=1}^{t}(x_{i..}-x_{...})^2$	$\sigma^2 + \dfrac{rq}{t-1}\sum_{i=1}^{t}(\tau_i^2)$	$\sigma^2 + q\sigma_{\tau\beta}^2 + rq\sigma_\tau^2$	$\sigma^2 + q\sigma_{\tau\beta}^2 + \dfrac{rq}{t-1}\sum_{i=1}^{t}(\tau_i^2)$
Blocks	$r-1$	$\dfrac{tq}{r-1}\sum_{j=1}^{r}(x_{.j.}-x_{...})^2$	$\sigma^2 + \dfrac{tq}{r-1}\sum_{j=1}^{r}(\beta_j^2)$	$\sigma^2 + q\sigma_{\tau\beta}^2 + tq\sigma_\beta^2$	$\sigma^2 + tq\sigma_\beta^2$
Tr × Bl	$(t-1)(r-1)$	$\dfrac{q}{(t-1)(r-1)}\sum_t\sum_j(x_{ij.}-x_{i..}-x_{.j.}+x_{...})^2$	$\sigma^2 + \dfrac{q}{(t-1)(r-1)}\sum_t\sum_j(\tau\beta)_{ij}^2$	$\sigma^2 + q\sigma_{\tau\beta}^2$	$\sigma^2 + q\sigma_{\tau\beta}^2$
Samples	$tr(q-1)$	$\dfrac{1}{tr(q-1)}\sum_t\sum_j\sum_k(X_{tjk}-x_{tj.})^2$	σ^2	σ^2	σ^2
Total:	$trq-1$	None	None	None	None

Each sampling Ms is distributed as

$$\frac{E\{Ms\}\cdot\chi^2_{\nu_i}}{\nu_i}$$

where ν_i = DF for Ms

Samples Ms is Error Ms for T, B, and T × B Mean Squares

Samples Ms is Error Ms for T×B. The T×B Ms = Error Ms for T and B

Samples Ms = Error Ms for T × B and B; T × B Ms = Error Ms for Treatments Ms.

certain sample Mean Squares have sampling F distributions under specified assumptions and hypotheses. It has been stated that any Mean Square of the sort considered in a valid analysis of variance has a sampling distribution described by

(8.54)
$$\frac{\chi^2_{\nu_i} \cdot [E(\text{Mean Square}_i)]}{\nu_i}$$

where ν_i is the DF for the ith Mean Square, Mean Square$_i$. For example: referring to Table 8.52 and the random model, the sampling distribution of the Treatments × Blocks Mean Square (column 3 from the left) is the same as the sampling distribution of

(8.55)
$$\frac{\chi^2_{(t-1)(r-1)}(\sigma^2 + q\sigma^2_{\tau\beta})}{(t-1)(r-1)}$$

Similarly, the sampling distribution of the corresponding Samples Mean Square is that of

(8.56)
$$\frac{\chi^2_{tr(q-1)}(\sigma^2)}{tr(q-1)}$$

If the hypothesis $H_0(\sigma^2_{\tau\beta} = 0)$ is true, the two sampling distributions in Quantities 8.55 and 8.56 have a common factor σ^2, so their ratio is of the form

$$\frac{\chi^2_1/\nu_1}{\chi^2_2/\nu_2}$$

which is an $F[(t-1)(r-1), tr(q-1)]$ distribution, because these sampling Mean Squares are derived from independent parts of the Total Sum of Squares. This result justifies using the designated F distribution to test $H_0(\sigma^2_\beta = 0)$. Furthermore, it justifies the statement, in Table 8.52, that for the random model the Samples Mean Square is the proper Error term for the Treatments × Blocks Mean Square.

It is seen in Table 8.52 that, if the hypothesis $H_0(\sigma^2_\beta = 0)$ is true, the Blocks Mean Square for the mixed-effects model is distributed as

$$(\sigma^2)\chi^2_{r-1}/(r-1)$$

hence, the Samples Mean Square is the proper denominator for an F test. Unless one assumed that both $H_0(\sigma^2_\beta = 0)$ and $H_0(\sigma^2_{\tau\beta} = 0)$ were true, the Treatments × Blocks Mean Square would not be a proper denominator for an F test of Blocks Mean Square, and if one did assume both hypotheses were true, what would one learn from the resulting F test? The following summary of proper and useful F tests is derived from this sort of reasoning and mathematics, and is shown in Table 8.52 in brief.

(*a*) With a fixed-effects RCB model use the Samples Mean Square to test any other Mean Square that is of interest.

(*b*) With a random-effects RCB model use the Samples Mean Square to test the Treatments × Blocks Mean Square, which tests $H_0(\sigma_{\tau\beta}^2 = 0)$, and use the Treatments × Blocks Mean Square to test the other Mean Squares as desired, regardless of the acceptance or rejection of $H_0(\sigma_{\tau\beta}^2 = 0)$.

(*c*) With a mixed-effects model with Treatments fixed and an RCB design use the Samples Mean Square to test either the Treatments × Blocks Mean Square or the Blocks Mean Square, but use the Treatments × Blocks Mean Square to test the Treatments Mean Square. Again, it should be noted that these statements hold, regardless of the outcomes of any of the other F tests in the same analysis of variance.

It should be emphasized that the foregoing statements are partially the consequence of certain assumptions made in the model. For example, in the mixed model, it was assumed that, if Treatments are fixed and Blocks are random, then $\sum_{i=1}^{t} (\tau\beta) = 0$ but $\sum_{j=1}^{r} (\tau\beta)_{ij} \neq 0$. Although it is believed that the point of view taken is reasonable and is the more common point of view, the reader is invited to read M. B. Wilks and O. Kempthorne, *J. Am. Stat. Assoc.* 50: 1144, 1955, and Scheffe, *Ann. Math. Stat.* 27: 251, 1956, on this matter.

Models for more complex experiments will be considered in later chapters, but the foregoing discussion of CR and RCB experiments covers some of the most widely used designs, especially those used in biological research. It also gives the basic procedures used in deriving expected Mean Squares.

PROBLEMS

1. Suppose that a psychologist is going to study the rapidity with which a certain breed of laboratory animal will learn to perform some certain act. The experimenter will be supposed to have three methods for training these animals and to use 20 animals under each method. He does not claim that the three methods to be employed are representative of any whole class of methods of teaching this skill to these animals, but simply that they are three specific methods which have been devised by psychologists for this purpose. Assuming that within the ith method the measurement of speed of learning is an $N(\mu, \sigma^2)$ variate, write down the appropriate model for this experiment and also the expected Mean Squares in the corresponding analysis of variance.

2. Assume for Problem 1 that the three methods in the experiment are actually a random sample of a whole class of possible such methods. What is now the appropriate model for the experiment, and what are the expected Mean Squares?

3. Suppose that for Problem 1 the 60 animals needed for this experiment naturally fall into four fixed blocks as follows: Block 1 = animals from source 1, Block 2 = animals from source 2, etc. If Method 1 is employed with 5 animals selected at random from each Block, and similarly for the other two methods, what is the proper analysis of variance with Methods regarded as a fixed effect? What are the Expected Mean Squares in terms of Table 8.52, if the Blocks are considered random effects and the Treatments fixed effects?

4. Suppose that for a nutrition study on beef cattle five diets are to be studied with Black Angus yearling steers. The measurement to be taken is the average daily gain during a suitable period of time. If 50 such steers are to be grouped into 5 Blocks on the basis of anticipated gain and two steers within each Block assigned at random to each of five specific diets which are of interest to the experimenter, what are the statistical model for the experiment, the analysis of variance, and the expected Mean Squares?

5. What change would you make in your answer to Problem 4 if these 5 diets were to be regarded as a random sample of high-roughage diets in general?

6. Suppose the steers of Problem 4 were first to be divided into ten classes on the basis of predicted efficiency of gain, as decided by a competent judging team. Thereafter, each diet (Treatment) would be assigned one steer at random from each of the ten efficiency levels. Regard the ten efficiency levels as Blocks with fixed effects, and then do as in Problem 4 with the necessary changes.

7. Make up an experimental set-up of your planning, fully describe it, write out the analysis of variance, and write down the expected Mean Squares. Thereafter, state what F tests would be appropriate, and justify them in terms of the information in Section 8.5.

8. Suppose a mixed-effects design has Tillage Methods as fixed effects and Blocks of Land as random effects. If there are five Methods and six Blocks, what is the sampling distribution of the Error Mean Square, assuming no interaction between Methods and Blocks? What is the sampling distribution of the Blocks Mean Square? If there actually are no true Tillage effects, what is the sampling distribution of the Methods Mean Square?

9. Referring to Problem 4, what is the sampling distribution of the Diets Mean Square, if there are true diet effects? If there are no diet effects? In which case would Diets Mean Square divided by Error Mean Square be an F?

REVIEW PROBLEMS

1. Flip a nickel 100 times and record H or T after each toss, according as heads or tails is uppermost after the flip. How does your total number of H's compare with the expectation for an unbiassed coin? What population did you sample, as nearly as you can tell?

2. How would you draw a random sample of the leaves on a tree, to study the incidence of a specific disease of some sort?

3. Suppose that someone has properly constructed a population containing 10,000 numbers which essentially conform to an $N(30, 9)$ distribution. If you are about to draw a random sample of size $n = 25$ from this population, what is the probability that the 10th number drawn exceeds 31? What is the probability that the mean, $\bar{x}$, of your sample will exceed 31?

4. Suppose that someone gives you a coin of a sort you have never seen before, and you do not know whether it is perfectly balanced with respect to occurrence of heads and tails on tosses or not. You designate one side Heads, and then you toss this coin 200 times, obtaining 115 Heads. What is the CI_{90} on the true percentage of Heads, p_H, and what does this tell you about the unbiassedness of this coin?

5. Suppose that for two measurements, X, and Y (such as age and height) it is reasonable to assume that the jth Y associated with the ith X is linearly related to X_i as follows: $Y_{ij} = \alpha + \beta X_i + \epsilon_{ij}$, where the ϵ_{ij} are NID$(0, \sigma^2)$. Given the following hypothetical data, estimate β by means of a CI$_{90}$ and interpret this interval:

X (age):	12	14	16	18	20	22	24	26
Y (height):	13.2	17.7	20.0	26.9	28.1	32.2	40.8	42.1
X (age):	28	30	32	34	36	38	40	
Y (height):	43.9	49.7	55.0	60.1	62.3	67.0	70.6	

6. Suppose that a horticulturist wishes to study the effects of colored transparent plastics on the growth of a specific plant under greenhouse conditions. A random sample of 30 measurements is to be taken under each of six specific plastics (not a sample of plastics of any sort). Write out the analysis of variance and the expected Mean Squares for this experiment, assuming normality of distribution as needed and also homogeneity of variance within the plastics.

7. If a random sample of six types of clear plastic is used in Problem 6 to study the effect of type of clear plastic on this plant's growth, how would the analysis of variance computed for Problem 6 have to be changed?

8. Referring to Problem 6, suppose there are to be four types of plastic under each of six colors. If both Type and Color are regarded as fixed effects, what are the expected values of the Color and Samples Mean Squares, respectively, if there are 10 samples per Color and Type?

9. What is the sampling distribution of the Plastics Mean Square in Problem 7, if there are no Plastic effects? If there are Plastic effects? How do these compare with the sampling distribution of the Error Mean Square?

10. Given the following analysis of variance from an experiment in which Treatments are random and Blocks are fixed, make all possible F tests, stating H_0 each time, and draw all appropriate conclusions:

Source of variation	DF	Sample Mean Square
Treatments (random)	8	81.52
Blocks (fixed)	4	172.6
Treatments × Blocks	32	141.3
Samples	90	45.68
Total about x...	134	

11. Justify the F test used in Problem 10 to test $H_0(\sigma_\tau^2 = 0)$ against $H_a(\sigma_\tau^2 \neq 0)$, where τ refers to Treatment Effects of the usual sort for the model involved.

12. Sample the five sections of this chapter with all samples of size $n = 8$ to see whether the true average percentage of adjectives relative to the number of words in each sentence is the same for the five sections. Use $\alpha = 0.10$.

13. Make up a sample of size $n = 20$ presumably from a normal bivariate population and such that $H_0(\rho = 0.4)$ is rejected in favor of $H_a(\rho > 0.4)$. Use $\alpha = 0.10$.

14. Make up two sets of data with $n_1 = 8$ and $n_2 = 10$, presumably from $N_1(\mu_1, \sigma^2)$ and $N_2(\mu_2, \sigma^2)$ and such that $H_0[(\mu_1 \leqslant \mu_2) \mid (\sigma_1^2 = \sigma_2^2 = \sigma^2)]$ will be accepted instead of $H_a[(\mu_1 > \mu_2) \mid (\sigma_1^2 = \sigma_2^2 = \sigma^2)]$. Use $\alpha = 0.10$ and the t test.

15. Do Problem 15, but with $\alpha = 0.05$, and use the G test.

16. What is the sampling distribution of Treatments × Blocks Mean Squares for experiments such as that implied for Problem 10?

17. Make up an example with six groups of data and $r = 7$ for each, such that the Duncan NMRT and the Fisher LSD will produce two different decisions with $\alpha = 0.10$.

18. Suppose that a bank clerk has a key ring holding seven keys. If it takes a specific *pair* of keys to open a certain safety deposit box, what is the probability that two keys chosen at random will open this box? What is the probability that the box will be opened on the *second* such try? *Within* two such tries?

Chapter 9

More Complex Analyses of Variance

9.1 INTRODUCTION

The student now has been introduced to some relatively simple situations, in which the analysis of variance, devised by R. A. Fisher in the nineteen-twenties, is useful in the interpretation of experimental research data. These experiences have included several experimental designs—CR and RCB with and without samples within Treatments and Blocks—and three types of mathematical model: fixed, random, and mixed. At this point it should be helpful to review the assumptions and points of view appropriate to each different situation before considering the more complex designs. It will be recalled that the following terms have been employed.

Experimental unit: A plot of land, individual person, pig, chicken, cake, or whatever physical unit or part of a unit the experimenter is using as the basis of the measurements to be taken during an experiment.

Treatment: Any actual treatment, method of handling something, variety or material, or any action to be taken relative to a grouping of the experimental units studied during an experiment.

Block: Any predetermined subgroup of the experimental units, formed before any Treatments are applied and formed in the hope of reducing basic sampling error among units within the same Block. Blocks usually contain equally many experimental units during any given experiment, namely 1 or q for each Treatment.

Sampling variance: The true actual or conceptual variance, σ^2, of experimental units within the same Treatment and Block around their own mean caused by random errors.

Interaction: The failure of the different Treatments in an experiment to maintain the same rank order in different Blocks, after proper allowance has been made for sampling error.

Main effects: The potential overall advantage or disadvantage of one of the major classifications, such as Blocks or Treatments, under the conditions sampled. It is the main effects which may interact.

Expected Mean Square: What a sample Mean Square in an analysis of variance is estimating or, put another way, the long-run average of the sample Mean Squares corresponding to a given Source of Variation.

Mathematical analyses of the kind presented previously make it possible to choose the correct denominator for each F test. These choices were summarized, at the end of Chapter 8, for a two-way (Treatment-Block) classification of the experimental units when one or more observations are being taken under each two-way class. The proper and valid F tests are determined by means of the sampling distributions of the Mean Squares, which, in turn, depend upon the expected Mean Squares.

It also is recalled that two other matters of interest in the analysis of variance have been included in previous discussions, namely useful identities and assumptions made regarding mathematical models used in the analysis of variance. For example, the identity

$$X_{ij} - x.. \equiv (x_{i.} - x..) + (x_{.j} - x..) + (X_{ij} - x_{i.} - x_{.j} + x..)$$

which is true regardless of any assumptions about the X_{ij}, leads to the corresponding identity involving Sums of Squares, such as the following:

$$\sum_{i=1}^{t} \sum_{j=1}^{r} (X_{ij} - x..)^2 \equiv r \sum_{i=1}^{t} (x_{i.} - x..)^2 + t \sum_{j=1}^{r} (x_{.j} - x..)^2$$
$$+ \sum_{i=1}^{t} \sum_{j=1}^{r} (X_{ij} - x_{i.} - x_{.j} + x..)^2$$

Thus it is shown that the Total Sum of Squares about the grand mean, $x..$, can be expressed in terms of three nonoverlapping and presumably independent Sums of Squares: one from the t Treatments, one from the r Blocks, and one from Sampling Error.

If there are q samples per Treatment and Block, the identity

$$X_{ijk} - x... \equiv (x_{i..} - x...) + (x_{.j.} - x...)$$
$$+ (x_{ij.} - x_{i..} - x_{.j.} + x...) + (X_{ijk} - x_{ij.})$$

has been shown to lead to the corresponding identity in terms of Sums of Squares, as follows:

$$\sum_{i}^{t}\sum_{j}^{r}\sum_{k}^{q}(X_{ijk} - x\ldots)^2 \equiv rq\sum_{i=1}^{t}(x_{i..} - x\ldots)^2 + tq\sum_{j=1}^{r}(x_{.j.} - x\ldots)^2$$

$$+ q\sum_{i}^{t}\sum_{j}^{r}(x_{ij.} - x_{i..} - x_{.j.} + x\ldots)^2$$

$$+ \sum_{i}^{t}\sum_{j}^{r}\sum_{k}^{q}(X_{ijk} - x_{ij.})^2$$

Identities of this sort also can be established for sampling situations in which more than two criteria of classification are present for each experimental unit, as will be shown in a later section.

With regard to the assumptions accompanying each experimental model and the corresponding analysis of variance, it is recalled that any one of three general points of view can be taken in a given experimental situation involving t Treatments and r Blocks. These are as follows.

(*a*) *Fixed-effects model:* Only the specific t Treatments and r Blocks in this experiment are of interest, and no attempt will be made to consider them representative of classes of Treatments and Blocks, respectively.

(*b*) *Random-effects model:* The Treatments and the Blocks in this experiment constitute random samples of defined classes of Treatments and Blocks, respectively. The particular Treatments and Blocks which happen to be drawn for this particular experiment are of no interest in themselves; it is the variance among the X_{ijk} which Treatments and Blocks of this sort may cause that is of interest. That is, we wish to know whether Treatments and Blocks of the sorts sampled constitute significant sources of variation under the circumstances sampled, and perhaps we may wish to measure these variances.

(*c*) *Mixed-effects model:* One of the sources of variation is a fixed effect and the other is a random effect, as described earlier.

It also is assumed in any of the above-described models that the experiment will be so conducted that there will be a valid way of measuring the magnitude of the random error variance which is needed in any F test. That is, there necessarily must be an ϵ_{ijk} in the model, and it must satisfy the usual assumptions made regarding such ϵ's; namely, they are NID(0, σ^2), regardless of Treatment and Block or any other source of variation that may be present in a more complex experiment.

The basic concepts of the analysis of variance already have been presented. Now attention will be turned to more complex analyses produced by some or all of the following circumstances:

(*a*) Each experimental unit has more than two general classifications, for example, Treatment, Variety, Fertilizer, and Block.

(*b*) The sort of measurement taken does not fulfill all the assumptions necessary for an analysis of variance regarding normality, homogeneity of variance, and additivity.

(*c*) Part of the planned data is missing.

These more complex situation will be considered in turn in the following sections.

9.2   THREE OR FOUR CRITERIA OF CLASSIFICATION OF EACH EXPERIMENTAL UNIT

The only new ideas and methods to be considered in this section are (*a*) how to compute three-factor and four-factor interaction Sums of Squares and (*b*) the interpretation of these more complex interactions.

Suppose that an experimenter wishes to study the effects of three factors and their interactions in terms of some measurement which is of interest. For example, a poultry scientist might wish to study the effects on egg production of different breeds of chicken, different diets for them, and different artificial daylengths, as well as the interrelations among these factors.

A variety of assumptions could be made if a Mixed Model were assumed to be preferable for this study, but the major points of interest regarding computations and interpretations of interactions can be illustrated more simply with a Fixed Model, so this model will be assumed for this illustration.

To be specific about this poultry science example, suppose there are three breeds to be studied (White Rock, White Leghorn, and Rhode Island Red), two diets (medium and high level of protein), and three daylengths (short, medium, and long). The possible *main effects* on egg production are (*a*) breeds averaged over the specific diets and daylengths to be studied in this experiment, (*b*) diets averaged over the specific breeds and daylengths to be studied in this experiment, and (*c*) daylengths averaged over the breeds and diets to be studied in this experiment.

It is entirely possible that White Leghorns would respond to the protein levels differently from Rhode Island Reds or White Rocks. If so, this would be an example of a two-factor, or first-order, interaction, to be designated a *Breed × Diet interaction*. There also might be Breed × Daylength and Diet × Daylength interactions of the same order.

In addition to the main effects (Breed, Diet, and Daylength) and the first-order interactions (Breed × Diet, Breed × Daylength, and Diet × Daylength) there might be a three-factor, or second-order, interaction; that is, the way in which breeds interact with the protein levels may depend upon daylength in some manner. This sort of interaction will be designated a Breed × Diet × Daylength interaction. For the sake of brevity this interaction may be written as the B × D × DL interaction. Similarly, B × D, B × DL, and D × DL will be used to designate the first-order interactions described earlier.

Tables 9.21, 9.22, 9.23, 9.24, and 9.25 have been constructed to illustrate the meaning and interpretation of a second-order interaction, as well as to

TABLE 9.21.   ILLUSTRATION OF A THREE-WAY CLASSIFICATION WITH
SIGNIFICANT MAIN EFFECTS BUT NO INTERACTIONS (MODEL I)

	Chicken						Daylength sums
Daylength	1		2		3		
Diet	High	Medium	High	Medium	High	Medium	
Short	12	8	14	10	11	7	
	16	10	16	7	14	4	
	10	7	11	12	9	10	
	9	9	13	11	10	8	
	13	6	16	10	12	5	
	60	40	70	50	56	34	
		100		120		90	310
Medium	13	10	17	9	13	9	
	15	12	12	13	9	11	
	9	7	15	7	17	7	
	11	11	18	9	14	10	
	14	8	17	11	13	9	
	62	48	79	49	66	46	
		110		128		112	350
Long	19	11	18	14	17	11	
	23	14	21	16	21	8	
	20	8	14	10	13	15	
	16	12	15	12	16	12	
	15	12	16	16	16	9	
	93	57	84	68	83	55	
		150		152		138	440
Breed sums:		360		400		340	1100

TABLE 9.22.   ANALYSIS OF VARIANCE FOR TABLE 9.21 (FIXED-EFFECTS MODEL)

Source of variation	DF	*Sum of Squares*	*Mean Squares*	F	*Decision on* H_0
Breeds	2	62.2223	31.11	5.37	reject
Diets	1	471.5112	471.5	81.45	,,
Daylengths	2	295.5556	147.8	25.53	,,
Breed × Diet	2	0.3554	0.1777	0.03	accept
Breed × Daylength	4	15.3777	3.844	0.66	,,
Diet × Daylength	2	6.4888	3.244	0.56	,,
Breed × Diet × Day-length	4	33.2446	8.311	1.44	,,
Chickens same B, D, DL	72	416.8000	5.789		
Total about x...	89	1301.5556			

TABLE 9.23.   ILLUSTRATION OF A THREE-WAY CLASSIFICATION WITH A
SIGNIFICANT SECOND-ORDER INTERACTION BUT NO
SIGNIFICANT FIRST-ORDER INTERACTION

| Daylength | Chicken breed | | | | | | Daylength sums |
| | 1 | | 2 | | 3 | | |
Diet	High	Medium	High	Medium	High	Medium	
Short	12	13	16	8	10	15	
	8	16	19	11	12	11	
	14	9	12	6	10	19	
	11	14	15	10	8	14	
	15	13	18	5	10	16	
	60	65	80	40	50	75	
		125		120		125	370
Medium	17	10	11	15	12	15	
	13	6	14	21	9	11	
	21	13	10	17	13	18	
	19	11	9	10	11	12	
	15	10	11	12	15	19	
	85	50	55	75	60	75	
		135		130		135	400
Long	11	14	12	13	15	9	
	8	10	16	16	11	5	
	15	12	9	14	18	13	
	10	18	11	10	12	10	
	11	16	12	12	19	8	
	55	70	60	65	75	45	
		125		125		120	370
Breed sums:		385		375		380	1140

show how to compute analyses of variance with interactions of the first and second orders involved. It is recalled that the arithmetic required for analyses of variance is the same, regardless of the particular mathematical model involved, *up to the point of making the appropriate F tests.*

Using the data of Table 9.21, the following computations are needed for an analysis of variance.

$$\text{Total Sum of Squares} = 12^2 + 16^2 + \cdots + 15^2 + 12^2 + 9^2 - \frac{(1100)^2}{90}$$

$$= 14{,}746 - 13{,}444.4444 = 1301.5556, \quad \text{with 89 DF}$$

Breed Sum of Squares $= \dfrac{360^2 + 400^2 + 340^2}{30} - 13{,}444.4444 = 62.2223$,

with 2 DF

Daylength Sum of Squares $= \dfrac{310^2 + 350^2 + 440^2}{30} - 13{,}444.4444$

$= 295.5556$, with 2 DF

Diet Sum of Squares $= \dfrac{653^2 + 447^2}{45} - 13{,}444.4444 = 471.5112$, with 1 DF

Subclass Sum of Squares $= \dfrac{60^2 + 40^2 + \cdots + 83^2 + 55^2}{5} - 13{,}444.4444$

$= 14{,}329.2000 - 13{,}444.4444 = 884.7556$,

with 17 DF

Chickens same B, D, DL Sum of Squares = Total Sum of Squares

$-$ Subclass Sum of Squares

$= 416.8000$, with 72 DF

The computation of the Breed $\times$ Diet Interaction Sum of Squares is based upon the following table of breed-diet sums:

		Breed			Breed-Diet Subclass Ss	
Diet	1	2	3	*Sum*	$= 215^2 + 233^2 + \cdots + 135^2 =$	209,678.0000;
High	215	233	205	653	divided by 15 $=$	13,978.5333
Med.	145	167	135	447	$-$ (correction) $=$	$-13{,}444.4444$
Sum:	360	400	340	1100	difference $=$	534.0889
					$-$ (Breed Ss $+$ Diet Ss) $=$	-533.7335
					Breed $\times$ Diet Ss $=$	0.3554
						with 2 DF

The Breed $\times$ Daylength interaction is computed as follows:

		Breed			Breed-Daylength Ss $=$	138,176.0000;
Day-	1	2	3	*Sum*	divided by 10 $=$	13,817.6000
length					$-$ (correction) $=$	$-13{,}444.4444$
Short	100	120	90	310		
Med.	110	128	112	350	Breed $\times$ Daylength Subclass Ss $=$	373.1556
Long	150	152	138	440	$-$ (Breed Ss $+$ Daylength Ss) $=$	-357.7779
Sum:	360	400	340	1100	Breed $\times$ Daylength Ss $=$	15.3777
						with 4 DF

The Diet × Daylength interaction Sum of Squares is computed similarly, by means of a Diet-Daylength table of sums as follows:

Diet	Short	Med.	Long	Sum
High	186	207	260	653
Med.	124	143	180	447
Sum:	310	350	440	1100

Daylength

Diet-Daylength SS = 213,270.0000;
divided by 15 = 14,218.0000
− (correction) = − 13,444.4444
_____
Diet-Daylength Subclass Ss = 773.5556
− (Diet Ss + Daylength Ss) = − 767.0668
_____
Diet × Daylength Ss = 6.4888
with 2 DF

Then the Breed × Diet × Daylength Sum of Squares is:

Subclass Ss − (Breed Ss + Diet Ss + Daylength Ss

$$+ \text{B} \times \text{DL Ss} + \text{B} \times \text{D Ss} + \text{D} \times \text{DL Ss})$$

$$= 884.7556 - 851.5110 = 33.2446 \quad \text{with 4 DF}$$

These calculations now can be combined into the analysis of variance for the data of Table 9.21, which also shows the proper F tests for this fixed-effects experimental model. This is shown in Table 9.22.

One of the multiple-comparison procedures described earlier now can be used to test for specific differences among populations means, since this is a fixed-effects model. It is apparent that the Breed, Diet, and Daylength main effects are significant, but there are no detectable interactions among these main effects. Following are more specific analyses used to pinpoint the probable individual differences among Breeds, Diets, and Daylengths, respectively:

For Breeds:

Breed	Mean	Conclusions
2	13.3	Breed 2 > breed 1 ≅ breed 3, after proper
	< *	account is taken of sampling error
1	12.0	
	< ns	
3	11.3	

$$\text{LSD}^* = 1.993\sqrt{5.789(2/30)} = 1.24, \quad \text{for } \alpha = 0.05$$

(The symbol < * between 13.3 and 12.0 indicates that those means are significantly different at the 5% level of significance as judged by Fisher's LSD at the 5% level. The symbol < ns indicates nonsignificance in the same sense.)

For Diets:

Diet	Mean	Conclusions
High	14.5	High > Medium, after due allowance for
	< *	sampling error
Medium	9.9	

$$\text{LSD}^* = 1.993\sqrt{5.789(2/45)} = 1.01, \quad \text{for } \alpha = 0.05$$

For Daylengths:

Day-length	Mean	Conclusions
Long	14.7	Long > Medium > Short, after due allow-
	< *	ance for sampling error
Medium	11.7	
	< *	
Short	10.3	

LSD* = 1.24, as for Breeds,   for $\alpha = 0.05$

Other multiple-comparison procedures, such as Duncan's NMRT, can be used if this seems preferable in any given situation.

Table 9.23 presents some hypothetical data designed to illustrate sampling situations that include a second-order interaction but not first-order interactions. The computations of the numbers in Table 9.24 are the same as illustrated earlier, so these will not be shown in detail again.

TABLE 9.24.   ANALYSIS OF VARIANCE FOR TABLE 9.23: FIXED-EFFECTS MODEL WITH THREE-FACTOR INTERACTION STATISTICALLY SIGNIFICANT

Source of variation	DF	Mean Square	F
Breed	2	0.8334	0.10
Diet	1	4.444	0.56
Daylength	2	10.00	1.25
Breed × Diet	2	6.944	0.87
Breed × Daylength	4	0.8333	0.10
Diet × Daylength	2	2.111	0.26
Breed × Diet × Daylength	4	125.6	15.76*
Chickens	72	7.972	
Total about $x \ldots$:	89		

* Indicates significance at the 5% level and rejection of hypothesis tested.

It is clear from Table 9.24 that only $H_0[\text{all } (\tau\beta\gamma)_{ijk} = 0]$ is rejected in the model,

$$X_{ijkl} = \mu + \tau_i + \beta_j + \gamma_k + (\tau\beta)_{ij} + (\tau\gamma)_{ik} + (\beta\gamma)_{jk} + (\tau\beta\gamma)_{ijk} + \epsilon_{ijkl}$$

where γ_k measures the effect of the kth Daylength in the same way that γ_i has been defined to measure Treatment effects in general relative to μ.

What does this mean to the experimenter? The decisions made from each of the F tests indicated in Table 9.24 are as follows.

(a) The means $x_{1\ldots}$, $x_{2\ldots}$, and $x_{3\ldots}$ are only randomly variable about $x\ldots$, as shown by the $F(2, 72) = 0.10$; hence, it is concluded that all the τ_i in the model are zero; that is, $H_0(\text{all } \tau_i = 0)$ is accepted over $H_a(\text{some } \tau_i \neq 0)$.

(*b*) Similarly, H_0(all $\beta_j = 0$) is accepted over H_a(some $\beta_j \neq 0$), because $F(1, 72) = 0.56$ is far below $F_{0.05}(1, 72) = 3.98$.

(*c*) Similarly, H_0(all $\gamma_k = 0$) is accepted with $\alpha = 0.05$.

(*d*) With regard to the Breed × Diet Interaction, the means in the following table,

	Breed:			
Diet	1	2	3	
Medium	$x_{11..}$	$x_{21..}$	$x_{31..}$	
High	$x_{12..}$	$x_{22..}$	$x_{32..}$	$x....$

are only randomly dispersed about the grand mean, $x....$, after due account is taken of the overall Breed and Diet variations by subtracting out their Sums of Squares. Hence, H_0[all $(\tau\beta)_{ij} = 0$] is accepted over H_a[some $(\tau\beta)_{ij} \neq 0$].

(*e*) Similarly for the Breed × Daylength and Diet × Daylength interactions.

(*f*) With regard to the Breed × Diet × Daylength interaction, the means in the following table are *more dispersed* than can be explained reasonably by sampling variation, overall Breed differences, overall Diet differences, overall Daylength differences, Breed × Diet interaction, Breed × Daylength interaction, and Diet × Daylength interaction.

	Breed:					
	1		2		3	
Daylength	*Diet*		*Diet*		*Diet*	
	Med.	*High*	*Med.*	*High*	*Med.*	*High*
Short	$x_{111.}$	$x_{112.}$	$x_{211.}$	$x_{212.}$	$x_{311.}$	$x_{312.}$
Medium	$x_{121.}$	$x_{122.}$	$x_{221.}$	$x_{222.}$	$x_{321.}$	$x_{322.}$
Long	$x_{131.}$	$x_{132.}$	$x_{231.}$	$x_{232.}$	$x_{331.}$	$x_{332.}$

$$x....$$

Therefore it is concluded that H_0[all $(\tau\beta\gamma)_{ijk} = 0$] should be rejected in favor of H_a[some $(\tau\beta\gamma)_{ijk} \neq 0$]. In other words, there *are* Breed effects, there *are* Diet effects, there *are* Daylength effects, and there *are* first-order interactions among those three main effects, but they occur in such manner that they cancel each other out except in the form of the second-order interaction, Breed × Diet × Daylength.

The experimenter then needs to make a detailed study of differences within the three-way table of means. This is illustrated in Table 9.25; but, of course, other decisions could be made, say between means in columns.

The following information can be derived from Table 9.25 by the use of Fisher's LSD*, the least significant difference at the 5% level.

(*a*) With the short daylength the high and medium protein diets are equal for breed 1 but unequal for the other two breeds. However, the superior diet for breed 2, in terms of egg production, is the inferior diet for breed 3. This is a Breed × Diet interaction *within the short daylength*.

(*b*) With the medium daylength the diets differ significantly when used on breed 1 and breed 2, but the direction of superiority is reversed. This is another "internal" interaction within the medium daylength, but when these results are compared with those for the short daylength, an "external" type of interaction is revealed: the diets differ from each other from breed to

TABLE 9.25.   SUBCLASS MEANS FOR TABLE 9.23, EACH MEAN
BASED ON FIVE OBSERVATIONS

	Chicken breed					
	1		2		3	
Daylength						
Diet	High	Medium	High	Medium	High	Medium
Short	12 ns 13		16 ← * 8		10 * → 15	
Medium	17 ← * 10		11 * → 15		12 ns 15	
Long	11 ns 14		12 ns 13		15 ← * 9	
LSD* = 3.6						
	H > M for medium DL		H > M for short DL		H < M for short DL	
	H ≅ M for other DL		H < M for medium DL		H ≅ M for medium DL	
			H ≅ M for long DL		H > M for long DL	

LSD* is the Fisher least significant difference at the 5% level.

ns between two numbers means that those sample means are not significantly different.

* between two numbers means those sample means are significantly different at the 5% level.

An arrow → shows the number which is significantly the greater.

breed with the short daylength differently from the way they differ from each other from breed to breed with the medium daylength. This is a second-order Breed × Diet × Daylength interaction.

(*c*) With the long daylength the diet difference is significant only with breed 3. This is a different Breed × Diet interaction within this daylength from that noted with either the short or the medium daylength, so here is additional indication of the second-order Breed × Diet × Daylength inter-

action. As stated earlier, the failure of the Diet × Breed first-order interaction to be the same (after due allowance for sampling error) for all three
daylengths is a second-order, or three-factor, interaction. Obviously, one
could as well speak of the failure of the Diet × Daylength first-order interaction to be the same for all three breeds as another interpretation of the
second-order interaction here, and similarly for the failure of a Breed × Daylength first-order interaction to be the same from one diet to another, after
due allowance is made for random sampling error.

TABLE 9.26.   OUTLINE OF THE ANALYSIS OF VARIANCE FOR THE THREE-
FACTOR FIXED-EFFECTS EXPERIMENT WITH q SAMPLES PER
A-B-C COMBINATION OF MAIN EFFECTS

Source of variation	DF	Expected Mean Squares
Factor A	$t - 1$	$\sigma^2 + \dfrac{rsq}{t-1} \sum_{i=1}^{t} (\tau_i^2)$
Factor B	$r - 1$	$\sigma^2 + \dfrac{tsq}{r-1} \sum_{j=1}^{r} (\beta_j^2)$
Factor C	$s - 1$	$\sigma^2 + \dfrac{trq}{s-1} \sum_{k=1}^{s} (\gamma_k^2)$
Interaction A × B	$(t-1)(r-1)$	$\sigma^2 + \dfrac{sq}{(t-1)(r-1)} \sum_i \sum_j (\tau\beta)_{ij}^2$
Interaction A × C	$(t-1)(s-1)$	$\sigma^2 + \dfrac{rq}{(t-1)(s-1)} \sum_i \sum_k (\tau\gamma)_{ik}^2$
Interaction B × C	$(r-1)(s-1)$	$\sigma^2 + \dfrac{tq}{(r-1)(s-1)} \sum_j \sum_k (\beta\gamma)_{jk}^2$
Interaction A × B × C	$(t-1)(r-1)(s-1)$	$\sigma^2 + \dfrac{q}{(t-1)(r-1)(s-1)} \sum_i \sum_j \sum_k (\tau\beta\gamma)_{ijk}^2$
Samples in A, B, C	$trs(q-1)$	σ^2
Total about x...	$trsq - 1$	

The strong, and reversed, interactions among the three factors (or main
effects) of Table 9.22 account for the fact that only the Breed × Diet × Daylength Mean Square is significantly larger than the Chicken Mean Square,
because certain main effects and first-order interactions are cancelling each
other's effects on egg production. For this sort of reason one must be careful
in the interpretation of such experiments that one does not falsely conclude
that there are no effects when, in fact, several significant effects are cancelling

each other. This is why one can have significant interactions and non-significant main effects according to the F tests possible in an analysis of variance for a fixed-effects design. This raises the question whether it is even useful in such an experiment to test main effects and lower-order interactions when a higher-order interaction is significant. Probably the best procedure is to make tables like Table 9.25 as soon as the corresponding interaction is determined significant and thereafter use some one of the multiple-comparison procedures to pinpoint the important sources of variation.

TABLE 9.27.   EXPECTED MEAN SQUARES FOR AN ANALYSIS OF VARIANCE
WITH FACTORS A AND C FIXED AND FACTOR B RANDOM IN MODEL:
$X_{ijkl} = \mu + \tau_i + \beta_i + \gamma_k + (\tau\beta)_{ij} + (\tau\gamma)_{ik} + (\beta\gamma)_{jk} + (\tau\beta\gamma)_{ijk} + \epsilon_{ijkl}$
(ASSUME: $\sum_{k=1}^{s} (\beta\gamma)_{jk} = 0$ BUT $\sum_{j=1}^{r} (\beta\gamma)_{jk} \neq 0$)

Source of variation	DF	Expected Mean Square
Factor A (f)	$(t-1)$	$\sigma^2 + sq\sigma^2_{\tau\beta} + \dfrac{rsq}{t-1}\sum_{i=1}^{x} (\tau_i^2)$
Factor B (r)	$(r-1)$	$\sigma^2 + \qquad\quad + tsq\sigma^2_{\beta}$
Factor C (f)	$(s-1)$	$\sigma^2 + rq\sigma^2_{\beta\gamma} + \dfrac{trq}{s-1}\sum_{k} (\gamma_k^2)$
A $\times$ B	$(t-1)(r-1)$	$\sigma^2 + sq\sigma^2_{\tau\beta}$
A $\times$ C	$(t-1)(s-1)$	$\sigma^2 + q\sigma^2_{\tau\beta\gamma} + \dfrac{rq}{(t-1)(s-1)}\sum_{i}\sum_{k} (\tau\gamma)^2$
B $\times$ C	$(r-1)(s-1)$	$\sigma^2 + tq\sigma^2_{\beta\gamma}$
A $\times$ B $\times$ C	$(t-1)(r-1)(s-1)$	$\sigma^2 + q\sigma^2_{\tau\beta\gamma}$
Samples	$trs(q-1)$	σ^2
Total:	$trsq - 1$	

(f) = fixed effect, (r) = random effect

The outline of the analysis of variance and expected mean squares for the three-factor fixed-effects model written earlier is shown in Table 9.26.

Table 9.26 shows (as usual for a fixed-effects design) that the Samples Mean Square is the only valid denominator to be chosen for each F test, because, with any hypothesis stating that the τ_i, β_j, γ_k, or any combinations of these, in interaction terms are zero, the corresponding expected Mean Squares each becomes σ^2.

With a random-effects model the expected Mean Squares would involve only variances. For example, for the A $\times$ B interaction with $(t-1)(r-1)$ DF one has $\sigma^2 + q\sigma^2_{\alpha\beta\gamma} + sq\sigma^2_{\alpha\beta}$ and for the A main effect one has $\sigma^2 + q\sigma^2_{\alpha\beta\gamma} + sq\sigma^2_{\alpha\beta} + rq\sigma^2_{\alpha\gamma} + rsq\sigma^2_{\alpha}$. One problem with the multifactor random model is testing useful hypotheses. For example, no other expected Mean Square differs from the expected Factor A Mean Square by only one term. How would one test $H_0(\sigma_\alpha^2 = 0)$ against $H_a(\sigma_\alpha^2 \neq 0)$? No exact test exists, because with $H_0(\sigma_\alpha^2 = 0)$ the sampling distribution of the Factor A Mean Square is

$$\frac{(\sigma^2 + q\sigma_{\alpha\beta\gamma}^2 + sq\sigma_{\alpha\beta}^2 + rq\sigma_{\alpha\gamma}^2)\chi_{t-1}^2}{t - 1}$$

and no other mean square has a distribution with this same quantity in parentheses, so an F ratio cannot be obtained. Approximate F tests are available, however, but will not be given here.

With the mixed-effects model the Mean Squares for fixed effects will involve only interactions with random effects, as in Table 8.52, and the random effects will involve only interactions with other random effects. Table 9.27 gives the expected Mean Squares for a three-factor model with one random and two fixed main effects.

Although models and identities have been presented before, it will be helpful to the discussion of this table to give them again for the three-factor case with subsampling, as follows.

(9.21)   Model: $X_{ijkl} = \mu + \tau_i + \beta_j + \gamma_k + (\tau\beta)_{ij} + (\tau\gamma)_{ik} + (\beta\gamma)_{jk}$
$$+ (\tau\beta\gamma)_{ijk} + \epsilon_{ijkl}$$

where appropriate assumptions are made about fixed and random effects, about distributions of random effects, and about statistical independence. Whatever these assumptions, the following identity

(9.22) $X_{ijkl} - x\ldots \equiv (X_{ijkl} - x_{ijk.}) + (x_{ijk.} - x_{ij..} - x_{i.k.} - x_{.jk.}$
$$+ x_{i...} + x_{.j..} + x_{..k.} - x\ldots)$$
$$+ (x_{ij..} - x_{i...} - x_{.j..} + x\ldots)$$
$$+ (x_{i.k.} - x_{i...} - x_{..k.} + x\ldots)$$
$$+ (x_{.jk.} - x_{.j..} - x_{..k.} + x\ldots) + (x_{i...} - x\ldots)$$
$$+ (x_{.j..} - x\ldots) + (x_{..k.} - x\ldots)$$

leads to the identity in Sums of Squares which clarifies the analysis of variance. The latter identity need not be repeated here, because its form is almost completely suggested by Identity 9.22. Instead, it is pointed out that the terms of Identity 9.22, which in turn produce the terms of the identity for

$$\sum_i \sum_j \sum_k \sum_l (X_{ijkl} - x\ldots)^2$$

are obtained by adding the X_{ijkl} over appropriate classifications. For example, $x_{i...}$ is obtained by summing the X's over the B classification, the C classification, and within cell, if A is the effect measured by γ_k. Moreover, the i is kept as a general index, and there is no summing for $i = 1$ to t.

As noted earlier, *it will be assumed herein* that, whenever summing of unsquared terms is done over a fixed effect, the sum will be zero, because all possible such effects are included in this experiment. In contrast, whenever summing of unsquared terms is done over a random effect, the sum will *not* be zero. It should be noted that in the determination of the value of a mean such as $x_{i...}$ the i is not involved in the summations, so the matter of whether the A effect is fixed or random is ignored as being irrelevant.

To illustrate, suppose that the A and C effects are fixed whereas the B effect is random. This would be true, for example, if the A's were fixed Treatments and the C's were specifically selected varieties, whereas the B's were a random sample of sandy loam soils. Then the mean $x_{i...}$ is obtained by summing the right-hand side of Equation 9.21 over the B classification and then over the C classification, including summing within each cell as one came to it under either classification. Because the B factor is random, the $\sum_{j=1}^{r} (\beta_j) \neq 0$ and, for example, $\sum_{j=1}^{r} (\tau\beta)_{ij} \neq 0$, but $\sum_{k=1}^{s} (\beta\gamma)_{jk} = 0$ because the C effect is fixed; hence, for a given i all the $(\beta\gamma)_{jk}$ which exist are included in this experiment. When this same type of reasoning is applied to $(x_{i...} - x....)$, which is the only variable part of the A factor's Mean Square, one finds that

$$(9.23) \qquad E(A\ Ms) = \sigma^2 + sq\sigma_{\tau\beta}^2 + \frac{rsq}{t-1} \sum_{i=1}^{t} (\tau_i^2)$$

The $\sigma_{\tau\beta\gamma}^2$ term is missing, because the $(\tau\beta\gamma)_{ijk}$ terms sum to zero for a fixed i when summed from $k = 1$ to s over the fixed C classification. The $(\tau\gamma)_{ik}$ terms sum to zero for the same reason.

The final table so obtained is shown in Table 9.27.

It should become clear from a study of Table 9.27 that, if the subscripts which refer to the main effect in question or the subscripts which refer to the factors in an interaction are ignored, the only terms remaining in the expected Mean Square other than the first and last, which are there regardless of assumptions, are those in which the remaining subscripts refer to random effects.

Table 9.27 indicates the following proper F tests, among others, for the indicated tests of hypotheses:

(*a*) Test H_0(all $\tau_i = 0$) by means of

$$F[t - 1, (t - 1)(r - 1)] = \frac{\text{factor A Ms}}{\text{A} \times \text{B Ms}}$$

but test $H_0(\sigma_\beta^2 = 0)$ by means of

$$F[r - 1, trs(q - 1)] = \frac{\text{factor B Ms}}{\text{samples Ms}}$$

(*b*) Test $H_0(\sigma_{\tau\beta}^2 = 0)$ by means of

$$F[(t - 1)(r - 1), trs(q - 1)] = \frac{\text{A} \times \text{B Ms}}{\text{samples Ms}}$$

but test $H_0[\text{all } (\tau\gamma)_{ik} = 0]$ by means of

$$F[(t-1)(s-1), (t-1)(r-1)(s-1)] = \frac{A \times C \text{ Ms}}{A \times B \times C \text{ Ms}}$$

These conclusions point out again the value of the expected Mean Squares, even though their derivation is a bit beyond the mathematical level assumed for readers of this text.

The rule given above, for determining which terms will appear in expected Mean Squares, can be applied to other combinations of fixed and random effects and to more complex factorial-type experiments.

PROBLEMS

1. Suppose that a person in charge of quality control in a certain factory wishes to study the interrelations among three methods of inspection, five selected and trained inspectors, and mid-morning versus mid-afternoon inspections and their effects upon a certain measurement. Assuming that five articles are measured by each inspector under each method and at each time of day, write down the outline of the analysis of variance and explain how you would compute the Method × Inspector × Time-of-Day interaction.

2. Write down the statistical model for Problem 1, fully defining all symbols.

3. Write down the specific algebraic identity you would use to analyze the Total Sum of Squares into its independent parts.

4. Write down the expected Mean Square for Methods × Inspector and also the expected Mean Square for the proper error term for the Method × Inspector Mean Square.

5. Suppose that, with reference to Problem 1, the inspectors are considered a random sample of trained inspectors. How would the answer to Problem 2 now change? How about the answer to Problem 3?

6. Suppose that an industrial statistician wishes to study the quality of some product as produced by different machines and different operators. To this end he sets up the study as follows. The four different types of machine in existence are each to be operated by a random sample of 10 operators, each of whom will operate each machine for a designated period of time. During each period an operator normally will produce thousands of the items in question, so a random sample of five of these items will be drawn from each operator's work on each machine, a total of 200 items. Write down and fully define the statistical model for this experiment. Note that there are just 10 operators, all told, in this experiment.

7. Referring to Problem 6, write down the squares' identity with specific numbers wherever possible, and also write down as specifically as possible the algebraic expression for the Operator's Mean Square.

8. Referring to Problem 6, write down the expression for the sampling distribution of the Machine's Mean Square as specifically as possible.

9. Given the following table of data from a hypothetical three-factor experiment, use the computations to do an analysis of variance through the F tests. Also justify two of the F's as true F tests under the H_0's by means of the appropriate expected Mean Squares.

A *factor* (*fixed*)

B *factor* (*random*)	A₁			A₂			A₃			B_j *Sums*
	C₁	C₂	C₃ (*random*)	C₁	C₂	C₃	C₁	C₂	C₃	
	3	0	8	7	17	10	7	6	15	
	1	2	3	4	9	8	2	10	11	
B₁	5	−1	7	0	12	5	9	5	8	
	4	4	2	6	10	4	11	5	13	
	$\overline{13}$	$\overline{5}$	$\overline{20}$	$\overline{17}$	$\overline{48}$	$\overline{27}$	$\overline{29}$	$\overline{26}$	$\overline{47}$	
			38			92			102	232
	4	5	12	7	11	14	5	8	−3	
	0	1	7	2	11	6	11	14	2	
B₂	6	3	8	11	8	9	3	3	4	
	−2	9	11	5	10	12	6	6	0	
	$\overline{8}$	$\overline{18}$	$\overline{38}$	$\overline{25}$	$\overline{40}$	$\overline{41}$	$\overline{25}$	$\overline{31}$	$\overline{3}$	
			64			106			59	229
A_t Sums:			102			198			161	461

Total SS = 4275.00   Total S = 461

$(461)^2/72 = 2951.68$ $\dfrac{102^2 + 198^2 + 161^2}{24} = 3147.04$

$\dfrac{232^2 + 229^2}{36} = 2951.81,$ $\dfrac{38^2 + 92^2 + \cdots + 59^2}{12} = 3260.42,$

$$\dfrac{13^2 + 5^2 + 20^2 + 17^2 + \cdots + 31^2 + 3^2}{4} = 3743.75$$

	A *factor*					C *factor*		
	A₁	A₂	A₃			C₁	C₂	C₃
C₁	21	42	54		B₁	59	79	94
C₂	23	88	57		B₂	58	89	82
C₃	58	68	50			117	168	176
	102	198	161					

$\dfrac{21^2 + 42^2 + \cdots + 50^2}{8} = 3391.38,$ $\dfrac{59^2 + 79^2 + \cdots + 82^2}{12} = 3047.25,$

$$\dfrac{117^2 + 168^2 + 176^2}{24} = 3037.04$$

9.3 NESTED (OR HIERARCHICAL) CLASSIFICATIONS

In certain research situations every factor is not combined with every other factor, as in a three-way classification, for example. Instead, one has B random samples *within* each A class, C random samples *within* each sample

B *within* each A class, etc. By contrast, in an RCB design all Treatments appear equally frequently in every Block, and all Blocks are equally represented within each Treatment. Within each Treatment-Block combination there may be q random samples, however.

As an example of a nested classification, a poultry scientist might have 10 proven sires and wish to mate each sire to a separate random sample of dams (hens) of a specified genetic composition and age. Then within each family of chicks so produced a random sample of offsprings is to be taken. Diagrammatically one has the following, assuming equally many dams per sire and equally many chicks in each family:

Proven Sire

S_1 S_2 $\cdots$ S_t

$D_{11}\cdots D_{1r}$ $D_{21}\cdots D_{2r}$ $D_{t1}\cdots D_{tr}$

This is in contrast to a scheme under which each dam is mated to each sire, which then would be the two-way classification considered earlier.

To illustrate the analysis of data obtained from such a study, we shall assume:

(*a*) Sire effects are fixed and are measured by τ_i relative to a properly defined μ, so $\sum \tau_i = 0$.

(*b*) Dam-within-sire effects are random and are measured by a β_{ij} for the jth sample dam mated to the ith proven sire. It also is assumed that the β_{ij} are NID(0, σ_β^2) variates regardless of sire. Thus, homogeneity of variance from dam to dam within sire is assumed.

(*c*) The random observations within each sire-dam family have an effect measured by ϵ_{ijk}, where the ϵ_{ijk} are NID(0, σ^2) variates for all i, j, and k.

The mathematical model for the kth chick from the jth dam mated to the ith sire is as follows:

(9.31) $$X_{ijk} = \mu + \tau_i + \beta_{ij} + \epsilon_{ijk}$$

where:

μ = the grand average X for all chicks conceivably produced by these specific sires and all dams represented by those in these samples

τ_i = the potential fixed effect of the ith sire mated to the dams sampled by this experiment

β_{ij} = the random effect of the jth sample dam mated to the ith sire.

The identity used with this model is:

(9.32) $\quad X_{ijk} - x\ldots \equiv (X_{ijk} - x_{ij.}) + (x_{ij.} - x_{i..}) + (x_{i..} - x\ldots)$

which justifies the following identity in Sums of Squares, as usual:

(9.33) $\quad \displaystyle\sum_{i=1}^{t} \sum_{j=1}^{r} \sum_{k=1}^{q} (X_{ijk} - x\ldots)^2 \equiv \sum_i \sum_j \sum_k (X_{ijk} - x_{ij.})^2$

$$+ q \sum_i \sum_j (x_{ij.} - x_{i..})^2 + qr \sum_i (x_{i..} - x\ldots)^2$$

Total Ss $\equiv$ (Samples within dam, within sire Ss)

$$+ \text{(Dams within sire Ss)} + \text{(Sires Ss)}$$

In the usual way it is determined that the analysis of variance is as shown in Table 9.31.

TABLE 9.31. ANALYSIS OF VARIANCE FOR A NESTED CLASSIFICATION
WITH q CHICKS FROM EACH OF r DAMS WITHIN
EACH OF t SIRES

Source of variation	DF	Sample Mean Squares
Sires	$t - 1$	$\dfrac{rq}{t-1} \displaystyle\sum_{i=1}^{t} (x_{i..} - x\ldots)^2$
Dams within Sire	$t(r - 1)$	$\dfrac{q}{t(r-1)} \displaystyle\sum_i \sum_j (x_{ij.} - x_{i..})^2$
Chicks in family	$tr(q - 1)$	$\dfrac{1}{tr(q-1)} \displaystyle\sum_i \sum_j \sum_k (X_{ijk} - x_{ij.})^2$
Total about $x\ldots$	$trq - 1$	none

By definition and from Model 9.31 it is found that

$$x_{i..} = \frac{1}{rq} \sum_{j=1}^{r} \sum_{k=1}^{q} (X_{ijk}) = \mu + \tau_i + \beta_{i.} + \epsilon_{i..}$$

$$x\ldots = \frac{1}{trq} \sum_i \sum_j \sum_k (X_{ijk}) = \mu + 0 + \beta.. + \epsilon\ldots$$

Hence,

$$x_{i..} - x\ldots = \tau_i + (\beta_{i.} - \beta..) + (\epsilon_{i..} - \epsilon\ldots)$$

$$= \tau_i + \frac{1}{tr} [t(\beta_{i1} + \cdots + \beta_{ir}) - (\beta_{11} + \cdots + \beta_{tr})]$$

$$+ \frac{1}{trq} [(t - 1)(\epsilon_{i11} + \cdots + \epsilon_{irq}) - (\epsilon_{111} + \cdots + \epsilon_{trq})]$$

$$= \tau_i + \frac{1}{tr} [(t - 1)(\beta_{i1} + \cdots + \beta_{ir}) - (\beta_{11} + \cdots + \beta_{i-1,r}$$

$$+ \beta_{i+1,r} + \cdots + \beta_{tr})] + \text{above expression in } \epsilon\text{'s}$$

Therefore,

$$E[(x_{i..} - x...)^2] = \tau_i^2 + \frac{1}{t^2 r^2}[(t-1)^2 r \sigma_\beta^2 + r(t-1)]\sigma_\beta^2$$

$$+ \frac{1}{t^2 r^2 q^2}(t-1)^2 rq\sigma^2 + rq(t-1)\sigma^2$$

$$= \tau_i^2 + \frac{(t-1)}{rt}\sigma_\beta^2 + \frac{(t-1)}{trq}\sigma^2, \quad \text{for each } i$$

It then follows in the usual manner that the expected Mean Square for Sires is:

$$E(\text{Sires Ms}) = \frac{qr}{t-1}\sum_{i=1}^{t}(\tau_i^2) + q\sigma_\beta^2 + \sigma^2$$

After this process of deriving the Expected Mean Squares is applied to the other sample Mean Squares of Table 9.31, one obtains Table 9.32.

TABLE 9.32.   ANALYSIS OF VARIANCE AND EXPECTED MEAN
SQUARES FOR TABLE 9.31: SIRE EFFECTS ASSUMED
FIXED, OTHERS ASSUMED RANDOM

Source of variation	DF	*Expected Mean Square*
Sires	$t - 1$	$\sigma^2 + q\sigma_\beta^2 + \dfrac{qr}{t-1}\sum_{i=1}^{t}(\tau_i^2)$
Dams same sire	$t(r-1)$	$\sigma^2 + q\sigma_\beta^2$
Chicks same family	$tr(q-1)$	σ^2
Total about $x...$	$trq - 1$	

To test H_0(all $\tau_i = 0$) against H_a(some $\tau_i \neq 0$), one would use

$$F[(t-1), t(r-1)] = (\text{Sires Ms})/(\text{Dams Ms})$$

because the Sires Sampling Ms has the sampling distribution of

$$(\sigma^2 + q\sigma_\beta^2)\chi_{t-1}^2/(t-1)$$

if the H_0 is true, and the Dams Same Sire Ms has the sampling distribution of $(\sigma^2 + q\sigma_\beta^2)\chi_{t(r-1)}^2/t(r-1)$. The ratio of these two quantities is

$$\frac{\chi_{t-1}^2/(t-1)}{\chi_{t(r-1)}^2/t(r-1)}, \quad \text{which is } F[(t-1), t(r-1)]$$

as required for the test. If the main classification (Sires in the preceding example) in a hierarchical, or nested, experiment is a random effect, the only change in the argument above is that the τ_i are NID(0, σ_τ^2) variates, and thus the expected Sires Mean Square becomes

$$\sigma^2 + q\sigma_\beta^2 + qr\sigma_\tau^2$$

The ideas and results so far discussed in this section can be extended to several hierarchical levels: for example, main class A, B's within each A, C's within each B within each A. To illustrate, suppose that a of the A's are chosen at random, then a random sample of b of the B's is drawn within each A, a random sample of c of the C's within each B within each A, and a random sample of d of the D's within each C within each B within each A. With this random-effects model the analysis of variance and the expected Mean Squares are as shown in Table 9.33 for the model

$$X_{ijkl} = \mu + \tau_i + \beta_{ij} + \gamma_{ijk} + \epsilon_{ijkl}$$

where:

μ = the grand average X over all conceivable X's so sampled

τ_i = the random effect of A_i relative to the grand average, μ, so that the τ_i are NID(0, σ_τ^2) variates for each i

β_{ij} = the random effect of the jth sample B under the ith sample A, so that the β_{ij} are NID(0, σ_β^2) variates for all i and j

γ_{ijk} = the random effect of the kth sample C within the jth sample B within the ith sample A, so that the γ_{ijk} are NID(0, σ_γ^2) variates for all i, j, and k

ϵ_{ijkl} = the random sampling error within the last subclassification, so that the ϵ_{ijkl} are NID(0, σ^2) variates for all i, j, k, and l

TABLE 9.33.   ANALYSIS OF VARIANCE AND EXPECTED MEAN SQUARES
FOR THE TRIPLY NESTED EXPERIMENT WITH THE IMMEDIATELY
PRECEDING MODEL, ALL EFFECTS RANDOM

Source of variation	DF	*Expected Mean Square*
A effects	$a - 1$	$\sigma^2 + d\sigma_\gamma^2 + cd\sigma_\beta^2 + bcd\sigma_\tau^2$
B's within A's	$a(b - 1)$	$\sigma^2 + d\sigma_\gamma^2 + cd\sigma_\beta^2$
C's within B's within A's	$ab(c - 1)$	$\sigma^2 + d\sigma_\gamma^2$
D's within C's within B's within A's	$abc(d - 1)$	σ^2
Total about x...	$abcd - 1$	

The various tests that might be of interest relative to Table 9.33 and the hypotheses they test are shown in Table 9.34. It is convenient to show these tests in terms of ratios of sample mean squares abbreviated as shown in that table.

TABLE 9.34.   F TESTS FOR INDICATED H_0'S FOR A RANDOM-EFFECTS
MULTIPLY NESTED EXPERIMENT WITH THE MODEL
$$X_{ijkl} = \mu + \tau_i + \beta_{ij} + \gamma_{ijk} + \epsilon_{ijkl}$$

H_0	F *in terms of ratios of sample Mean Squares*
$\sigma_\gamma^2 = 0$	(C within B and A)/(D within C, B, and A)
$\sigma_\beta^2 = 0$	(B within A)/(C within B and A)
$\sigma_\tau^2 = 0$	(A effect)/(B within A)

The DF for the numerator and denominator, in that
order, for these respective F tests are

$$[ab(c-1), abc(d-1)]; \quad [a(b-1), ab(c-1)], \quad \text{and}$$
$$[(a-1), a(b-1)].$$

If there are unequal numbers of samples within some or all levels of
nesting, the situation becomes much more complex, *and the F tests become
inexact.* Table 9.35 was taken from R. L. Anderson and T. A. Bancroft's

TABLE 9.35.   OUTLINE OF THE ANALYSIS OF VARIANCE FOR A TRIPLY
NESTED EXPERIMENT WITH a OF MAIN CLASS A, b_i B UNITS WITHIN
THE iTH A CLASS, c_{ij} C UNITS WITHIN THE jTH B CLASS,
AND d_{ijk} D UNITS WITHIN THE kTH C CLASS

Source of variation	DF	*Coefficients of variances in expected Mean Squares*			
		σ^2	σ_c^2	σ_b^2	σ_a^2
A's	$a - 1$	1	$\sum_i \sum_j \sum_k (n_{ijk}^2 \cdot f_i)$	$\sum_i \sum_j (n_{ij}^2 \cdot f_i)$	$\sum_i (n_i^2 \cdot f_i)$
B's within A's	$\sum_i b_i - a$	1	$\sum_i \sum_j \sum_k (n_{ijk}^2 \cdot f_{ij})$	$\sum_i \sum_j (n_{ij}^2 \cdot f_{ij})$	
C's within B's	$\sum_i \sum_j c_{ij} - \sum_i b_i$	1	$\sum_i \sum_j \sum_k (n_{ijk} \cdot f_{ijk})$		
D's within C's	$n - \sum_i \sum_j c_{ij}$	1			

Each A unit has a total of n_i samples, the jth B unit under the ith class has n_{ij}
samples, and the kth C unit under the jth B and the ith A has n_{ijk} samples. Taken from
R. L. Anderson and T. A. Bancroft, *Statistical Theory in Research*, McGraw-Hill,
New York, 1952, with the permission of the authors and of the publisher.

Statistical Theory in Research (McGraw-Hill, New York, 1952) to present a
general outline of the analyses for a random-effects triply nested design with
unequal numbers of subsamples in the various hierarchical classifications.
Table 9.36 then presents a specific example of this more complex analysis.

TABLE 9.36. ILLUSTRATION OF THE USE OF TABLE 9.35 IN A TRIPLY
NESTED EXPERIMENT WITH UNEQUAL NUMBERS OF
OBSERVATIONS IN THE SUBCLASSES

A_1					A_2				
B_{11}		B_{12}			B_{21}			B_{22}		B_{23}		
C_{111} C_{112}		C_{121} C_{122} C_{123}			C_{211} C_{212} C_{213}			C_{221} C_{222}		C_{231} C_{232} C_{233}		

C_{111}	C_{112}	C_{121}	C_{122}	C_{123}	C_{211}	C_{212}	C_{213}	C_{221}	C_{222}	C_{231}	C_{232}	C_{233}
2	−1	4	5	8	7	8	7	11	4	3	4	11
3	3	−1	5	4	2	11	12	9	7	5	4	13
5	1	0	3	—	5	5	9	—	4	8	6	9
2	1	—	2	12	3	8	6	20	—	7	11	—
—	1	3	5		3	—	6		15	4	0	33
12	—				—	32	—			3	—	
	5		20			20			40			25
												30

$a = 2$; $b_1 = 2$, $b_2 = 3$; $c_{11} = 2$, $c_{12} = 3$, $c_{21} = 3$, $c_{22} = 2$, $c_{23} = 3$; $n_1 = 19$, $n_2 = 33$; $n_{11} = 9$, $n_{12} = 10$, $n_{21} = 14$, $n_{22} = 5$, $n_{23} = 14$; $n_{111} = 4$, $n_{112} = 5$, $n_{121} = 3$, $n_{122} = 5$, $n_{123} = 2$, $n_{211} = 5$, $n_{212} = 4$, $n_{213} = 5$, $n_{221} = 2$, $n_{222} = 3$, $n_{231} = 6$, $n_{232} = 5$, $n_{233} = 3$. It is seen that:

$$\sum_i^2 n_i = \sum_i^2 \sum_j^{b_i} n_{ij} = \sum_i^2 \sum_j^{b_i} \sum_k^{c_j} n_{ijk} = n = 52$$

In this table

$$f_i = (1/n_i - 1/n)/(a - 1),$$

$$f_{ij} = (1/n_{ij} - 1/n_i)/(\sum b_i - a),$$

$$f_{ijk} = (1/n_{ijk} - 1/n_{ij})/\left(\sum \sum c_{ij} - \sum b_i\right).$$

The use of Table 9.35 is illustrated in Table 9.36 by means of some
hypothetical data from a triply nested experiment. When the specific numbers

TABLE 9.37. ILLUSTRATION OF TABLE 9.35 WITH DATA OF
TABLE 9.36, RANDOM MODEL

Source of variation	Coefficients of variances in E(Ms)'s				
	DF	σ^2	σ_c^2	σ_b^2	σ_a^2
A's	1	1	4.74	11.93	27.41
B's within A's	3	1	3.85	9.53	
C's within B's within A's	8	1	3.92		
D's within C's within B's within A's	39	1			
Total about x...	51				

of Table 9.36 are used in Table 9.35, one obtains Table 9.37. The computations required to obtain the numbers in this table are as follows:

$$\sum_i \sum_j \sum_k (n_{ijk}^2 \cdot f_i)$$

$$= n_{111}^2 \cdot f_1 + n_{112}^2 \cdot f_1 + n_{121}^2 \cdot f_1 + n_{122}^2 \cdot f_1 + n_{123}^2 \cdot f_1 + n_{211}^2 \cdot f_2 + n_{212}^2 \cdot f_2$$
$$\quad + n_{213}^2 \cdot f_2 + n_{221}^2 \cdot f_2 + n_{222}^2 \cdot f_2 + n_{231}^2 \cdot f_2 + n_{232}^2 \cdot f_2 + n_{233}^2 \cdot f_2$$
$$= (16 + 25 + 9 + 25 + 4)(1/19 - 1/52)$$
$$\quad + (25 + 16 + 25 + 4 + 9 + 36 + 25 + 9)(1/33 - 1/52)$$
$$79(0.0334) + 149(0.0141) = 4.74$$

$$\sum_i \sum_j \sum_k (n_{ijk}^2 \cdot f_{ij})$$

$$= (1/3)(16 + 25)(1/9 - 1/19) + (1/3)(9 + 25 + 4)(1/10 - 1/19)$$
$$\quad + (1/3)(25 + 16 + 25)(1/14 - 1/33) + (1/3)(4 + 9)(1/5 - 1/33)$$
$$\quad + (1/3)(36 + 25 + 9)(1/14 - 1/33)$$
$$= (1/3)[41(0.0585) + 38(0.0474) + 66(0.0381) + 13(0.1667) + 70(0.0381)]$$
$$= 3.85$$

$$\sum_i \sum_j \sum_k (n_{ijk}^2 \cdot f_{ijk})$$

$$= (1/8)[16(0.1389) + 25(0.0889) + 9(0.2333) + 25(0.1000) + 4(0.4000)$$
$$\quad + 25(0.1286) + 16(0.1786) + 25(0.1286) + 4(0.3000) + 9(0.1335)$$
$$\quad + 36(0.0952) + 25(0.1286) + 9(0.2619)]$$
$$= 3.92$$

$$\sum_i \sum_j (n_{ij}^2 \cdot f_i)$$

$$= (81 + 100)(9.0334) + (196 + 25 + 196)(0.0141) = 11.93$$

$$\sum_i \sum_j (n_{ij}^2 \cdot f_{ij})$$

$$= (1/3)[81(0.0585) + 100(0.0474) + 196(0.0381) + 25(0.1667)$$
$$\quad\quad\quad\quad\quad\quad\quad\quad\quad\quad\quad\quad + 196(0.0381)]$$

$$\sum_i (n_i^2 \cdot f_i)$$

$$= 361(0.0334) + 1089(0.0141) = 27.41$$

It is evident from Table 9.36 that, all effects being random effects, the expected Mean Square for the A effect is $\sigma^2 + 4.74\sigma_c^2 + 11.93\sigma_b^2 + 27.41\sigma_a^2$ which, under $H_0(\sigma_a^2 = 0)$, becomes $\sigma^2 + 4.74\sigma_c^2 + 11.93\sigma_b^2$. This expected Mean Square is not now identical with any other Mean Square for this analysis; therefore, there is no proper Error by which to test $H_0(\sigma_a^2 = 0)$. Some approximate, and usually satisfactory, tests have been suggested by Anderson and Bancroft (cited above) and by G. W. Snedecor (*Statistical Methods*, 5th edition, Iowa State Press, 1956), among others. The student is referred to these sources for additional information.

PROBLEMS

1. Suppose that the following data were obtained from an experiment employing nested (hierarchical) classifications:

Classification A

A_1				A_2				A_3			
B_{11}	B_{12}	B_{13}	B_{14}	B_{21}	B_{22}	B_{23}	B_{24}	B_{31}	B_{32}	B_{33}	B_{34}
3.6	4.6	6.2	1.9	4.2	3.7	2.8	3.6	3.2	2.4	4.0	2.1
5.2	1.9	3.0	2.8	2.6	3.9	3.3	2.5	1.9	3.0	2.7	1.8
1.3	3.3	4.8	3.2	6.8	4.6	5.0	3.4	2.7	2.8	3.6	3.2
4.4	3.2	5.1	2.9	7.2	4.2	3.9	4.0	2.8	3.9	3.2	3.6
3.1	2.7	4.2	3.6	3.9	3.5	4.5	3.1	3.5	2.7	3.0	2.7

Assuming fixed A's, random B's within A's, and random samples within B's within A's, write down the model and do the analysis of variance.

2. Omit two columns of B's at random under each A, and do as directed in Problem 1.

3. Omit at random (by a table of random numbers) the following data from Problem 1 by columns from the first to the twelfth inclusive:

Col. No.	Omission	Col. No.	Omission
1	1st no.	7	3rd, 4th nos.
2	3rd no.	8	none
3	1st, 5th nos.	9	5th no.
4	2nd no.	10	none
5	none	11	1st, 4th nos.
6	2nd, 4th, 5th nos.	12	none

Then do the analysis of variance, and draw appropriate conclusions.

9.4 STATISTICAL ANALYSIS OF DATA WHICH DO NOT SATISFY THE ASSUMPTIONS OF THE ANALYSIS OF VARIANCE: TRANSFORMATIONS

In the models studied so far three specific properties of the measurements (for example, X_{ijk}) were assumed. These properties were normality of the random errors, ϵ_{ijk}, independence of the ϵ_{ijk} among themselves and of τ_i, β_j, etc., and homogeneity of variance for the ϵ_{ijk} regardless of main effects involved. What does one do if some or all assumptions appear to be unsatisfied?

In the case of decided nonnormality, for example, one could turn to one of the nonparametric methods that have been devised to replace the analysis of variance in situations in which normality cannot be assumed reasonably. Another possible action is to use an appropriate algebraic transformation of the data to a new scale of measurement, which may bring the data into satisfactory accord with the assumptions of the model and of the analysis of variance. This may be preferable, if successful, because it generally is believed that a normal analysis of variance produces more information than usually is obtainable from a nonparametric test. It seems to be true in a number of important situations that nonnormality, nonadditivity, and heterogeneity of variance have a common cause and can be cured, or at least alleviated, by properly transforming the data to another scale of measurement. Three such statistical transformations in fairly common use are the square root of $X+a$, the logarithm of $X+a$, and the arc sine of $\sqrt{X}$ as a percent, where X is the measurement actually taken and a is a real constant.

There are at least two general ways to decide which, if any, transformation is most likely to be successful in the sense described previously. One way is to follow general rules that describe the situation in which a given transformation often is successful. For example, when counts of insects are to be analyzed statistically, a prior square-root transformation to either $\sqrt{X}$ or $\sqrt{X+a}$ may produce numbers to which the analysis of variance can be applied with better results than if the obvious nonnormality and heterogeneity of variance had been ignored. Sometimes it is convenient to convert such counts into percentages. Under those circumstances it may be helpful to apply the so-called angular transformation, $Y_i = \arcsin \sqrt{100\, X_i/n}$, before performing an analysis of variance. Or, finally, if the effects under study are likely to be multiplicative rather than additive (if they exist at all) the logarithmic transformation $Y_i = \log(X + a)$ may change the data into numbers which satisfactorily conform to the assumptions made during an analysis of variance.

Another way to determine the need for, and type of, transformation in a given experimental situation is to use the fact that the sampling mean ($\bar{x}$) and the sampling variance (s^2) are uncorrelated for groups of data from a normal population; this is true for no other type of population. The analysis of variance is designed for studying samples from normal populations, so one essentially seeks an algebraic transformation which will normalize the given data. With some of the more common nonnormal populations there is a detectable relationship between $\bar{x}$ and s^2, so one starts by graphing the observed relationship between these two sample statistics and derives thereafter a transformation which appears to remove any relationship between $\bar{x}$ and s^2. After applying a specific transformation, one judges its success by regraphing the transformed sampling mean and variance, to see whether they no longer appear to be mathematically related, and then one tests for homogeneity of variance and additivity. This is the process which produced the rules stated earlier for using square-root, logarithmic, and arc sine transformations.

In view of the fact that the mathematical derivation of any transformation is beyond the level of this course, the following discussion is chiefly graphic and is followed by a summary which attempts to tie together the graphs and the recommended transformations. However, for the benefit of those who have had integral calculus, it is pointed out that the *form* of the suggested transformation, $Y_i = f(X_i)$, is obtained from $Y = \int \dfrac{C\,d\bar{x}}{s_X(\bar{x})}$, where C is a constant and s_X is the standard deviation of X as a function of $\bar{x}$. For example, if graphic analysis suggests that the variance of X is linearly related to $\bar{x}$, then the standard deviation is of the form $s_X(\bar{x}) = \sqrt{\bar{x} + a}$, so $Y = \int \dfrac{C\,d\bar{x}}{\sqrt{\bar{x} + a}} = K\sqrt{\bar{x} + a}$. This result suggests that a square-root transformation of the X's might normalize the data. If $s_X^2 = a\bar{x}^2 + b\bar{x} + c$, a quadratic relationship between $\bar{x}$ and s^2, it turns out by integration that the general form of the suggested transformation is $Y = K \log(\bar{x} + k)$; hence, a logarithmic transformation is tried when the relationship between $\bar{x}$ and s^2 appears to be quadratic.

If X is a binomial variate, so that $\sigma_X^2 = npq$, but X is expressed as a fraction of the total sample number, n, it is found that $\sigma_{X/n}^2 = pq/n$. This variance can be written as

$$\frac{1}{n}[p(1 - p)] = \frac{1}{n}(p - p^2) = \frac{1}{n}[1/4 - (p^2 - p + 1/4)]$$

$$= \frac{1}{n}[1/4 - (p - 1/2)^2]$$

so that $\sigma_{X/n}^2$ is in the form $\dfrac{1}{n}(a^2 - u^2)$. Therefore, the form of the transfor-

mation suggested is $Y = \displaystyle\int \dfrac{C\,d\bar{x}}{\sqrt{a^2 - \bar{x}^2}} = \arcsin \sqrt{X/n}$ as a percent, as noted earlier.

Clearly, this procedure by which transformations are derived is not a rigorous mathematical process; it only suggests the most promising transformation one should try. It remains, after using such a transformation, to show that it has at least greatly improved the validity of the assumptions made for the model and for the analysis of variance.

Table 9.41 shows some simulated counts of houseflies found on dairy cattle in the field. It is expected that such counts usually will increase during the day, so the data were chosen to show this sort of trend. In addition, the variance is made to increase in a predetermined way as the count level increases.

When the $(\bar{x}, s^2)$ pairs from Table 9.41 are plotted on the usual rectangular coördinate system, one obtains Figure 9.41. The dots on this figure clearly suggest that the sample mean and variance have a curvilinear relationship which reasonably can be considered quadratic, so it is suggested, as described above, that a logarithmic transformation $Y = \log(X + a)$ would bring these data much nearer to satisfying the assumptions of the analysis of variance than they are now. Table 9.42 shows the transformed data and the new sample means and variances. The crosses in Figure 9.41 show the relationship between $\bar{y}$ and s_Y^2 when a is taken as 1.

TABLE 9.41.   SIMULATED FLY COUNTS ON DAIRY CATTLE, TO ILLUSTRATE
A CURVILINEAR RELATIONSHIP BETWEEN SAMPLING
MEAN AND VARIANCE

	8 A.M.	10 A.M.	1 P.M.	3 P.M.	5 P.M.	7 P.M.
	18	13	18	42	17	16
	5	7	25	17	75	30
	5	5	9	32	23	113
	5	17	8	24	21	25
	2	4	10	14	24	28
	3	5	14	23	19	19
	5	10	5	11	43	40
	2	2	20	30	25	55
	4	9	11	9	35	27
	5	16	7	11	34	21
	2	3	10	16	17	60
	4	5	7	11	27	46
$\bar{x}$:	5.0	8.0	12.0	20.0	30.0	40.0
s^2:	18.36	25.45	36.91	107.01	263.09	727.82

When the sample means and variances of the transformed data shown in Table 9.42 are plotted into Figure 9.41 (as crosses), it is seen that the sample mean and variance are essentially unrelated, as they should be when samples are drawn from a normal population. The variances for the different hours of the day also seem now to be homogeneous, whereas they formerly were not. Therefore, it appears from this graphic evidence that the logarithmic transformation has been successful. More objective measures of the success of a transformation will be considered later.

Obviously, when one uses a transformation of some observed data before doing an analysis of variance, one must be assuming that the sources of variation which were important before transformation still will be so after it, and that no unrealistic sources of variation will be made to seem important by a transformation. As long as one uses transformations which are such that as X increases Y increases and for each X there is but one Y, and vice versa, these assumptions seem reasonable. The three transformations which have been described so far are of this sort.

TABLE 9.42.   RESULTS OF LOGARITHMIC TRANSFORMATION $Y = \log(X + 1)$
APPLIED TO THE MEASUREMENTS OF TABLE 9.41

	8 A.M.	10 A.M.	1 P.M.	3 P.M.	5 P.M.	7 P.M.
	1.279	1.146	1.279	1.633	1.255	1.230
	0.778	0.903	1.415	1.255	1.881	1.491
	0.778	0.778	1.000	1.519	1.380	2.057
	0.778	1.255	0.954	1.398	1.342	1.415
	0.477	0.699	1.041	1.176	1.398	1.462
	0.602	0.778	1.176	1.380	1.301	1.301
	0.778	1.041	0.778	1.079	1.643	1.613
	0.477	0.477	1.322	1.491	1.415	1.748
	0.699	1.000	1.079	1.000	1.556	1.447
	0.778	1.230	0.903	1.079	1.544	1.342
	0.477	0.602	1.041	1.230	1.255	1.785
	0.699	0.778	0.903	1.079	1.447	1.672
$\bar{y}$:	0.717	0.891	1.074	1.277	1.451	1.547
s_Y^2:	0.047	0.062	0.036	0.042	0.033	0.056

Consider next the data, shown in Table 9.43, which involve a linear
rather than a quadratic relationship between the observed sample means
and variances. In this circumstance it is believed, as explained earlier, that a
square-root transformation, $Y = \sqrt{X + a}$, often will normalize the data in
the sense described before.

TABLE 9.43.   HYPOTHETICAL HOUSEFLY COUNTS ON DAIRY CATTLE,
ILLUSTRATING THE NEED FOR A SQUARE-ROOT TRANSFORMATION

	8 A.M.	10 A.M.	1 P.M.	3 P.M.	5 P.M.	7 P.M.
	5	75	95	26	121	159
	51	8	15	30	25	42
	10	10	20	113	54	65
	14	35	24	25	40	61
	3	30	30	28	58	49
	25	20	25	29	75	42
	12	16	35	40	36	48
	7	22	17	55	49	64
	13	32	19	27	29	72
	46	15	17	21	38	51
	4	13	50	40	46	58
	14	24	13	46	29	45
$\bar{x}$:	17	25	30	40	50	63
s_X^2:	252.55	322.55	525.82	627.82	700.91	1009.27

When the sample mean, $\bar{x}$, and the sample variance, $s_{\bar{x}}^2$, from Table 9.43 are plotted against each other, Figure 9.42, it is clear that they are probably linearly related, when allowance is made for sampling error. On

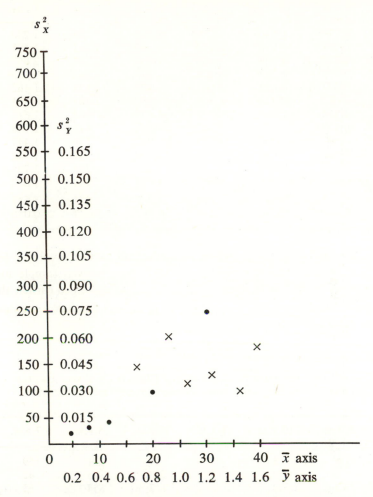

Figure 9.41. Relationships between sample mean and variance before (·) and after (x) of the logarithmic transformation $Y \log (X + 1)$.

the mathematical basis explained earlier a square-root transformation, $Y = \sqrt{X + a}$, was applied to the data of Table 9.43 to obtain Table 9.44. After a bit of preliminary experimentation it was decided that the a in $X = \sqrt{X + a}$ should be taken as zero.

Figure 9.42 suggests that after the transformation $Y = \sqrt{X}$ the sample mean and variance are, at the worst, only very weakly related. Thus, this square-root transformation seems to have fulfilled its purpose of making the sampling mean and variance independent of each other, as they should be in the sampling of normal populations.

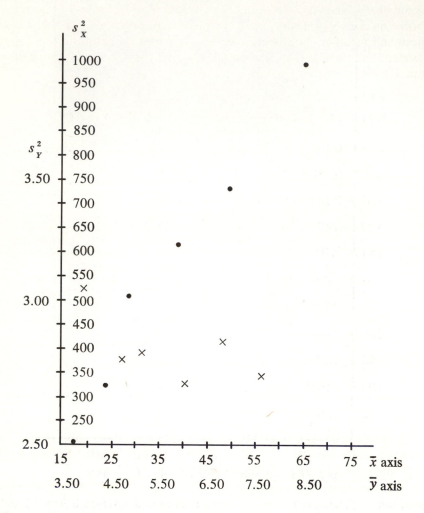

Figure 9.42.   Relationship between sample mean and variance before (·) and after (x) of the square-root transformation $Y = \sqrt{X}$ to data of Table 9.43.

Naturally, transformations of data do not always work as well in practice as they appear to have done in these prepared examples, but the examples do illustrate what one is trying to accomplish by transformations of experimental data. The examples also show how to judge the success of a transformation graphically.

A third, rather commonly used, transformation is the arc sine, or angular, transformation $Y_i = \arcsin \sqrt{100\ X_i/n}$; that is, the counts, say, are expressed as percentages of the total number observed. For example, it might be that 68 out of 100 leaves had a certain blight, so $X/n = 68\%$. Basically, this transformation is employed when there is a linear relationship between the sample mean and variance, as explained earlier. This transformation is sufficiently standard that there are tables by means of which the X's can be transformed into Y's very simply.

TABLE 9.44.   SQUARE-ROOT TRANSFORMATION $Y = \sqrt{X}$ APPLIED
TO DATA OF TABLE 9.43

	8 A.M.	10 A.M.	1 P.M.	3 P.M.	5 P.M.	7 P.M.
	2.24	8.66	9.75	5.10	11.00	12.61
	7.14	2.83	3.87	5.48	5.00	5.48
	3.16	3.16	4.47	10.63	7.35	8.06
	3.74	5.92	4.90	5.00	6.32	7.81
	1.73	5.48	5.48	5.29	7.62	7.00
	5.00	4.47	5.00	5.39	8.66	6.48
	3.46	4.00	5.92	6.32	6.00	6.93
	2.65	4.69	4.12	7.42	7.00	8.00
	3.61	5.66	4.36	5.20	5.39	8.49
	6.78	3.87	4.12	4.58	6.16	7.14
	2.00	3.61	7.07	6.32	6.78	7.62
	3.74	4.90	3.61	6.78	5.39	6.71
$\bar{y}$:	3.77	4.77	5.22	6.13	6.89	7.78
s_Y^2:	3.03	2.78	2.80	2.70	2.77	2.75

In summary, it can be said that the use of a square-root, logarithmic, or arc sine transformation before one applies the analysis of variance is intended to produce some or all of the following benefits.

(a) The variances from group to group will be homogeneous, or very nearly so.

(b) The transformed measurements will conform to the normal distribution satisfactorily.

(c) The effects to be studied in the experiment will, on the transformed scale of measurement, satisfy the usual assumptions of additivity in the model $X_{ij} = \mu + \tau_i + \beta_j + \epsilon_{ij}$, so the Error Variance can be estimated successfully. If a more complex model is involved, then the concept of, and test for, additivity needs to be extended accordingly. This procedure will not be given here but can be found in an article by J. W. Tukey in *Biometrics* 11: 111–13, 1955.

TABLE 9.45.   DATA OF TABLE 8.31 TRANSFORMED BY $Y = \log_{10}(X + 1)$
PLUS TUKEY'S TEST FOR NONADDITIVITY

Block	8 A.M.	10 A.M.	1 P.M.	3 P.M.	5 P.M.	7 P.M.	Sum	$y_{.j}$	$d_j = y_{.j} - y_{..}$	$p_j = \sum_{i}^{6} Y_{ij} \times (y_{i.} - y_{..})$
I	1.28	1.15	1.28	1.63	1.26	1.23	7.83	1.30	$+0.14$	0.0518
II	0.78	0.90	1.42	1.26	1.88	1.49	7.73	1.29	$+0.13$	0.5635
III	0.78	0.78	1.00	1.52	1.38	2.06	7.52	1.25	$+0.09$	0.7422
IV	0.78	1.26	0.95	1.40	1.34	1.42	7.15	1.19	$+0.03$	0.3415
V	0.48	0.70	1.04	1.18	1.40	1.46	6.26	1.04	-0.12	0.6232
VI	0.60	0.78	1.18	1.38	1.30	1.30	6.54	1.09	-0.07	0.4688
VII	0.78	1.04	0.78	1.08	1.64	1.61	6.93	1.16	0	0.5389
VIII	0.48	0.48	1.32	1.49	1.42	1.75	6.94	1.16	0	0.8135
IX	0.70	1.00	1.08	1.00	1.56	1.45	6.79	1.13	-0.03	0.4627
X	0.78	1.23	0.90	1.08	1.54	1.34	6.87	1.14	-0.02	0.3425
XI	0.48	0.60	1.04	1.23	1.26	1.78	6.39	1.06	-0.10	0.7323
XII	0.70	0.78	0.90	1.08	1.45	1.67	6.58	1.10	-0.06	0.6018
Sum:	8.62	10.70	12.89	15.33	17.43	18.56	83.53			$\sum p_j = 6.2827$
$y_{i.}$:	0.72	0.89	1.07	1.28	1.45	1.55			$1.16 = y_{..}$	

$d_i = y_{i.} - y_{..}$
$\quad -0.44 \quad -0.27 \quad -0.09 \quad +0.12 \quad +0.29 \quad +0.39$

$P = \sum (d_j p_j) = -0.080119$ $\sum (d_j^2) = 0.0797$ $\sum (d_i^2) = 0.5252.$

To test nonadditivity:

$$\frac{P^2}{\sum (d_i^2) \cdot \sum (d_j^2)} = \frac{0.00641905}{0.04185844} = 0.1534 = \text{corresponding Ss.}$$

Source of variation	DF	Sum of Squares	Mean Square
Hour of Day	5	6.2798	1.256*
Block	11	0.4789	0.04354 ns
Gross Hour × Block	55	2.5586	
(Nonadditivity	1	0.1534	0.1534) ns
Net Hour Block	54	2.4052	0.04454

Conclude that nonadditivity has been cured or enough alleviated for the analysis of variance now to be performed legitimately, as far as additivity is concerned.

* means statistically significant at the 5% level.
ns means statistically nonsignificant.

The parentheses around the line for nonadditivity indicate that this Source of Variation is a portion of the one above it.

One may check these hopes quite adequately, if one wishes to invest the additional time and labor. However, it probably is sufficient to use the best available transformation, check to see whether the relationship between sample mean and sample variance is nonexistent *after* transformation, and then, if these checks turn out affirmatively, proceed with an analysis of variance on the transformed data.

Another matter of concern, when the data may not satisfy the assumptions of the proposed model, is nonadditivity. This was mentioned earlier, so reference is made to the data of Table 8.31, simulating counts of houseflies on dairy cattle. Tukey's test for nonadditivity in the model $X_{ij} = \mu + \tau_i + \beta_j + \epsilon_{ij}$ indicated nonadditivity. When the mean and variance by hour of day are plotted against each other, one finds a quadratic relationship, so the logarithmic transformation is suggested. Table 9.45 shows the results of this transformation in detail and the test for nonadditivity after this transformation.

With reference to Table 9.45, it is found that:

(*a*) There no longer is an apparent relation between the sampling mean and variance. This is shown by graph and by the fact that the linear correlation coefficient between $\bar{y}$ and s_Y^2 is but $r = -0.166$, with 4 DF, which is clearly nonsignificant at any reasonable level of significance.

(*b*) The hour-of-day variances among the Y's now are homogeneous. Hence, it seems (though admittedly not proved herein) that this logarithmic transformation has essentially "cured" nonadditivity, nonnormality, and heterogeneity of variance. The analysis of variance on the transformed data now can be accepted as being reasonably valid and useful.

PROBLEMS

1. Given the following hypothetical data,

	1	2	3	*Method:* 4	5	6	7
	160	14	48	3	2	28	10
	35	58	11	0	13	31	0
	80	5	20	0	19	19	3
	150	92	15	4	5	5	5
	28	40	9	1	10	3	5
	15	21	33	1	3	0	1
Σ:	468	230	136	9	52	86	24
$\bar{x}$:	78	38	23	2	9	14	4
s^2:	4046	1055	227	3	43	181	13

plot $\bar{x}$ against s^2 (on vertical axis), decide which transformation might work, and do it with the a in $(X + a) = 1, 2, 5, 7,$ and 10, successively. Summarize the effect of changing a, and decide whether any of the transformations tried has been successful.

2. Suppose the following practice data are counts of infected plants inspected in each experimental unit. There are five plots of each of five Treatments in a CR design with fixed effects.

	Treatment:				
	1	2	3	4	5
	10	10	14	42	52
	7	25	13	20	22
	18	16	32	25	30
	5	19	20	15	40
	5	10	21	28	16
Sum:	45	80	100	130	160
Mean:	9	16	20	26	32
$s_{\bar{x}}^2$:	29.5	40.5	57.5	104.5	206.0

Decide which transformation is most likely to "normalize" these data (in case any transformation is needed), apply it, recompute the means and variances, and decide whether the transformation you used was successful.

3. Convert the counts of Problem 2 into arc sines, assuming these are counts per 100, and then show by graphs the effect of this transformation on the relationship between sampling mean and variance.

4. Apply Tukey's test for additivity to the data of Problem 2 after assuming that the rows of data are blocks.

5. Apply Tukey's test for additivity to the data of Problem 2 after using the arc sine transformation. Assume the Blocks described in Problem 4.

6. Make up a set of data presumably from a CR experiment with 6 Treatments and 5 samples per Treatment, such that a square-root transformation seems likely to normalize these data. Then perform that transformation, and determine graphically whether it probably was successful.

7. Do as in Problem 6 but with the purpose of making the logarithmic transformation the proper one to use.

8. Apply Tukey's test for additivity to Problem 1 before and after using a $\log(X + 6)$ transformation. Draw appropriate conclusions.

9. Take any newspaper and do as follows. (1) Take an article containing at least 500 words and count out and mark 5 sets of 100 words each. (2) Do as in (1) for a total of 6 articles. (3) Within each set of 100 words count the number of adverbs. (4) Formulate a table, such as for Problem 1, with Article and Number of Adverbs as headings, so there are six columns with 5 numbers in each. Compute $\bar{x}$ and s^2 for each article, and plot them to see whether there appears to be a relationship between $\bar{x}$ and s^2. If so, decide which transformation should be tried, and try it.

9.5 STATISTICAL ANALYSIS OF DATA WHICH DO NOT SATISFY THE ASSUMPTIONS OF THE ANALYSIS OF VARIANCE: MISSING DATA

It may happen that some of the data which were to be taken during an experiment are not obtainable for one or more of the experimental units involved or else were taken and lost. For example, an animal might get loose and trample some plots in an experiment or eat the plants to be measured.

If this sort of accident occurs in a CR design, one simply does an analysis of variance in the usual way for unequal numbers within Treatments, and the assumptions of the analysis of variance are not impaired by this accident. However, if data are missing from an RCB design with but one observation per Treatment and Block, the experiment is unbalanced by missing data, because some Treatments are not represented in one or more Blocks at all. If a Block from which a Treatment is missing is especially good or especially bad, the Treatment comparisons will be biassed by the missing data.

Nothing can be done to remedy this trouble completely, but it is generally believed that the best way out of this partially unsatisfactory situation is to calculate replacements for the missing data in such a way as to minimize the estimate of the Error Variance. Thereafter, a correction can be introduced to alleviate the bias caused by missing data. That will not be done here, however, because there is a better way to compute missing data *and* correct for bias caused thereby, which will be introduced in the chapter on the analysis of covariance.

To illustrate the process of replacing missing data and the principle of minimizing the Error Variance, consider the data of Table 9.51, in which an X appears in place of the missing data in one cell of this table. The appropriate analysis of variance, without correction for bias, also is shown in the table.

If the process shown in this table is performed when there are t Treatments and r Blocks, one obtains the following formula for computing

TABLE 9.51.   ILLUSTRATION OF TECHNIQUE FOR REPLACING MISSING DATA IN A RANDOMIZED COMPLETE BLOCK DESIGN WITH $q = 1$

Block	Treatment				Block sum
	A	*B*	*C*	*D*	
I	13	3	17	7	40
II	10	5	X	5	$20 + X$
III	17	12	13	13	55
Treatment Sum:	40	20	$30 + X$	25	$115 + X$

Source of variation	DF	Sum of Squares	Mean Square
Treatments	3	$(3X^2 + 10X + 875)/12$	
Blocks	2	$(1855 - 110X + 2X^2)/12$	
Error	6	$(6X^2 - 130X + 1289)/12$	$(6X^2 - 130X + 1289)/72 = s^2$

The Error Mean Square is made a minimum by calculus, if $12X - 130 = 0$; or, $X = 65/6$.

replacements for one missing measurement in an RCB design with one experimental observation per Treatment and Block. The X_{ij} stands for a missing value to be supplied for the ith Treatment and the jth Block. The formula obtained upon minimizing the Error Mean Square by simple calculus is

(9.51)
$$X_{ij} = \frac{tT_i + rB_j - G}{(t - 1)(r - 1)}$$

where:

T_i = the total of the numbers actually taken for Treatment i

B_j = the total of the numbers actually taken for Block j

G = the grand total of the $tr - 1$ numbers actually obtained during the experiment

It is necessary, after one computes a value to be used in place of one missing number, to reduce the Error DF and the Total DF each by 1. This also is logical, because the missing number supplied by Formula 9.51 certainly is not subject to the usual random variation, because it is computed in such a way as to minimize the Error Variance.

If more than one number is missing from an experiment, the analysis of variance may be biassed more than if but one number is missing, but it is still feasible and preferable to compute replacements for the missing numbers, using the principle of minimizing the Error Variance. This process is an iterative one as follows:

(*a*) Put an X_{ij} in any one of the places where data are missing.

(*b*) In each of the other places where data are missing put the best estimate you know for the missing numbers, considering the Block and Treatment involved. Guides for this process can be obtained from the corresponding Treatment and Block means when they are considered relative to the grand mean. Actually, any numbers could be used, but it usually will speed up the iterative process to put in the best possible estimates.

(*c*) Use Formula 9.51 as before, as though only this one X_{ij} were missing.

(*d*) Insert the X_{ij} computed, remove any one of the other numbers which originally were missing, put X_{ij} in this place, and recompute a number for this place in the table, using Formula 9.51 as before. Be sure to recompute the necessary totals for this formula after putting in the first X_{ij} computed.

(*e*) Continue this process of iteration in a rotation of your own choosing, until no number changes when recomputed.

(*f*) Reduce the Total and Error DF's each by the number of missing measurements.

To illustrate this process of iteration, consider the data in Table 9.52, in which two units X and Y originally were missing. A "guessed" value for Y can be computed logically as follows:

Y = grand mean + (mean A − grand mean) + (mean V − grand mean)

  = 12.28 − 0.28 − 0.28 = 11.72

TABLE 9.52.   ILLUSTRATION OF ITERATIVE PROCESS OF REPLACING MORE
THAN ONE MISSING MEASUREMENT IN A RANDOMIZED COMPLETE
BLOCK DESIGN WITH $q = 1$, X and Y THE MISSING DATA

Block	Treatment				Block	
	A	B	C	D	Sum	Mean
I	8	11	16	5	40	10
II	13	24	X	8	$(45) = B_{II}$	(15)
III	19	22	24	7	72	18
IV	8	8	9	3	28	7
V	Y	15	14	7	(36)	12
Treatment Sum:	(48)	80	$(63) = T_C$	30	(221)	(12.28)
Treatment Mean:	(12)	16	(15.75)	6		

The numbers in parentheses are the sums and means exclusive of the missing data.

When this value for Y is inserted into Table 9.52, one obtains, for the computations needed in the formula $X_{C,II}$, $T_C = 63$, $B_{II} = 45$, and $G = 232.72$. The results obtained with Formula 9.51 are as follows:

$$X_{C,II} = \frac{4(63) + 5(45) - 232.72}{3(4)} = 20.36$$

This computed size for $X_{C,II}$ now is inserted into Table 9.52 in the place of X, and another number is computed for $Y_{A,V}$ by using the same T_C and B_{II} that Y would have had before the first X was computed, because X and Y do not have either a Treatment or a Block in common. The G now changes to 241.25. Thus,

$$Y_{A,V} = \frac{4(48) + 5(36) - 241.36}{12} = 10.89$$

This number is smaller than the "expected value" first computed. This new estimate for Y is put in place of the 11.72 formerly computed, and another $X_{C,II}$ now is computed with Formula 9.51. In this case, $T_C = 63$, $B_{II} = 45$ (again), and $G = 231.89$, so the second computed estimate of $X_{C,II}$ is

$$X_{C,II} = \frac{4(63) + 5(45) - 231.89}{12} = 20.43$$

which differs from the previous calculation of $X_{C,II}$ by 0.07. This new $X_{C,II}$ changes the G to 241.43 for the computation of another estimate of $Y_{A,V}$ from

$$Y_{A,V} = \frac{4(48) + 5(36) - 241.25}{12} = 10.88$$

This new estimate of $Y_{A,V}$ is but 0.01 smaller than that obtained previously, so G only changes to 231.88 for the computation of another estimate of $X_{C,II}$ from

$$X_{C,II} = \frac{4(63) + 5(45) - 231.88}{12} = 20.43$$

which is the same as the immediately preceding estimate of $X_{C,II}$; hence, this iterative process of successive approximations ends with $X_{C,II} = 20.43$ and $T_{A,V} = 10.88$. These choices minimize the Error Variance, which now has but $12 - 2 = 10$ DF.

In case there are more than two missing numbers, the same process is used but is more difficult, and the Mean Squares in the analysis of variance have greater bias. As already noted, we shall present another method of replacing missing data, after the analysis of covariance is presented. This procedure also will provide a correction for bias in the same general operation, so it is the preferred method in practice.

PROBLEMS

1. Given the following table of data with a missing number, compute a replacement for the missing datum which will minimize the Error Variance in the subsequent analysis of variance:

		Variety of Wheat:			
Block	*Ponca*	*Concho*	*Pawnee*	*Tenmarq*	*Block sum*
I	62.1	missing	58.1	60.1	180.3
II	38.5	29.3	40.2	45.1	153.1
III	55.0	49.7	50.6	48.5	203.8
IV	70.3	68.8	67.7	65.0	271.8
V	74.1	75.0	82.0	70.0	301.1
Var. Sum:	300.0	222.8	298.6	288.8	1110.1

2. Referring to Problem 1, assume that the number in Block IV under Pawnee also is missing, and compute replacements for the missing data by the iterative procedure.

3. Do the analysis of variance for Problem 2, including the appropriate F test and a full interpretation of the results.

4. Given the following practice data, compute the missing values on the principle of minimizing the Error Variance.

		Treatment:			
Block	*A*	*B*	*C*	*D*	*E*
1	3.5	4.8	4.1	missing	4.2
2	missing	4.6	3.9	2.9	3.8
3	2.8	3.0	2.7	2.3	3.2
4	2.3	missing	2.1	1.9	2.5

5. Do the analysis of variance for Problem 4.

9.6   VARIANCE COMPONENTS

Suppose that the statistical model for a random-effects design is

(9.61) $$X_{ijk} = \mu + \tau_i + \beta_j + (\tau\beta)_{ij} + \epsilon_{ijk}$$

where the τ_i, β_j, $(\tau\beta)_{ij}$, and the ϵ_{ijk} are NID variates with zero means and variances of σ_τ^2, σ_β^2, $\sigma_{\tau\beta}^2$, and σ^2, respectively. In this situation it is true that

(9.62) $$\sigma_{X_{ijk}}^2 = \sigma_\tau^2 + \sigma_\beta^2 + \sigma_{\tau\beta}^2 + \sigma^2$$

and so the variances for Treatments, Blocks, Interaction, and Error are *components* (nonoverlapping additive parts) of the Total variance of the X_{ijk}. The result shown in Equation 9.62 is established as follows by using the methods of Chapter 8:

$$
\begin{aligned}
\text{Variance of } X_{ijk} &= \mathrm{E}\{(X_{ijk} - \mu)^2\} \\
&= \mathrm{E}\{(\mu + \tau_i + \beta_j + (\tau\beta)_{ij} + \epsilon_{ijk} - \mu)^2\} \\
&= \mathrm{E}\{\tau_i^2 + \beta_j^2 + (\tau\beta)_{ij}^2 + \epsilon_{ijk}^2 + \text{crossproducts}\} \\
&= \mathrm{E}\{\tau_i^2\} + \mathrm{E}\{\beta_j^2\} + \mathrm{E}\{(\tau\beta)_{ij}^2\} + \mathrm{E}\{\epsilon_{ijk}^2\} + \text{zeros}
\end{aligned}
$$

Hence,

$$\sigma_{X_{ijk}}^2 = \sigma_\tau^2 + \sigma_\beta^2 + \sigma_{\tau\beta}^2 + \sigma^2$$

as stated in Equation 9.62. The analysis of variance provides a process for estimating the *variance components*. If the experiment has equal numbers of observations in the subclasses, one can obtain efficient estimators of the variance components. Moreover, the variances of these estimates can be estimated.

Estimates of the variance components σ_τ^2, σ_β^2, $\sigma_{\tau\beta}^2$, and σ^2 are obtained by equating the sample Mean Squares with their corresponding expected Mean Squares and solving for the latter as estimates. For example, consider the analysis in Table 9.61.

When the sample Mean Squares of this table are set equal to the expected Mean Squares, the σ^2's replaced by $\hat{\sigma}^2$'s, and solutions sought for these linear

TABLE 9.61.   ANALYSIS OF VARIANCE FOR A HYPOTHETICAL EXPERIMENT WITH RANDOM EFFECTS, 5 TREATMENTS, 6 BLOCKS, AND 3 SAMPLES WITHIN EACH TREATMENT AND BLOCK

Source of variation	DF	Sample Mean Square	Expected Mean Square
Treatments	4	36.55	$\sigma^2 + 3\sigma_{\tau\beta}^2 + 18\sigma_\tau^2$
Blocks	5	21.00	$\sigma^2 + 3\sigma_{\tau\beta}^2 + 15\sigma_\beta^2$
Treatment × Block	20	3.90	$\sigma^2 + 3\sigma_{\tau\beta}^2$
Samples	60	3.15	σ^2
Total about $x..$	89		

simultaneous equations in the *variance components*, one obtains $\hat{\sigma}^2 = 3.15$, $\hat{\sigma}^2_{\tau\beta} = 0.25$, $\hat{\sigma}^2_{\beta} = 1.14$, and $\hat{\sigma}^2_{\tau} = 1.81$. Furthermore, 5% F tests of $H_0(\sigma^2_{\tau} = 0)$, $H_0(\sigma^2_{\beta} = 0)$, and $H_0(\sigma^2_{\tau\beta} = 0)$, respectively, indicate that only $\sigma^2_{\tau\beta}$ is likely to be zero.

One can obtain formulas for the variances of these estimates of the variance components by using information previously presented regarding the sampling distributions of the sample Mean Squares. The distribution of the Treatment Mean Square for the situation of Table 9.61 is that of $(\sigma^2 + 3\sigma^2_{\tau\beta} + 18\sigma^2_{\tau})\chi^2_4/4$. The variance of any chi-square variate is twice its degrees of freedom, so the variance of χ^2_4 is 8. The expression in the σ's is a constant, so its effect is to multiply the variance of the variate by

$$(\sigma^2 + 3\sigma^2_{\tau\beta} + 18\sigma^2_{\tau})^2/16.$$

Thus, the variance of the Treatment Mean Square is $(\sigma^2 + 3\sigma^2_{\tau\beta} + 18\sigma^2_{\tau})^2/2$. In a similar manner it is found that the variance of the Treatments × Blocks Mean Square is $(\sigma^2 + 3\sigma^2_{\tau\beta})^2/10$.

The estimate of σ^2_{τ} was obtained by subtracting the Treatments × Blocks Mean Square from the Treatments Mean Square and dividing by 18. Those Mean Squares are independent variates, hence the variance of $\hat{\sigma}^2_{\tau}$ is

$$\frac{1}{18^2}\left[\frac{(\sigma^2 + 3\sigma^2_{\tau\beta} + 18\sigma^2_{\tau})^2}{2} + \frac{(\sigma^2 + 3\sigma^2_{\tau\beta})^2}{10}\right]$$

which can only be estimated from the analysis of variance in Table 9.61, because the σ^2's are unknown. The estimated variance of $\hat{\sigma}^2_{\tau}$ is, therefore,

$$\frac{1}{324}\left\{\frac{(\hat{\sigma}^2 + 3\hat{\sigma}^2_{\tau\beta} + 18\hat{\sigma}^2_{\tau})^2}{2} + \frac{(\hat{\sigma}^2 + 3\hat{\sigma}^2_{\tau\beta})^2}{10}\right\} = 2.0664$$

Hence the estimated standard deviation of the variance component σ^2_{τ} is $\sqrt{2.0664} \cong 1.44$.

A number of problems relative to variance components remain unsolved, but the preceding discussion shows how these components can be estimated and give a procedure for approximating the standard deviation of an estimated variance component.

PROBLEMS

1. Calculate an approximate standard deviation for the estimate of the interaction component of variance in Table 9.61.

2. Given the following analysis of variance, estimate all of the variance components and their standard errors:

Source of variation	DF	Mean Square
Sires	6	293.0
Dams within Sire	21	75.8
Chicks same Dam and Sire	112	20.3
Total:	139	

3. Estimate all variance components and their standard deviations for Problem 1 of Section 9.3, after assuming a fully random model.

9.7 SAMPLING ERROR VERSUS EXPERIMENTAL ERROR

In some experimental studies one may do subsampling which raises the question which is the valid error variance for certain possible F tests. As usual, much depends upon the assumptions made. These should be set forth in the model chosen during the planning of the experiment.

In an RCB design with t Treatments, r Blocks, and q samples per Treatment and Block, one can take either of two points of view:

(*a*) The Blocks are sufficiently different that they might interact with Treatment effects. If this is the logical point of view, it has been discussed previously from the model:

$$(9.71) \qquad X_{ijk} = \mu + \tau_i + \beta_j + (\tau\beta)_{ij} + \epsilon_{ijk}$$

(*b*) The Blocks are different (or they would not have been used), but they are not different in such a way that a meaningful interaction should be expected or could be interpreted usefully. From this point of view, one could use the model

$$(9.72) \qquad X_{ijk} = \mu + \tau_i + \beta_j + \epsilon_{ij} + \delta_{ijk}$$

where $\sum \tau_i = \sum \beta_j = 0$, the ϵ_{ij} are NID$(0, \sigma_e^2)$ for all i and j, and the δ_{ijk} are NID$(0, \sigma_s^2)$ for all i, j, and k. Under this model and these assumptions the expected Mean Squares are obtained in the usual way and found to be as in Table 9.71.

TABLE 9.71.   ANALYSIS OF VARIANCE AND EXPECTED MEAN SQUARES FOR THE FIXED-EFFECTS MODEL $X_{ijk} = \mu + \tau_i + \beta_j + \epsilon_{ij} + \delta_{ijk}$

Source of variation	DF	Expected Mean Square
Treatments	$t - 1$	$\sigma_s^2 + q\sigma_e^2 + \dfrac{rq}{t - 1}\sum (\tau_i^2)$
Blocks	$r - 1$	$\sigma_s^2 + q\sigma_e^2 + tq/(r - 1)\sum (\beta_j^2)$
Experimental error	$(r - 1)(t - 1)$	$\sigma_s^2 + q\sigma_e^2$
Subsample error	$rt(q - 1)$	σ_s^2

If, relative to Table 9.71, a random-effects model had been assumed, the τ_i and β_j being NID$(0, \sigma_\tau^2)$ and NID$(0, \sigma_\beta^2)$ variates, respectively, this would affect the summation terms in Table 9.71. They would be replaced by $rq\sigma_\tau^2$ and $tq\sigma_\beta^2$, respectively, reading from the top of the table downward.

It is seen, then, that the Subsamples Mean Square would be used as the denominator of the F test only when testing $H_0(\sigma_e^2 = 0)$ against $H_a(\sigma_e^2 > 0)$.

The Experimental Error Mean Square would be used for the other two possible F tests.

Although the preceding conclusions seem obvious in view of the models, one might raise a question of experimental design. Why should one ever wish to test $H_0(\sigma_e^2 = 0)$? Is it not true in almost any study of this sort that only the Treatment and Block effects are of major interest? If this is true, it might be argued that one should increase the number of degrees of freedom for estimating the so-called experimental error and reduce, or even eliminate, the number of subsamples. There also is a philosophical question regarding these models: if the Experimental Error and the Subsampling Error truly are different, what is the difference between the ϵ_{ij} in one model and the $(\tau\beta)_{ij}$ in the other? There are experimental situations in which these two sorts of error *could* be different, but it is important that the experimenter be clear on this matter at the outset of the experiment. For example, in a soils and variety study, with varieties as Treatments and soil types as Blocks, it may be of interest to measure the interaction between variety and soil type; hence, the model with the $(\tau\beta)_{ij}$ term should be used. On the other hand, a poultry scientist might define daylengths as Treatments and areas of a poultry range as Blocks but have individual cages within Treatment and Block. A true Area × Daylength interaction might seem unrealistic in this situation; but it might be that the apparent Area × Daylength "interaction" represents a different sort of variance from the cage-to-cage variance. In this situation it would seem preferable to use the model with the ϵ_{ij} and the δ_{ijk} terms and study two sorts of error variance. If an analysis of variance indicates that σ_e^2 is decidedly larger than σ_s^2, in the next such study one probably should reduce the number of samples within the same Treatment and Block, so that the total resources used would be utilized better.

PROBLEMS

1. Verify the expected Mean Square for Blocks in Table 9.71.
2. What is the sampling distribution of the sample Mean Square for Experimental Error in Table 9.71 in terms of a chi-square distribution?

9.8   ORTHOGONAL SETS OF COMPARISONS

There are research situations in which certain specific individual Treatment comparisons are planned in advance and can be made more efficiently and meaningfully by means of individual F tests than one of the multiple-comparison procedures. To illustrate, suppose a botanist is going to study the effects of three mercurial and two organic types of seed treatments against a certain type and race of smut on barley. It is supposed, for illustration, that the three mercurial treatments are three rates of the same compound, namely, 1, 3, and 5 parts per million. In most such instances the experimenter would like to know the following:

(a) Is there a linear response (in effectiveness) when the rate of the mercurial compound is changed uniformly from 1 to 3 parts per million?

(b) Is there a quadratic response to the rate change described in (a)?

(c) Do the two organic treatments differ significantly in their average effects?

(d) Do the mercurial treatments averaged over all three rates differ materially from the average effect of the two organic treatments?

These four questions can be shown to correspond to four individual F tests, each accounting for 1 DF among the 4 DF for the five seed treatments. Moreover, the four corresponding Sums of Squares are nonoverlapping parts of the Treatment Sum of Squares with 4 DF. Such a set of independent comparisons is said to constitute an *orthogonal set* of individual comparisons.

The formulas for the four independent Sums of Squares described earlier will be derived, so that the student may see the general manner in which such formulas are obtained, in case he should need to derive some of his own later. Consider first the comparison of the two organic compounds. One simply makes an F test with 1 DF for the numerator Mean Square. This process is exhibited by the following diagram and algebra:

$$\frac{S_1^2 + S_2^2}{k} - \frac{(S_1 + S_2)^2}{2k} = \text{Organic Sum of Squares}$$

$$= \frac{2S_1^2 + 2S_2^2 - S_1^2 - S_2^2 - 2S_1 S_2}{2k}$$

$$= \frac{(S_1 - S_2)^2}{2k} = \frac{(1S_1 - 1S_2)^2}{k[1^2 + (-1)^2]}$$

$$
\begin{array}{cc}
0_1 & 0_2 \\
\end{array}
$$

$$
k\left\{
\begin{array}{cc}
- & - \\
- & - \\
\vdots & \vdots \\
- & -
\end{array}
\right\}k
$$

Sum: $S_1 \quad S_2$

The numerator of the Organics Ss can be designated briefly by $(+1, -1)$, with the understanding that these numbers are the coefficients of S_1 and S_2, respectively, and remembering that the algebraic sum so indicated always will be squared. The denominator for the Organics Ss is just k(sum of squares of the coefficients of S_1 and S_2).

Consider next the computation of the Mercurials Ss. The linear trend

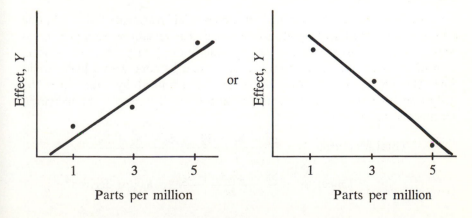

Effect, Y — Parts per million (1, 3, 5)   or   Effect, Y — Parts per million (1, 3, 5)

in the effects of uniformly increasing the rate of application will be considered first. The meaning of the term "linear effect of increasing the rate uniformly" is shown by the diagrams on page 385.

The measurement of a linear trend will be made, as illustrated previously, by calculating the reduction in the $\sum (y^2)$ achieved by taking account of the linear trend of effect, Y, with increasing rate, X. This process of measurement for the present situation is shown in the diagram and in the calculations below. The equally spaced rates are coded as $X = 0$ (for 1 ppm), 1 (for 3 ppm), and 2 (for 5 ppm) by subtracting 1 and dividing by 2. It is assumed that there are k trials at each rate. The following algebra follows precisely the procedures used in Chapter 6 for linear regression analyses.

Rate, X	Effect, Y	
0	Y_{01}	$\sum (X^2) = 5k$ $\sum (XY) = 1 \sum (Y_1\text{'s}) + 2 \sum (Y_2\text{'s})$
.	.	$(\sum X)^2/3k = 3k$ $\qquad\qquad = 1S_1 + 2S_2$
.	.	$\overline{}$
.	.	$\sum (x^2) = 2k$
0	Y_{0k}	$\dfrac{(\sum X)(\sum Y)}{n} = 3k(S_0 + S_1 + S_2)/3k$
Sum: $\overline{0}$	S_0	Hence $\sum (xy) = -1S_0 + 0S_1 + 1S_2.$
1	Y_{11}	Therefore, the reduction in $\sum (y^2)$ assignable to linear
.	.	trend with X is obtained as usual by
.	.	
.	.	$[\sum (xy)]^2/\sum (x^2) = \dfrac{(-1S_0 + 1S_2)^2}{2k}$, or is
1	Y_{1k}	
Sum: $\overline{k}$	S_1	$\qquad\qquad\qquad = \dfrac{(-1S_0 + 1S_2)^2}{k[(-1)^2 + (+1)^2]}$
2	Y_{21}	The reduction attributable to linear trend of Y on X
.	.	can be denoted by the coefficients $-1, 0, +1$, with the
.	.	same understanding noted before.
2	Y_{2k}	
Sum: $\overline{2k}$	S_2	

The Sum of Squares for the three mercurial treatments has 2 DF, one of which is for the linear trend just discussed. The remaining Sum of Squares with its 1 DF measures the additional reduction in $\sum (y^2)$ achieved by using a quadratic trend line after doing all that could be done with a linear trend line. The corresponding Sum of Squares is obtained by subtracting the reduction for linear trend from the Total Sum of Squares for the mercurial treatments, as follows:

$$\text{Total Mercurial Ss} = \frac{S_0^2 + S_1^2 + S_2^2}{k} - \frac{(S_0 + S_1 + S_2)^2}{3k}$$

$$\text{Linear Ss} = \frac{S_0^2 - 2S_0S_2 + S_2^2}{2k}, \qquad \text{as just derived}$$

Hence,

Added quadratic reduction

$$= \frac{1}{6k} (6S_0^2 + 6S_1^2 + 6S_2^2 - 2S_0^2 - 2S_1^2 - 2S_2^2 - 4S_0S_1 - 4S_0S_2$$
$$- 4S_1S_2 - 3S_0^2 + 6S_0S_2 - 3S_2^2)$$

$$= \frac{1}{6k} (1S_0 - 2S_1 + 1S_2)^2$$

Again, the denominator, $6k$, can be written as $k[(+1)^2 + (-2)^2 + (+1)^2]$. This is the Sum of Squares for the additional reduction in $\sum (y^2)$ achieved by using a quadratic curve after fitting the linear trend line.

Three of the four degrees of freedom for the five seed treatments now have been accounted for. The remaining one is for the comparison of the organic and mercurial compounds. There are $2k$ organic samples and $3k$ mercurial samples. The F testing procedure for comparing them is as follows:

$$Ss = \frac{(S_1 + S_2)^2}{2k} + \frac{(S_3 + S_4 + S_5)^2}{3k}$$
$$- \frac{(S_1 + \cdots + S_5)^2}{5k}$$
$$= \frac{1}{30} (15S_1^2 + 30S_1S_2 + 15S_2^2 + \cdots$$
$$- 12S_4S_5)$$
$$= (3S_1 + 3S_2 - 2S_3 - 2S_4 - 2S_5)^2/30k;$$

or

$$= \frac{(3S_1 + 3S_2 - 2S_3 - 2S_4 - 2S_5)^2}{k[(+3)^2 + (+3)^2 + (-2)^2}$$
$$+ (-2)^2 + (-2)^2],$$

with 1 DF

This is the form previously used for the Sums of Squares for the individual comparisons.

The whole set of orthogonal individual comparisons just discussed for the seed treatments can be represented concisely as in Table 9.81, which will be called a plus-minus diagram, for obvious reasons. This scheme also provides an easy guide to the necessary arithmetic computations.

Each individual Sum of Squares (which also is a Mean Square) in Table 9.81 would be tested against the proper Error Mean Square. For example, with an RCB design with fixed effects the analysis would be as shown in Table 9.82.

It is seen from this table that instead of the 10 possible pairwise Treatment comparisons, which could have been made by some multiple-comparison procedure, four specific comparisons are made, and these correspond in some sense to the number of independent comparisons suggested by the four degrees of freedom for Treatments. Furthermore, there is an exact F

TABLE 9.81. SCHEMATIC REPRESENTATION OF A SET OF ORTHOGONAL
COMPARISONS INVOLVING TWO ORGANIC AND THREE MERCURIAL
SEED TREATMENTS AT THE RATES 1, 3, AND 5 PARTS PER MILLION
FOR THE MERCURIALS, k SAMPLES ASSUMED PER TREATMENT

Comparison	Treatment					Sum of Squares	DF
	O_1	O_2	M_1	M_2	M_3		
(Sum)	(S_1)	(S_2)	(S_3)	(S_4)	(S_5)		
Organic$_1$ vs. Organic$_2$	-1	$+1$	0	0	0	$(-S_1 + S_2)^2/2k$	1
Linear Mercurial	0	0	-1	0	$+1$	$(-S_3 + S_5)^2/2k$	1
Quadratic Mercurial	0	0	$+1$	-2	$+1$	$(S_3 - 2S_4 + S_5)^2/6k$	1
Organic vs. Mercurial	$+3$	$+3$	-2	-2	-2	$(3S_1 + 3S_2 - 2S_3 - 2S_4 - 2S_5)^2/30k$	1

test appropriate to each such comparison. With any of the multiple-comparison methods introduced herein, the true probability of a Type I error often was unknown, so, if a set of orthogonal comparisons exist which also fits the purposes of a given study, they should be used in preference to any other multiple-comparisons procedure.

The orthogonality of a proposed set of $t - 1$ comparisons can be tested by performing the following two arithmetic computations:

(a) See whether the sum of the numbers in each row of the plus-minus diagram is zero.

(b) See whether the sum of the products of the corresponding row elements of every pair of rows is zero. For example, in the illustration above,

$$(-1)(0) + (+1)(0) + (0)(-1) + (0)(0) + (0)(+1) = 0$$

$$(-1)(0) + (+1)(0) + (0)(+1) + (0)(-2) + (0)(+1) = 0, \quad \text{etc.}$$

It can be stated categorically that, if any Treatment or combination of Treatments is used in exactly the same form more than once, the set will not be orthogonal. In general, however, one just applies the above-described tests.

TABLE 9.82. ANALYSIS OF VARIANCE FOR RANDOMIZED COMPLETE
BLOCK DESIGN WITH TREATMENTS ANALYZED AS IN TABLE 9.81

Source of variation	DF	Sample Mean Square
O_1 versus O_2	1	$(1S_1 - 1S_2)^2/2k$
Linear M effect	1	$(-1S_3 + 1S_5)^2/2k$
Quadratic M effect	1	$(1S_3 - 2S_4 + 1S_5)^2/6k$
O's versus M's	1	$(+3S_1 + 3S_2 - 2S_3 - 2S_4 - 2S_5)^2/30k$
Blocks	$r - 1$	usual
Error	$4(r - 1)$	usual
Total about $x \ldots$:	$5r - 1$	none

If a logical set of orthogonal comparisons does not suggest itself, one can use a nonorthogonal set with $t - 1$ DF or one of the multiple-comparison procedures available in the literature. It also should be pointed out that there is more than one possible orthogonal set for each given experimental situation. Which set, if any, is used will depend upon the purposes of the experiment.

As long as the X measurements are equally spaced along their scale of measurement, the methods just illustrated can be extended to other experimental situations of this same sort. In fact, there are tables of the coefficients, such as $-1, 0, +1$, for many standard situations in which regression analyses are appropriate, for example, the Fisher-Yates tables cited earlier.

If the X measurements are unequally spaced, the *linear effect* of increasing X can be measured by means of coefficients obtained in the following manner. Suppose the X's can be coded to become 0, 1, 2, 4, and 8. The mean of these numbers is 3. The required coefficients, which describe the proper procedure, are obtained from $0 - 3$, $1 - 3$, $2 - 3$, $4 - 3$, and $8 - 3$, or $-3, -2, -1, +1, +5$. These numbers would be used precisely as previously illustrated; that is

Linear Ss and Ms

$$= (-3S_1 - 2S_2 - 1S_3 + 1S_4 + 5S_5)^2/k(9 + 4 + 1 + 1 + 25), \quad \text{or}$$

$$= (-3S_1 - 2S_2 - 1S_3 + 1S_4 + 5S_5)^2/40k$$

If the mean of the coded number is not an interger, one proceeds as follows. Let $X = 0, 1, 3, 5,$ and 9, whose mean is 18/5. The required coefficients are obtained from $0(5) - 18$, $1(5) - 18$, $3(5) - 18$, $5(5) - 18$, and $9(5) - 18$, or $-18, -13, -3, +7, +27$.

If one wishes to study nonlinear trends, one does the following:

(*a*) If the X's are equally spaced, use the coefficients given in the Fisher-Yates table or some other source.

(*b*) If the X's are unequally spaced, use the above-described procedure for the linear effect, and consult D. Robson's article in *Biometrics* 15: 187, 1959, which gives a general procedure for nonlinear effects.

One very useful application of orthogonal comparisons is found in certain factorial experiments, in which two or three factors, say A, B, and C, each at two or more levels are combined in all possible ways. It may be that one wishes to study individual main effects and their interactions, and it may be that these main effects can be studied best in terms of trends with an equally spaced X measurement. To illustrate, consider the following fertilizer experiment involving three levels of each of the two elements, nitrogen and phosphorus, as follows:

N: 0, 100, and 200 pounds per acre

P: 0, 20, and 40 pounds per acre

The nine combinations are 0N, 0P; 0N, 20P; 0N, 40P; 100N, 0P; 100N, 20P; 100N, 40P; 200N, 0P; 200N, 20P; and 200N, 40P. These nine Treatments may be designated 0, 0; 0, 1; 0, 2; 1, 0; 1, 1; 1, 2; 2, 0; 2, 1; and 2, 2; respectively. There will be 8 DF for Treatments, so the plus-minus diagram will have eight rows, each describing a study of an effect of interest. These are displayed in Table 9.83.

TABLE 9.83.   AN ORTHOGONAL SET OF EIGHT COMPARISONS FOR A FACTORIAL (3 × 3) EXPERIMENT IN WHICH THREE LEVELS OF N ARE COMBINED WITH THREE LEVELS OF P

Comparison	Treatment								
	0, 0	0, 1	0, 2	1, 0	1, 1	1, 2	2, 0	2, 1	2, 2
(Sum)	(S_1)	(S_2)	(S_3)	(S_4)	(S_5)	(S_6)	(S_7)	(S_8)	(S_9)
Linear N, N_L	−1	−1	−1	0	0	0	+1	+1	+1
Quadratic N, N_Q	+1	+1	+1	−2	−2	−2	+1	+1	+1
Linear P, P_L	−1	0	+1	−1	0	+1	−1	0	+1
Quadratic P, P_Q	+1	−2	+1	+1	−2	+1	+1	−2	+1
$N_L \times P_L$	+1	0	−1	0	0	0	−1	0	+1
$N_L \times P_Q$	−1	+2	−1	0	0	0	+1	−2	+1
$N_Q \times P_L$	−1	0	+1	+2	0	−2	−1	0	+1
$N_Q \times P_Q$	+1	−2	+1	−2	+4	−2	+1	−2	+1

The interaction coefficients are obtained formally by multiplying together the corresponding coefficients of the main effects involved. For example, the following coefficients appear in Table 9.83 for the linear nitrogen effect and the linear phosphorus effect:

$$N_L: \quad -1 \quad -1 \quad -1 \quad 0 \quad 0 \quad 0 \quad +1 \quad +1 \quad +1$$
$$P_L: \quad -1 \quad 0 \quad +1 \quad -1 \quad 0 \quad +1 \quad -1 \quad 0 \quad +1$$

Therefore, by simple multiplication vertically one obtains for the $N_L \times P_L$ interaction:

$$N_L \times P_L: \quad +1 \quad 0 \quad -1 \quad 0 \quad 0 \quad 0 \quad -1 \quad 0 \quad +1$$

It is noted that all rows of numbers add to zero. All sums of products of corresponding row coefficients also are zero, because these are orthogonal comparisons.

As illustrated earlier, the coefficients in each row of a plus-minus diagram, such as Table 9.83, serve as guides to the computation of the Sum of Squares computations for the individual comparisons. The divisor is obtained as described earlier. To illustrate, $N_L \times P_L$ Ss = $(S_1 - S_3 - S_7 + S_9)^2/20$, where the $20 = 5[(+1)^2 + (-1)^2 + (-1)^2 + (+1)^2]$, assuming 5 samples of each of the nine nitrogen-phosphorus combinations. If the $N_L \times P_L$ Sum of Squares (which also is the Mean Square) is found to be statistically significant at a designated α level when compared with a proper error term, this result indicates that the linear response (of whatever is measured) to a uniform increase in the nitrogen level changes linearly as the phosphorus level is increased uniformly. This concept is illustrated in the diagrams. Thus, successive 20-pound increases in the phosphorus level

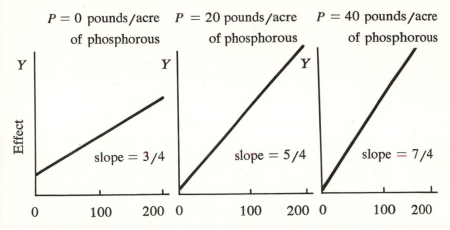

caused the rate of increase in Y per 100 pounds of nitrogen to change from 3/4 to 5/4 to 7/4, a linear change.

A different sort of $N_L \times P_L$ interaction is exhibited by the next diagrams. In this hypothetical experimental situation adding phosphorus in 20-pound increments first eliminated the beneficial linear effects of adding nitrogen and then (at the 40-pound level of phosphorus) caused the added nitrogen to be

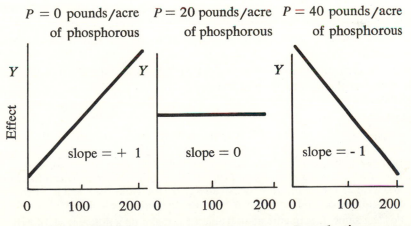

linearly harmful. Thus the slope of the *Y–N* line went from $+1$ to 0 to -1. This still is a linear change in the N_L effect, and therefore is an $N_L \times P_L$ effect, but this is somewhat different from the $N_L \times P_L$ illustrated by the previous example.

To exhibit an $N_L \times P_Q$ interaction, the change in the linear response to added nitrogen must be made to change quadratically. For example, consider the next diagrams. It now is observed that the decrease in the linear trend of

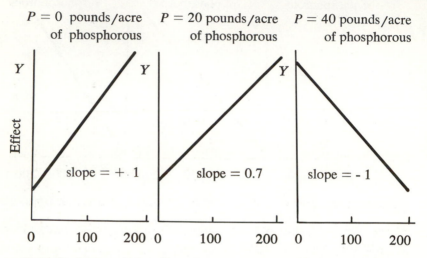

Y with increasing nitrogen as the amount of phosphorus is increased uniformly from 0 to 20 to 40 pounds/acre is a *nonuniform* decrease with respect to Y, namely a decrease from $+1$ to $+0.7$ (a change of -0.3) to -1.0 (a change of -1.7). This certainly is not a linear change. With only three levels of phosphorus we necessarily describe it as quadratic, even though with more levels of phosphorus it really might be the start of some other mathematical change.

In practice it often is very helpful to draw such sketches as these, to help interpret the results of an experiment.

PROBLEMS

1. Suppose that the Treatment sums for Table 9.81 were $S_1 = 200$, $S_2 = 250$, $S_3 = 290$, $S_4 = 270$, and $S_5 = 310$, with $k = 6$. If the Error Mean Square is 20.0 with 25 DF, compute each Mean Square for Table 9.81, test it for statistical significance, and interpret the results for the entire study.

2. For the same Treatments as in Table 9.81, make up a different set of orthogonal comparisons, and demonstrate their orthogonality.

3. If the coded X measurements are -1, 4, 7, and 9, what are the coefficients needed to calculate the Sum of Squares for the linear effect of increasing X uniformly?

4. Refer to the Robson reference given earlier and calculate the Sum of Squares for the quadratic effect of increasing X uniformly under the conditions of Problem 3.

5. Make up a plus-minus diagram for an orthogonal set of comparisons for a factorial experiment with factor A at three levels (equally spaced), factor B at two levels, and factor C at two levels.

6. Given the following data on the 3×3 factorial fertilizer experiment considered earlier, compute the Sum of Squares for $N_L \times P_L$, and interpret it with $\alpha = 0.05$. With $\alpha = 0.10$.

Treatment:	00	01	02	10	11	12	20	21	22
Sum:	30	25	25	45	60	70	70	85	105

Do the same, given also that $k = 4$ and the Error Ms $= 17$ with 24 DF.

7. Given the following data on an experiment in which three levels of nitrogen, 0, 50, and 100 pounds/acre are combined with two levels of potash (K), 20 and 40 pounds/acre,

Treatment:	01	02	11	12	21	22
Sum:	18.1	20.2	43.2	50.8	31.0	36.2

compute the $N_L \times K$ interaction Sum of Squares. Also draw a sketch of the nitrogen effect.

8. Make a complete plus-minus diagram for Problem 7 for a set of orthogonal Treatment comparisons.

9. Suppose the nitrogen rates of Problem 7 had been 0, 60, and 100 pounds/acre. Compute the Mean Square for the linear effect of nitrogen with the data given in Problem 7.

10. Suppose that an experiment designed to study the amount of storage of a certain toxicant in white rat livers involved the rates 1, 2, 3, 4, 5, and 6 parts per million. Suppose also that rats at the three initial ages of 16, 24, and 32 days are to be used. Make up a set of hypothetical data for which the $R_L \times A_Q$ interaction should be significant.

REVIEW PROBLEMS

1. Given the following data for a hypothetical experiment in which Treatments are considered fixed effects and the other sources of variation random effects, do a complete analysis of variance, including all valid F tests, all useful multiple comparisons, and their interpretations. Do not write out the mathematical model.

| | Treatment: | | | | | | | | |
Variety	T_1 Spacing S_1	S_2	T_2 Spacing S_1	S_2	T_3 Spacing S_1	S_2	T_4 Spacing S_1	S_2	Variety sum
V_1	5	8	5	6	9	3	10	12	
	3	11	9	12	7	5	11	9	
	7	5	7	9	5	4	15	12	
V Sum:	15	24	21	27	21	12	36	33	
V-T Sum:	39		48		33		69		189
V_2	10	8	12	6	12	11	9	11	
	5	7	14	11	7	12	6	8	
	6	12	10	7	5	7	12	8	
V Sum:	21	27	36	24	24	30	27	27	
V-T Sum:	48		60		54		54		216
V_3	13	9	8	14	20	12	7	9	
	10	12	9	8	11	9	11	12	
	7	12	13	11	14	9	6	6	
V. Sum:	30	33	30	33	45	30	24	27	
V-T Sum:	63		63		75		51		252
Tr. Sum:	150		171		162		174		657 Grand sum

2. Write down the mathematical model in full for Problem 1 and also the expected Mean Squares.

3. Estimate the Variety variance component, σ_V^2 for Problem 1, and then estimate its variance.

4. Compute the Samples Within-Treatment, Variety, and Spacing Sums of Squares directly from deviations from means.

5. Given the following data from a hierarchical experiment, do a complete analysis of variance:

A_1:			A_2:			A_3:		
B_{11}	B_{12}	B_{13}	B_{21}	B_{22}	B_{23}	B_{31}	B_{32}	B_{33}
5	7	3	10	8	5	4	-1	6
-2	3	-1	7	3	11	2	8	0
6	2	7	4	7	8	6	8	6
9	12	9	21	18	24	12	15	12

6. Write out the expected Mean Squares for Problem 5, and justify therefrom the proper F test for $H_0(\sigma_\beta^2 = 0)$ versus $H_a(\sigma_\beta^2 > 0)$.

7. Write down the simplest expression possible for the sampling distribution of the A effects sample Mean Square for Problem 5.

8. Omit the following data from Problem 5 and then do as in Table 9.36 for the remaining experiment: B_{13} completely, B_{31} completely, the 6 under B_{11}, the 4 under B_{21}, and the two 6's under B_{33}.

9. Referring to Problem 8, determine whether an exact F test exists for testing $H_0(\sigma_A^2 = 0)$. Explain your answer.

10. Make up your own problem with Sources of Variation as in Problem 1, but one which will display a significant ($\alpha = 0.10$) Treatment × Variety × Spacing interaction.

11. Given the following data from a hypothetical experiment on seed Treatments along the same pattern as that used earlier for illustration, make up the specific plus-minus diagram for these data, do the analysis of variance completely, and interpret the individual comparisons graphically in the light of the analysis of variance.

O_1	O_2	M_0	M_1	M_2		
37	55	48	56	50		
53	60	44	50	38	Total SS = 91,384	
46	53	43	58	35		
41	49	42	63	45	Treatment SS = 721,700	
50	42	32	48	46		
38	44	36	60	53		
48	48	40	46	46		
47	49	45	59	47		
360	400	330	440	360	1890	
45	50	41.25	55	45		

12. Suppose that 100 Paiute Indians are in a ravine. Twenty-eight are braves, twenty are squaws, and the rest are children. A rock falls from a cliff and kills one Indian. What is the probability that a brave was killed? That a child was not killed? That, if the victim was not a child, it was a squaw?

13. Given that a sample of size $n = 20$ is going to be taken from a binomial population, what region of rejection would you use to test $H_0(p = 0.30)$ against $H_a(p = 0.60)$? Against $H_a(p > 0.30)$? Why?

14. Suppose that an experiment is to involve four methods of production to be tried in a sample of 5 localities. Ten of the products are to be measured appropriately from each method at each location. Write down the statistical model for this experiment. Then write out as specifically as possible the formula for the Methods Mean Square.

15. Referring to Problem 14, write down the mathematical description of the sampling Mean Square for Localities.

16. Suppose that a person is throwing darts at a target which has (1) a small bull's eye marked "10," (2) a ring around the bull's eye marked "5," (3) a second ring outside the first ring marked "3," and (4) an outer ring marked "1." Suppose the probabilities of hitting these four areas are as follows: (a) bull's eye, $p_1 = 1/20$; (b) first ring, $p_2 = 1/8$; (c) second ring, $p_3 = 1/4$; (d) outer ring, $p_4 = 1/5$. Thus, the probability of missing the target is 3/8. What is the probability that on three independent throws the sum of the scores will be exactly 10?

17. Derive the expected Locations Mean Square for Problem 14. What is the distribution of the sample Locations Mean Square?

18. Referring to Problem 16, what is the probability of a total score of *at least* 5?

19. Draw a random sample of size $n = 25$ from Table 6.11 and compute the CI_{90} on ρ. On β, assuming the X's fixed. Is $H_0(\rho = 0)$ acceptable over $H_a(\rho \neq 0)$? What about $H_0(\rho = 0.50)$ versus $H_a(\rho > 0.50)$? Use $\alpha = 0.05$.

20. Given the following two random samples from populations π_1 and π_2, use Klotz's Normal Scores Test to decide whether the dispersions of the populations are probably different:

    X_1:   10.7, 3.1, -8.7, 4.0, 0.9, 6.7, 15.2, -1.9, 5.3, 6.4, 4.2, and 2.7

    X_2:   22.5, 10.9, 38.8, 19.4, 20.2, 29.7, 50.6, 26.6, 25.7, 32.0, 40.9,

    and 32.9

21. Do Problem 20 by Mood's Square-Root Test.

22. Assume Normality as needed, and do Problem 20 by the F ratio test.

23. Use the data of Problem 20 to test $H_0[(\mu_1 = \mu_2) \mid (\sigma_1^2 = \sigma_2^2)]$ against $H_a[(\mu_1 > \mu_2) \mid (\sigma_1^2 = \sigma_2^2)]$. Use $\alpha = 0.10$.

Chapter 10

Simple Analysis of Covariance

10.1 INTRODUCTION

In some types of experimental research it is interesting and useful to take two (or more) numerical measurements, X_i and Y_i, on each experimental unit, even though the measurement of major interest in the study is the Y_i. It is recalled from earlier discussion that, if it is appropriate to assume that the jth measurement made when $X = X_i$ is representable by

$$(10.11) \qquad Y_{ij} = \alpha + \beta x_i + \epsilon_{ij}$$

then the fraction $(\sum xy)^2/\sum (x^2)$ of the $\sum (y^2)$ can be said to be accounted for in terms of the linear trend of Y with increasing X. Under these circumstances, it is useful to write the estimated average Y when $X = X_i$ as

$$(10.12) \qquad \hat{Y}_{ij} = \hat{Y}_i = \bar{y} + bx_i$$

where $b = \sum (xy)/\sum (x^2)$. Thus, $\hat{Y}_i$ is an estimate of μ_{yx_i}, the true average Y for all $X = X_i$. Moreover, it has been shown that we may write $\sum (Y_i - \hat{Y}_i)^2 = \sum (y^2) - (\sum xy)^2/\sum (x^2)$ and may say that by taking account of the linear relationship between X and Y we can reduce the apparent variability among the Y's, as measured by $\sum (y^2)$, by the fraction $(\sum xy)^2/\sum (x^2)$. From this point of view, we are attempting to increase the precision of a study of the Y measurement by showing that some of its previously unexplained variability is associated with the variation of a concomitant measurement X.

397

Another way to approach this matter is to adjust the Y's for their corresponding X measurements and thereafter analyze the adjusted Y's. But how should one adjust Y's for their corresponding X's? And how should one allow for the fact that any possible adjustment depends on sampling estimates of all parameters involved? If the Y_i and the X_i truly are linearly related, we are entitled to say that, if an X_2 is k units larger than an X_1, we expect (on the average) Y_2 to be kb units larger than Y_1 if b is positive and to be kb units smaller than Y_1 if the regression coefficient, b, is negative, so that Y tends to decrease as X increases. In view of this feature of any linear trend, the adjustment of Y's for different X's is made by subtracting (so as to equalize) from the observed Y_{ij} the quantity bx_i. Symbolically, the adjusted Y_{ij} is computed from the following equation:

(10.13) $$\text{Adjusted } Y_{ij} = Y_{a_{ij}} = Y_{ij} - bx_i$$

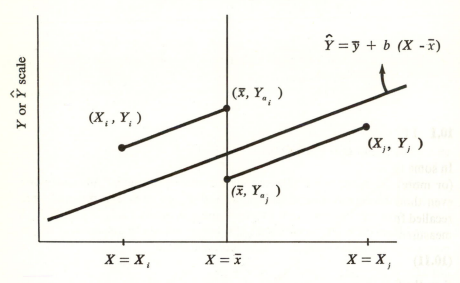

Figure 10.11. Illustration of the concept of an adjusted Y when the X's are not subject to sampling error and there is a linear relationship between X and Y. The Y_{a_i} and Y_{a_j} are directly comparable, having the same $X = \bar{x}$.

Graphically, one is doing as shown in Figure 10.11 and is bringing all observed points to the vertical line $X = \bar{x}$ along lines parallel to line of Equation 10.12, because this "eliminates" X from additional consideration. It is borne in mind, however, that the $Y_{a_{ij}}$ depend on the estimate, b, which is a random variable.

When observed Y's have been adjusted for their concomitant X measurements, they then have the *same* X, namely $X = \bar{x}$. This adjustment process reduces the original two-variable problem to an analysis of variance on the adjusted Y's, but it must be remembered that these adjustments were made by means of a sampling estimate of the linear relationship between X and Y. Hence, the analysis of covariance can be described as an analysis of variance performed on the adjusted Y's *with due allowance for sampling error in these adjustments*. The need to take proper account of the sampling error in the b of the $Y_{a_{ij}} = Y_{ij} - bx_i$ makes an analysis of covariance considerably more complex than an analysis of variance for the same set of Y's alone, even though the mathematical model has but one additional, and simple, term.

PROBLEMS

1. Given the following pairs of (X, Y) observations, compute the adjusted values, $Y_{a_{ij}}$:

X:	1.2	1.8	3.2	4.7	5.4	6.5
Y:	-2.3	0.6	3.9	9.0	9.8	14.2

2. Given the scatter diagram and the least-squares regression line $\hat{Y}_i = \bar{y} + bx_i$, adjust the Y's linearly for X by geometric operations, and record the approximate $Y_{a_{ij}}$ so obtained.

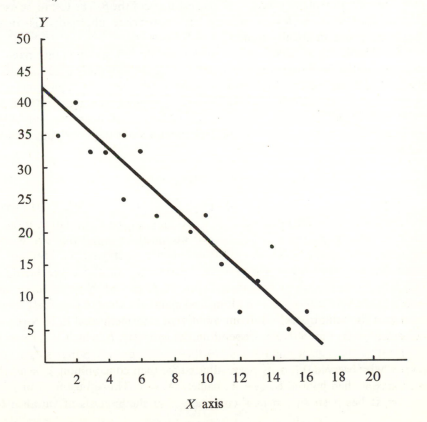

3. Make a scatter diagram for the data of Problem 1, draw in what appears to be the best fitting straight line, and geometrically determine the adjusted Y's.

10.2 SOME MATHEMATICAL CONSIDERATIONS AND POINTS OF VIEW

If one is planning a completely randomized (CR) experimental design involving t Treatments and r observations per Treatment, there is the initial matter of the homogeneity of the regression relationships between the X measurement and the Y measurement from Treatment to Treatment. Conceivably, the different Treatments could be associated with different linear relationships between X and Y or with none at all. We shall only consider in some detail those situations in which it is reasonable, perhaps after an appropriate test of significance, to assume that the basic relationship

$$Y_{ij} = \alpha + \beta x_i + \epsilon_{ij}$$

is the same for all t Treatments in a given study. If this is true, the common β for all t Treatments is estimated by combining the information in the samples from the t Treatments to obtain a pooled estimate of the β. The test to be used to test $H_0(\beta_1 = \cdots = \beta_t = \beta)$ against an appropriate alternative is an F test developed heuristically somewhat as follows.

(*a*) The least possible sum of squares of deviations of points from a linear trend line is obtained if the Method of Least Squares is used to obtain the line, and the least possible pooled Sum of Squares for t Treatments will be obtained if the Method of Least Squares is applied separately to the data from each Treatment, the resulting $\sum_i \sum_j (Y_{ij} - \hat{Y}_i)^2$ being pooled. This procedure does not assume that all Treatment β's are the same, but it does assume that

$$\sigma^2_{y_1 \cdot x_1} = \cdots = \sigma^2_{y_t \cdot x_t} = \sigma^2_{y \cdot x}$$

(*b*) If $H_0[(\beta_1 = \cdots = \beta_t = \beta) \mid (\sigma^2_{y_1 \cdot x_1} = \cdots = \sigma^2_{y_t \cdot x_t} = \sigma^2_{y \cdot x})]$ is   true, we can obtain a better estimate of β by pooling all the information in all t samples. Moreover, the $\sum \sum (Y_{ij} - \hat{Y}_i)^2$ obtained by using this *one b* will be quite close to the $\sum \sum (Y_{ij} - \hat{Y}_i)^2$ obtained by applying the Method of Least Squares separately within each Treatment. On the other hand, if $H_0[(\beta_1 = \beta_2 = \cdots = \beta_t = \beta) \mid (\sigma^2_{y_1 \cdot x_1} = \cdots = \sigma^2_{y_t \cdot x_t} = \sigma^2_{y \cdot x})]$ is, in fact, *untrue*, then the $\sum \sum (Y_{ij} - \hat{Y}_i)^2$ obtained by using *one b* will be quite different from that Sum of Squares obtained by applying the Method of Least Squares separately within each Treatment and pooling the $\sum \sum (Y_{ij} - \hat{Y}_i)^2$ for $i = 1,$ $\cdots, t$. It is through a comparison of these two Sums of Squares that one judges whether $H_0[(\beta_1 = \beta_2 = \cdots = \beta_t = \beta) \mid (\sigma^2_{y_1 \cdot x_2} = \cdots = \sigma^2_{y_t \cdot x_t} = \sigma^2_{y \cdot x})]$ is an acceptable hypothesis.

(*c*) It has been shown mathematically that the analysis of variance of

Table 10.21 does, in fact, test $H_0[(\beta_1 = \cdots = \beta_t = \beta) \mid (\sigma^2_{y_1 \cdot x_1} = \cdots = \sigma^2_{y_t \cdot x_t} = \sigma^2_{y \cdot x})]$ against the alternative that *some* β's are unequal. As can be seen, it is necessary to assume homogeneity of variance about the regression lines within Treatments, even though the β's might be unequal. Table 10.21 outlines the procedure in a general way.

TABLE 10.21.   TEST OF $H_0[(\beta_1 = \cdots = \beta_t = \beta) \mid (\text{EQUAL } \sigma^2_{y \cdot x})]$
VERSUS ITS NEGATION

Source of variation	DF	Sum of Squares	Mean Square
About pooled one-*b* regression lines within Treatments	$tr - t - 1$	S_1	
About individual Least-Squares regression lines within Treatments	$t(r - 2)$	S_2	M_2
Difference for testing homogeneity of *b*'s	$t - 1$	$S_1 - S_2$	M_3

$F[(t - 1), t(r - 2)] = M_3/M_2$ tests $H_0[(\beta_1 = \cdots = \beta_t) \mid (\sigma^2_{y \cdot x})\text{'s equal})]$.

The pooled Error *b* needed to obtain the S_1 Sum of Squares in Table 10.21 is computed from the following formula:

(10.21)   Error $b = b_E = (\text{pooled } \sum xy)/(\text{pooled } \sum x^2)$

Furthermore, the S_1 Sum of Squares itself can be shown to be computable from

(10.22) $S_1 = \text{pooled } \sum (y^2) - (\text{pooled } \sum xy)^2/(\text{pooled } \sum x^2)$

for the following reasons:

(a) For a given Treatment, $\hat{Y}_{ij} = \bar{y}_i + b(X_i - \bar{x}_i)_1$, where b is from Equation 10.21, and

$$\sum_j (Y_{ij} - \hat{Y}_i)^2 = \sum_j (y_{ij} - b_{xi})^2 = \sum_j y^2_{ij} - 2b \sum_j (x^2_{ij} y_{ij}) + b^2 \sum_j x^2_{ij}$$

(b) Pooled $\sum_j (Y_{ij} - \hat{Y}_{ij})^2 = \text{pooled } \sum_j y^2_{ij} - 2b\left[\text{pooled } \sum_j (x_{ij} y_{ij})\right]$

$$+ b^2\left[\text{pooled } \sum_j (x^2_{ij})\right]$$

$$= \text{pooled } \sum_j (y^2_{ij}) - \frac{(\text{pooled } \sum_j x_{ij} y_{ij})^2}{\text{pooled } \sum_j (x^2_{ij})},$$

as stated.
The S_2 Sum of Squares is simply:

(10.23) $S_2 = [\sum (y^2_1) - (\sum x_1 y_1)^2/(\sum x^2_1)] + \cdots + [\sum (y^2_t)$
$$- (\sum x_t y_t)^2/(\sum x^2_t)]$$

The discussion in this section is illustrated in Tables 10.22 and 10.23 and Figure 10.21.

TABLE 10.22. HYPOTHETICAL DATA ON STUDENTS' ACE SCORES AND
THEIR GRADES IN AN EXAMINATION GIVEN THREE CLASSES TAUGHT
BY THREE DIFFERENT TEACHERS COVERING THE SAME
MATERIAL AND GIVING THE SAME
EXAMINATION

	Teacher 1		Teacher 2		Teacher 3	
	X (ACE)	Y (Grade)	X (ACE)	Y (Grade)	X (ACE)	Y (Grade)
	70	72	90	70	115	76
	72	76	93	73	110	73
	75	72	95	68	118	72
	76	76	96	76	122	82
	80	82	97	78	125	78
	81	76	102	72	125	87
	85	80	105	76	130	85
	88	78	108	86	133	88
	91	86	110	80	135	82
	92	86	115	82	119	81
	98	86	117	85	140	88
	100	90	120	90	140	92
Sum:	1,008	960	1,248	936	1,512	984
Mean:	84	80	104	78	126	82
$\sum X^2$:	85,764		130,906		191,558	
$\sum x^2$:	1,092		1,114		1,046	
$\sum Y^2$:	77,192		73,518		81,128	
$\sum y^2$:	392		510		440	
$\sum XY$:	81,234		97,998		124,558	
$\sum xy$:	594		654		574	
	$68.89 = \sum y_1^2$		$126.05 = \sum y_2^2$		$125.01 = \sum y_3^2$	
	$-\dfrac{(\sum x_1 y_1)^2}{\sum (x_1^2)}$		$-\dfrac{(\sum x_2 y_2)^2}{\sum (x_2^2)}$		$-\dfrac{(\sum x_3 y_3)^2}{\sum (x_3^2)}$	
b_i:	0.5440		0.5871		0.5488	

TABLE 10.23. TEST OF $H_0[(\beta_1 = \beta_2 = \beta_3 = \beta) \mid (\sigma_{y_i x_i}^2$ ARE EQUAL FOR ALL $i)]$
VERSUS H_a(SOME β'S ARE UNEQUAL) FOR
DATA IN TABLE 10.22

Source of variation	DF	Sum of Squares	Mean Square
About error regression lines within Teacher, using *one b* namely b_E	32	321.19	
About Least-Squares regression lines within Teacher, using three Least-Squares *b*'s	30	319.95	10.665
Difference for testing homogeneity of Least-Squares *b*'s	2	1.24	0.620

$F(2, 30) = 0.620/10.665$ is less than $F(2, 30)$ at 5% level; therefore, accept H_0.

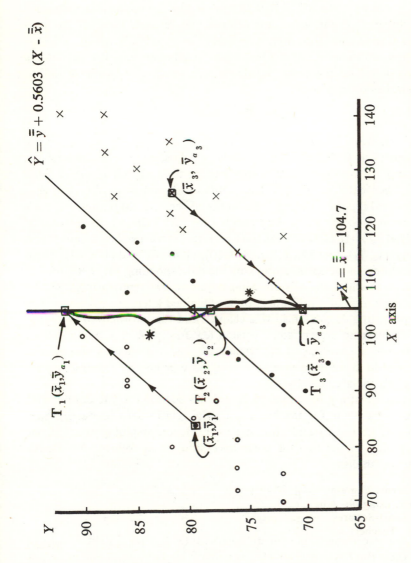

Figure 10.21. Adjusted data from Table 10.22, equalized at $X = \bar{\bar{x}} = 104.7$. $\circ$ = student under Teacher 1 (T_1), $\bullet$ = student under Teacher 2 (T_2), $\times$ = student under Teacher 3 (T_3), $\boxdot$ = mean point for class, and $\triangle$ = grand mean point.

The following calculations are relevant to Table 10.22:
pooled $\sum (x^2) = 3252$,   pooled $\sum (y^2) = 1342$, and pooled $\sum (xy) = 1822$. Hence, the pooled Sum of Squares from the regression lines within each teacher but with slope b_E is $1342 - (1822)^2/3252 = 321.19$, with 32 DF.

The pooled Sum of Squares about the three least-squares regression lines is $68.89 + 126.05 + 125.01 = 319.95$ and is the minimum possible such Sum of Squares. From these calculations one obtains Table 10.23. It is concluded from Table 10.23 that $b_1 = 0.5440$, $b_2 = 0.5871$, and $b_3 = 0.5488$ (the sampling estimates of the β_i for the three teachers) are, in fact, estimating the same population regression coefficient, β; hence, it is proper to adjust all Y's (grades) by means of

(10.24) $$Y_{a_i} = Y_{ij} - b_E x_i$$

where $b_E = $ (pooled $\sum xy$)/(pooled $\sum x^2$) and the $x_i = X_i - \bar{x}$, where $\bar{x}$ is the grand mean X of this study. The process of adjusting Y's for their X's is shown graphically in Figure 10.21 along with the final position of the adjusted Y's on the vertical line, $X = \bar{x}$. The points on $X = \bar{x}$ were obtained, geometrically speaking, by "sliding" the points of the original scatter diagrams on lines parallel to the Error Regression Line, until these lines intersected $X = \bar{x}$. The b_E is $1822/3252 = 0.5603$ and the three teacher mean points are $(\bar{x}_1, \bar{y}_1)$, $(\bar{x}_2, \bar{y}_2)$, and $(\bar{x}_3, \bar{y}_3)$, or $(84, 80)$, $(104, 78)$, and $(126, 82)$. These points are shown in the figure along with the corresponding Error Regression Line, relative to which the Y's are being adjusted. The figure also shows the results of some tests of significance, to be explained later.

The preceding discussion in this chapter and the information in Figure 10.21 are designed to present some general features, problems, and points of view relative to the analysis of covariance. As with the analysis of variance, it is beneficial to make these points of view more precise by stating a mathematical model for a given study.

The teacher study of Table 10.21 was based upon a CR design with allowance to be made for teacher effects, the relationship between grades (Y) and ACE scores (X), and sampling error. Hence, assuming fixed teacher effects, a logical model for this covariance study is as follows, for the jth student in the ith class:

(10.25) $$Y_{ij} = \mu + \tau_i + \beta(X_i - \mu_x) + \epsilon_{ij}$$

where:

$\mu = $ the true mean grade for all conceivable students taught by any of these three specific teachers, and involving the subject and examinations involved in this study

$\tau_i = $ the fixed effect of Teacher i on grades in this subject *after due allowance for the students' ACE* (American Council on Education) *scores*

β = the true regression of Y on X within teachers and for the situation studied in this experiment

μ_x = the true mean ACE score for all students represented by this study

ϵ_{ij} = NID$(0, \sigma^2_{y \cdot x})$ variates for all i, j combinations.

It is helpful to a better understanding of the points of view in an analysis of covariance to rewrite Model 10.25 in two alternative forms. In the form

$$(10.26) \qquad\qquad Y_{ij} - \tau_i = \mu + \beta(X_i - \mu_x) + \epsilon_{ij}$$

it is seen that teacher effects have been removed from the Y's (linearly), before a linear regression relationship is defined; therefore, the β is the regression coefficient between X and Y *internal* to the classes. This is the Error type of regression, as noted earlier. In the form

$$(10.27) \qquad\qquad Y_{ij} - \beta(X_i - \mu_x) = \mu + \tau_i + \epsilon_{ij}$$

the left-hand side of this equation is seen to be an adjusted Y, while the right-hand side is the usual model for a CR experimental design and the subsequent analysis of variance. Thus, Form 10.27 reëmphasizes a previous statement, that an analysis of covariance is basically an analysis of variance performed upon the adjusted Y's. It also is noted again that the τ_i refer to teacher effects *after adjustment for ACE scores*.

PROBLEMS

1. Given the following practice data, make a scatter diagram for each Treatment and judge by eye whether or not $H_0[(\beta_1 = \beta_2 = \cdots = \beta_5 = \beta) \mid$ (equal $\sigma^2_{y_i \cdot x}$)] is acceptable, so that a covariance analysis is in order:

Treatment:

1		2		3		4		5	
X	Y	X	Y	X	Y	X	Y	X	Y
1.1	13	7.0	11	3.8	18	0.6	11	4.8	23
3.6	5	4.2	21	5.6	7	3.8	3	5.8	20
0.9	12	5.9	19	4.1	14	1.3	10	9.6	13
2.4	8	3.3	26	4.7	12	1.7	5	3.9	28
1.7	9	6.5	15	5.0	8	2.2	8	7.2	17
2.2	7	5.4	19	4.3	16	2.5	3	6.1	19

2. Use the data in Problem 1 to compute the least-squares $\sum (Y_i - \hat{Y}_i)^2$ for each Treatment separately, and test for homogeneity of variance around the regression lines; that is, test $H_0(\sigma^2_{y_1 \cdot x_1} = \cdots = \sigma^2_{y_5 \cdot x_5} = \sigma^2_{y \cdot x})$ against its negation, using $\alpha = 0.10$.

3. Use the data in Problem 1 to test $H_0[(\beta_1 = \cdots = \beta_5 = \beta)] \mid$ (equal $\sigma^2_{y_i \cdot x_i})]$ versus its negation, with $\alpha = 0.10$.

4. Write down the specific model for an analysis of covariance for Problem 1 three different ways, and state all assumptions clearly.

5. Make a graph similar to Figure 10.21 for Problem 1.

6. Make up an example with four Treatments and eight measurements per Treatment, such that $H_0[(\beta_1 = \cdots = \beta_4 = \beta) \mid (\text{equal } \sigma^2_{y_i \cdot x_i})]$ is *not* acceptable with $\alpha = 0.10$.

7. Make up an example as in Problem 6 but such that $H_0(\sigma^2_{y_1 \cdot x_1} = \cdots = \sigma^2_{y_4 \cdot x_4} = \sigma^2_{y \cdot x})$ is not acceptable.

8. Make the scatter diagrams for Table 10.22, and therefrom verify the adjusted means in Figure 10.21.

10.3 THE ANALYSIS OF COVARIANCE TABLE

The mathematical justification of the computational procedures used in even the simplest analysis of covariance is beyond the mathematical level of this discussion; hence, only the method itself will be shown, plus some heuristic justification of certain procedures and the interpretations of the types of results obtained. This will be done specifically for the teacher study being used for illustration of the meaning of the analysis of covariance and then more generally for an RCB experimental design. Table 10.31 summarizes the analysis of covariance for the data of Table 10.22.

TABLE 10.31. ANALYSIS OF COVARIANCE FOR TABLE 10.22 DERIVED
FROM A HYPOTHETICAL COMPLETELY RANDOMIZED
EXPERIMENT

Source of variation	DF	$\Sigma(x^2)$	$\Sigma(xy)$	$\Sigma(y^2)$	$\Sigma(y^2) - \dfrac{(\Sigma xy)^2}{\Sigma x^2}$	DF	Mean Squares	
							Sample	Expected
Teachers	2	10,592	528	96				
Error (students)	33	3,252	1,822	1,342	321.19	32	10.04	$\sigma^2_{y \cdot x}$
Total	35	13,844	2,350	1,438				
Teachers + Error	35	13,844	2,350	1,438	1,039.09	34		
Difference for testing adjusted Teachers Mean Square:					719.90	2	359.95	$\sigma^2_{y \cdot x} + \dfrac{12}{2} \Sigma \tau_i^2$

The line designated "Teachers + Error" in Table 10.31 is identical with the line for "Total" in the left-hand part of this table, but this will not be true in more complex analyses of covariance. All that can be said usefully about this line now is that the calculations shown are necessary for a proper account of the sampling error of the b_E used to adjust the Y's for their different X's.

The chief purpose of the analysis of covariance in Table 10.31 is to test for teacher effects on grades after proper adjustment for differences in ACE scores among the students involved in this study. The teacher effects, after linear adjustment for X, are measured by the τ_i in the Models 10.25, 10.26, and 10.27. If the τ_i all are zero, the teachers are considered to be equal in effectiveness. On the H_0(all $\tau_i = 0$), the $F(2, 32) = 359.95/10.04 = 35.85$ $\gg F_{0.05}(2, 32)$; therefore H_0 is rejected and it is concluded that *some* $\tau_i \neq 0$.

To summarize, the following conclusions are supported by the computations in, and below, Table 10.31.

(*a*) Not all τ_i are zero; so, after due allowance is made linearly for the students' ACE scores, some of these teachers are more effective than others as regards the production of high grades on examinations in this subject.

(*b*) The estimate of β is $b_E = 1822/3252 = 0.5603$, and this coefficient is statistically significant, because

$$F(1, 32) = \frac{(1822)^2/3252}{10.04} = \frac{1020.81}{10.04} = 101.69 \gg F_{0.05}(1, 32)$$

so it is believed that there probably is a linear relationship between grades and ACE scores within the same teacher's class among these three teachers.

(*c*) If analyses of variance are computed for X and Y separately, the following $F(2, 33)$'s are obtained: For X alone, $F(2, 33) = 5296/98.55 > F_{0.05}(2, 33)$; therefore, the average ACE scores for the three teachers' classes are definitely from different levels of such scores. For Y alone, $F(2, 33) = 48/40.67 < F_{0.05}(2, 33)$; therefore, the average grades under those three teachers are essentially at the same level, if *differences in level of ACE scores for the three classes are ignored.*

(*d*) The Error Variance of Y before adjustment for the X's is $s_y^2 = 1342/33 = 40.67$, but *after* adjustment for different X's it becomes $s_{y \cdot x}^2 = 10.04$, only one fourth of its unadjusted size. Hence, the analysis of covariance has increased the precision of the test of teacher effects on grades by reducing the amount of sampling variance against which teacher performance must be judged. In some experiments the substantial reduction in Error Variance is the chief gain from using the analysis of covariance instead of an analysis of variance, which ignores the X measurements.

In general it is obvious that the analysis of covariance has uncovered teacher differences which were obscured until the analysis of covariance removed the distorting effects of differences in level of ACE scores among the three classes. Furthermore, the testing was made more precise by reducing the Error Variance to one fourth of its original size when adjustment was made for different X's.

When there are more sources of variation than are recognized with a CR design, the analysis of covariance is more complex. Table 10.32 shows the general analysis for an RCB design. The extra row of computations, "Teacher + Error," was used in Table 10.31 for generality, even though this is just "Total" for a CR design. The more general procedure is illustrated in Table 10.32 for an RCB design with t Treatments, r Blocks, and q samples within each Treatment and Block.

TABLE 10.32.   DIRECTIONS FOR ANALYSIS OF COVARIANCE FOR RANDOMIZED COMPLETE BLOCK DESIGN WITH t FIXED TREATMENTS, r FIXED BLOCKS, AND q SAMPLES PER TREATMENT AND BLOCK

Source of variation	DF	$\sum x^2$	$\sum xy$	$\sum y^2$	$\sum y^2 - (\sum xy)^2/\sum x^2$	DF	Sample Ms	Expected Ms
Treatments	$t-1$	T_{xx}	T_{xy}	T_{yy}	none	—		
Blocks	$r-1$	B_{xx}	B_{xy}	B_{yy}	none	—		
Treatments × Blocks	$(t-1)(r-1)$	TB_{xx}	TB_{xy}	TB_{yy}	none			
Samples (Error)	$tr(q-1)$	S_{xx}	S_{xy}	S_{yy}	$S_{yy} - \dfrac{S_{xy}^2}{S_{xx}} = A$	$tr(q-1)-1$	E Ms	$\sigma_{y\cdot x}^2$
Treatments + Error		$T_{xx}+S_{xx}$	$T_{xy}+S_{xy}$	$T_{yy}+S_{yy}$	$(T_{yy}+S_{yy}) - \dfrac{(T_{xy}+S_{xy})^2}{(T_{xx}+S_{xx})} = B$			
Difference for testing adjusted Treatments $=T_a=B-A$						$t-1$	T_a Ms	$\sigma_{y\cdot x}^2 + \dfrac{r}{t-1}\sum \tau_i^2$

Use Blocks+Error computations and similar calculations for testing adjusted Blocks Ms=B_a Ms. Similar remarks hold for Treatments × Blocks Ms.

The ratio $F[t - 1, \ tr(q - 1) - 1] = T_a \text{ Ms}/E \text{ Ms}$ is used to test H_0(all $\tau_i = 0$) against H_a(some $\tau_i \neq 0$), remembering that the τ_i are the adjusted Treatment constants.

The symbolic analysis of covariance shown in Table 10.32 is illustrated by means of the data in Table 10.33. The fact that the X's are at fixed intervals, some of which are the same for different cells, causes the analysis to be easier and to look different from the general covariance analysis. It does not, however, affect the new procedures being illustrated.

TABLE 10.33.   HYPOTHETICAL DATA CORRESPONDING TO
TABLE 10.32, MIXED MODEL

Blocks (random)	Treatments (Fixed effect)								Block sum	
	1		2		3		4			
	X	Y	X	Y	X	Y	X	Y	X	Y
	2.0	35.0	2.5	35.9	3.0	43.6	3.5	50.3		
	2.5	24.2	3.0	30.0	3.5	31.3	4.0	40.7		
I	3.0	25.7	3.5	33.0	4.0	35.3	4.5	44.5		
	3.5	14.8	4.0	20.3	4.5	23.8	5.0	35.0		
	4.0	8.5	4.5	18.4	5.0	23.0	5.5	28.6		
	15.0	108.2	17.5	137.6	20.0	156.7	22.5	199.1	75	601.6
	2.0	28.8	2.5	40.2	3.0	41.5	3.5	52.8		
	2.5	20.0	3.0	38.7	3.5	40.0	4.0	40.5		
II	3.0	24.5	3.5	28.2	4.0	25.0	4.5	43.3		
	3.5	16.2	4.0	32.0	4.5	27.5	5.0	32.9		
	4.0	10.3	4.5	24.1	5.0	18.6	5.5	25.6		
	15.0	99.8	17.5	163.2	20.0	152.6	22.5	195.1	75	610.7
	2.0	32.5	2.5	41.5	3.0	44.7	3.5	37.9		
	2.5	22.9	3.0	43.1	3.5	46.5	4.0	27.6		
III	3.0	25.0	3.5	30.1	4.0	37.8	4.5	34.5		
	3.5	15.7	4.0	35.2	4.5	39.2	5.0	25.2		
	4.0	7.5	4.5	26.5	5.0	32.0	5.5	19.0		
	15.0	103.6	17.5	176.4	20.0	200.2	22.5	144.2	75	624.4
Treatment sum:	45.0	311.6	52.5	477.2	60.0	509.5	67.5	538.4	225	1836.7

The following calculations come from Table 10.33.

Total $\sum (y^2)$	$= 6249.36$	Total $\sum (xy)$	$= -108.27$
Total $\sum (x^2)$	$= 48.75$	Treatments $\sum (y^2)$	$= 2060.80$
Treatments $\sum (xy)$	$= 178.18$	Treatments $\sum (x^2)$	$= 18.75$
Blocks $\sum (y^2)$	$= 13.07$	Blocks $\sum (xy)$	$= 0$
Blocks $\sum (x^2)$	$= 0$	$T \times B \sum (y^2)$	$= 802.75$
$T \times B \sum (xy)$	$= 0$	$T \times B \sum (x^2)$	$= 0$
Samples $\sum (y^2)$	$= 3372.74$	Samples $\sum (xy)$	$= 286.45$
Samples $\sum (x^2)$	$= 30.00$ by subtraction		

TABLE 10.34. ANALYSIS OF COVARIANCE FOR TABLE 10.33, MIXED MODEL $Y_{tjk} = \mu + \beta(X_{tj} - \mu_{tj.}) + \tau_t + \gamma_j + (\tau\gamma)_{tj} + \epsilon_{tjk}$

Source of variation	DF	$\sum(x^2)$	$\sum(xy)$	$\sum(y^2)$	$\sum(y^2) - \frac{(\sum xy)^2}{\sum x^2}$	DF	Mean observed	Mean Square expected
Treatments (f)	3	18.75	178.18	2,060.80				
Blocks (r)	2	0	0	13.07				
T × B	6	0	0	802.75				
Samples	48	30.00	−286.45	3,372.74	637.62	47	13.57	$\sigma_{y\cdot x}^2$
Total	59	48.75	−108.27	6,249.36				
"Treats + Samples"		48.75	−108.27	5,433.54	5,193.08			
Adjusted Treats. Ss = 5,193.08 − 637.62 = 4,555.46						3	1,518.49	$\sigma_{y\cdot x}^2 + 5\sigma_{\tau\gamma}^2 + 5\sum\tau_t^2$
"Blocks + Samples"		30.00	−286.45	3,385.81	2,568.45			
Adjusted Blocks Ss = 2,568.45 − 637.62 = 1,930.83						2	965.42	$\sigma_{y\cdot x}^2 + 20\sigma_\gamma^2$
"T × B + Samples"		30.00	−286.45	4,175.49	1,607.04			
Adjusted T × B Ss = 1,607.04 − 637.62 = 969.42						6	161.57	$\sigma_{y\cdot x}^2 + 5\sigma_{\tau x}^2$

$F(6, 47) = 161.57/13.57 = 11.91$; therefore, reject $H_0(\sigma_{\tau\gamma}^2 = 0)$. $F(3, 6) = 1518.49/161.57 = 9.40$; therefore, reject $H_0(\text{all } \tau_t = 0)$.

$F(2, 47) = 965.42/13.57 = 71.14$; therefore, reject $H_0(\sigma_\gamma^2 = 0)$.

Therefore the analysis of covariance for Table 10.33 can be completed as follows and is shown in Table 10.34.

Samples $[\sum (y^2) - (\sum xy)^2/\sum (x^2)] = 637.62$ with 47 DF, so the Samples Mean Square on Y after adjustment for X is $s_{y \cdot x}^2 = 13.57$. The Within-Treatment regression coefficient is $b_E = -9.548$, which is significant with $\alpha = 0.05$; therefore, there appears to be a useful linear relationship between X and Y within cells.

PROBLEMS

1. Given the hypothetical data of Problem 1, Section 10.2, assume that pairs of rows of data are Blocks, so that Block 1 includes the first two rows, Block 2 includes the next two rows, and Block 3 includes the last two rows; hence, $q = 2$. Do an analysis of covariance as completely as possible, and draw appropriate conclusions.

2. Given the following hypothetical data, perform an analysis of covariance including separate analyses on X and Y. Assume homogeneity of variance about the regression lines within fertilizer, and also assume homogeneity of regression coefficients.

	Fertilizer 1		Fertilizer 2		Fertilizer 3	
	X	Y	X	Y	X	Y
	210	100	155	65	155	55
	150	50	150	55	160	55
	200	105	170	65	165	65
	180	75	175	75	185	70
	190	80	185	75	185	80
	220	110	195	90	200	85
	170	60	205	85	205	90
	170	70	210	100	215	105
	190	90	215	95	220	105
	220	100	220	100	220	100
Sum:	1900	840	1880	805	1910	810
Mean:	190	84.0	188	80.5	191	81.0
$\sum (x^2)$:	4800		5510		5540	
$\sum (y^2)$:		3690		2272.5		3340
$\sum(xy)$:	4000		3435		4215	
b:		0.8333		0.6234		0.7608
$\dfrac{(\sum xy)^2}{\sum (x^2)}$:	3333.33		2141.42		3206.90	

3. Test $H_0(\beta_1 = \beta_2 = \beta_3 = \beta)$ against H_a(some β's are unequal) by means of the data of Problem 2. Use $\alpha = 0.10$, and draw appropriate conclusions.

4. Test $H_0(\sigma_{y_1 \cdot x_1}^2 = \sigma_{y_2 \cdot x_2}^2 = \sigma_{y_3 \cdot x_3}^2 = \sigma_{y \cdot x}^2)$ against its negation by means of the data of Problem 2. Use $\alpha = 0.10$, and draw appropriate conclusions.

5. Make a scatter diagram for fertilizer 2 in Problem 2, and draw in a free-hand linear regression line which seems to fit the points of the scatter diagram best. Then show graphically what the Method of Least Squares does. Also estimate $\sum (Y_i - \hat{Y}_i)^2$ from your graph.

6. What information is contained in the following computations from the lines for "Treatments (f)" and "Total" in Table 10.34:
   (a) $178.18/18.75 = 9.50$
   (b) $2,060.80 - (178.18)^2/18.75 = 367.57$
   (c) $(-108.27)/48.75 = -2.20$
   (d) $6,249.36 - (-108.27)^2/48.75 = 6008.90$?

7. What is the sampling distribution of the Adjusted Treatments Mean Square for experiments like that summarized in Table 10.34?

8. Write down the statistical model and the Expected Mean Squares for an experiment with a random sample of eight type A Treatments, a fixed set of four type B Treatments, and three random observations within each of the 32 A-B combinations.

10.4 MULTIPLE COMPARISONS FOLLOWING AN ANALYSIS OF COVARIANCE

The same general problems arise here as for an analysis of variance, but their solutions are more complicated. If but two Treatments are involved, one can make a t test and know what the probability of a Type I error is, but often, if there are more than two Treatment means to compare, the multiple-t type of testing may be subject to an excessive Type I error rate. However, if the protection of a prior F test is used, by means of an analysis of covariance, much can be learned with, as this author believes, little additional risk of Type I error and a near-maximum power of avoiding Type II error.

An adjusted Treatment mean, $\bar{y}_{a_i}$, can be calculated from

(10.41) $$\bar{y}_{a_i} = \bar{y}_i - b_E(\bar{x}_i - \bar{x})$$

where b_E is the Error regression coefficient from the analysis of covariance. From Equation 10.41 the difference between two adjusted Treatment means, $\bar{y}_{a_i}$ and $\bar{y}_{a_j}$, is

(10.42) $$\bar{d}_{a_{ij}} = (\bar{y}_i - \bar{y}_j) - b_E(\bar{x}_i - \bar{x}_j)$$

Assume homogeneity of variance about the trend lines for the Treatments i and j, as was assumed in the performance of an analysis of covariance. If it is logical also to assume that the sample means are independent and that the X's are not subject to sampling error, one can calculate

(10.43) $$s_{\bar{d}_a}^2 = s_{y \cdot x}^2 \left[2/r + \frac{(\bar{x}_i - \bar{x}_j)^2}{E_{xx}} \right]$$

where E_{xx} is the Error $\sum (x^2)$. Furthermore, it can be shown that

$$(10.44) \qquad \frac{\bar{d}_{a_{ij}} - (\mu_{a_i} - \mu_{a_j})}{s_{\bar{d}_a}} = t, \qquad \text{with the Error DF}$$

Note that $s_{\bar{d}_a}^2$ is not calculated from $s_{\bar{y}_{a_i}}^2 + s_{\bar{y}_{a_j}}^2$ because the $\bar{y}_{a_i}$ and $\bar{y}_{a_j}$ are not independent.

To illustrate the preceding discussion, reference is made to Table 10.31, which produced a significant F test of the Teacher Mean Square after a linear adjustment of the students' grades for their ACE scores. The following pertinent information was obtained:

(a) The $b_E = 1822/3252 = 0.5603$
(b) $\bar{x}_1 = 84$, $\bar{x}_2 = 104$, $\bar{x}_3 = 126$, and $\bar{\bar{x}} = 104.67$
(c) $\bar{y}_1 = 80$, $\bar{y}_2 = 78$, and $\bar{y}_3 = 82$
(d) $s_{y \cdot x}^2 = 10.04 = $ adjusted Error Variance with 32 DF
(e) $r = 12$ observations per Teacher
(f) Error $\sum (x^2) = 3252 = E_{xx}$

It is found from Equations 10.41 and 10.42 that

$$\bar{y}_{a_1} = 80 - 0.5603(-20.67) = 91.58$$
$$\bar{y}_{a_2} = 78 - 0.5603(-0.67) = 78.38$$
$$\bar{y}_{a_3} = 82 - 0.5603(+21.33) = 70.05$$

Hence,

$$\bar{d}_{a_{12}} = 13.20, \qquad \bar{d}_{a_{13}} = 21.53, \qquad \bar{d}_{a_{23}} = 8.33$$

The standard deviations of the differences between adjusted $\bar{y}$'s are computed as

$$s_{\bar{d}_{a_{12}}} = 10.04(2/12 + 400/3252) = 1.705$$
$$s_{\bar{d}_{a_{13}}} = 10.04(2/12 + 1768/3252) = 2.668$$
$$s_{\bar{d}_{a_{23}}} = 10.04(2/12 + 484/3252) = 1.780$$

Hence, the following t tests result: $t_1 = 7.75$, $t_2 = 8.07$, and $t_3 = 4.68$, each with 32 DF. Each of the hypotheses $H_0(\mu_{1a} = \mu_{2a})$, $H_0(\mu_{1a} = \mu_{3a})$, and $H_0(\mu_{2a} = \mu_{3a})$ is rejected with $\alpha = 0.05$, and the respective negations are accepted. In general, it is concluded that $\mu_{3a} < \mu_{2a} < \mu_{1a}$ or that Teacher 1 is the most effective, Teacher 2 next most effective, and Teacher 3 the poorest, as measured by grades, and after due allowance is made for the ACE scores of their students. These conclusions are shown in Figure 10.21 by the adjusted mean points T_1, T_2, and T_3.

PROBLEMS

1. Given the following data from a hypothetical RCB design, perform an analysis of covariance and draw all appropriate conclusions.

Treatments:

Block	A		B		C		Block sums	
	X	Y	X	Y	X	Y	X	Y
I	2	8	20	30	14	20	36	58
II	17	27	12	21	9	16	38	64
III	4	12	21	36	26	34	51	82
IV	19	27	19	30	18	27	56	84
V	14	22	26	41	23	27	63	90
VI	10	18	14	23	16	25	40	66
VII	16	22	11	22	22	28	49	72
VIII	8	13	9	22	28	30	45	65
IX	20	26	7	18	15	19	42	63
X	13	23	25	36	24	32	62	91
Treatment Sums:	123	198	164	279	195	258	482	735

2. Make the three scatter diagrams appropriate to Problem 1, and decide by eye whether the $X - Y$ relations are likely to be linear and whether the relationship between X and Y is likely to be the same (ignoring level) for all three Treatments.

3. Using the samples of Problem 1, test $H_0(\sigma^2_{y_1 \cdot x_1} = \sigma^2_{y_2 \cdot x_2} = \sigma^2_{y_3 \cdot x_3} = \sigma^2_{y \cdot x})$.

4. Compute for Problem 1 the magnitudes of $\bar{y}_{a_2}$ and $s_{\bar{y}_{a_2}}$.

5. Using the data of Problem 1, test $H_0(\beta_1 = \beta_2 = \beta_3 = \beta)$, ignoring the Block designation so the design becomes a CR design.

6. Compute a CI_{90} on $(\mu_{1_a} - \mu_{2_a})$ for Problem 1, and interpret this interval.

7. Write down the mathematical model for the experiment visualized in Problem 1. Fully define all symbols used.

10.5 SUPPLYING MISSING DATA BY MEANS OF THE ANALYSIS OF COVARIANCE

In the previous discussion of this subject in Chapter 9, the following was stated.

(*a*) If *m* measurements originally planned to be taken in an experiment are unobtainable or are lost, they should be estimated in such a way that the Error Sum of Squares is minimized. This was done in Chapter 9, to obtain formulas for missing data.

(*b*) When missing data are supplied under the minimizing procedure for a CR or an RCB design (the only ones considered herein), the Treatment Sum of Squares will tend to be larger than, or equal to, the Sum of Squares that would have been obtained if no data had been lost. Therefore, a correction for bias needs to be subtracted from the Treatment Sum of Squares when missing data have been supplied by the above-described procedure.

The use of a formula for a missing measurement has been illustrated in Chapter 9, but no correction for bias was introduced there, because it was more efficient to perform the whole operation by means of an analysis of covariance, especially when only one number was missing. Irma Coons

(*Biometrics* 13: 387–405, 1957) has called attention to the following procedures, originally suggested in part by M. S. Bartlett (*J. Roy. Stat. Soc.,* Suppl., 4: 137–70, 1937) and R. L. Anderson (*Biometrics* 2: 41–47, 1946):

(*a*) If the measurements of interest are called Y's, let $Y = 0$ where the number is missing.

(*b*) Introduce a concomitant variable $X = -n$ corresponding to $Y = 0$, and put 0's elsewhere for the X's (the n is the total number of numbers, including the 0 for Y).

(*c*) Perform an analysis of covariance.

The analysis of covariance automatically will produce an *un*biassed test of the Treatments Mean Square. Moreover, nb_E is the best estimate of the missing Y, in the sense of minimizing the Error Variance.

TABLE 10.51.   TABLE 9.51 WRITTEN AS A COVARIANCE PROBLEM
(THE Y IN C-II WAS MISSING)

Block	Treatment								Block sum	
	A		B		C		D			
	X	Y	X	Y	X	Y	X	Y	X	Y
I	0	13	0	3	0	17	0	7	0	40
II	0	10	0	5	$-12 = -n$	0	0	5	-12	20
III	0	17	0	12	0	13	0	13	0	55
Treatment sum:	0	40	0	20	-12	30	0	25	-12	115

Consider Table 10.51, which is just Table 9.51 written as a covariance problem. It is found from this table that:

$$\begin{aligned}
\text{Total} \sum (x^2) &= 144 - 144/12 = 132 \\
\text{Total} \sum (y^2) &= 1437 - (115)^2/12 = 334.9167 \\
\text{Total} \sum (xy) &= 0 - (115)(-12)/12 = 115 \\
\text{Treatments} \sum (x^2) &= 144/3 - 144/12 = 36 \\
\text{Treatments} \sum (y^2) &= 72.9167 \\
\text{Treatments} \sum (xy) &= -360/3 - (-115) = -5 \\
\text{Blocks} \sum (x^2) &= 144/4 - 12 = 24 \\
\text{Blocks} \sum (y^2) &= 154.1667 \\
\text{Blocks} \sum (xy) &= -240/4 - (-115) = 55
\end{aligned}$$

Using these computations, one obtains the analysis of covariance shown in Table 10.52, which gives the correct test of the Treatments Mean Square after its having been adjusted for bias during the same process of covariance analysis.

It can be determined from Table 10.52 that $b_E = 65/72 = 0.9028$ and that $nb_E = 12(0.9028) = 10.83$, the value computed earlier for the missing X in Table 9.51. Although no correction for bias was used in Table 9.51,

TABLE 10.52. ANALYSIS OF VARIANCE AFTER CORRECTION FOR A MISSING NUMBER IN TABLE 9.51

Source of variation	DF	$\Sigma (x^2)$	$\Sigma (xy)$	$\Sigma (y^2)$	$\Sigma (y^2) - \dfrac{(\Sigma xy)^2}{\Sigma (x^2)}$	DF	Mean Square
Treatment	3	36	−5	72.9167			
Blocks	2	24	55	154.1667			
Error	6	72	65	107.8333	49.1527	5	9.8309
Total	11	132	115	334.9167			
Treatments + Error	9	108	60	180.7500	147.4166	8	
Difference for testing adjusted Treatment MS:					98.2639	3	32.754

$F(3, 5) = 32.754/9.8309 = 3.33 < F_{0.05}(3, 5)$; therefore,
$$H_0[(\mu_1 = \cdots = \mu_4) \mid (\sigma_1^2 = \cdots = \sigma_4^2)]$$
is accepted instead of its negation.

it can be shown that the Mean Square for Treatments in Table 10.52 is precisely the same as would have been obtained had the recommended correction for bias (see Snedecor, 5th edition, p. 310, for example) been subtracted during an analysis of variance on the data of Table 9.51. Thus, the analysis of covariance has been shown to be useful in the analysis of experiments which have one planned number missing. Only the RCB design has been illustrated herein, but Coons has shown that the method is much more widely applicable than this.

When an analysis of covariance is being used to supply a missing value for an experiment and to make correction for the resulting bias in the Treatment Mean Square, some authors suggest letting X equal either $+1$ or -1, whereas Coons suggests using $-n$ for that X. This will result in the Error b's being the negative of the missing value and it will not be necessary to multiply by n. If the Coons $-n$ is used, the $\Sigma (x^2)$'s are directly computable from $n(\mathrm{DF})$. Thus,

$$\text{Treatments } \Sigma (x^2) = 12(3) = 36$$
$$\text{Blocks } \Sigma (x^2) \qquad = 12(2) = 24$$
$$\text{Error } \Sigma (x^2) \qquad = 12(6) = 72$$
$$\text{Total } \Sigma (x^2) \qquad = 12(11) = 132$$

as shown in Table 10.52. If -1 had been used in Table 10.51 in place of the -12, the X Sums of Squares would have been as follows:

$$\text{Treatments } \Sigma (x^2) = 3/12 = 0.2500$$
$$\text{Blocks } \Sigma (x^2) \qquad = 2/12 = 0.1667$$
$$\text{Error } \Sigma (x^2) \qquad = 6/12 = 0.5000$$
$$\text{Total } \Sigma (x^2) \qquad = 11/12 = 0.9167$$

In general, these $\Sigma (x^2)$'s are just $(\mathrm{DF})/n$, so they still are easily computed. If one considers the decimals thus produced in the covariance analysis, it may be thought easier to follow Coons' suggestion.

If more than one Y is missing, the covariance analysis becomes more complex, as does the procedure illustrated in Chapter 9. It now is necessary to employ what is called multiple covariance analysis. The process shown in Chapter 9 also would need to be extended to include the calculation of a correction for bias when several numbers are missing after an experiment has been finished. This process also would be much more complex. The basic principles are the same, so the reader is referred to previous references for the actual procedures used.

REVIEW PROBLEMS

1. Perform an analysis of covariance on the following data to determine the missing measurement and to correct the Treatment Sum of Squares for bias:

Treatment:

	1		2		3		4		Block sum	
Block	X	Y	X	Y	X	Y	X	Y	X	Y
1	0	30	0	36	0	24	0	28	0	118
2	0	15	0	18	0	12	0	20	0	65
3	0	27	−24	0	0	20	0	30	−24	77
4	0	15	0	13	0	10	0	11	0	49
5	0	23	0	27	0	18	0	25	0	93
6	0	22	0	24	0	18	0	24	0	88
Tr. sum:	0	132	−24	118	0	102	0	138	−24	490

2. Do Problem 1, using −1 in place of the −24 shown for one X.

3. Write down the model for Problem 1, and discuss the probable validity of the assumptions required in an analysis of covariance.

4. Given the following coded data on breaking loads of concrete beams at 7 days of curing and the maximum air temperature in the field where the beams where being made, test for Slump effect. Y = Breaking Load and X = temperature.

Level of slump:

Low		Medium		High	
X	Y	X	Y	X	Y
6	165	6	83	20	250
19	60	16	127	11	220
11	203	11	318	16	200
11	187	16	190	19	213
11	287	0	180	23	140
23	287	13	220	15	203
15	173	13	238	9	185
9	185			0	232
5	202				
21	93				

5. Test specifically $H_0(\beta_N = \beta_M = \beta_H = \beta)$ with the data of Problem 4. Use $\alpha = 0.10$ and the alternative hypothesis that some of the β's are unequal.

6. For the data of Problem 4 test $H_0(\mu_{a_L} = \mu_{a_H})$ against $H_a(\mu_{a_L} < \mu_{a_H})$ by a t test and with $\alpha = 0.05$. Draw appropriate conclusions.

7. Given the following data on Breaking Loads (Y) and level of Water-Cement ratio, test for the effect of Water-Cement ratio on Breaking Load after adjustment for different X's.

Water-Cement ratio:

Low		Medium		High	
X	Y	X	Y	X	Y
20	250	11	187	6	83
6	165	11	287	11	220
16	200	23	287	16	127
11	203	15	173	19	60
11	318	9	185	19	213
15	203	9	185	16	190
0	180	13	220	23	140
0	232			13	238
5	202				
21	93				

The X has the same meaning as in Problem 4; that is, it is a temperature measurement.

8. Discuss specifically the usefulness of covariance analysis in Problem 7 as compared with the simpler analysis of variance, ignoring temperature.

9. In an attempt to learn about temperature effects on the time, Y, required for sorghum to mature, a variable X, the total degree-hours below 60° F. during the whole growing season, was studied with six varieties, planted in triplicate at each of three locations in Kansas. The following data were obtained on X and Y.

Variety:

	1		2		3		4		5		6	
Location	X	Y	X	Y	X	Y	X	Y	X	Y	X	Y
I	582	55	596	65	596	68	596	72	596	66	582	59
	454	55	454	62	454	64	475	70	454	61	454	57
	46	48	187	58	210	62	258	73	187	58	46	51
II	320	51	320	62	320	66	320	72	320	61	320	56
	299	53	299	62	299	66	339	78	299	60	299	57
	178	51	192	59	201	65	234	79	192	62	192	56
III	257	59	279	74	279	79	279	79	279	70	279	65
	267	57	304	81	313	82	313	90	267	71	267	63
	237	61	313	76	313	78	488	92	313	76	267	60

Make a within-variety scatter diagram over all locations and decide whether linear covariance analysis seems justified.

10. Perform an analysis of covariance on the data of Problem 9, to test H_0 (all $\tau_i = 0$) against its negation, where τ_i refers to a fixed variety effect in the usual model. Draw appropriate conclusions.

11. What is the expected Location Mean Square for Problem 9, assuming Locations and Varieties are fixed sets rather than random samples? Write an expression for the sampling distribution of the observed Locations Mean Square.

12. Is there a significant correlation between X and Y from variety to variety in Problem 9 when these are considered over all three locations? Use $\alpha = 0.10$.

13. Suppose that an experiment involving one type of measurement, X, has been conducted under two different conditions with the following results:

Condition 1	Condition 2
$\bar{x}_1 = 43.1$	$\bar{x}_2 = 40.2$
$s_1^2 = 7.40$	$s_2^2 = 5.07$
$n_1 = 16$	$n_2 = 21$

Test $H_0(\mu_1 = \mu_2)$ against $H_a(\mu_1 > \mu_2)$ with $\alpha = 0.10$, and draw appropriate conclusions. Test $H_0(\mu_1 \leq \mu_2)$ against $H_a(\mu_1 > \mu_2)$, and comment.

14. Suppose there are 10 fleas on a rope leading from a ship to the shore, and three are carrying bubonic plague. If three fleas jump on a rat going along the rope to the shore, what is the probability that at least one bubonic-plague-carrying flea is on shore?

15. Referring to Problem 13, test $H_0(\mu_1 - \mu_2 = 2)$ against $H_a(\mu_1 - \mu_2 > 2)$ when $\alpha = 0.10$.

16. Make up hypothetical data to which it would be logical and valid to apply Klotz's Normal Scores Test. Use this test on your data and draw appropriate conclusions.

17. Apply a range analysis of variance to the X data of Problem 9, with $\alpha = 0.05$, and draw appropriate conclusions.

Chapter 11

Multiple Linear Regression and Correlation Analysis

11.1 INTRODUCTION

Experimental situations in which it is desirable to take two numerical measurements, X_i and Y_i, on the ith experimental unit already have been studied in Chapter 6 under the heading "Linear Regression and Correlation." This sort of regression and correlation will be called *simple*, in contrast to the *multiple* type of the present chapter.

In Chapter 6 it was assumed that the jth Y measurement taken when $X = X_i$ could be expressed mathematically as:

(11.11) $$Y_{ij} = \alpha + \beta(X_i - \mu_x) + \epsilon_{ij}$$

where $\alpha = $ a constant, $\mu_x = $ the mean of the specific X's involved in the study, $\beta = $ the slope of the population regression line $\mu_{Y_i} = \alpha + \beta(X_i - \mu_x)$, and the ϵ_{ij} are assumed to be NID$(0, \sigma^2_{y \cdot x})$ variates. These concepts are shown graphically in Figure 11.11.

When the coefficients of

(11.12) $$\mu_{Y_i} = \alpha + \beta(X_i - \mu_x)$$

were estimated from sampling data by the Method of Least Squares, it was found that the a and b in the corresponding sample equation,

(11.13) $$\hat{Y} = a + b(X - \bar{x})$$

are computed from $a = \bar{y}$ and $b = \sum (xy)/\sum (x^2)$.

The logical extension of the two-variable situation is to assume that Y is linearly related to two or more X's or $X_1, \cdots, X_s$, in the regression sense and to assume that, in general,

(11.14) $Y = \alpha + \beta_1(X_1 - \mu_1) + \cdots + \beta_s(X_s - \mu_s) + \epsilon$

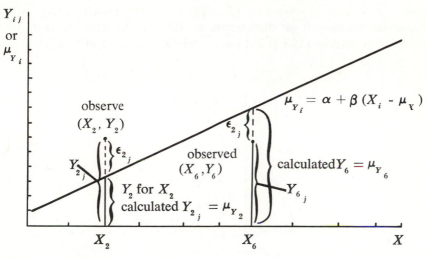

Figure 11.11. Illustration of meaning of Formula 11.11 when population regression line is known.

If there are but two X's, Formula 11.14 becomes the more specific formula

(11.15) $Y_{ijk} = \alpha + \beta_1(X_{1i} - \mu_1) + \beta_2(X_{2j} - \mu_2) + \epsilon_{ijk}$

for the kth Y measurement taken with the (X_i, X_j) combination of the two X's, where:

α = a constant
β_1 = the slope of the regression *plane* in the X_1 direction
β_2 = the slope of the regression *plane* in the X_2 direction
ϵ_{ijk} = the amount by which the point $(X_{1i}, X_{2j}, Y_{ijk})$ is above ($+$) or below ($-$) the regression plane

(11.16) $\mu_{Y_{ij}} = \mu_{Y_i} = \alpha + \beta_1(X_{1i} - \mu_1) + \beta_2(X_{2j} - \mu_2)$

Figure 11.12 shows these concepts for a particular case.

As usual, the equation for, and location of, the true regression plane are unknown; hence, the equation for the μ_{Y_i} of Formula 11.16 is estimated from the equation

(11.17) $\hat{Y}_i = a + b_1(X_{1i} - \bar{x}_1) + b_2(X_{2j} - \bar{x}_2)$

by applying the Method of Least Squares. Given a set of fixed X_1's and X_2's, in combination, it is necessary to estimate the α, β_1, and β_2 by means of the a, b_1, and b_2 in such a way that the variance of the sample points about the sample plane, Equation 11.17, is minimized.

It is convenient to use but one summation sign, $\sum$, to indicate summation over all sets of observations (X_{1i}, X_{2i}, Y_i) rather than to carry multiple symbols throughout all discussions, so this will be done. It also is convenient to assume there is but one sample Y measurement for each (X_1, X_2) combination.

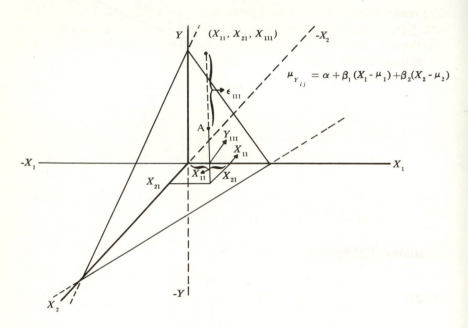

Figure 11.12.   Illustration of Formulas 11.15 and 11.16. The point A is on the regression plane.

11.2 DETERMINATION OF THE LEAST-SQUARES MULTIPLE REGRESSION PLANE WHEN AN X_1 AND AN X_2 ARE ASSOCIATED WITH EACH Y

If but two X measurements are associated with Y, the least-squares principle requires that the a, b_1, and b_2 in Equation 11.17 be so chosen that the quantity

(11.21) $$U = \sum_{\text{all samples}} (Y_k - \hat{Y}_k)^2 = \sum (Y_k - a - b_1 x_{1k} - b_2 x_{2k})^2$$

be minimized, where $x_{1k} = X_{1k} - \bar{x}_1$ and similarly for x_{2k}, as usual. By calculus (which, however, is not assumed herein to be known to the student) it is found that the following linear simultaneous equations need to be solved for a, b_1, and b_2, in order that $\sum (Y_k - \hat{Y}_k)^2$ may be minimized:

(11.22)
$$\begin{cases} a = \bar{y} \\ b_1 \sum (x_1^2) + b_2 \sum (x_1 x_2) = \sum (x_1 y) \\ b_1 \sum (x_1 x_2) + b_2 \sum (x_2^2) = \sum (x_2 y) \end{cases}$$

The reader is reminded that the quantities $\bar{y}$, $\sum (x_1^2)$, $\sum (x_1 x_2)$, $\sum (x_2^2)$, $\sum (x_1 y)$, and $\sum (x_2 y)$ are computable constants obtained from a set of sampling data; it is the a, b_1, and b_2 which are unknown. For example, consider the following set of hypothetical data:

X_1	X_2	Y	
1	21	14	$\sum (x_1^2) = 52$
5	15	20	$\sum (x_2^2) = 214$
3	13	10	$\sum (x_1 x_2) = -33$
0	4	16	$\sum (x_1 y) = 117$
8	5	33	$\sum (x_2 y) = -151$
7	8	27	
Σ: 24	66	120	
Mean: 4	11	20	

Equations 11.22 become

(11.23)
$$\begin{cases} a = 20 \\ 52b_1 - 33b_2 = 117 \\ -33b_1 + 214b_2 = -151 \end{cases}$$

The solution for a is immediate, namely $a = 20$. The solutions for b_1 and b_2 require the solution of a set of simultaneous linear equations by whatever one of several available procedures one prefers. One convenient procedure for this simplest situation of multiple regression is to use determinants and obtain

$$b_1 = \frac{\begin{vmatrix} 117 & -33 \\ -151 & 214 \end{vmatrix}}{\begin{vmatrix} 52 & -33 \\ -33 & 214 \end{vmatrix}} = \frac{(117)(214) - (-151)(-33)}{(52)(214) - (-33)^2} = 1.998$$

$$b_2 = \frac{\begin{vmatrix} 52 & 117 \\ -33 & -151 \end{vmatrix}}{\text{(same)}} = \frac{-3,991}{10,039} = -0.398$$

Therefore, the sample estimate of the equation of the multiple linear regression *plane* becomes

(11.24)
$$\hat{Y} = 20 + 1.998(X_1 - 4) - 0.398(X_2 - 11)$$
$$= 1.998X_1 - 0.398X_2 + 16.4$$

If $X_1 = 0$ and $X_2 = 4$, as was true for one set of the sample data, then

$$\hat{Y} = 1.998(0) - 0.398(4) + 16.4$$
$$= 14.8$$

as compared with the $Y = 16$ observed when $X_1 = 0$ and $X_2 = 4$. This *estimated average* Y for $X_1 = 0$ and $X_2 = 4$ is 1.2 units less than the Y observed when $X_1 = 0$ and $X_2 = 4$, but this is not at all surprising, because observed Y's are subject to sampling error. Although the estimate, $\hat{Y}$, of μ_Y is subject to sampling error, it is based upon all available information in this sample and, hence, should be a more reliable estimate of μ_Y when $X_1 = 0$ and $X_2 = 4$ than is a single observation at these values of X_1 and X_2.

In view of the fact that the $\sum (x_1^2)$, $\sum (x_2^2)$, $\sum (x_1 x_2)$, $\sum (x_1 y)$, $\sum (x_2 y)$, and $\sum (y^2)$, which are generally called the corrected Sums of Squares and products for X_1, X_2, and Y, will have different numbers of significant digits and different decimal places, it often is convenient to transform Equations 11.22 so that they involve only simple linear correlation coefficients and the corresponding regression coefficients. The a always will be $\bar{y}$, so this equation will be disregarded in the following.

Consider the equation $\sum (x_1^2)b_1 + \sum (x_1 x_2)b_2 = \sum (x_1 y)$. We wish deliberately to create in this equation the correlation coefficients $r_{12} = $ the correlation between X_1 and X_2 and the $r_{yi} = $ the correlations between X_i and Y for $i = 1$ and 2. If the coefficient of b_2 were divided by $\sqrt{\sum x_1^2} \cdot \sqrt{\sum x_2^2}$, it would become r_{12}; hence, one divides through the above equation by $\sqrt{\sum x_1^2} \cdot \sqrt{\sum x_2^2}$, as follows:

$$\frac{\sum (x_1^2)}{\sqrt{\sum x_1^2} \sqrt{\sum x_2^2}} b_1 + \frac{\sum (x_1 x_2)}{\sqrt{\sum x_1^2} \sqrt{\sum x_2^2}} b_2 = \frac{\sum (x_1 y)}{\sqrt{\sum x_1^2} \sqrt{\sum x_2^2}}$$

or

$$\sqrt{\frac{\sum x_1^2}{\sum x_2^2}} b_1 + r_{12} \cdot b_2 = r_{y1} \sqrt{\frac{\sum (y^2)}{\sum x_2^2}}$$

or, multiplying through by $\sqrt{\sum x_2^2 / \sum y^2}$, one obtains

(11.25)
$$\sqrt{\frac{\sum x_1^2}{\sum y^2}} b_1 + r_{12} \sqrt{\frac{\sum x_2^2}{\sum y^2}} b_2 = r_{y1}$$

In view of the fact that $\sqrt{\sum x_i^2/(n-1)} = s_i$ and $\sqrt{\sum y^2/(n-1)} = s_y$, Equation 11.25 may be written as $(s_1/s_y)b_1 + r_{12}(s_2/s_y)b_2 = r_{y1}$, if one wishes. Or, if one measures X_1, X_2, and Y in *standard measure about the mean and in units of the standard deviation*, one obtains

(11.26)
$$\begin{cases} 1 \cdot b'_1 + r_{12}b'_2 = r_{y1} \\ r_{12}b'_1 + 1 \cdot b'_2 = r_{y2} \end{cases}$$

as the so-called *normal equations in standard measure*. When all correlations are calculated to the same number of decimals, one obtains the following set of equations for the illustration being used in this section:

(11.27)
$$1b'_1 - 0.31282b'_2 = +0.84351$$
$$-0.31282b'_1 + 1b'_2 = -0.53662$$

If these be solved for b'_1 and b'_2, one obtains $b'_1 = 0.7489$ and $b'_2 = -0.3023$. When these b's are multiplied by $\sqrt{\sum y^2 / \sum x_1^2}$ and $\sqrt{\sum y^2 / \sum x_2^2}$, respectively, one obtains $2.6674(0.7489) = 1.998 = b_1$, as obtained before, and $1.3149(-0.3023) = -0.398 = b_2$ as obtained before, because $\sqrt{\sum x_1^2 / \sum y^2}\, b_1$ was set equal to b'_1 and $\sqrt{\sum x_2^2 / \sum y^2}\, b_2$ was set equal to b'_2 to give these *standard partial regression coefficients*, b'_1 and b'_2.

When but two X's, X_1 and X_2, are associated with Y, the general formulas for b_1 and b_2 are found to be as follows:

(11.28)
$$b_1 = \frac{\sum (x_1 y) \cdot \sum (x_2^2) - \sum (x_1 x_2) \cdot \sum (x_2 y)}{\sum (x_1^2) \cdot \sum (x_2^2) - [\sum x_1 x_2]^2}$$

$$b_2 = \frac{\sum (x_2 y) \cdot \sum (x_1^2) - \sum (x_1 x_2) \cdot \sum (x_1 y)}{\text{(same)}}$$

or, if standard measure and correlations are used, one obtains from Equations 11.26

(11.29)
$$b'_1 = \frac{r_{y1} - r_{y2}r_{12}}{1 - r_{12}^2}, \qquad b'_2 = \frac{r_{y2} - r_{12}r_{y1}}{1 - r_{12}^2}$$

PROBLEMS

1. Use Formulas 11.28 and 11.29 to compute the b_i and b'_i for the illustrative data of Section 11.2.

2. Compute the $\hat{Y}_i$ for the illustrative data of Section 11.2, and show that $\sum \hat{Y}_i = \sum Y_i$, within the accuracy kept.

3. Compute the simple linear correlation between the Y_i and $\hat{Y}_i$ requested in Problem 2. Then compare this correlation with

$$R^2_{y \cdot 12} = \frac{r_{y1}^2 + r_{y2}^2 - 2r_{12}r_{y1}r_{y2}}{1 - r_{12}^2}$$

The $R_{y \cdot 12}$ is called the *multiple linear correlation coefficient* between Y and the two X's, X_1 and X_2.

4. Plot the regression plane:

$$\hat{Y} = 20 + 1.998(X_1 - 4) - 0.398(X_2 - 11)$$
$$= 1.998X_1 - 0.398X_2 + 7.630$$

on a three-dimensional coördinate system. Then plot each sample point on this same coördinate system.

5. Convert the equation of Problem 4 into standard measure.

6. Given the following data, compute the least-squares regression equation for $\hat{Y}$, and the multiple R.

X_1:	2	4	6	8	10	11	15
X_2:	21	17	16	12	11	10	-3
Y:	20	27	33	38	45	46	50

7. Referring to Problem 6, obtain the least-squares equation $\hat{Y}_1 = a + b(X_1 - \bar{x}_1)$, and compute each $\hat{Y}_1$. Then compute $\sum (Y - \hat{Y}_1)^2$. Next use $\hat{Y} = a + b_1 (X_1 - \bar{x}_1) + b_2 (X_2 - \bar{x}_2)$ and compute $\sum (Y - \hat{Y})^2$. How do $\sum (Y - \hat{Y}_1)^2$ and $\sum (Y - \hat{Y})^2$ compare in size? Comment.

11.3 SOLUTION OF THE NORMAL EQUATIONS WHEN Y IS ASSOCIATED WITH TWO OR MORE X's

Previous illustrations have shown one way to solve the normal equations when only X_1 and X_2 are related to Y in a multiple linear regression equation. When more than two X's are required, the solution of the normal equations becomes sufficiently complex that special methods have been developed for this purpose. Herein attention will be concentrated on solution of the normal equations in the form of Equations 11.26, because it seems easier to maintain a uniform number of decimal places. The simple correlation coefficients used in this method also furnish useful information in themselves.

One routine for solving Equations 11.26 and obtaining other useful information simultaneously is outlined in Table 11.31. It follows the pattern of the Doolittle Method. The steps in forming this table are as follows:

Step 1.   Write down the following starting framework obtained from obvious sources:

Column:

Line	(1)	(2)	(3)	(4)	(5)	(6)
1	1	r_{12}	r_{y1}	1	0	0
2		1	r_{y2}	0	1	0
3			1	0	0	1
4	1	r_{12}	r_{y1}	1	0	0
5	1	r_{12}	r_{y1}	1	0	0

TABLE 11.31.   OUTLINE OF SOLUTION OF TWO NORMAL EQUATIONS BY A COMPUTATIONAL ROUTINE

	1	2	3	4	5	6
1	1	r_{12}	r_{y1}	1	0	0
2		1	r_{y2}	0	1	0
3			1	0	0	1
4	1	r_{12}	r_{y1}	1	0	0
5	1	r_{12}	r_{y1}	1	0	0
6		$(1-r_{12}^2)$	$r_{y2}-r_{12}r_{y1}$	$0-(1)r_{12}$	$1-0(r_{12})$	0
7		1	$\left(\dfrac{r_{y2}-r_{12}r_{y1}}{1-r_{12}^2}\right)$	$\left(\dfrac{-r_{12}}{1-r_{12}^2}\right)$	$\left(\dfrac{1}{1-r_{12}^2}\right)$	0
8			$1-r_{y1}^2-\dfrac{(r_{y2}-r_{12}r_{y1})^2}{1-r_{12}^2}$ $=1-\left\{\dfrac{r_{y1}^2+r_{y2}^2-2r_{12}r_{y1}r_{y2}}{1-r_{12}^2}\right\}$ $=1-R_{y\cdot12}^2$	$0-1(r_{y1})-\dfrac{-r_{12}(r_{y2}-r_{12}r_{y1})}{1-r_{12}^2}$ $=-\left\{\dfrac{r_{y1}-r_{12}r_{y2}}{1-r_{12}^2}\right\}$ $=-b_1'$	$0-0(r_{y1})-\dfrac{1(r_{y2}-r_{12}r_{y1})}{1-r_{12}^2}$ $=-\left\{\dfrac{r_{y2}-r_{12}r_{y1}}{1-r_{12}^2}\right\}$ $=-b_2'$	$1-0-0=1$

Step 2. From the 1 in line 2, column 2, subtract the product of the numbers in lines 4 and 5, column 2, namely r_{12}^2. From the r_{y2} in line 2, column 3, subtract the product of the r_{12} in line 5, column 2, and the r_{y1} in line 4, column 3. This produces $r_{y2} - r_{12}r_{y1}$. From the 0 in line 2, column 4, subtract the product of the r_{12} in line 5, column 2, and the 1 of line 4, column 4. This produces $0 - 1r_{12}$. From the 1 in line 2, column 5, subtract the product of the r_{12} in line 5, column 2, and the 0 of line 4, column 5. The result is $1 - 0 = 1$ in line 6, column 5. Finally, from the 0 in line 2, column 6, subtract the product of the r_{12} in line 5, column 2, and the 0 of line 4, column 6, namely 0. These operations produce the following:

Column:

Line	2	3	4	5	6
6	$1 - r_{12}^2$	$r_{y2} - r_{12}r_{y1}$	$-r_{12}$	1	0

If each member of line 6 is divided by $1 - r_{12}^2$, one obtains

Column:

Line	2	3	4	5	6
7	1	$\dfrac{r_{y2} - r_{12}r_{y1}}{1 - r_{12}^2}$	$\dfrac{-r_{12}}{1 - r_{12}^2}$	$\dfrac{1}{1 - r_{12}^2}$	0

Step 3. From the 1 in line 3, column 3, subtract the following products: $r_{y1}r_{y1} = r_{y1}^2$ from lines 4 and 5, column 3, and $(r_{y2} - r_{12}r_{y1})\left(\dfrac{r_{y2} - r_{12}r_{y1}}{1 - r_{12}^2}\right)$ from lines 6 and 7, column 3. The net result of these subtractions, after simplification, is

$$1 - \frac{r_{y1}^2 + r_{y2}^2 - 2r_{12}r_{y1}r_{y2}}{1 - r_{12}^2}, \quad \text{which is } 1 - R_{y \cdot 12}^2$$

Step 4. From the 0 of line 3, column 4, subtract the following products: $r_{y1}1 = r_{y1}$ from lines 4 and 5, columns 3 and 4, respectively, and $\left(\dfrac{r_{y2} - r_{12}r_{y1}}{1 - r_{12}^2}\right)(-r_{12})$ from lines 6 and 7, columns 3 and 4, respectively. The simplified result of these operations is

$$-\left(\frac{r_{y1} - r_{12}r_{y2}}{1 - r_{12}^2}\right), \quad \text{which is } -b_1'$$

Step 5. From the 0 of line 3, column 5, subtract the following products: $r_{y1}(0) = 0$ from lines 4 and 5, columns 3 and 5, respectively, and $\left(\dfrac{r_{y2} - r_{12}r_{y1}}{1 - r_{12}^2}\right)(1)$ from lines 6 and 7, columns 3 and 5, respectively. The simplified result of these operations is

$$-\left(\frac{r_{y2} - r_{12}r_{y1}}{1 - r_{12}^2}\right), \quad \text{which is } -b_2'$$

These results are summarized in Table 11.31.

TABLE 11.32.   APPLICATION OF TABLE 11.31 TO ILLUSTRATIVE NUMERICAL
EXAMPLE OF SECTION 11.2

Row	1	2	Column 3	4	5	6
1	1	−.31282	.84351	1	0	0
2		1	−.53662	0	1	0
3			1	0	0	1
4	1	−.31282	.84351	1	0	0
5	1	−.31282	.84351	1	0	0
6		.90214	−.27275	.31282	1	
7		1	−.30234	.34675	1.10848	
			$1 - R^2_{y\cdot12} = .20603$	.74893	.30234	1
				$(= -b'_1)$	$(= -b'_2)$	

$R^2_{y\cdot12} = 1 - 0.20603 = 0.79397$; hence $R \cong 0.892$

Table 11.32 shows a numerical illustration of Table 11.31, based on the illustrative example considered in Section 11.2. The reader should verify these computations until the routine is learned.

If more than two auxiliary variables are measured with Y, it is assumed that basically

(11.31) $Y = \alpha + \beta_1(X_1 - \mu_1) + \beta_2(X_2 - \mu_2) + \cdots + \beta_s(X_s - \mu_s) + \epsilon$

Geometrically, the points $(X_1, \cdots, X_s, Y)$ are in an $(s + 1)$-dimensional space, and one is fitting a hyperplane to the observed sample points by the Method of Least Squares. The normal equations for the b's in

(11.32) $\hat{Y} = a + b_1(X_1 - \bar{x}_1) + \cdots + b_s(X_s - \bar{x}_s)$

are the following:

(11.33) $\begin{cases} \sum (x_1^2)\cdot b_1 \ + \ \sum (x_1 x_2)\cdot b_2 + \cdots + \sum (x_1 x_s)\cdot b_s = \sum (x_1 y) \\ \sum (x_1 x_2)\cdot b_1 + \sum (x_2^2)\cdot b_2 \ + \cdots + \sum (x_2 x_s)\cdot b_s = \sum (x_2 y) \\ \quad\vdots \qquad\qquad\quad \vdots \qquad\qquad\quad \vdots \qquad\qquad \vdots \\ \sum (x_1 x_s)\cdot b_1 + \sum (x_2 x_s)\cdot b_2 + \cdots + \sum (x_s^2)\cdot b_s \ \ = \sum (x_s y) \end{cases}$

As before, one can use standard measure and correlation coefficients and change Equations 11.33 into the following:

(11.34) $\begin{cases} 1\cdot b'_1 \ + \ r_{12} b'_2 + \cdots + r_{1s} b'_s = r_{y1} \\ r_{12} b'_1 + 1\cdot b'_2 \ + \cdots + r_{2s} b'_s = r_{y2} \\ \quad\vdots \qquad\quad \vdots \qquad\qquad \vdots \qquad \vdots \\ r_{1s} b'_1 \ + r_{2s} b'_2 + \cdots + 1\cdot b'_s = r_{ys} \end{cases}$

TABLE 11.33. COMPUTATIONS FOR THREE X'S

X_1	X_2	X_3	Y	Unit matrix			
1	.096907	−.317985	.388338	1	0	0	0
	1	−.098086	.692360	0	1	0	0
		1	−.430532	0	0	1	0
			1	0	0	0	1
1	.096907	−.317985	.388338	1	0	0	0
1	.096907	−.317985	.388338	1	0	0	0
	.990609	−.067271	.654727	−.096907	1	0	0
	1	−.067909	.660934	−.097826	1.009480	0	0
		.894317	−.262584	.311404	.067909	1	0
		1	−.293615	.348203	.075934	1.118172	0
			.339364	−.232856	−.640995	.293615	1

$$b_1' = +0.232856, \quad b_2' = +0.640995, \quad b_3' = -0.293615.$$
$$R_{y\cdot123}^2 = 0.660636, \quad \text{so } R_{y.123} \cong 0.813.$$

Calculations:

$$.990609 = 1 - (.096907)^2$$
$$-.067271 = -.098086 - (.096907)(-.317985)$$
$$.654727 = .692360 - (.096907)(.388338)$$
$$-.096907 = 0 - (.096907)(1)$$
$$.894317 = 1 - (-.317985)^2 - (-.067909)(-.067271)$$
$$-.262584 = -.430532 - (-.317985)(.388338) - (-.067909)(.654727)$$
$$.311404 = 0 - (-.317985)(1) - (-.067909)(-.096907)$$
$$.067909 = 0 - (-.317985)(0) - (-.067909)(1)$$
$$.339364 = 1 - (.388338)^2 - (.654727)(.660934) - (-.262584)(-.293615)$$
$$-.232856 = 0 - (.388338)(1) - (.660934)(-.096907) - (.293615)(.311404)$$
$$-.640995 = 0 - (.388338)(0) - (.660934)(1) - (-.293615)(.067909)$$
$$.293615 = 0 - (.388338)(0) - (.660934)(0) - (-.293615)(1)$$

The computational scheme of tables 11.31 and 11.32 can be extended readily to the solution of Equations 11.34, or of Equations 11.33, if desired. This is shown for $s = 3$ in Table 11.33. The variables in this linear multiple regression problem are as follows:

$Y =$ number of days from the planting of a plot of sorghum until its maturity according to a set standard

$X_1 =$ total degree-hours air temperature was below 60°F. at night (7 P.M.–6 A.M.) during time from planting to maturity

$X_2 =$ total degree-hours air temperature was above 70°F. at night during the period from 30 days after planting until maturity

$X_3 =$ total degree-hours air temperature was above 70°F. in the daytime (6 A.M.–7 P.M.) during the third ten days after planting.

There were 25 sets of observations (X_1, X_2, X_3, Y). Referring to Table 11.33, one learns the following:

(a) The multiple linear regression equation for estimating μ_Y from X_1, X_2, and X_3 is

$$\hat{Y} = \bar{y} + \sqrt{\frac{\sum y^2}{\sum x_1^2}}(0.232856)(X_1 - \bar{x}_1) + \sqrt{\frac{\sum y^2}{\sum x_2^2}}(0.640995)(X_2 - \bar{x}_2)$$

$$- \sqrt{\frac{\sum y^2}{\sum x_3^2}}(0.293615)(X_3 - \bar{x}_3)$$

Given the sample data, one could obtain a specific equation for $\hat{Y}$.

(b) In view of the fact that the correlation between the observed Y's and the corresponding computed $\hat{Y}$'s is $R_{y.123} = 0.813$, it is concluded that about 66 percent (R^2) of the observed variability among the Y's, as measured by $\sum(y^2)$, is assignable to multiple linear regression on X_1, X_2, and X_3, because $R_{y.123} \cong 0.66$.

Additional information, obtainable from tests of significance and from partial correlation coefficients, is needed and will be obtained in succeeding sections.

PROBLEMS

1. Given the following practice data, obtain:
   (a) The normal equations for b_1 and b_2.
   (b) The normal equations for b_1' and b_2'.
   (c) The equation for the least-squares regression plane in its simplest form.
   (d) The graph of this plane and the points from this sample.

X_1	X_2	Y	Given
3	9	14	$\sum(x_1^2) = 92$
8	6	10	$\sum(x_1 y) = -61$
7	8	11	$\sum(x_2^2) = 34$
-2	11	16	$\sum(x_1 x_2) = -51$
4	10	13	$r_{y1} = -0.98132$
10	4	8	
Σ: 30	48	72	

2. Given the following *correlation matrix*, compute b_1', b_2', b_3', b_4', and $R_{y.1234}$:

X_1	X_2	X_3	X_4	Y
1	.096907	$-.317985$	.540403	.388338
	1	$-.098086$	$-.188100$	.692360
		1	$-.442823$	$-.430532$
			1	.383116
				1

3. Do Problem 2 with the X's in the order X_2, X_3, X_1, and X_4. Draw appropriate conclusions about the effect of changing the order of the variables in the computational routine.

4. The following data are similar to those for Table 11.33 but pertain to temperature on what might be called warm nights during the growing season. Specifically,
   $X_1 =$ total degree-hours about 70°F. *after* 30 nights from date of planting
   $X_2 =$ total degree-hours above 70°F. at night all season

X_3 = total degree-hours above 70°F. during the first 20 nights after planting

X_4 = total degree-hours above 70°F. after 20 nights

Y = total days from planting to maturity

These data are from an actual experiment conducted by the Kansas Agricultural experiment station. They pertain to the sorghum variety Norghum.

X_1	X_2	X_3	X_4	Y
1	.75528	.27524	.92901	.21358
	1	.59189	.85825	−.13420
		1	.27815	.09398
			1	−.02635
				1

Perform a full linear multiple regression analysis and answer the following questions:

(a) What is the equation of the estimated linear regression plane by the Method of Least Squares in standard measure?

(b) What fraction of the variation $\sum (y^2)$ can one associate with variation among the X's?

(c) How much more is $\sum (y^2)$ reduced by adding X_3 to the analysis, after X_1 and X_2 already are used?

(d) Does it seem reasonable that both X_1 and X_4 should be kept in the analysis?

5. The following data are from another variety of sorghum but are the same otherwise. Answer the same questions as posed in Problem 4.

X_1	X_2	X_3	X_4	Y
1	.69473	.04008	.94475	.58139
	1	.73520	.49671	.40550
		1	−.22268	.05753
			1	.49984
				1

6. It has been thought by some that the most important temperature-summation variables related to the time it takes sorghum to mature are those produced by hot days. Given the following variables and data, answer the questions below:

X_1 = total degree-hours above 90°F. during the second 10 days after planting

X_2 = total degree-hours above 90°F. during the daytime and after 20 days from planting

X_3 = total degree-hours above 90°F. during the daytime and after 30 days from planting

X_4 = total degree-hours above 90°F. during the daytime and during the first 20 days

Y = days to maturity

X_1	X_2	X_3	X_4	Y
1	.46047	.18565	.70137	.30056
	1	.68243	.45736	.36024
		1	.16978	−.15126
			1	.31852
				1

(a) If $\hat{Y} = \bar{y} + b_1(X_1 - \bar{x}_1) + \cdots + b_4(X_4 - \bar{x}_4)$, what is the correlation between $\hat{Y}$ and Y?

(b) What fraction of $\sum (y^2)$ is "explained" by these four X's?

(c) Is the order in which the X's are written above probably the best one to use? Why?

(d) Do you think some of these X's might as well have been omitted? Why?

11.4   TESTING THE RELATIVE IMPORTANCE OF X's INCLUDED IN A MULTIPLE LINEAR REGRESSION STUDY

The importance of X_1 in explaining the $\sum (y^2)$, if it is assumed that

$$(11.41) \qquad Y = \alpha + \beta(X_1 - \mu_x) + \epsilon$$

is measured by $(\sum x_1 y)^2 / \sum (x_1^2)$ or $r_{y1}^2 \sum (y^2)$. By analogy, the benefit derived from using

$$(11.42) \qquad Y = \alpha + \beta_1(X_1 - \mu_1) + \beta_2(X_2 - \mu_2) + \epsilon$$

instead of Equation 11.41 can be measured by $(R_{y \cdot 12}^2 - r_{y1}^2) \sum (y^2)$, because:

$R_{y \cdot 12}^2 \cdot \sum (y^2)$ measures the amount by which $\sum (y^2)$ is reduced if one uses Equation 11.42 as compared to using no X's at all

$r_{y1}^2 \cdot \sum (y^2)$ measures the amount by which $\sum (y^2)$ is reduced if one uses Equation 11.41 as compared to not using X_1.

Thus, *the additional reduction* in $\sum (y^2)$ obtained by using both X_1 and X_2 instead of just X_1 is, as stated, the difference

$$(11.43) \qquad (R_{y \cdot 12}^2 - r_{y1}^2) \cdot \sum (y^2)$$

One degree of freedom is associated with $r_{y1}^2 \cdot \sum (y^2)$, and the significance of this reduction in $\sum (y^2)$ is measured by

$$F(1, n-2) = \dfrac{\dfrac{r_{y1}^2 \sum (y^2)}{1}}{\dfrac{(1 - r_{y1}^2) \sum y^2}{n-2}} = \dfrac{(n-2)r_{y1}^2}{(1 - r_{y1}^2)}$$

It is reasonable and true that $(R_{y \cdot 12}^2 - r_{y1}^2) \sum (y^2)$ should have 1 DF and that the significance of the additional reduction in $\sum (y^2)$ achieved by bringing X_2 into the regression analysis in addition to X_1 is measured by

$$F(1, n-3) = \dfrac{\dfrac{(R_{y \cdot 12}^2 - r_{y1}^2) \sum y^2}{1}}{\dfrac{(1 - R_{y \cdot 12}^2) \sum (y^2)}{n-3}} = \dfrac{(n-3)(R_{y \cdot 12}^2 - r_{y1}^2)}{(1 - R_{y \cdot 12}^2)}$$

If a multiple linear regression analysis involves X_1, X_2, X_3, and Y, it is concluded that:

(a) The "success" achieved by using X_1 alone with Y is measured by

$$F(1, n - 2) = \frac{(n - 2)r_{y1}^2}{1 - r_{y1}^2}$$

(b) The significance of the additional reduction of $\sum(y^2)$ achieved by adding X_2 *after* X_1 is measured by

$$F(1, n - 3) = \frac{(n - 3)(R_{y \cdot 12}^2 - r_{y1}^2)}{1 - R_{y \cdot 12}^2}$$

(c) The significance of the additional reduction of $\sum(y^2)$ achieved by adding X_3 *after using X_1 and X_2* is measured by

$$F(1, n - 4) = \frac{(n - 4)(R_{y \cdot 123}^2 - R_{y \cdot 12}^2)}{1 - R_{y \cdot 123}^2}$$

These ideas obviously can be extended to s X's. However, one should note that the Error Mean Square has but $n - v$ DF, where $v = s + 1$.

The computational scheme in Table 11.33 can be extended quite simply to include these three tests. This is done in the lower left corner of Table 11.41.

It is concluded from Table 11.41 that:

(a) X_1 probably should be kept in this analysis, but this is a little uncertain with $\alpha = 0.05$.

(b) X_2 most certainly should be kept in this study, either by itself or in addition to X_1.

(c) The reduction in $\sum(y^2)$ achieved by adding X_3 to the multiple linear regression, even after X_1 and X_2 already have been included, is significant, so all three X's should be used in the analysis.

(d) About a third ($33.9^+\%$) of the $\sum(y^2)$ remains unexplained, even after X_1, X_2, and X_3 have been considered in a linear multiple relationship to Y, because $1 - R_{y \cdot 123}^2 = 0.339364$.

To clarify further the tests of significance made in Table 11.41, consider Table 11.42, in which the hypotheses tested and the decisions made are set forth specifically.

It may be of interest to test each individual b_i for significance in

$$\hat{Y} = a + b_1(X_1 - \bar{x}_1) + b_2(X_2 - \bar{x}_2) + b_3(X_3 - \bar{x}_3)$$

that is, to test $H_0(\beta_1 = 0)$ or $H_0(\beta_2 = 0)$ or $H_0(\beta_3 = 0)$, each against its negation, $H_a(\beta_i \neq 0)$. This can be done by means of the t test

(11.44) $$t = \frac{b_i - \beta_i}{s_{b_i}} = \frac{b_i' - \beta_i'}{s_{b_i'}}, \qquad \text{with } n - v \text{ DF}$$

TABLE 11.41.   EXTENSION OF TABLE 11.33 TO INCLUDE TESTS OF IMPORTANCE
OF X_1, X_2, AND X_3 IN ACCOUNTING FOR $\sum (y^2)$; $n = 25$

X_1	X_2	X_3	Y	Unit matrix			
1	.096907	− .317985	.388338	1	0	0	0
	1	− .098086	.692360	0	1	0	0
		1	− .430532	0	0	1	0
			1	0	0	0	1
1	.096907	− .317985	.388338	1	0	0	0
1	.096907	− .317985	.388338	1	0	0	0
	.990609	− .067271	.654727	− .096907	1	0	0
	1	− .067909	.660934	− .097826	1.009480	0	0
		.894317	− .262584	+ .311404	.067909	1	0
		1	− .293615	.348203	.075934	1.118172	0
			.339364	− .232856	− .640995	.293615	1

$F[1, (n - v)]$	$(n - v)$	Δ	
4.08^{near}*	23	.150806	$.849194 = 1 -- r_{y1}^2 = 1 - (.388338)^2$
22.86*	22	.432732	$.416462 = 1 - R_{y \cdot 12}^2 = 1 - (.388338)^2$
			$\qquad\qquad - (.654727)(.660934)$
4.77*	21	.077098	$.339364 = 1 - R_{y \cdot 123}^2 = 1 - (.388338)^2$
			$\qquad\qquad - (.654727)(.660934)$
			$\qquad\qquad - (-.262584)(-.293615)$

$+0.150806 = r_{y1}^2$, $0.432732 = R_{y \cdot 12}^2 - r_{y1}^2$,   and $0.077098 = R_{y \cdot 123}^2 - R_{y \cdot 12}^2$.
A 5% level of significance was used.

Δ's are the differences between 1 and r_{y1}^2, $R_{y \cdot 12}^2$ and r_{1y}^2, etc.
* means significant at the 5% level and "near *" means almost so.

as soon as we have a formula for s_{b_i} or $s_{b_i'}$. To that end, an addition needs to
be made to Table 11.41. This process is shown in Table 11.43.

The standard deviations for b_2' and b_3' are $s_{b_2'} = 0.1280$ and $s_{b_3'} = 0.1344$.
These b_i' are called *sample standard partial regression coefficients.* As noted
earlier, they can be converted to partial regression coefficients, in the original

TABLE 11.42.   SUPPLEMENT TO TABLE 11.41, SHOWING H_0'S AND DECISIONS
FOR EACH F TEST OF TABLE 11.41 WITH $\alpha = 0.05$

$F[1, (n - v)]$	H_0 tested vs. negation	Decision
4.08^{near}*	$\beta = 0$ in $\mu_y = \alpha_1 + \beta(X_1 - \mu_1)$	Probably reject H_0
22.86*	$\beta_{12} = 0$ in $\mu_y = \alpha_2 + \beta_{11}(X_1 - \mu_1)$	Definitely reject H_0
	$\qquad\qquad\qquad + \beta_{12}(X_2 - \mu_2)$	
4.77*	$\beta_{23} = 0$ in $\mu_y = \alpha_3 + \beta_{21}(X_1 - \mu_1)$	Reject H_0
	$\qquad + \beta_{22}(X_2 - \mu_2) + \beta_{23}(X_3 - \mu_3)$	

TABLE 11.43.   EXTENSION OF TABLE 11.41 TO INCLUDE CALCULATION
OF THE $s_{b_i'}$; $n = 25$

X_1	X_2	X_3	Y			*Unit matrix*	
1	.096907	$-.317985$	.388338	1	0	0	0
	1	$-.098086$	.692360	0	1	0	0
		1	$-.430532$	0	0	1	0
			1	0	0	0	1
1	.096907	$-.317985$	.388338	1	0	0	0
1	.096907	$-.317985$	.388338	1	0	0	0
	.990609	$-.067271$	.654727	$-.096907$	1	0	0
	1	$-.067909$	.660934	$-.097826$	1.009480	0	0
		.894317	$-.262584$	.311404	.067909	1	0
		1	$-.293615$	.348203	.075934	1.118172	0
			.339364	$-.232856$	$-.640995$	.293615	1
			1	$-.686154$	-1.888812	.865192	2.946689

$$\begin{pmatrix} 1.117912 & -.074180 & .348203 \\ -.074180 & 1.014637 & .075934 \\ .348203 & .075934 & 1.118172 \end{pmatrix} = (m_{ij})$$

$1.117912 = 1 + (-.096907)(-.097826) + (.311404)(.348203)$
$-.074180 = (1)(-.097826) + (.067909)(.348203)$
$.348203 = (1)(.348203)$
$1.014637 = (1)(1.009480) + (.067909)(.075934)$
$1.118172 = (1)(1.118172)$

Notation: $m_{11} = 1.117912$, the number in row 1, column 1, of (m_{ij})
$m_{12} = -0.074180$, the number in row 1, column 2, of (m_{ij}); etc.
Definition: The standard deviation of b_i' is

$$s_{b_i}' = \sqrt{\frac{(1 - R_{y.123}^2)m_{ii}}{n - v}}, \qquad i = 1, 2, 3$$

where v = number of variables including Y and n = number of (X_1, X_2, X_3, Y) observations.
For example,

$$s_{b_1}' = \sqrt{\frac{0.339364(1.117912)}{25 - 4}} = 0.1344.$$

units of measure, simply by multiplication by $\sqrt{\sum (y^2)/\sum (x_i^2)}$. For a given set of samples, this is a constant for a given i; hence, one can convert the standard deviation, s_{b_i}', into the standard deviation s_{b_i} by multiplication by this same factor, namely $\sqrt{\sum (y^2)/\sum (x_i^2)}$. Thus, the t test, $t_1 = (b_i' - \beta_i')/s_{b_i'}$, is identically the same as $t_2 = (b_i - \beta_i)/s_{b_i}$, when β_i' or β_i taken $= 0$; so the results of a t_i test may be interpreted in terms of the original units for b_i and β_i if one prefers. This is done in Table 11.44.

TABLE 11.44. t TESTS OF HYPOTHESES REGARDING β_i's; DATA OF
TABLE 11.43

t test	H_0 *tested by* t
$t_1 = (0.232856 - 0)/0.1344 = 1.73;$	$\beta_1 = 0$ in $\mu_Y = \alpha + \beta_1(X_1 - \mu_1)$ $+ \beta_2(X_2 - \mu_2) + \beta_3(X_3 - \mu_3);$
21 DF; $P \cong 0.10$	
$t_2 = (0.640995 - 0)/0.1280 = 5.01;$	$\beta_2 = 0$ in $\mu_Y = \alpha + \beta_1(X_1 - \mu_1)$ $+ \beta_2(X_2 - \mu_2) + \beta_3(X_3 - \mu_3);$
21 DF; $P < 0.05$	
$t_3 = (-0.293615 - 0)/0.1344 = 2.19;$	$\beta_3 = 0$ in $\mu_Y = \alpha + \beta_1(X_1 - \mu_1)$ $+ \beta_2(X_2 - \mu_2) + \beta_3(X_3 - \mu_3);$
21 DF; $P < 0.05$	

P is the probability of a t being at least as large as this t_i, $i = 1, 2,$ and 3, if H_0 is true.

It should be noted carefully at this point that the tests of significance in Tables 11.42 and 11.44 are identical in *only one place*: the $F(1, 21) = 4.77$ of Table 11.42 is identical with the $t_3 = 2.19$, 21 DF, of Table 11.44. In fact, $(2.19)^2 \cong 4.77$; that is, this $t^2 =$ this F to the accuracy maintained.

PROBLEMS

1. Extend Problem 2, Section 11.3, to include the four t tests of the b_i, with $i = 1$ to 4, and draw appropriate conclusions.
2. If in Tables 11.41 and 11.43 the order of the X's is changed to X_3, X_1, X_2, what F test and t test become identical?
3. Extend Problem 1, Section 11.3, to include the two t tests of the b's.
4. Given the following correlation matrix from a study of some factors (P, Te, M, and T_{15}) affecting the loaf volume (Y) of bread, do as complete a multiple linear regression analysis as possible, given $n = 22$.

P	Te	M	T_{15}	Y
1	.39898	$-.45282$	.50853	.53886
	1	$-.23130$	.93796	.53772
		1	$-.42557$	$-.47839$
			1	.61335
				1

5. Extend Problem 4, Section 11.3, to include t tests of the b_i''s. Which F is which t^2?
6. Extend Problem 5, Section 11.3, to include t tests of the b_i''s. Which F is which t^2?
7. Extend Problem 6, Section 11.3, to include t tests of the b_i''s. Which F is which t^2?

11.5 PARTIAL CORRELATION COEFFICIENTS

If an experimenter is involved in a study in which several measurements are to be taken on each experimental unit, he may wish at some point in his experiment to study the relationship between one particular pair of measurements, X_i and X_j. If all the variables are linearly related to each other, this could be done in either of two general ways:

(a) Ignore the other measurements entirely, and compute the simple linear correlation, $r_{X_i X_j}$.

(b) Linearly adjust the X_i and X_j for their relationships to the other variables, and then compute the simple linear correlation between adjusted X_i and X_j *with the other measurements held at fixed values*. Such a correlation is called a *partial linear correlation*, as contrasted with the simple linear correlation, for which all other variables are ignored rather than held fixed.

If the v X's in a study basically have a multivariate normal distribution, the two-dimensional normal distribution of any two X's *for a given set of values for the other $v - 2$ variables* is independent of those $v - 2$ variables. One consequence of this fact is that the formula for the partial linear correlation coefficient between any X_i and X_j does not depend on the values at which the other $v - 2$ variables are fixed.

With $v = 3$, the partial linear correlation between X_1 and X_2 is measured by

$$(11.51) \qquad r_{12 \cdot 3} = \frac{r_{12} - r_{13} r_{23}}{\sqrt{(1 - r_{13}^2)(1 - r_{23}^2)}}$$

if sampling data are used to compute this coefficient, so the r_{12}, r_{13}, and r_{23} are computed from the sampling data.

If there are four X's (X_1, X_2, X_3, and X_4) in a multivariate normal distribution, the sample estimate of the coefficient of partial linear correlation between X_1 and X_2, X_3 and X_4, assumed fixed, is given by

$$(11.52) \qquad r_{12 \cdot 34} = \frac{r_{12 \cdot 3} - r_{14 \cdot 3} r_{24 \cdot 3}}{\sqrt{(1 - r_{14 \cdot 3}^2)(1 - r_{24 \cdot 3}^2)}}$$

R. A. Fisher ("The distribution of the partial correlation coefficient," *Metron* 3: 329, 1924) has shown that the sampling distribution of a linear partial correlation coefficient for a multivariate normal distribution is the same as that of the simple linear correlation coefficient, r, *except* that it has $n - v$ degrees of freedom instead of $n - 2$, where v is the total number of variables. Hence, the procedures discussed previously for tests of significance and confidence intervals apply with this modification.

Quite often the partial correlation coefficient is of interest in a situation in which multiple correlation analysis also is useful; hence, it may be doubly worth while to compute the partial correlations from an extension of Table 11.43. This consists of extending the 3×3 matrix (m_{ij}) into a 4×4 matrix (M_{ij}) merely by continuing the process of computing (m_{ij}) one step in each case, plus the fourth row and column, which come directly from previous calculations. The (M_{ij}) matrix for Table 11.43 is

$$(M_{ij}) = \begin{pmatrix} 1.277687 & .365641 & .146738 & -.686154 \\ .365641 & 2.225356 & -.478650 & -1.888812 \\ .146738 & -.478650 & 1.372205 & .865192 \\ -.686154 & -1.888812 & .865192 & 2.946689 \end{pmatrix}$$

in which:

$M_{11} = 1.277687$
$\quad = m_{11} + (-.232856)(-.686154)$ from column 6 of Table 11.43
$M_{12} = .365641$
$\quad = m_{12} + (-.640995)(-.686154)$ from columns 6 and 7 of Table 11.43

$\cdot \quad \cdot \quad \cdot \quad \cdot \quad \cdot \quad \cdot \quad \cdot \quad \cdot \quad \cdot \quad \cdot \quad \cdot \quad \cdot \quad \cdot \quad \cdot$

$M_{33} = 1.372205$
$\quad = m_{33} + (.293615)(.865192)$ from column 7 of Table 11.43
$M_{14} = -.686154$
$\quad = (1)(-.686154)$ from columns 5 and 8 of Table 11.43
$M_{24} = -1.888812$
$\quad = (1)(-1.888812)$ from columns 6 and 8 of Table 11.43
$M_{34} = .865192$
$\quad = (1)(.865192)$ from columns 7 and 8 of Table 11.43
$M_{44} = 2.946689 = (1)(2.946689)$ from column 8 of Table 11.43

Naturally, in practice the (M_{ij}) is placed just below (m_{ij}) in a table such as Table 11.43.

The coefficient of linear partial correlation between X_i and X_j is computed by means of the following formula:

(11.53)
$$r_{ij \cdot \text{others}} = \frac{-M_{ij}}{\sqrt{(M_{ii})(M_{jj})}}$$

For Table 11.43 the following partial correlations are computed; using the same notation as used for those variables, Y playing the role of X_4:

$(a) \quad r_{y1 \cdot 23} = \dfrac{-M_{y1}}{\sqrt{(M_{11})(M_{yy})}} = \dfrac{-(-0.686154)}{\sqrt{(1.277687)(2.946689)}}$

$\qquad\qquad = +0.3536$ ns, whereas simple $r_{y1} = 0.388338$[near*]

(b) $r_{y2 \cdot 13} = \dfrac{-M_{y2}}{\sqrt{(M_{22})(M_{yy})}} = \dfrac{-(-1.888812)}{\sqrt{(2.225356)(2.946689)}}$

$= +0.7376^*,$ whereas simple $r_{y2} = 0.692360^*$

(c) $r_{y3 \cdot 12} = \dfrac{-M_{y3}}{\sqrt{(M_{33})(M_{yy})}} = \dfrac{-(0.865192)}{\sqrt{(1.372205)(2.946689)}}$

$= -0.4303^*,$ whereas simple $r_{y3} = -0.430532^*$

(d) $r_{12 \cdot y3} = \dfrac{-M_{12}}{\sqrt{(M_{11})(M_{22})}} = \dfrac{-(0.365641)}{\sqrt{(1.277687)(2.225356)}}$

$= -0.2168 \text{ ns},$ whereas simple $r_{12} = 0.096907 \text{ ns}$

(e) $r_{13 \cdot y2} = \dfrac{-M_{13}}{\sqrt{(M_{11})(M_{33})}} = \dfrac{-(0.146738)}{\sqrt{(1.277687)(1.372205)}}$

$= -0.1108 \text{ ns},$ whereas simple $r_{13} = -0.317985 \text{ ns}$

(f) $r_{23 \cdot y1} = \dfrac{-M_{23}}{\sqrt{(M_{22})(M_{33})}} = \dfrac{-(-0.478650)}{\sqrt{(2.225356)(1.372205)}}$

$= +0.2739 \text{ ns},$ whereas simple $r_{23} = -0.098086 \text{ ns}$

Each of these partial correlation coefficients has $n - v = 25 - 4 = 21$ DF, whereas the simple correlation coefficients each have $25 - 2 = 23$ DF.

In general, and with a 5% level of significance, it is concluded that:

(a) If all *other* X's (or Y's) are at fixed values, only Y and X_2, and Y and X_3, are significantly linearly correlated.

(b) If all other variables are left random and ignored, Y and X_2, and Y and X_3, are significantly linearly correlated, but all other pairs are not; hence the simple and partial correlations are producing the same conclusions.

It is apparent that correlations between variables should be carefully interpreted. In the case of $r_{y2.13}$, for example, all other possible variables are not even considered. What if an X_4 were brought into the study? Could it seriously change the estimate of the relationship between Y and X_2? Part of the answers to these questions lies in the multiple correlation coefficient R, because R^2 measures the extent to which the other variables "account for" the variation observed among the Y's (any of the variables could play the role of Y in this correlation discussion, because we now are assuming a multinormal distribution). Thus, if $R^2_{y.123}$ is near unity, it seems that all of the variables importantly related to Y have been brought into the study, and the addition of another variable should not materially affect the partial correlations with Y. On the other hand, if $R^2_{y.12}$, say, is well below unity, and there is another measurement, X_3, such that $R^2_{y.123}$ is near unity, the meanings and sizes of some of the partial correlations could be quite different under these two circumstances. These points are illustrated by the data of Table 11.51.

TABLE 11.51. HYPOTHETICAL MULTIPLE AND PARTIAL CORRELATION DATA AND COMPUTATIONS

X_1	X_2	X_3	Y	
15	32	0	35	$\sum (x_1^2) = 539.4286, \quad \sum (x_1 x_2) = 54.5714$
2	19	15	10	
5	14	11	9	$\sum (x_1 x_3) = -324, \quad \sum (x_1 y) = 700, \quad \sum (x_2^2) = 776.9286$
19	3	1	30	
11	17	13	20	$\sum (x_2 x_3) = -191, \quad \sum (x_2 y) = 339, \quad \sum (x_3^2) = 490$
10	25	7	23	
23	15	6	28	$\sum (x_3 y) = -766, \quad \sum (y^2) = 1466$
12	13	18	8	
10	11	4	29	$r_{12} = 0.08430, \quad r_{13} = -0.63019, \quad r_{1y} = 0.78716, \quad r_{23} = -0.30956$
4	6	20	4	
10	25	7	18	$r_{2y} = 0.31765, \quad r_{3y} = -0.90379$
9	18	9	14	
16	17	3	32	$R_{y \cdot 12}^2 = 0.68322, \quad R_{y \cdot 123}^2 = 0.90224$
0	10	12	6	

$r_{y1 \cdot 2} = 0.80478**, \quad r_{y1 \cdot 23} = 0.67941*$

$r_{y2 \cdot 1} = 0.40890 \text{ ns}, \quad r_{y2 \cdot 13} = 0.25604 \text{ ns}$

$r_{12 \cdot y} = -0.28341 \text{ ns}, \quad r_{12 \cdot y3} = -0.28039 \text{ ns}$

** denotes statistical significance at the 1% level.
ns denotes nonsignificance with $\alpha = 0.05$.

It is observed from Table 11.51 that:

(*a*) The partial correlations involving Y changed enough, when X_3 was added, to change levels of significance in one instance and change noticeably the correlation in another instance. In both instances it is reasonable that under some circumstances both changes could have been important.

(*b*) The partial correlation between X_1 and X_2 was not affected by the addition of X_3, possibly because X_1 and X_2 probably were not related anyway.

If the simple linear correlation between two variables X_i and X_j is notably larger than the partial linear correlation between X_i and X_j when some other variables are held fixed, it is reasonable to believe the simple correlation was produced in part by their common relationship to the other variables. If, however, the partial linear correlation is larger than the simple, it is concluded that the other variables, which were ignored in the simple correlation, were obscuring the basic linear relationship between X_i and X_j to some extent.

PROBLEMS

1. Given the following correlation matrix, compute the b_i''s for the indicated four-variable multiple regression equation with $n = 63$.

X_1	X_2	X_3	Y
1	.58928	−.25699	.46941
	1	−.33117	.13815
		1	.21358
			1

2. With the data for Problem 1 test $H_0(\beta_2 = 0)$ in $Y = \alpha + \beta_1(X_1 - \mu_1) + \beta_2(X_2 - \mu_2) + \epsilon$, and draw appropriate conclusions.

3. With the data of Problem 1 compute $r_{y2 \cdot 13}$ and test it for significance by means of a t test. By means of an F test.

4. Compute and interpret the $R_{y \cdot 123}$ for Problem 1.

5. Compare r_{y1} and $r_{y1 \cdot 23}$ for Problem 1, and draw appropriate conclusions.

6. Write down the standard normal equations for Problem 1.

7. Compute the standard deviation of b_3' for Problem 1. How could b_3 be computed therefrom, given the necessary additional information?

8. Given the following correlation matrix for a sample of size $n = 61$, test $H_0(\rho_{14 \cdot 23y} = 0)$ with $\alpha = 0.10$, where $\rho_{14 \cdot 23y}$ is the true partial correlation between X_1 and X_4.

X_1	X_2	X_3	X_4	Y
1	.90730	−.03082	.41749	.41393
	1	−.13638	.26101	.45269
		1	−.21489	.58139
			1	.09942
				1

9. Make up a problem with $n = 10$ and three variables, X_1, X_2, and Y, such that both X's are statistically useful with $\alpha = 0.10$.

10. Compute all the partial correlations with Y for the data of Section 11.3.

11.6   SUMMARY

If it is assumed that a measurement Y, which is subject to sampling error, is linearly related to s measurements, $X_1, \cdots, X_s$, which are not subject to sampling error (or at least the sampling error is very low compared to Y), the Y can be written as

(11.61) $$Y = \alpha + \beta_1(X_1 - \mu_1) + \cdots + \beta_s(X_s - \mu_s) + \epsilon$$

where the α's and β's are real constants, the μ's are the true means of the respective X's, and the ϵ represents random error. It is usual to assume the ϵ's are $NID(0, \sigma^2_{y \cdot x_1 \ldots x_s})$, in order that certain desirable tests of significance and estimations may be done validly. The β_i are called partial regression coefficients.

If, for lack of information about these population parameters, we use

(11.62) $$\hat{Y} = a + b_1(X_1 - \bar{x}_1) + \cdots + b_s(X_s - \bar{x}_s)$$

as an estimate of the true average Y for a given set of X's, it is necessary to estimate the α (by a), and the β_i (by b_i's) from a sample of n sets of observations: $(X_{11}, \cdots, X_{s1}), \cdots, (X_{1n}, \cdots, X_{sn})$. If this is done by the Method of Least Squares, one obtains $a = \bar{y}$ and the following *normal equations* from which to obtain $b_1, \cdots, b_s$:

(11.63)
$$
\begin{cases}
\sum (x_1^2)b_1 + \cdots + \sum (x_1 x_s)b_s = \sum (x_1 y) \\
\quad \cdot \quad \cdot \quad \cdot \quad \cdot \quad \cdot \quad \cdot \quad \cdot \\
\sum (x_1 x_s)b_1 + \cdots + \sum (x_s^2)b_s = \sum (x_s y)
\end{cases}
$$

Computational procedures have been developed for solving these equations for the b's (or for b_i''s after changing to standard measure) and for computing a number of other useful statistics. Table 11.61 has been prepared to summarize these computations and to provide a basis for the conclusions drawn after this table. This table was derived from data similar to the sorghum data of Table 11.33. The variables are as follows:

$Y = $ Number of days from the planting of a plot of sorghum until its maturity in a defined sense

$X_1 = $ Total degree-hours air temperature was below 60°F. at night (7 P.M. to 6 A.M.) during time from planting until maturity

$X_2 = $ Total degree-hours air temperature was below 70°F. at night from 30 nights after planting until maturity

$X_3 = $ Total degree-hours air temperature was above 70°F. at night from 30 days after planting until maturity

$X_4 = $ Total degree-hours air temperature was < 70°F. during the first 20 nights

$X_5 = $ Total degree-hours air temperature was > 70°F. during the first 10 days (6 A.M. to 7 P.M.) after planting

For the sake of reminding the reader of the assumptions involved, it will be assumed for the correlation analysis illustrated in this same table that the X_1, X_2, X_3, X_4, X_5, and Y have a multivariate normal distribution. When the correlations in the correlation matrix are used to compute regression coefficients, they merely play the role of transformed functions of sums of squares and products.

The following conclusions, among others, can be drawn from Table 11.61:

(a) It is quite doubtful that X_5 is contributing enough to this study to justify its inclusion after X_1, X_2, X_3, and X_4 are already included. This conclusion is justified by the $F(1, 56)$ test, the test of b_5' by a t test, or the test of the partial regression coefficient, $r_{y5 \cdot 1234}$, by a t test—all of which are identical tests as used herein.

TABLE 11.61. MULTIPLE AND PARTIAL CORRELATION AND REGRESSION ILLUSTRATION; $n = 62$, $\alpha = 0.05$

X_1	X_2	X_3	X_4	X_5	Y	Unit matrix					
1	.78388	−.35859	.81681	.44050	.45037	1	0	0	0	0	0
	1	−.45338	.48789	.35292	.47258	0	1	0	0	0	0
		1	−.30304	.23476	.29439	0	0	1	0	0	0
			1	−.57927	.40453	0	0	0	1	0	0
				1	−.34023	0	0	0	0	1	0
					1	0	0	0	0	0	1

X_1	X_2	X_3	X_4	X_5	Y						
1	.78388	−.35859	.81681	−.44050	.45037	1	0	0	0	0	0
1	.78388	−.35859	.81681	−.44050	.45037	−.78388	−2.03325	1	2.59383	1	0

X_1		X_3	X_4	X_5	Y						
.38553		−.17229	−.15239	−.00762	.11954	.00828	.44689	1	.33546	−.01236	.29623
1		−.44689	−.39528	−.01977	.31007	.01042	.56254	1.25878	.53750	−.01981	.83192
		.79442	−.07824	.07340	.50931	−1.12585	.43929	.09848		.81263	−.77722
		1	−.09848	.09239	.64111	−4.25042	1.65845	.37179		1.30206	−2.18271
			.26488	−.21525	.13407			3.77529	1	1	−.69249
			1	−.81263	.50615					1.60228	−1.94476
				.62411	−.07758						−.40513
				1	−.12431						−1.13775
					.35608						+.12431
					1						+.34911
											1
											2.80836

$$(m_{ij}) = \begin{pmatrix} 7.76499 & -4.15949 & -.39844 & -4.88929 & -.78618 \\ -4.15949 & 3.75407 & .71922 & 2.09524 & .53750 \\ -.39844 & .71922 & 1.29564 & .35569 & -.01981 \\ -4.88929 & 2.09524 & .35569 & 4.83338 & 1.30206 \\ -.78618 & .53750 & -.01981 & 1.30206 & 1.60228 \end{pmatrix}$$

$$(M_{ij}) = \begin{pmatrix} 8.01144 & -4.80608 & -.97455 & -5.22633 & -.68276 & .83192 \\ -4.80608 & 5.45052 & 2.23073 & 2.97952 & .26617 & -2.18272 \\ -.97455 & 2.23073 & 2.64237 & 1.14358 & -.26156 & -1.94476 \\ -5.22633 & 2.97952 & 1.14358 & 5.29432 & 1.16063 & -1.13775 \\ -.68276 & .26617 & -.26156 & 1.16063 & 1.64568 & +.34911 \\ .83192 & -2.18271 & -1.94476 & -1.13775 & +.34911 & 2.80836 \end{pmatrix}$$

F[1, (n − v)] and sig.	(n − v)	△	
			.79717
2.88 ns	59	.03707	
			.76010
43.68*	58	.32652	
			.43358
10.58*	57	.06786	
			.36572
1.54 ns	56	.00964	
			.35608

$$s_{b_i^1} = \sqrt{\dfrac{m_{ii}(1 - R^2_{y \cdot 12345})}{n - v}}$$

$$s_{b_5^1} = \sqrt{\dfrac{1.602284(0.35608)}{56}} = 0.100937$$

$$t_2 = \dfrac{+0.12431 - 0}{0.100937} = 1.2316$$

$$r_{y1 \cdot 2345} = \dfrac{-0.83192}{\sqrt{8.01144(2.80836)}} = -0.17539 \text{ ns}$$

$$r_{y2 \cdot 1345} = \dfrac{+2.18272}{\sqrt{5.45052(2.80836)}} = +0.55791*$$

$$r_{y3 \cdot 1245} = \dfrac{+1.94476}{\sqrt{2.64237(2.80836)}} = +0.71391*$$

$$r_{y4 \cdot 1235} = \dfrac{+1.13775}{\sqrt{5.29432(2.80836)}} = +0.29506*$$

$$r_{y5 \cdot 1234} = \dfrac{-(+0.34911)}{\sqrt{1.64568(2.80836)}} = -0.16239 \text{ ns}$$

$$t_1^2 = \dfrac{r^2_{y5 \cdot 1234}(n - v)}{1 - r^2_{y5 \cdot 1234}} = 1.52 = F(1, 56) \text{ above}$$

$$t_2^2 = 1.52 \text{ again as for F(1, 56) and } t_1^2$$

(b) $R^2_{y \cdot 12345} = 1 - 0.35608 = 0.64392$; hence, more than one third of the $\sum (y^2)$ still is not accounted for. This means there probably are other important X_i not yet considered, so some thought and effort should be devoted to finding one or more additional X's which add significantly to the further reduction of the $\sum (Y - \hat{Y})^2$.

(c) It is somewhat doubtful that X_2 contributes importantly to this study after X_1 already is being included, but the F(1, 59) is below the 10% level slightly, and the $R^2_{y \cdot 12345}$ is sufficiently far from 1.0 that it probably is wise to leave X_2 in this study, unless better additional X's are found.

(d) It was found that $r_{y1 \cdot 2345}$, $r_{y4 \cdot 1235}$, and $r_{y5 \cdot 1234}$ were respectively less than the corresponding simple r's. Although these differences cannot be tested for significance, it may be that the original r's were due in part to help from other variables related to X_1, X_4, and X_5.

(e) It was observed that $r_{y2 \cdot 1345}$ and $r_{y3 \cdot 1245}$ were substantially larger than r_{y2} and r_{y3}, so it is felt that the relationships between X_2 and Y and between X_3 and Y were somewhat obscured by the X_1, X_4, and X_5 until this partial correlation analysis revealed the apparently stronger linear relationship to Y.

(f) The following specific hypotheses were tested and accepted with $\alpha = 0.05$:

(a) $\beta_2 = 0$ in $Y = \alpha + \beta_1(X_1 - \mu_1) + \beta_2(X_2 - \mu_2) + \epsilon$ (but would not have been accepted with a 10% level.)

(b) $\beta_1 = 0$ in $Y = \alpha + \beta_1(X_1 - \mu_1) + \beta_2(X_2 - \mu_2) + \cdots$
$+ \beta_5(X_5 - \mu_5) + \epsilon$

(c) $\beta_5 = 0$ in $Y = \alpha + \beta_1(X_1 - \mu_1) + \beta_2(X_2 - \mu_2) + \cdots$
$+ \beta_5(X_5 - \mu_5) + \epsilon$

(d) $\rho_{y1 \cdot 2345} = 0$

(e) $\rho_{y5 \cdot 1234} = 0$

(g) The following specific hypotheses were tested and rejected with $\alpha = 0.05$.

(a) $\beta = 0$ in $Y = \alpha + \beta(X_1 - \mu) + \epsilon$

(b) $\beta = 0$ in $Y = \alpha + \beta(X_2 - \mu) + \epsilon$

(c) $\beta = 0$ in $Y = \alpha + \beta(X_3 - \mu) + \epsilon$

(d) $\beta = 0$ in $Y = \alpha + \beta(X_4 - \mu) + \epsilon$

(e) $\beta = 0$ in $Y = \alpha + \beta(X_5 - \mu) + \epsilon$

(f) $\beta_3 = 0$ in $Y = \alpha + \beta_1(X_1 - \mu_1) + \beta_2(X_2 - \mu_2)$
$+ \beta_3(X_3 - \mu_3) + \epsilon$

(g) $\beta_4 = 0$ in $Y = \alpha + \beta_1(X_1 - \mu_1) + \cdots + \beta_4(X_4 - \mu_4) + \epsilon$

(h) $\rho_{y2 \cdot 1345} = 0$

(i) $\rho_{y3 \cdot 1245} = 0$

(j) $\rho_{y4 \cdot 1235} = 0$

(k) $\beta_2 = 0$ in $Y = \alpha + \beta_1(X_1 - \mu_1) + \beta_2(X_2 - \mu_2) + \cdots$
$+ \beta_5(X_5 - \mu_5) + \epsilon$

(*l*) $\beta_3 = 0$ in $Y = \alpha + \beta_1(X_1 - \mu_1) + \beta_2(X_2 - \mu_2) + \cdots$
$\qquad\qquad + \beta_5(X_5 - \mu_5) + \epsilon$

(*m*) $\beta_4 = 0$ in $Y = \alpha + \beta_1(X_1 - \mu_1) + \beta_2(X_2 - \mu_2) + \cdots$
$\qquad\qquad + \beta_5(X_5 - \mu_5) + \epsilon$

In view of the apparent complexity of a table such as Table 11.61, it should be emphasized that modern digital computers can be programmed to produce in a printed form all the results discussed herein, and can do so very rapidly. One could describe some of the computations in Table 11.61 in terms of mathematical operations with matrices, but this will not be done herein. Anyone familiar with matrix algebra probably already knows this, and those not familiar with it can use routinely the methods given above or seek aid from a computing center.

REVIEW PROBLEMS

1. Suppose that two indistinguishable sacks contain, respectively, 5 blue and 7 white marbles, 3 blue and 6 white marbles. If a sack is chosen at random and thereafter one marble is drawn at random, what is the probability of drawing a white marble?

2. Referring to set-up of Problem 1, but drawing a pair of marbles simultaneously, what is the probability of drawing a pair of white marbles?

3. Suppose that on a certain 10-mile stretch of two-lane highway there are 20 legal passing zones with the following lengths: 8 are 1/10 mile, 6 are 1/8 mile, 5 are 1/6 mile, and 1 is 1/5 mile. These passing zones are distributed at random as far as a driver can tell. A car travelling 70 miles per hour comes up to a car travelling 60 miles per hour just as they approach a passing zone. If each car is 6 yards long, and if the car which is passing comes just to the rear of the car being passed but in the passing lane just as they reach the passing zone, what is the probability that the car in the passing lane can get 20 yards ahead of the other car before the passing zone ends, if both cars maintain their speeds?

4. Given the following data on two samples from $N(\mu_1, \sigma^2)$ and $N(\mu_2, \sigma^2)$ populations, test $H_0(\mu_1 \le \mu_2)$ against $H_a(\mu_1 > \mu_2)$, α being chosen as 0.10. How many ways could you make this test?

$\qquad X_1:\qquad -2.7,\ 0.5,\ -1.4,\ 2.0,\ 3.8,\ 0.9,$ and 1.6
$\qquad X_2:\qquad 4.2,\ -1.3,\ 2.2,\ 0.9,\ 3.6,\ 3.5,$ and 2.9

5. Suppose in Problem 4 the hypotheses were $H_0(\mu_1 = \mu_2)$ versus $H_a(\mu_1 \ne \mu_2)$; use an analysis of variance to make this test with $\alpha = 0.10$. How is this $F(1, 10)$ related to the t of Problem 4? What is the sampling distribution of the Between-Groups Mean Square under a fixed-effects model? Under a random-effects model?

6. Take a random sample of 20 sentences from Sections 11.1 and 11.2, and also from Sections 11.3 and 11.4 of this book. Classify each word as Noun, Verb, Adjective or Adverb, or Other. Construct a 2×4 contingency table and test the hypothesis that there is no association between section of chapter and frequencies of the word types.

7. Make up two sets of pairs of measurements (X_i, Y_i) such that $n = 6$ and $r \cong -0.4$ for one set and -0.8 for other. Thereafter regard each set as a

random sample from a normal bivariate population and test $H_0(\rho_1 = \rho_2)$ against $H_a(\rho_1 < \rho_2)$ with $\alpha = 0.10$.

8. Which of the following statements are true?
   (a) The hypotheses $H_{01}(\mu = 17)$ and $H_{02}(\mu = 19)$ both could be acceptable as judged by the same test criterion and with the same-sized region of rejection and the same sample data.
   (b) The power of any test of significance always will be increased by increasing the sample size, if all other pertinent conditions remain the same.
   (c) Mood's Square Rank Test is used to test two samples for difference in dispersion about the median.
   (d) Given random samples $X_1, \cdots, X_n$, the difference (largest X − smallest X) has a sampling distribution.

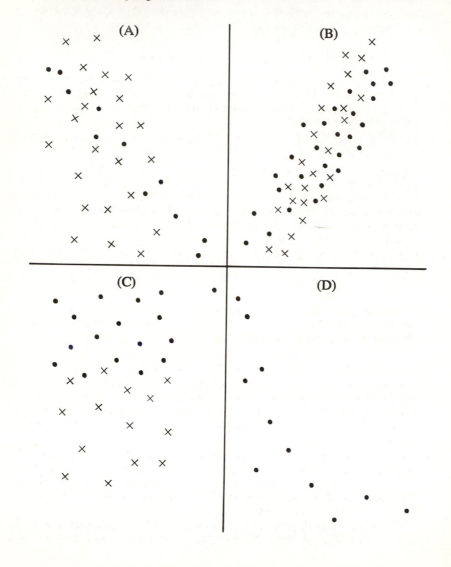

(e) If random samples of size $n = 16$ are to be drawn from an $N(10, 25)$ population, the quantity $(X_1 + \cdots + X_{16})/8$ will have a symmetrical distribution with standard deviation 10.

9. Given the scatter diagrams on page 448, answer the questions.
   (a) In which case(s) would the $H_0(\beta_1 = \beta_2)$ be likely to be rejected?
   (b) In which case(s) might it be necessary to use a special method, because an assumption usually made appears to be unjustifiable?
   (c) In which case(s) is linearity of regression in doubt?
   (d) In which case(s) is b negative?
   (e) For which case is r the largest without regard to sign?

10. Given the following hypothetical analysis of variance, do all appropriate statistical tests, including Fisher's LSD and Duncan's NMRT, if justified. Use $\alpha = 0.10$.

Source of Variation	DF	Mean Square
Manufacturing Method (fixed)	3	350.0
Locality (fixed)	9	110.9
M × L	27	68.52
Plant within M and L	80	75.31
Total about $x..$	119	

Method Means: $x_{1.} = 30$, $x_{2.} = 32$, $x_{3.} = 34$, $x_{4.} = 38$
Locality Means: $x_{.1} = 31.9$, $x_{.2} = 34.5$, $x_{.3} = 30.7$, $x_{.4} = 33.0$, $x_{.5} = 35.2$, $x_{.6} = 33.6$, $x_{.7} = 28.6$, $x_{.8} = 32.7$, $x_{.9} = 40.0$, $x_{.10} = 34.8$

11. Write down the statistical model for Problem 10, defining all symbols clearly.

12. How would the F tests for Problem 10 change, if all effects were random? How would the multiple-comparison procedures be affected?

13. Answer the questions of Problem 12 for Methods fixed and Localities random.

14. Given the following hypothetical analysis of variance for a nested type of experiment, estimate all of the variance components:

Source of Variation	DF	Mean Square
Geographical Area	4	201.9
Cities within Area	10	140.7
Households within City within Area	285	6.851
Total about $x..$	299	

Assume three cities per area, and 20 households per city.

15. Estimate the standard deviations of the estimated variance components for Problem 14.

16. Do all useful F tests from Problem 14, and draw appropriate conclusions.

17. Write down the statistical model for Problem 14, making all assumptions clear.

18. Suppose one is going to conduct a CR experiment with 25 animals divided into five groups of 5 animals each. In how many physically different ways could those 25 animals be assigned to five treatments? What is the statistical model for this design? What does its ϵ term mean?

19. Graph the binomial frequency distribution for $b(X; 18, 0.3)$. What are its mean and variance?

20. What is the standard deviation of the difference in numbers of heads tossed on two independent sets of 15 and 20 tosses, respectively, of an unbiassed coin?

Chapter 12

Curvilinear Regression Analysis

12.1 INTRODUCTION

The discussions of regression in Chapters 6 and 11 have assumed linear models. In situations involving but two measurements, a fixed X and a random Y, the model

$$Y_{ij} = \alpha + \beta X_i + \epsilon_{ij}$$

expresses the assumption that the true *means* of the Y_{ij} for $i = 1, 2, \cdots, n$ lie exactly on a straight line: $\mu_{Y_i} = \alpha + \beta X_i$ with random variation of the Y_{ij} about that line. With s fixed X's and a random variable Y, the linear model

$$Y_{ij\ldots s} = \alpha + \beta_1 X_{1i} + \cdots + \beta_s X_{si} + \epsilon_{ij\ldots s}$$

expresses the assumption that the true *means* of the $Y_{ij\ldots s}$ lie exactly on a hyperplane, $\mu_{Y_i} = \alpha + \beta_1 X_{1i} + \cdots + \beta_s X_{si}$, the Y's varying randomly and vertically therefrom. These two situations have been studied in earlier chapters.

There are useful and interesting situations in which the relationships among some or all of the measurements are nonlinear, that is, are curvilinear. For example, plant and animal growths relative to time (age) frequently are curvilinear. Figure 12.11 illustrates a portion of an age-weight relationship supposedly observed in a group of animals. In such a circumstance an exponential model might seem appropriate; for example, some form of

(12.11) $Y_{ij} = \alpha k^{X_i} + \epsilon_{ij}$

In some other type of study it might be that the maximum average Y's occurred for intermediate values of X. For example, consider the scatter diagram of Figure 12.12, with a free-hand line drawn in to show the trend. The scatter diagram of this figure would be likely to suggest the model

(12.12) $$Y_{ij} = \alpha + \beta_1 X_i + \beta_2 X_i^2 + \epsilon_{ij}$$

because it seems likely that the true mean Y's for $X = 1, 2, \cdots, i, \cdots, n$ would lie on a parabola.

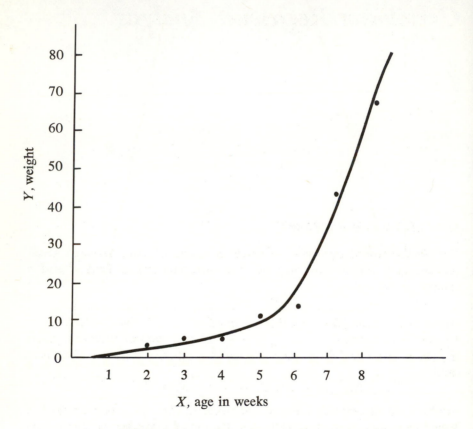

Figure 12.11.   An exponential scatter diagram.

If each Y measurement were being associated with two X measurements, X_1 and X_2, and if the relationship between X_1 and Y were quadratic when X_2 was fixed at a point and that between X_2 and Y were exponential when X_1 was fixed at a point, one might expect that the model

(12.13) $$Y_{ijk} = \alpha + \beta_1 X_{1i} + \beta_2 X_{1i}^2 + \beta_3 k^{X_{2j}} + \epsilon_{ijk}$$

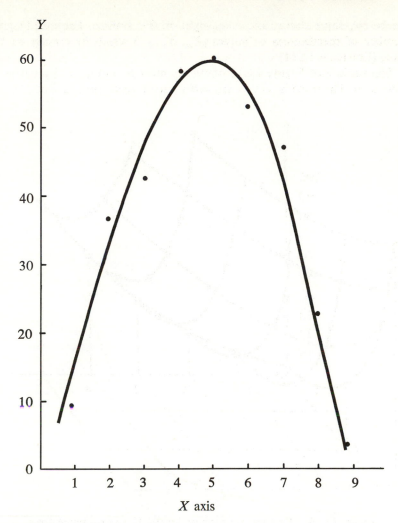

Figure 12.12.   A quadratic scatter diagram. The curve is free-hand.

would be useful. More specifically, the true model might be

$$Y_{ijk} = 1 + 2X_{1i} + 3X_{1i}^2 + 4e^{X_{2j}} + \epsilon_{ijk}$$

so that the means of the Y distributions in three dimensions for a specific pair of values of X_1 and X_2 would fall on the curved surface:

(12.14) $\mu_{Y_{ij}} = 1 + 2X_{1i} + 3X_{1i}^2 + 4e^{X_{2j}}$

Figure 12.13 depicts a portion of such a true regression surface. The actual points $(X_{1i}, X_{2j}, Y_{ijk})$ would be distributed in three-space about this surface:

some below, some above, and some right on this surface. Table 12.11 gives a number of specific sets of values $(X_{1i}, X_{2j}, \mu_{ij})$ which lie exactly on the surface (Equation 12.14).

The surface of Figure 12.13 obviously must be estimated by means of sample data. The same is true of any other curved regression surface.

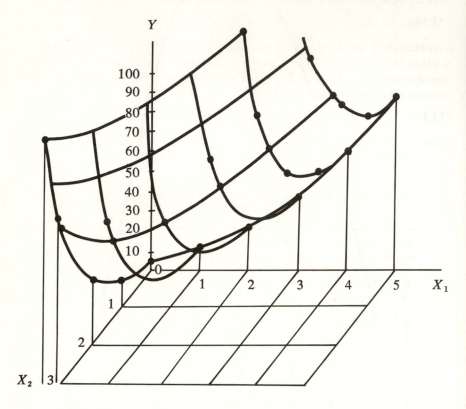

Figure 12.13. Portion of graph of Model 12.14 in three-space.

Mathematically it usually is not feasible, or best, to estimate a curvilinear surface directly. Instead, it is preferable to transform the curvilinear relationship into a linear relationship; that is, one geometrically transforms a curved surface into a plane—which will, however, be in $(s + 1)$-dimensional space.

Everyone is somewhat familiar with quadratic equations and the characteristic parabolic curve shown in Figure 12.12; so this type of curvilinear regression will be considered in some detail as an illustration of the transformation procedure used.

If Model 12.12 is the logical one for a given situation, as suggested by the scatter diagram or by theory, the sample data must be used to estimate the quadratic equation

(12.15) $$\mu_{Y_i} = \alpha + \beta_1 X_i + \beta_2 X_i^2$$

This equation is rectified (that is, made linear) by the substitutions $Z_1 = X$ and $Z_2 = X^2$, so that we have now shifted attention to the equation

(12.16) $$\mu_{Y_i} = \alpha + \beta_1 Z_{1i} + \beta_2 Z_{2i}$$

Geometrically speaking, a shift has been made from a curve in two-space to a plane in three-space. This might seem to be complicating the situation by transforming from plane geometry to solid geometry, but the solutions of the normal equations for a, b_1, and b_2 in

(12.17) $$\hat{Y}_i = a + b_1 z_{1i} + b_2 z_{2i}$$

where $z_{1i} = Z_{1i} - \bar{z}_1$ and $z_{2i} = Z_{2i} - \bar{z}_2$, are much easier to obtain than the corresponding ones obtained directly from the quadratic equation.

TABLE 12.11.   SOME POINTS ON THE CURVILINEAR REGRESSION PLANE
$$\mu_{Y_{ij}} = 1 + 2X_{1i} + 3X_{1i}^2 + 4e^{X_{2j}}$$

X_{1i}	X_{2j}	$\mu_{Y_{ij}}$	X_{1i}	X_{2j}	$\mu_{Y_{ij}}$	X_{1i}	X_{2j}	$\mu_{Y_{ij}}$
0	0	5	2	0	21	4	0	61
0	1	12	2	0.5	24	4	1	68
0	2	31	2	1	28	4	2	87
0	3	81	2	1.5	35	4	3	137
0	3.5	133	2	2	47	4	3.5	190
1	0	10	2	2.5	66	5	0	90
1	0.5	13	2	3	97	5	1	97
1	1	17	2	3.5	150	5	2	116
1	1.5	24	3	0	38	5	3	166
1	2	36	3	1	45			
1	2.5	55	3	2	64			
1	3.0	86	3	3	114			
1	3.5	138	3	3.5	167			

To illustrate the procedures described above, consider the following sampling data:

X:	1	2	3	4	5	6	7	8	9
Y:	10	37	43	59	61	54	48	24	5

which produced Figure 12.12. When the substitutions given above are made, one obtains:

Z_1:	1	2	3	4	5	6	7	8	9
Z_2:	1	4	9	16	25	36	49	64	81
Y:	10	37	43	59	61	54	48	24	5

Proceeding by the Method of Least Squares for multiple linear regression, as described in Chapter 11, one obtains the following least-squares regression equation:

$$\hat{Y}_i = 31.8Z_{1i} - 3.27Z_{2i} - 17.6$$

The sum of squares of vertical deviations of the sample Y's from this plane is the least it can be from any plane.

If one replaces the Z_1 and Z_2 by X and X^2, respectively, one obtains the following quadratic equation:

(12.18) $$\hat{Y}_i = 31.8X_i - 3.27X_i^2 - 17.6$$

The graph shown in Figure 12.12 is a free-hand line, drawn to show that the observed trend in the scatter diagram is essentially quadratic. Equation 12.18 is the least-squares curvilinear fit to the scatter diagram (as will be pointed out in a later section), and its graph will have a minimum $\sum_{i=1}^{9}(Y_i - \hat{Y}_i)^2$, even though the actual minimization was accomplished from a plane.

If Equation 12.13 is thought to be the actual situation (though this would be hard to recognize), then the substitutions

$$Z_1 = X_1, \qquad Z_2 = X_1^2, \qquad \text{and} \quad Z_3 = e^{X_2}$$

will rectify this curvilinear relationship and geometrically replace a curved surface in three-space by a hyperplane in four-dimensional space. Thereafter, the methods of Chapter 11 again apply.

If the true relationship between X_i and the mean Y_i is $\mu_{Y_i} = \alpha + \beta k^{X_i}$, then $\log \mu_{Y_i}$ and X_i are linearly related and the $\log Y_i$ essentially follows a linear regression model. This means that if the Y_i scale is laid off nonuniformly on a logarithmic scale, the scatter diagram will suggest a linear model. This is a useful tool in practice; in fact, it is so useful that graph paper is readily available for this purpose. It is called *semilog paper*. This paper is illustrated by the data of Table 12.12 and the scatter diagram of Figure 12.14.

TABLE 12.12.   FITTING A LEAST-SQUARES LINE AFTER A LOGARITHMIC TRANSFORMATION OF THE DATA

X	Y	$\log Y = Z$	
0	2	0.301	$\sum(x^2) = 240$ $\sum(xz) = 37.572$
2	7	0.845	$\sum(z^2) = 5.920365$
4	10	1.000	$b = 0.1566$
6	24	1.380	$\therefore \hat{Z}_i = 0.1566X_i + 0.405$ is the equa-
8	40	1.602	tion of the least-squares equation for
10	110	2.041	$\log_{10} Y_i = Z_i$.
12	190	2.279	
14	400	2.602	
16	750	2.875	
$\bar{x} = 8$		$\bar{z} = 1.658$	

If in another situation the basic relationship between X_i and the true mean of the Y_i for $X = X_i$ is of the form

$$(\mu_{Y_i})^\gamma = \delta \cdot X_i^\xi$$

a logarithmic transformation on both sides of the equation will produce $\gamma \log \mu_{Y_i} = \log \delta + \xi \log X_i$. Hence, one again can use linear regression models with $\hat{Z}_i = \log Y_i$, $W_i = \log X_i$, and $\hat{Z}_i = a + bW_i$ as an estimate of $\mu_{Z_i} = \alpha + \beta W_i$. Graphing of the observed data on *log-log graph paper*, in which both axes are on log scales, will produce an essentially linear scatter diagram.

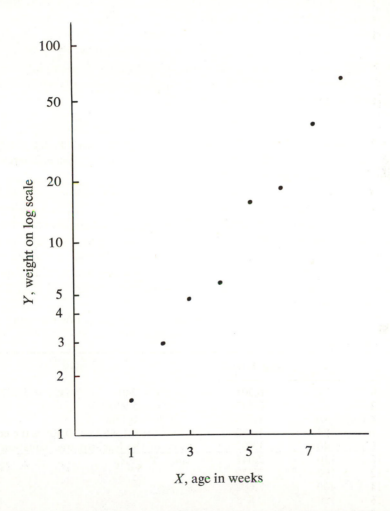

Figure 12.14.   Logarithmic transformation used to produce linearity of trend for Table 12.12.

To illustrate, consider the following data patterned after the specific relationship $(\mu_{Y_i})^{1/2} = 0.45X_i^{2/3}$:

X_i:	4	6	8	10	15	24	27	35
Y_i:	1.3	2.5	2.0	6.3	7.0	15.1	15.5	24.0

If both the X scale and the Y scale are measured in logarithmic units, as shown in Figure 12.15, one obtains a scatter diagram which clearly suggests

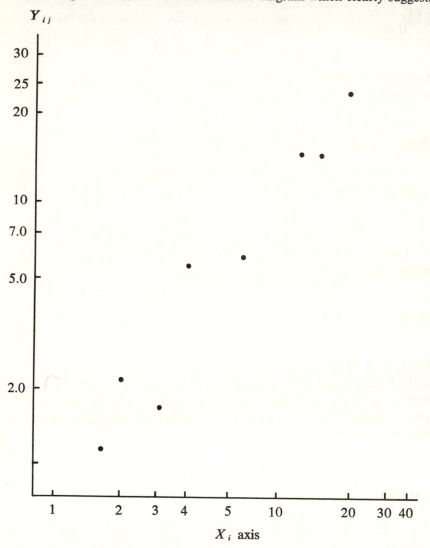

Figure 12.15. Illustration of log-log transformation to produce linear regression. Both scales are in units of $\log_{10}$.

a linear relationship between $\log X_i$ and mean $\log Y_i$, that is, the model

$$\mu_{\log Y_i} = \alpha + \beta \log X_i$$

Thus, one would assume

(12.19) $$\hat{Z}_i = a + b(\log X_i - \overline{\log X_i})$$

and would so choose the a and b of this equation as to minimize the $\sum (Z_i - \hat{Z}_i)^2$, which is minimizing the $\sum (\log Y_i - \log Y)^2$ rather than the $\sum (Y_i - \hat{Y}_i)^2$, but this is the only feasible way of fitting a line to Figure 12.15.

If the relationship between X and Y is of the type

$$XY = \alpha$$

it obviously could be made linear by use of logarithms, but it may be simpler to solve for $Y = \alpha/X$ and set $W = 1/X$. This produces the linear model

$$Y_{ij} = \alpha W_i + \epsilon_{ij}$$

Hence, one uses the sample regression relationship

$$\hat{Y}_i = aW_i$$

It is found by the Least-Squares method that

$$a = \frac{\sum (YW)}{\sum (W^2)}$$

One final curvilinear form, among the many possible, will be considered in this section, and this is the polynomial form

$$Y = \alpha + \beta_1 X + \beta_2 X^2 + \cdots + \beta_s X^s + \epsilon$$

The transformation $Z_i = X^i$ suggests the sample regression equation

$$\hat{Y} = a + b_1 z_1 + b_2 z_2 + \cdots + b_s z_s$$

This is the multiple linear regression form considered in Chapter 11, so those methods now apply. Obviously, the interpretation of this sort of analysis must recognize the curvilinearity of the true regression line. In some situations special methods can be employed for polynomial regression, as will be discussed in Section 12.2.

PROBLEMS

1. Given the following data,

X:	1.5	2.1	3.0	4.4	5.9	6.5	7.0
Y:	3	10	16	90	325	700	1000

(a) Make a scatter diagram of these data on arithmetic graph paper.
(b) Make a scatter diagram of these data on semilog graph paper. Draw appropriate conclusions.

2. Using a log transformation of the Y data of Problem 1, obtain the least-squares linear regression equation for $Z = \log Y$ as a linear function of X.

3. Suppose that the following data have been observed under conditions which suggest that $\mu_{Y_i} = \alpha + e^{\beta X_i}$:

X_i:	0	2	4	6	8	10	12	14	16
Y_i:	2	7	10	24	40	110	190	400	750

Suggest a logical transformation to secure a linear relationship, and then determine the appropriate least-squares regression equation. Discuss its meaning, and state what Sum of Squares has been minimized.

4. Make up a set of data which fit the general model $\mu_{Y_i} = \alpha + \beta_1 X + \beta_2 X^2$, but which, when transformed to a plane in three-space, will have a negative b_2.

5. If the data for Figure 12.12 are modified to end at $X = 7$, what effect will this have on the regression coefficients of the corresponding *linear* regression model?

6. For each of the following curvilinear models suggest a transformation of variables which will produce a linear model:
   (a) $Y_{ij} = \alpha + \beta \log X_i + \epsilon_{ij}$
   (b) $Y_{ij} = \alpha + X_i \log \beta + \epsilon_{ij}$
   (c) $Y_{ij} = \alpha + \beta e^{X_i} + \epsilon_{ij}$
   (d) $Y_{ij} = \alpha + \beta e^{X_i^2} + \epsilon_{ij}$
   (e) $Y_{ij} = \alpha e^{\beta X_i} + \epsilon_{ij}$
   (f) $Y_{ij} = \alpha + \beta_1 X_i^2 + \beta_2 X_i^3 + \epsilon_{ij}$
   (g) $X_i \cdot Y_{ij} = \alpha + \epsilon_{ij}$
   (h) $Y_{ij} = \alpha / X_i + \epsilon_{ij}$
   (i) $Y_{ijk} = \alpha + \beta_1 / X_{1i} + \beta_2 \log X_{2j} + \epsilon_{ijk}$

7. Make up a set of 10 pair of observations which:
   (a) follow Problem 6, part (g), exactly, ignoring the ϵ_{ij}.
   (b) follow Problem 6, part (g), in trend but have scatter about the regression curve.

12.2 USE OF SPECIAL METHODS IN SPECIAL CASES

Sometimes special situations occur frequently enough to justify the development of special methods. This is true of the model

(12.21) $$Y = \alpha + \beta_1 X^1 + \cdots + \beta_s X^s + \epsilon$$

It should be borne in mind, however, that the procedures of previous and of subsequent sections could be used, because they are the basic methods.

Fisher suggested a very neat and efficient way to handle polynomial regression when the X measurement is made at equal intervals along the X scale. The procedure has been used already in Section 9.8. Actually, the general idea of using orthogonal polynomials was originated in the nineteenth century by Tchebycheff, and many writers have used this concept since, but Fisher's procedures seem especially easy to use. Moreover, he and Yates (Fisher-Yates tables cited earlier) have provided convenient tables with which to carry out the method of orthogonal polynomials. Basically, one can look at this process as follows. If it is true that Y and X have a polynomial relationship (Equation 12.21), then set ξ_j equal to a polynomial of degree j in X, where the ξ_j also are *orthogonal* polynomials with $j = 1, 2, \cdots, s$. The term "orthogonal" carries the same meaning of independence as in Chapter 9. Thus, $\hat{Y}$ is now expressed as

(12.22)
$$\hat{Y} = a + B\xi_1 + C\xi_2 + \cdots + T\xi_s$$

in which ξ_1 is a linear function of X, ξ_2 is a quadratic function of X, etc. The advantage of orthogonality is that each part of this equation is independent of the others, so one can compute each regression coefficient separately and can test the significance of each term in Equation 12.22 quite readily. The interested reader is referred to Anderson and Bancroft, chap. 16, Snedecor, chap. 15, Fisher-Yates tables (all cited earlier), and R. A. Fisher, *Statistical Methods For Research Workers* (Oliver and Boyd, Edinburgh, 1936, chap. 5), and E. J. Williams, *Regression Analysis* (Wiley, New York, 1959, chap. 3), for additional and more specific information on this subject. At the same time the reader is reminded that this use of orthogonal polynomials is only a neat way to handle a special curvilinear regression problem which also is solvable by the substitution $Z_i = X^i$ and the use of familiar multiple linear regression procedures, as set forth in Chapter 11.

One point with regard to polynomial regressions deserves additional comment. Even though a polynomial be transformed into a multiple linear regression form by the substitution of $Z_i = X^i$ in Equation 12.21, certain tests of significance may be different. With a true multiple linear regression situation from the beginning, it is appropriate to test any b_i or b_i' for significance without regard to any other variable than X_i. However, if the basic regression is believed to be a polynomial regression, it obviously is somewhat different to test intermediate b_i''s as compared to testing the last b_i'. For example, if a cubic polynomial is assumed, so that

$$\hat{Y} = a + b_1 x_1 + b_2 x_2 + b_3 x_3$$

where $x_3 = (X^3 - \overline{x^3})$, the test of $H_0(\beta_3 = 0)$ is testing if there really is a cubic relationship between Y and X. If one concludes that the β_3 is equal to 0, then a test of $H_0(\beta_2 = 0)$ will have a different interpretation if $H_0(\beta_3 = 0)$ has been rejected. It seems most useful with an assumed polynomial regression to test $H_0(\beta_3 = 0)$ first. If this H_0 is rejected, one concludes the relationship between X and Y is cubic—assuming no higher degree is even considered. If $H_0(\beta_3 = 0)$ is accepted, then $H_0(\beta_2 = 0)$ logically should be tested with only a quadratic equation fitted. As the reader should recall, the F testing procedure previously described (as in Table 11.61, for example) will accomplish these successive tests, if interpreted from the *last* F back toward the first F shown.

In some kinds of statistical analysis it is useful to rectify the cumulative normal frequency distribution. As the reader should recall, this distribution has a symmetrical S shape centered on $\lambda = 0$ and with a vertical scale running from $P = 0$ to $P = 1.00$, where $P = \Pr\{\text{random } \lambda < \lambda_0\}$. Figures 12.21 and 12.22 show how the cumulative normal curve is rectified by means of a nonuniform λ scale. This nonuniform scale is so chosen that the scale distance between λ_i and λ_j is just the difference between $\Pr\{\lambda < \lambda_i\}$ and $\Pr\{\lambda < \lambda_j\}$ for the cumulative normal distribution. For example, $\Pr\{\lambda < 0\} = 0.500$, whereas $\Pr\{\lambda < -1\} = 0.160$; hence, the points $\lambda = 0$ and $\lambda = -1$ are 34 units apart on the nonuniform λ scale of Figure 12.22.

If one has some data which one suspects may be from a normal distribution, the cumulative distribution can be plotted above the nonuniform λ scale of Figure 12.22, or its equivalent, to see whether the resulting graph is essentially linear. Obviously, sampling and other errors will keep this rectified graph from being perfectly linear.

An alternative way to rectify a cumulative normal curve is to plot the X measurement (or some function thereof) on the horizontal against the λ measurement corresponding to the cumulative frequency for that X. To illustrate, suppose that the following data are obtained from a study of a fly spray when dosages X_i are applied to cages of 500 houseflies:

$X = $ Dosage (ppm):	1	2	3	4	5	6	7	8	9	10
$Y = $ killed (%):	4	2	8	30	36	82	84	96	92	98

In order to rectify the cumulative curve (it is assumed that any fly killed by dose d would have been killed by a stronger dose) by the method just described, one would need to convert to the standard normal, λ. The rectification can be accomplished by plotting dosage on the horizontal in terms of the λ which, in the standard normal, corresponds to the observed percent kill. The numbers required are as follows, Table III being used to obtain the λ's:

Percent kill	4	2	8	30	36	82	84	96	92	98
λ	-1.75	-2.05	-1.41	-0.52	-0.36	$+0.92$	$+1.00$	$+1.75$	$+1.41$	$+2.05$
X	1	2	3	4	5	6	7	8	9	10

When these λ's are plotted on the vertical scale against dosage X on the horizontal, one obtains Figure 12.23. The scatter diagram of this figure clearly suggests a linear relationship between X and λ. If $+5$ be added to the λ's above, the sum is what Fisher has called the *probit*. This topic is more fully discussed in a later section.

There are many curvilinear regression problems unmentioned here. The interested reader is invited to consult Williams' *Regression Analysis* (cited earlier) for additional information and references.

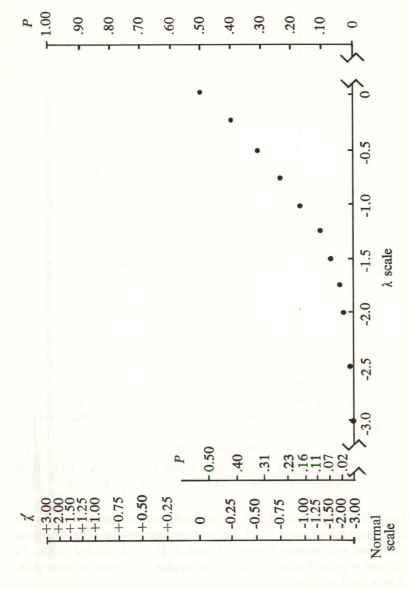

Figure 12.21.   First step in rectification of cumulative normal frequency distribution.

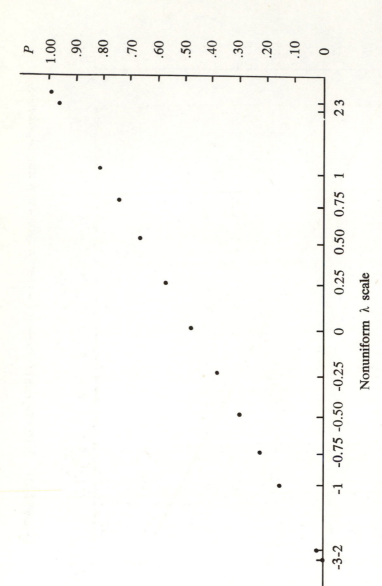

Figure 12.22.   Second step in rectification of the cumulative normal frequency curve. Nonuniform scale is based on the λ' scale of Figure 12.21.

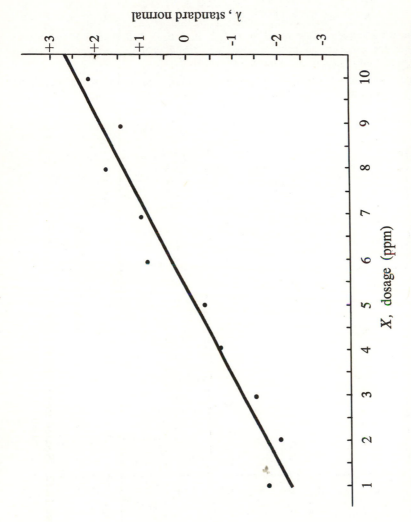

Figure 12.23. Scatter diagram of relationship between dosage (X) and normalized kill (λ).

PROBLEMS

1. Given the following hypothetical data, determine whether the relationship between X and Y is linear, quadratic, or cubic, by:
   (a) Making a scatter diagram.
   (b) Fitting $\hat{y} = a + b_1x + b_2x^2 + b_3x^3$ by Least Squares and testing for significance appropriately.

X:	0	1	2	3	4	5	6	7	8
Y:	-40	3	-13	20	5	2	-10	4	17

2. Make up a set of Y data for $X = 0, 1, 2, 3, 4, 5, 6, 7, 8, 9,$ and 10, such that the scatter diagram suggests a quadratic trend. Then fit a quadratic trend line by the Method of Least Squares.

3. Suggest for each of the following sketches a transformation which would be likely to produce a linear trend to replace this curvilinear trend.

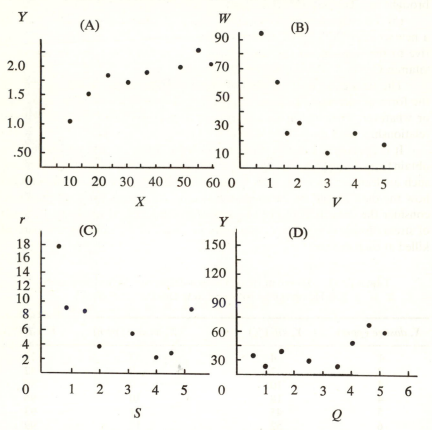

4. Referring to Problem 3, estimate the actual data from the scales for part (b) of the figure, rectify the apparent trend by means of an appropriate transformation, and derive the linear trend equation for the transformed data, *after making the transformed scatter diagram* to see whether your transformation has, in fact, produced essentially a linear trend.

5. Do as in Problem 4 for part (d) of the figure in Problem 3.

12.3 DOSAGE-RESPONSE CURVES WHEN QUANTAL RESPONSES ARE INVOLVED

In certain types of experimental research, plants or animals are subjected to some planned stresses in varying intensities designed to determine the relationship between the intensity of stress and the level of the associated response for a given type of organism and environment. These studies often have one of two purposes:

(*a*) To determine, and to use, the mathematical relationship between level of stress (often called *dosage*) and level of response to a given stress. For example, a toxicologist might wish to study the relationship between concentration of a certain toxic agent in a spray and the mortality of houseflies brought into contact with that spray.

(*b*) To evaluate (or assay) some agent of unknown strength, such as a new source of vitamin C, in terms of the responses of some organisms relative to the response of that same class of organisms to a known source of vitamin C.

The stresses to which a class of organisms are subjected also may be in the form of increasing times of exposure to a fixed amount of drug, x-rays, or whatever. This sort of an experiment would produce a dosage-response relationship, with time as the dosage.

It is appropriate at this point to ask what kinds of data one expects to obtain from dosage-response studies involving all-or-none (quantal) responses, such as death or survival, what assumptions one reasonably can make, and how the data should be handled statistically. As a basis for such inquiries, consider the data in Table 12.31 supposedly obtained by applying 12 levels of stress (dosages) to cages of 500 houseflies each and recording the percent killed at each dosage.

TABLE 12.31.   HYPOTHETICAL DOSAGE-RESPONSE DATA, ASSUMING 500 HOUSEFLIES USED AT EACH DOSAGE OF SPRAY

X, dosage (*ppm*)	Y, kill (%)	X, dosage (*ppm*)	Y, kill (%)
1	4	7	78
2	2	8	82
3	10	9	90
4	18	10	96
5	45	11	93
6	52	12	99

Figure 12.31 shows the dosage-response scatter diagram for these hypothetical experimental data.

In Figure 12.31 this particular dosage-response relationship is curvilinear in a manner suggesting some kind of S-shaped curve in the population sampled. One could simply regard the problem as one of empirically fitting a curve to the scatter diagram of Figure 12.31 without making any assumptions regarding the mechanism back of the response of flies to dosages of a toxin, and with no intention of making tests of hypotheses or of estimating any parameters of the population. From this point of view one seeks to rectify the scatter diagram by transformation of one or both measurements, X and Y. Two of the procedures which have been suggested and used will be discussed:

(*a*) Transform percent kill into "*probit kill*" by using

(12.31)   Probit kill $= \lambda + 5$

where λ is the standard normal variate used in Section 12.2. It may also be necessary in some cases, but not the present one, to transform the X to logarithms.

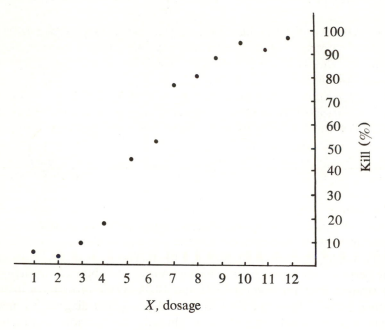

Figure 12.31. Scatter diagram for the data of Table 12.31 illustrating a dosage-response relationship.

(*b*) Transform the fraction killed at each dosage into *logits* by means of the formula

(12.32) $l = \text{logit } Y = \dfrac{Y}{100 - Y}$ for dosage X_i

where $Y = 1/(1 + e^{-(\alpha + \beta X)})$. It also could be necessary in some instances, but not in the present one, to use log X instead of X.

R. A. Fisher and C. I. Bliss have provided tables which convert "percent kill" into "probit kill." J. Berkson has provided tables which convert "fraction kill" into "logit kill." These have been used to prepare Table 12.32. Figure 12.32 was then prepared, to compare the transformed scatter diagrams. Then Figures 12.33 and 12.34 were prepared with the probit and logit graph papers (which are readily available and which reduce the work of graphing quite a bit).

TABLE 12.32.   DATA OF TABLE 12.31 TRANSFORMED TO
PROBITS AND TO LOGITS

X, dosage (ppm)	Y, kill (%)	$y = \lambda + 5$, probit kill	Logit kill
1	4	3.25	− 3.18
2	2	2.95	− 3.89
3	10	3.72	− 2.20
4	18	4.08	− 1.52
5	45	4.87	− 0.20
6	52	5.05	+ 0.08
7	78	5.77	1.27
8	82	5.92	1.52
9	90	6.28	2.20
10	96	6.75	3.18
11	93	6.48	2.59
12	99	7.33	4.60

The scatter diagrams of Figures 12.33 and 12.34 are not identical, but they are very much alike. Both suggest a successful rectification of the relationship between dosage and response. There are methods, which make use of the weighting schemes suggested by Fisher, Bliss, and others (for probits) and by Berkson (for logits), by which equations can be obtained for the best-fitting straight lines for Figures 12.33 and 12.34. These procedures involve weightings for the observed points. When fitting a scatter diagram by means of logits, it is recommended that the weight $n_i \hat{p}_i \hat{q}_i$ (in our notation) be used for l_i, where $\hat{p}_i$ is the observed fraction killed and $\hat{q}_i$ is $1 - \hat{p}_i$. The n_i is the number observed at dosage X.

The proponents of probits recommend a procedure involving the use of a provisional line and provisional probits, followed by an iterative procedure. Each observed point on the scatter diagram is given a weight $= Z^2/\hat{p}\hat{q}$, where Z is the normal ordinate corresponding to the probit kill for this point.

In the discussion of dosage-response data the conclusion has been come

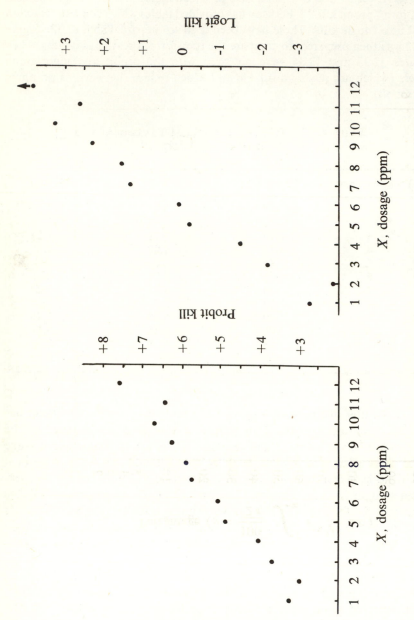

Figure 12.32. Probit and logit transformations of data of Table 12.31.

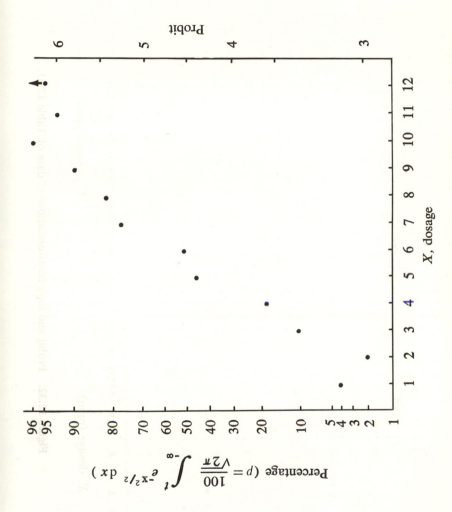

Figure 12.33.   Probit transformation for Table 12.32.

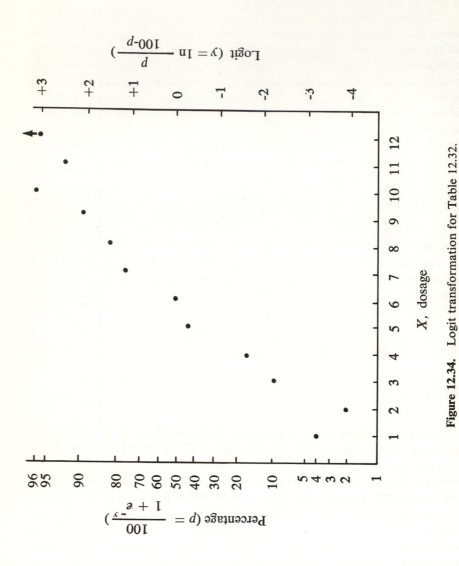

Figure 12.34. Logit transformation for Table 12.32.

to that from the purely empirical curve-fitting point of view the use of probits and the use of logits may lead to essentially the same rectification of the originally curvilinear data and to essentially the same fitted straight line. It is interesting to see what else can be done by these methods; this requires a look at the underlying assumptions.

Suppose that an organism has a tolerance for some particular sort of a stress placed upon it, and that different members of the same class (or species) of organism have different tolerances for this stress. Also assume that these tolerances plus random errors of observation and performance all combine to produce a normal curve of response to the stresses applied along some scale of such stresses. Then, if stresses are applied to groups of organisms at each level of stress, their all-or-none (quantal) responses should follow a cumulative normal curve. If this be the case, then probit analysis seems justified, is useful, and leads to tests of hypotheses and procedures of estimation as fully as the experimenter wishes to use this sort of analysis.

The logistic function

$$(12.33) \qquad Y = \frac{1}{1 + e^{-(\alpha + \beta X)}}$$

has been connected for many years with growth phenomena. For example, R. Pearl and L. J. Reed (*Proc. Nat. Acad. Sci.* 6: 275, 1920) used it to study population growth. It is seen by simple algebra applied to Equation 12.33 that

$$\frac{Y}{1 - Y} = \frac{\dfrac{1}{1 + e^{-(\alpha + \beta X)}}}{1 - \dfrac{1}{1 + e^{-(\alpha + \beta X)}}} = \frac{1}{e^{-(\alpha + \beta X)}} = e^{\alpha + \beta X};$$

Hence, $\log_e \left(\dfrac{Y}{1 - Y}\right) = \alpha + \beta X$. Therefore, logit $y = l = \log_e \left(\dfrac{Y}{1 - Y}\right) = \alpha + \beta X$, so that l and X are linearly related. This is the reason the logit transformation rectifies the logit function and rectifies certain scatter diagrams, as shown earlier. Berkson (*Biometrics* 7: 332, 1951) has pointed out that the logistic function also fits a number of physical phenomena. He contends that in many instances this function is a more dynamic and reasonable one to use than the cumulative normal, which is back of probit analysis. It certainly appears that in many cases the logistic procedure is easier and simpler to understand, *if* one is solely interested in curve-fitting and in the calculation of some descriptive constants, such as the mean lethal dose, the slope of the linear regression line, and some standard deviations.

If one wishes to do tests of significance and to compute and interpret confidence intervals, it appears best to use the probit transformation *if the assumption stated earlier appears to be satisfied*. Certainly, probit analysis and bioassay have become almost synonymous terms, probably because of the wide range of statistical procedures available if the assumption of normality made in probit analysis is reasonably acceptable.

The argument that the probit method is considerably more laborious than the logit method loses some of its force in view of the wide prevalence of so many digital and other high-speed computers. However, it still is illogical to waste machine time on a harder method if the assumptions behind a probit analysis seem unreasonable for a given situation or if the purpose of the analysis is purely one of curve-fitting.

There are many special forms of statistical analysis of dosage-response data as, for example, bioassay, in which one compares an unknown with a standard, but the field of dosage-response and, more particularly, of bioassay is too vast to be included in an introductory book in experimental statistics. The student is urged to read some of the references at the end of this chapter, if he is interested in pursuing this subject further.

REFERENCES

1. Berkson, J., "Application of the logistic function to bioassay," *J. Am. Stat. Assoc.* 39: 357–65, 1944.
2. Berkson, J., "Why I prefer logits to probits," *Biometrics* 7: 327–39, 1951.
3. Berkson, J., "A statistically precise and relatively simple method of estimating the bioassay with quantal response, based on the logistic function," *J. Am. Stat. Assoc.* 48: 565–99, 1953.
4. Bliss, C. I., "The comparison of dosage-mortality data," *Ann. Appl. Biol.* 22: 307–33, 1935.
5. Finney, D. J., *Probit Analysis: A Statistical Treatment of the Sigmoid Response Curve*, Cambridge Univ. Press, London.
6. Fisher, R. A., and Yates, F., *Statistical Tables for Biological, Agricultural and Medical Research*, Oliver and Boyd, London and Edinburgh.

PROBLEMS

1. C. I. Bliss (*J. Am. Pharm. Assoc.* 29: 466, 1940) gives a graph from which the following data on mortality of frogs administered Quabain were read:

Dose:	24	26	28	30	32	34	36	38
Cum. % kill:	1	4	18	40	68	85	95	99

Plot Dose (horizontal) versus Cumulative Percent Kill (vertical) on arithmetic paper. Then plot log dose against cum. % kill. Draw appropriate conclusions.

2. Plot log dose against probit on log-probit graph paper, and draw appropriate conclusions, for the data of Problem 1.

3. Convert the data of Problem 1 to logits, graph, and draw conclusions.

4. Do as in Problem 3, but use $X = $ log dose.

5. Use Reference 6 above, and fit a (log dose)-probit line to the data of Problem 1.

6. Use Reference 1 above, and fit a (log dose)-logit line to the data of Problem 1.

7. Given the following hypothetical dosage-response data simulating a study of the effects of a spray on flies, determine the basic relationship between dosage and response and calculate the corresponding linear regression line:

X (dose) ppm:	0.5	1	1.5	2	2.5	3
Y (cum. % kill):	10	20	40	60	85	93

8. Use the references suggested, plus others as needed, and apply logits to Problem 4.

REVIEW PROBLEMS

1. Given the following sketch of a hypothetical sampling distribution curve for a statistic ψ, do as directed below.

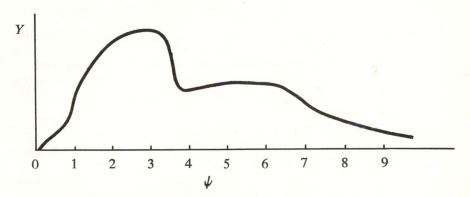

(*a*) Estimate the median ψ.

(*b*) Estimate the probability that a specified future random sample will produce a $\psi > 5$. A $\psi > 0$. A ψ between 3 and 5.

(*c*) Estimate the probability that two independent random samples will produce two ψ's, both of which exceed 5. Both of which exceed the median of ψ.

(*d*) Estimate the probability that three random samples will produce exactly two ψ's > 5 and one < 5. At least two ψ's > 5.

2. If a random sample of size 100 produces $X = 32$ A's and 68 not-A's, would you accept $H_0(p_A = 0.25)$ over $H_a(p_A > 0.25)$ if you chose $\alpha = 0.05$? What if $H_0(p_A \leqslant 0.25)$ is tested?

3. Given that a random sample from an $N(\mu, \sigma^2)$ population has produced

$$\Sigma X = 87.5, \quad \text{with } n = 12, \quad \Sigma X^2 = 653.25$$

what is the unbiassed estimate of σ^2? What is the GLB_{90} on σ^2 and what does it mean? What is the maximum-likelihood estimate of σ^2?

4. Given that a random sample from a normal bivariate population has produced $r = 0.504$ with $n = 12$,

    (a) Test $H_0(\rho = 0)$ against $H_a(\rho > 0)$ with $\alpha = 0.10$, and draw appropriate conclusions.

    (b) Compute a CI_{90} on ρ.

    (c) Compute a GLB_{90} on ρ.

5. Suppose that two random samples, each of size 12, have produced $r_1 = 0.504$ and $r_2 = 0.756$. Test $H_0(\rho_1 = \rho_2)$ against $H_a(\rho_1 \neq \rho_2)$. Against $H_a(\rho_1 < \rho_2)$. Use $\alpha = 0.10$, and draw all appropriate conclusions.

6. How large a sample does it take with r turning out to be 0.500 for $H_0(\rho = 0)$ to be rejected in favor of $H_a(\rho \neq 0)$, if $\alpha = 0.05$?

7. Suppose that an experimenter wishes to study four methods of some sort, each carried out by three operators representative of a certain degree of training. His purpose is to see:

    (a) Whether there are overall differences among these particular methods.

    (b) Whether operators with the level of training represented by the three used in the experiment are a significant source of variation in the measurement to be taken.

    (c) Whether the performances of operators at this level of training depend significantly on the method they are using.

    It is planned that each operator will perform each method five times. Write down and fully define the model for this experiment. Then write out the outline of the appropriate analysis of variance and the expected Mean Squares.

8. Referring to Problem 7, what is the sampling distribution of the Operators Mean Square? What is the proper Error Mean Square for testing the Operators Mean Square?

9. Make up a linear multiple regression problem in which there is a Y and two X's and in which Y and X_2 are significantly correlated, but in which it does not pay statistically to use X_2 after X_1 already has been used. Use $\alpha = 0.10$ and $n = 25$.

10. Make up a linear multiple regression problem for which r_{y1} is significant at the 10% level but $r_{y1.2}$ is not.

11. Make up a set of data on X and Y such that the scatter diagram will be linear on semilog graph paper.

12. Make up a scatter diagram such that the model $Y_{ij} = \alpha + \beta X_i + \epsilon_{ij}$, where the ϵ_{ij} are $N(0, \sigma^2)$, should be questioned, because there is a lack of homogeneity of variance for $X_1, \cdots, X_n$.

13. Sketch the sampling distribution of $(\bar{x} - 5)/s_{\bar{x}}$ for samples of size $n = 16$ from $N(5, \sigma^2)$, and mark on this sketch two different 5% regions of rejection for $H_0(\mu = 5)$. Also suggest an appropriate alternative hypothesis for each region of rejection.

14. Given the following correlation matrix, computations, and other indicated results, answer the questions below ($n = 21$):

    (a) What is the size of b_2' if $X_4 = Y$?

    (b) Which variables should one keep in a multiple linear regression analysis of X_4?

X_1	X_2	X_3	X_4	Unit matrix			
1	.76389	−.38131	.44856	1	0	0	0
	1	−.47578	.46285	0	1	0	0
		1	.27918	0	0	1	0
			1	0	0	0	1
1	.76389	−.38131	.44856	1	0	0	0
1	.76389	−.38131	.44856	1	0	0	0
	.41648	−.18450	.12020	−.76389	1	0	0
	1	−.44430	.28862	−1.83416	2.40109	0	0
		.77287	.50347	.04291	.44300	1	0
		1	.65143	.05552	.57320	1.29388	0
			.43613	−.25604	−.57720	−.65143	1
			1	−.58707	−1.32347	−1.49366	2.29290

$F(1, n-v)$	$n-v$	Δ				
4.79	19	.20121	.79879	2.40348	−1.80957	.05552
0.84	18	.03469	.76410	−1.80957	2.65502	.57320
12.78	17	.32797	.43613	.05552	.57320	1.29388

$$= (m_{ij})$$

$$\begin{pmatrix} 2.55379 & -1.47071 & .43795 & -.58707 \\ -1.47071 & 3.41894 & 1.43534 & -1.32347 \\ .43795 & 1.43534 & 2.26690 & -1.49366 \\ -.58707 & -1.32347 & -1.49366 & 2.29290 \end{pmatrix} = (M_{ij})$$

(c) What is the specific numerical formula for $s_{b'_2}$ if $X_4 = Y$?

(d) What are the size and meaning of $r_{X_4 X_3 . X_1 X}$?

15. Given the following data, use the Wilcoxon-Mann-Whitney test and Klotz's Normal Scores Test, and interpret the results so obtained:

X_1:   2.7, 11.4, 5.0, 5.5, 0.7, 16.2, 9.8, 7.2, 3.6, and 8.1
X_2:   17.5, 9.2, 8.7, 14.6, 0.5, 20.2, 10.7, 10.3, 12.2, and 2.7

16. Assume normality for the data of Problem 15 and then use the G test of $H_0(\mu_1 = \mu_2)$ versus $H_a(\mu_1 \neq \mu_2)$, assuming $\sigma_1^2 = \sigma_2^2$. Draw appropriate conclusions.

17. Assuming normality and $\sigma_1^2 \neq \sigma_2^2$ for the populations supposedly sampled in Problem 15, use the t' test to decide whether $H_0[(\mu_1 = \mu_2) \mid (\sigma_1^2 \neq \sigma_2^2)]$ is acceptable over $H_a[(\mu_2 > \mu_1) \mid (\sigma_1^2 \neq \sigma_2^2)]$.

18. Using the X_1 data of Problem 15, compute a CI_{90} on μ_1 by means of the t distribution and the G distribution in turn.

19. Make up data for a CR experiment with $t = 5$ and $r = 4$ and such that Hartley's F-max test will cause rejection of $H_0(\sigma_1^2 = \cdots \sigma_5^2 = \sigma^2)$ in favor of H_a(some σ_i^2 unequal) with $\alpha = 0.05$. Perform the test.

20. Draw a random sample of 10 sentences from each section of this chapter, compute the relative number of adverbs per sentence (that is, number of adverbs divided by number of words in the sentence), and test the hypothesis that the relative number of adverbs did not change from section to section.

21. Do as in Problem 20 but for the first section of each of the first 12 chapters of this text.

22. Draw a random sample of size $n = 20$ from Table 6.11, and compute therefrom the CI_{90} on the size of the next 28-weeks-old turkey to be obtained from that population.

Chapter 13

The Poisson and Negative Binomial Distributions

13.1 INTRODUCTION TO THE POISSON DISTRIBUTION

Suppose that some discrete events are occurring randomly in time or in space in such a way that:

(a) The probability that an event will occur in any specified portion of this time or space remains fixed for a useful period of observation.

(b) The occurrences of events in different segments of time or space are independent of each other.

(c) The occurrences of events within a given segment of time or space also are independent of each other.

For example, consider the following circumstances:

(1) During a given two-hour period telephone calls will come into a certain exchange in such a way that the number of calls during the ith five-minute interval is independent of the number of calls during the jth five-minute interval, with $i \neq j$. And, within any given five-minute interval, the calls will come in independently of each other. The number of calls, x_i, during the ith five-minute period within the designated two-hour period will be expected to be a Poisson variate.

(2) A virologist has introduced some virus particles into a solution and then has diluted and thoroughly mixed this solution several times to obtain a final solution which can be regarded as being composed of many one-cubic-

centimeter (1-cc.) volume units. Although attempts have been made to mix the virus particles into the liquid uniformly, the scarcity of particles and imperfectness of all mixing will cause some 1-cc. units to have no particles, others to have exactly one particle, others exactly two, etc. The numbers x_1 and x_2 of particles in two randomly drawn 1-cc. samples will be independent of each other in the sense that, if x_1 is known, this does not determine x_2 in any respect. Furthermore, the presence of particle A in a given 1-cc. sample does not hinder or enhance the occurrence of particle B in the same sample. The numbers x_i have a Poisson distribution.

If x_i is the number of telephone calls occurring during the ith observation on a Poisson process or x_i is the number of Poisson occurrences during some specified observation of a Poisson process, it turns out mathematically that for a given time or volume or interval the probability function for x_i is as follows:

(13.11)
$$\Pr\{x_i\} = \frac{e^{-\lambda}\lambda^{x_i}}{x_i!}, \qquad x_i = 0, 1, 2, \cdots \to \infty$$

where λ is the true average x_i for the situation sampled. For example, λ could be 3, equalling the average number of telephone calls per five-minute interval, or it could be 2, equalling the average number of virus particles per 1-cc. unit of volume of a given large volume of solution. The $\Pr\{x_i\}$ is the probability that a randomly chosen five-minute period will have x_i calls under the circumstances for which $\lambda = 3$, or it is the probability that a randomly drawn 1-cc. unit of a solution will have exactly x_i virus particles under circumstances in which $\lambda = 2$.

Other examples of situations which may involve a Poisson probability distribution are radioactive disintegrations being recorded by a Geiger counter, accidents to some individual worker over a specified period of time, mutations produced by irradiation, rare defects in some industrial product enumerated in time or over some length or mass of the product, weed seed in lawn grass considered per specified unit of volume, and machine stoppages caused by random events.

The Poisson probability function displayed in Equation 13.11 can be visualized (and derived mathematically) in another setting, namely, as an approximation to the binomial distribution $b(x_i; n, p)$ when p is quite small and n is quite large.

If in
$$b(x_i; n, p) = \binom{n}{x_i} p^{x_i}(1 - p)^{n - x_i}$$

the product $np \to \lambda$ as $p \to 0$ and $n \to \infty$, then it has been shown that

(13.12)
$$b(x_i; n, p) \to \frac{e^{-\lambda}\lambda^{x_i}}{x_i!}$$

Thus, the Poisson distribution may be regarded as the limiting form, or the rare-event form, of the binomial frequency distribution. How small the p

must be and how large the n, in practice, before one essentially is dealing with the Poisson distribution, is not known with precision; however, it is recalled that when p is not too small—say > 0.10—the $b(x_i; n, p) \rightarrow$ $N(np, npq)$. Thus, the binomial probability function "generates" two other distributions: the normal, when p is intermediate in size, and the Poisson, when p is extreme in size.

The name of the Poisson probability function comes from the fact that Simeon D. Poisson, who lived from 1781 to 1840, is believed to be the first person to derive Expression 13.12.

One can give a very useful and somewhat more general form of Equation 13.11 by supposing that

$$\lambda = \text{the average } x_i \text{ per unit of time}$$
$$t_i = \text{the number of units of time to obtain } x_i$$

Then one obtains the following probability function for x_i:

(13.13) $$\Pr\{x_i \mid \lambda, t_i\} = \frac{e^{-\lambda t_i}(\lambda t_i)^{x_i}}{x_i!}$$

TABLE 13.11.   FIVE POISSON DISTRIBUTIONS WITH $\lambda = 0.25, 0.50, 1.00,$ 3.00, AND 10.00, RESPECTIVELY

x_i	$\lambda = 0.25$	$\lambda = 0.50$	$\lambda = 1.00$	$\lambda = 3.00$	$\lambda = 10.00$
0	0.779	0.606	0.368	0.050	
1	0.195	0.303	0.368	0.149	0.000
2	0.024	0.076	0.184	0.224	0.002
3	0.002	0.013	0.061	0.224	0.008
4	0.000	0.002	0.015	0.168	0.019
5		0.000	0.003	0.101	0.038
6			0.001	0.050	0.063
7			0.000	0.022	0.090
8				0.008	0.113
9				0.003	0.125
10				0.001	0.125
11				0.000	0.114
12					0.095
13					0.073
14					0.052
15					0.035
16					0.022
17					0.013
18					0.007
19					0.004
20					0.002
21					0.001
Sum of $\Pr\{x_i\}$:	1.000	1.000	1.000	1.000	1.001

The Poisson distribution is a one-parameter, discrete, and nonsymmetrical distribution. Table 13.11 and Figure 13.11 present five specific Poisson distributions in both tabular and graphic form.

It is noted from the table and figure that for small λ the Poisson distributions are decidedly nonsymmetrical but, as λ increases, the distribution becomes nearly symmetrical.

It already has been said that the true mean of a Poisson distribution with parameter λ is $\mu_x = \lambda$. It also can be shown that the true variance for a Poisson distribution is $\sigma_x^2 = \lambda$. This result can be rationlized by noting that, for the binomial distribution, the variance is npq. If circumstances are such that $np \to \lambda$ as $n \to \infty$ and $p \to 0$, as for a Poisson rare-event process, then q must $\to 1$, so that $npq \to$ (quantity $\to \lambda$)(a quantity $\to 1$), or $(np)q \to \lambda$.

The fact that the mean and variance of a Poisson variate are equal can be used, at times, as a means of deciding that observed x's do have a Poisson distribution. If a variate is a binomial variate, its variance is $(np)q$, which is less than np, which is the mean, so the variance of a binomial variate is *less than* its mean, in contrast to the Poisson variate. In a later section it will be seen that another type of variate, the negative binomial, is typified by the fact that its variance is larger than its mean.

Another general property of Poisson variates which is useful is the fact that the sum of two independent Poisson variates with parameters λ_1 and λ_2 is a Poisson variate with parameter $\lambda = \lambda_1 + \lambda_2$. This can be shown as follows. It was stated in Chapter 1 that the probability of the simultaneous (or joint) occurrence of independent events is the product of their separate probabilities. Hence, for two independent Poisson variates x_1 and x_2,

$$\Pr\{x_1, x_2\} = \frac{e^{-\lambda_1}\lambda_1^{x_1}}{x_1!} \cdot \frac{e^{-\lambda_2}\lambda_2^{x_2}}{x_2!} = \frac{e^{-(\lambda_1+\lambda_2)}\lambda_1^{x_1}\lambda_2^{x_2}}{x_1!x_2!}$$

For the reason that it works out well to do so, the latter quantity can be written as

$$\frac{e^{-(\lambda_1+\lambda_2)}\lambda_2^{x_1+x_2}}{x!} \cdot \left(\frac{\lambda_1}{\lambda_2}\right)^{x_1} \cdot \frac{x!}{x_1!x_2!}$$

where $x = x_1 + x_2$. For some particular $x = x_1 + x_2$, and considering all combinations of x_1 and x_2 which sum to that x, one has

$$\Pr\{x\} = \frac{e^{-\lambda}\lambda_2^x}{x!} \cdot \sum_{x_1=0}^{x} \frac{x!}{x_1!(x-x_1)!}\left(\frac{\lambda_1}{\lambda_2}\right)^{x_1} \cdot (1)^{x-x_1}$$

where $\lambda = \lambda_1 + \lambda_2$. But the quantity being summed can be rewritten as follows:

$$\sum_{x_1=0}^{x} \frac{x!}{x_1!(x-x_1)!}\left(\frac{\lambda_1}{\lambda_2}\right)^{x_1}(1)^{x-x_1} \equiv \sum_{x_1=0}^{x}\binom{x}{x_1}\left(\frac{\lambda_1}{\lambda_2}\right)^{x_1}(1)^{x-x_1}$$

$$\equiv \left(1+\frac{\lambda_1}{\lambda_2}\right)^x \equiv \frac{(\lambda_1+\lambda_2)^x}{\lambda_2^x} = \frac{\lambda^x}{\lambda_2^x}$$

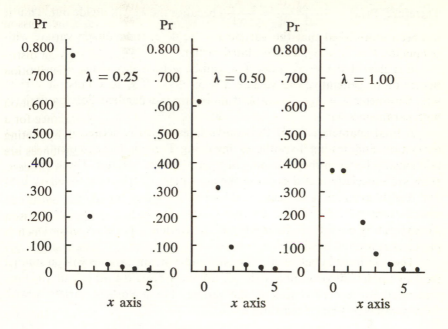

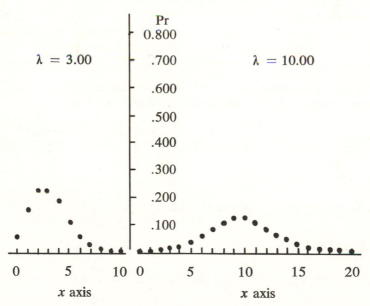

Figure 13.11.   Five specified Poisson probability distributions.

Therefore, $\Pr\{x\} = \dfrac{e^{-\lambda}\lambda_2^x}{x!} \cdot \dfrac{\lambda^x}{\lambda_2^x} = \dfrac{e^{-x}\lambda^x}{x!}$, because the λ_2^x will divide out. Thus it has been established that the variate $x = x_1 + x_2$ is a Poisson variate with parameter $\lambda = \lambda_1 + \lambda_2$, as was stated earlier.

It is clear that $x = x_1 + x_2 + x_3$ can be written as $x = (x_1 + x_2) + x_3$; hence, more generally, the variate $x = x_1 + \cdots + x_t$ is a Poisson variate with parameter $\lambda = \lambda_1 + \cdots + \lambda_t$ if the x_i are independent Poisson variates with parameters λ_i.

A final characteristic of Poisson variates which is needed in studies of estimation and testing hypotheses involving Poisson measurements is the relationship between the Poisson, chi-square, and s^2 variates. These relationships are especially useful because the chi-square distribution is fully tabled and readily available and because the relationships of the chi-square and s^2 distributions to the F distribution open the way to some very useful procedures for computing confidence intervals and for testing hypotheses when Poisson parameters are involved.

The relationship between chi-square and Poisson variates will be studied from two points of view: one with x as the variate and the other with the time t required for x occurrences as the variate. For a Poisson variate x with fixed parameter λ and fixed time t,

$$
\Pr\{x \leqslant x_0 \mid \lambda, t\} = \sum_{x=0}^{x_0} \frac{e^{-\lambda t}(\lambda t)^x}{x!},
$$

$$
= e^{-\lambda t}\left[1 + \frac{(\lambda t)^1}{1!} + \frac{(\lambda t)^2}{2!} + \cdots + \frac{(\lambda t)^{x_0}}{x_0!}\right]
$$

Furthermore, it is shown in courses in mathematical statistics that, for a chi-square variate with an even number of degrees of freedom,

$$
\Pr\{\chi_{2\nu}^2 \geqslant w_0\} = e^{-w_0/2}\left(1 + \frac{(w_0/2)^1}{1!} + \frac{(w_0/2)^2}{2!} + \cdots + \frac{(w_0/2)^{(2\nu-2)/2}}{(2\nu-2)/2!}\right)
$$

or, if $w_0/2$ is *set* $= \lambda t$,

$$
\Pr\{\chi_2^2 \geqslant 2\lambda t\} = e^{-\lambda t}\left(1 + \frac{(\lambda t)^1}{1!} + \frac{(\lambda t)^2}{2!} + \cdots + \frac{(\lambda t)^{(2\nu-2)/2}}{(2\nu-2)/2!}\right)
$$

which then shows that

(13.14) $\Pr\{\chi_{2\nu}^2 \geqslant 2\lambda t\} \equiv \Pr\left\{\text{Poisson } x \leqslant \dfrac{2\nu - 2}{2} \,\Big|\, \lambda, t\right\}$

Thus one can obtain the cumulative distribution of a Poisson variate from tables of the chi-square distributions, if λ is known.

To illustrate Identity 13.14, suppose that a Poisson process is such that the true average x is $\lambda = 1.5$ per unit of time and suppose that one has a situation in which $t = 10$ units of time. Then $\lambda t = 15$. The probability that a randomly observed 10 units of time will produce $x \leqslant 10$ is found from the following:

$$\Pr\{x \leqslant 10 \mid \lambda = 1.5 \text{ and } t = 10\} \equiv \Pr\{\chi_{22}^2 \geqslant 30\}$$

For, if $(2\nu - 2)/2 = 10$ in Identity 13.14, then 2ν must be 22. By Table XI, $\Pr\{\chi_{22}^2 \geqslant 30\} = 0.12$, approximately, so this is the solution to the problem as stated.

If one has a Poisson variate involved in a study and is merely using a chi-square distribution as an aid, a more convenient form of their relationship than that shown in Identity 13.14 is the following:

(13.15) $\Pr\{\text{Poisson } x < x_0 \mid \lambda, t\} \equiv \Pr\{\chi_{2x_0 + 2}^2 \geqslant 2\lambda t\}$

There is one problem with this identity, when t is fixed and x_0 is observed, namely that the occurrence of the x_0th Poisson event does not usually coincide exactly with the termination of time t. D. R. Cox (*Biometrika* 40: 354–60, 1953) has suggested using a chi-square variate with $2x_0 + 1$ degrees of freedom and treating $2\lambda t$ as a $\chi_{2x_0 + 1}^2$ variate even though t is supposed to be fixed. As will be seen in later sections, this scheme is sufficiently accurate to be employed in the computation of confidence intervals on λ and in testing hypotheses about two or more Poisson parameters.

If one takes the point of view that the number of Poisson events, x, is fixed in advance, and then lets t equal the time until the xth event occurs, t is the variate, in contrast to the case just discussed. As a matter of fact, this t has a $\chi_{2x}^2/2\lambda$ distribution exactly. This sort of sampling is called *inverse Poisson sampling*. Usually one expresses the distribution of t in the form

(13.16) $2\lambda t = \text{a } \chi_{2x}^2 \text{ variate}$

for a fixed x. This relationship will lead to some exact tests of $H_0(\lambda_1 = \lambda_2)$, as will be seen later.

As background for later discussions of Poisson variates it is useful here to recall some general information about the chi-square, F, and s^2 distributions. These points are as follows:

(*a*) If $\chi_{\nu_1}^2$ and $\chi_{\nu_2}^2$ are independently derived from $N(\mu_1, \sigma^2)$ and $N(\mu_2, \sigma^2)$ populations, so that $\sigma_1^2 = \sigma_2^2 = \sigma^2$, then

$$\frac{\chi_{\nu_1}^2/\nu_1}{\chi_{\nu_2}^2/\nu_2} = \text{an } F(\nu_1, \nu_2) \text{ variate} = \frac{\nu_2 \chi_{\nu_1}^2}{\nu_1 \chi_{\nu_2}^2}$$

(*b*) If s_i^2 is the unbiassed estimator of σ_i^2 based on ν_i degrees of freedom, then

$$\frac{\nu_i s_i^2}{\sigma^2} = \text{a } \chi_{\nu_i}^2 \text{ variate}$$

Thus it follows from the discussion earlier in this section that:

(*c*) In the case of *direct* Poisson sampling, in which t_i is fixed and an x_i

is observed as a random variable, if two Poisson processes are sampled simultaneously, then

(13.17) $\qquad \dfrac{t_1(2x_2 + 1)}{t_2(2x_1 + 1)} \cong$ an $F(2x_1 + 1, 2x_2 + 1)$, if $\lambda_1 = \lambda_2$

(*d*) In the case of *inverse* Poisson sampling, in which x_i is fixed and t is the random variable, if two Poisson processes are sampled simultaneously:

(13.18) $\qquad \dfrac{t_1 x_2}{t_2 x_1} =$ an $F(2x_1, 2x_2)$ exactly, if $\lambda_1 = \lambda_2$

(*e*) It is further observed that, in view of the relationship between s_i^2, F, and χ^2, the distribution of $2\lambda_i t_i$ for $i = 1, 2, \cdots, k$ can be related to the distribution of s_i^2, because

(13.19) $$2\lambda_i t_i = \chi_{2x_i}^2 = \frac{2x_i s_i^2}{\sigma_i^2}$$

Furthermore, it turns out mathematically that a test of the hypothesis $H_0(\lambda_1 = \cdots = \lambda_t = \lambda)$ can be accomplished through a test of homogeneity of variances.

It frequently will occur in practice that neither the variate x nor the time t will be fixed in advance of the actual sampling but, as D. R. Cox has pointed out, the distributions described herein are quite satisfactory as long as the determination of the x or of the t does not depend upon their observed sizes but upon some ancillary event which is essentially independent of the size of x or of t.

PROBLEMS

1. Suppose that a Poisson process is such that random events will occur, on the average, 5.1 times per unit of time. Write down the probability function specifically for x, the number of occurrences of this event, in t units of time. In 10 units of time.

2. Suppose that an average of 1.2 defects per 10 feet are to be found in some enameled wire which is being produced by a certain industrial process. What is the probability of observing exactly 3 such defects in a random sample of 50 feet of this wire, if the number of such defects is a Poisson variate? What is the probability of no more than 3 defects? Should the 50-foot sample be taken in one piece or in several pieces? Explain.

3. Suppose that, on the average, telephone calls come through a certain trunk line at the rate of five each 30 seconds and that the number of calls follows a Poisson distribution. If 10 calls in any 30-second interval will block the line, what is the probability that during a 30-second interval randomly chosen in advance the line will become blocked?

4. Suppose that under certain specific conditions radioactive particles are reaching a Geiger counter at the average rate of five per second. Assuming a Poisson distribution of numbers of particles, what is the probability function

for x, the number of counts, in randomly chosen 10-second intervals? In three independently selected such intervals?

5. Suppose that two separate and independent sources are being counted, as in Problem 4, with $\lambda_1 = 5$ for the first source and $\lambda_2 = 7$ for the second. Write down the probability function for x = the sum of the two counts.

6. Suppose the situation of Problem 4 obtains, but one is going to count until $x_i = 25$. What is the distribution of t, the time required to reach $x = 25$?

7. Suppose that, for a Poisson population, $\lambda = 2.5$. What is the probability that a randomly observed x will be 0? That x will be 0 or 1? That x will exceed 0?

8. Suppose that the mutation rate for an observable trait is four in one million. What is the probability function for the number (x) of such mutations observed from sets of 300,000 individuals, each of which could have mutated? If by means of irradiation this mutation rate can be increased to one in 30,000, what is now the probability function for x?

9. Suppose that the number of occurrences of pinholes in enameled wire is a random variable such that:
   (a) The probability of x pinholes in a randomly chosen 10-foot piece of this wire is the same as for the occurrence of x pinholes in 10 randomly chosen one-foot lengths of this wire.
   (b) The occurrences of pinholes in, say, one-inch lengths within one-foot lengths are independent of each other.
   (c) The average number of pinholes per 10-foot length is 0.5.
   What is the probability function for y = the number of pinholes in a random chosen 50-foot length of this wire?

10. Referring to Problem 9, suppose y is set at 4. What is the probability distribution of L = the length of wire which must be examined to find exactly four pinholes?

13.2   THE ESTIMATION OF A POISSON PARAMETER

When a random observation on a Poisson population with mean and variance each equal to λ has produced the number x, this x is the maximum-likelihood estimate of λ for the time or interval, or whatever, involved. This is point estimation. It more commonly is useful to determine a confidence interval on λ, with a predetermined confidence coefficient, $1 - \alpha$.

A $CI_{1-\alpha}$ could be determined approximately from Table 13.21 in a manner analogous to that in which Table 2.13 was used to place approximate confidence limits on the binomial parameter, p. It is noted, however, that just one "sample size" now is sufficient because, in the binomial sense, the sample size, n, is presumed to be infinite. Or, it can be said that we now are using continuous time or space instead of discrete counts of "trials." As in Table 2.13, each column of Table 13.21 is a separate Poisson distribution for a stated size of the parameter. The step boundary for the CI_{80} illustrated in the table is so drawn that, as nearly as possible, an extreme 10 percent of each

TABLE 13.21. TWENTY-FOUR SELECTED POISSON DISTRIBUTIONS USED TO ILLUSTRATE THE DETERMINATION OF AN APPROXIMATE $1 - \alpha$ CONFIDENCE INTERVAL FOR A POISSON PARAMETER WHEN A LARGE SAMPLE (PRESUMABLY INFINITE) HAS PRODUCED AN X NUMBER OF UNITS WITH A SPECIFIED TRAIT (α CHOSEN $= 0.20$ TO OBTAIN A CI_{80})

The size of the Poisson parameter

X	0.10	0.30	0.50	0.70	0.90	1.0	1.1	1.3	1.4	1.6	2.0	2.5	3.0	3.5	4.0	5.0	6.0	7.0	8.0	9.0	10	11	12	13
0	0.90	0.74	0.61	0.50	0.41	0.37	0.33	0.27	0.25	0.20	0.14	0.08	0.05	0.03	0.02	0.01	0.00	0.00						
1	0.09	0.22	0.30	0.35	0.37	0.37	0.37	0.35	0.35	0.32	0.27	0.21	0.15	0.11	0.07	0.03	0.01	0.01	0.00					
2	0.01	0.03	0.08	0.12	0.16	0.18	0.20	0.23	0.24	0.26	0.27	0.27	0.22	0.18	0.15	0.08	0.04	0.02	0.01	0.00				
3	0.00	0.00	0.01	0.03	0.05	0.06	0.07	0.10	0.11	0.14	0.18	0.21	0.22	0.22	0.20	0.14	0.09	0.05	0.03	0.02	0.01			
4		0.00	0.00	0.01	0.01	0.02	0.02	0.03	0.04	0.06	0.09	0.13	0.17	0.19	0.20	0.18	0.13	0.09	0.06	0.03	0.02	0.01	0.01	0.00
5			0.00	0.00	0.00	0.00	0.00	0.01	0.01	0.02	0.04	0.07	0.10	0.13	0.16	0.18	0.16	0.13	0.09	0.06	0.04	0.02	0.01	0.01
6										0.00	0.01	0.03	0.05	0.08	0.10	0.15	0.16	0.15	0.12	0.09	0.06	0.04	0.03	0.02
7											0.00	0.01	0.02	0.04	0.06	0.10	0.14	0.15	0.14	0.12	0.09	0.06	0.04	0.03
8												0.00	0.01	0.02	0.03	0.07	0.10	0.13	0.14	0.13	0.11	0.09	0.07	0.05
9													0.00	0.01	0.01	0.04	0.07	0.10	0.12	0.13	0.13	0.11	0.09	0.07
10														0.00	0.01	0.02	0.04	0.07	0.10	0.12	0.13	0.12	0.10	0.09
11															0.00	0.01	0.02	0.05	0.07	0.10	0.11	0.12	0.11	0.10
12																0.00	0.01	0.03	0.05	0.07	0.09	0.11	0.11	0.11
13																	0.01	0.01	0.03	0.05	0.07	0.09	0.11	0.11
14																		0.01	0.02	0.03	0.05	0.07	0.09	0.10
15																			0.01	0.02	0.03	0.05	0.07	0.09
16																			0.00	0.01	0.02	0.04	0.05	0.07
17																				0.01	0.01	0.02	0.04	0.06
18																				0.00	0.01	0.01	0.03	0.04
19																					0.00	0.01	0.02	0.03
20																					0.00	0.00	0.01	0.02
21																						0.00	0.01	0.01
22																							0.00	0.01
23																								0.00

By Table XVII, CI_{80} is $3.546 < \lambda < 9.922$, if $X = 6$.

distribution lies above, and also below, the horizontal line. Then, given any sample outcome, x, one draws an imaginary line to the right to the *first column of figures inside the step boundary*. The λ at the top of this column is the approximate lower confidence limit, L, for $\alpha = 0.20$. When that same imaginary line is extended to the right to the *last column of figures inside the step boundary*, the λ at the top of this column is the approximate upper confidence limit, U. For example, if x is observed to be 6, the CI_{80} is approximately $3.5 < \lambda < 10$. Table XVII, from an article by E. L. Crow and R. S. Gardner (*Biometrika* 46: 441, 1959), shows that this CI_{80} is very nearly the same as the more accurate published intervals.

Table XVII has been constructed for the more efficient and more accurate determination of confidence intervals for Poisson parameters. It is observed in general that these intervals are relatively long.

To illustrate the use of Table XVII again, suppose that a two-minute observation on a certain telephone exchange records 10 calls. By Table XVII, the CI_{80} on λ is $5.882 < \lambda < 15.205$ and the CI_{99} is $4.130 < \lambda < 20.676$. These intervals obviously are quite indefinite, so one surely would use as large an α as reasonable, in order to get a shorter and more useful interval. Obviously, a shorter interval cannot now be obtained by increasing sample size.

As in previous discussions of confidence intervals, one can place either a greatest lower bound or a least upper bound on a λ by taking all risk of error at one end of all Poisson distributions. In these instances, Table 13.21 displays diagrammatically either a GLB_{90} or an LUB_{90}. With tables such as Table XVII one merely employs the $\alpha = 0.20$ in Table XVII, or, alternatively, halves the α and finds $LUB_{90} = 15.205$. In view of the fact that:

(*a*) Even though times t_1 and t_2 be fixed and x_1 and x_2 be observed numbers of Poisson events, D. R. Cox (*Biometrika* 40: 354–60, 1953) has shown that $2\lambda_i t_i$ can be usefully regarded as having approximately a $\chi^2_{2x_i+1}$ distribution.

(*b*) If $\sigma_1^2 = \sigma_2^2$, then

$$\frac{\chi^2_{2x_1+1}}{2x_1+1} \div \frac{\chi^2_{2x_2+1}}{2x_2+1} = F(2x_1+1, 2x_2+1)$$

and, using (*a*),

$$\frac{2\lambda_1 t_1}{2x_1+1} \div \frac{2\lambda_2 t_2}{2x_2+1} = F(2x_1+1, 2x_2+1)$$

the following obtains:

(**13.21**) $\qquad \left(\dfrac{\lambda_1}{\lambda_2}\right)\dfrac{t_1(2x_2+1)}{t_2(2x_1+1)} =$ an $F(2x_1+1, 2x_2+1)$ variate

Using Equation 13.21, one can obtain an approximate but good confidence interval on the ratio λ_1/λ_2 because, before the Poisson samples are drawn, the inequality

(13.22) $$F_{1-\alpha/2}(2x_1 + 1, 2x_2 + 1) < \left(\frac{\lambda_1}{\lambda_2}\right)\frac{t_1(2x_2 + 1)}{t_2(2x_1 + 1)}$$
$$< F_{\alpha/2}(2x_1 + 1, 2x_2 + 1)$$

has probability $1 - \alpha$ to be realized when the data have been observed. Therefore, the $CI_{1-\alpha}$ on λ_1/λ_2 is obtained from Inequality 13.22 by multiplying through by $t_2(2x_1 + 1)/t_1(2x_2 + 1)$, to obtain the following approximate $CI_{1-\alpha}$:

(13.23) $$\frac{t_2(2x_1 + 1)}{t_1(2x_2 + 1)} \cdot F_{1-\alpha/2}(2x_1 + 1, 2x_2 + 1)$$
$$< \frac{\lambda_1}{\lambda_2} < \frac{t_2(2x_1 + 1)}{t_1(2x_2 + 1)} \cdot F_{\alpha/2}(2x_1 + 1, 2x_2 + 1)$$

To illustrate Formula 13.23, suppose that two Poisson processes are to be observed for numbers of events, x_1 and x_2, in fixed times, t_1 and t_2, respectively, equal to $t_1 = 20$ and $t_2 = 25$ units of time. If it subsequently is observed that $x_1 = 45$ events and $x_2 = 35$ events, and α is chosen $= 0.10$, the 90% confidence limits on the ratio λ_1/λ_2 are computed from

$$\left(\frac{25(91)}{25(71)}\right) \cdot F_{0.95}(91, 71) < \lambda_1/\lambda_2 < \left(\frac{25(91)}{20(71)}\right) \cdot F_{0.05}(91, 71)$$

Most F tables do not give values for $F_{0.95}$ equal to that F which will be exceeded by chance 95% of the time during random sampling. However, as noted earlier, $F_{0.95}(91, 71) = 1/F_{0.05}(71, 91)$, so $F_{0.95}(91, 71) = 1/1.445 = 0.692$ and $25(91)/20(71) = 1.602$. The final CI_{90} on λ_1/λ_2 is $1.11 < \lambda_1/\lambda_2 < 2.34$. One would feel quite secure in the statement that λ_1 is at least from one to two times the size of λ_2.

The student already is familiar with the uses of confidence intervals in tests of hypotheses. The same ideas hold true in Poisson sampling. For example, if examination of a random sample of 25 feet of a certain kind of wire reveals two defects of a well-defined sort, and if the frequency of such defects can be assumed reasonably to conform to a Poisson distribution, then with $\alpha = 0.10$ the 90% confidence interval on the true average number of such defects per 25 feet is

$$CI_{90}: \qquad 0.532 < \lambda < 5.976$$

according to Table XVII. Any H_0 about this λ which specifies a value between 0.52 and 5.976 is acceptable, whereas any H_0 which presumes λ to be outside these limits is unacceptable.

Equality 13.23, though an approximation, can be used to test hypotheses about the ratio λ_1/λ_2, including $\lambda_1/\lambda_2 = 1$ which is $H_0(\lambda_1 = \lambda_2)$. For example, suppose that radioactive distintegrations of some sort are to be counted under two circumstances, each of which produces a Poisson variate. Suppose also that one wishes to test $H_0(\lambda_1 = \lambda_2)$ against $H_a(\lambda_1 \neq \lambda_2)$ with $\alpha = 0.10$. If in the same fixed time, t, for each situation one counts $x_1 = 58$ and $x_2 = 75$ events, then by Inequality 13.23

$$\frac{t(117)}{t(151)} \cdot F_{0.95}(117, 151) < \frac{\lambda_1}{\lambda_2} < \frac{t(117)}{t(151)} \cdot F_{0.05}(117, 151)$$

The t's divide out, $117/151 = 0.775$, $F_{0.05}(117, 151) = 1.33$, and $F_{0.95}(117, 151) = 1/F_{0.05}(151, 117) = 0.752$; hence, the CI_{90} on λ_1/λ_2 is $0.583 < \lambda_1/\lambda_2 < 1.031$, which includes $\lambda_1/\lambda_2 = 1$; so H_0 is accepted.

If, in advance of the sampling, one had good reason to choose $H_a(\lambda_1 < \lambda_2)$ as the alternative hypothesis in the preceding example, an LUB_{90} would be obtained on λ_1/λ_2 by using the *upper* CI_{80} limit. The computations are as follows for $t_1 = t_2 = t$, $x_1 = 58$, and $x_2 = 75$:

$$0 < \lambda_1/\lambda_2 < \frac{t(117)}{t(151)} \cdot F_{0.10}(117, 151), \quad \text{or } 0 < \lambda_1/\lambda_2 < 0.85$$

Hence, $H_0(\lambda_1 = \lambda_2)$ would be rejected in favor of $H_a(\lambda_1 < \lambda_2)$. Obviously, one must not decide to use $H_a(\lambda_1 < \lambda_2)$ after the samples have been taken just to be able to reject H_0. The decision regarding the appropriate H_a must be made for logical reasons *before* the samples are taken.

PROBLEMS

1. Suppose that it reasonably can be assumed that the numbers of defects appearing in a product moving along a production line per five-minute inspection interval have a Poisson distribution. If during a randomly chosen such inspection interval $x = 2$ defects occur, what is the CI_{90} on the mean number of defects for such time intervals? What is the LUB_{90} on this λ, and what is its interpretation?

2. Suppose that two separate and independent observations as in Problem 1 produced $x_1 = 2$ and $x_2 = 0$. What is the CI_{90} on λ now?

3. Suppose that during a 10-second interval a Geiger counter records $x = 20$ "hits" from a certain source of radioactive disintegrations. Suppose also that such counts follow a Poisson distribution for a useful period of time. What is the LUB_{95} on the average number of particles hitting per 10-second interval? What is the CI_{95} on the variance for this Poisson population?

4. Suppose that a certain type and amount of irradiation applied to the fruit fly *Drosophila melanogaster* has produced the specific visible mutation, white eye, five times among 20,000 observed flies, each of which could have mutated. What is the CI_{80} on the true average number of mutations to "white eye" per 20,000 flies irradiated as in this experiment?

5. Suppose that a virologist puts some virus particles into a solution and dilutes it to suit his purposes. Then he draws out five random 1-cc. samples and finds them to contain 0, 3, 1, 1, and 2 particles, respectively. With α chosen as

0.10 what is the CI_{90} on the true average number of particles per cubic centimeter in this solution?

6. Referring to Problem 5, suppose that it takes at least three of those virus particles to infect a chick embryo. What can you say about the probability that a randomly drawn 1-cc. sample will contain enough virus particles to infect a chick embryo?

7. Suppose that a certain telephone exchange can only handle 25 connections per two-minute interval. If the true average number of calls per two-minute interval is 15, what is the probability that a future randomly chosen two-minute interval will exceed the capacity of the exchange?

8. Referring to Problem 7, what if the λ is unknown but five randomly chosen two-minute intervals produced $x = 18, 24, 20, 14$, and 9 calls, respectively. What, if anything, can you now say about the probability requested in Problem 7?

9. Suppose that one has the following sampling situation:
   (a) A Poisson process with parameter $\lambda_1 = 1.3$ is to be observed until $x_1 = 12$.
   (b) Another and independent Poisson process with parameter $\lambda_2 = 2.6$ is to be observed until $x_2 = 20$.
   (c) The times t_1 and t_2 until x_1 and x_2 Poisson events are observed under (a) and (b), respectively, are to be determined.
   What is the probability that t_1 will be at least $2t_2$ as nearly as you can determine from existing tables?

10. Suppose it is hypothesized that for two independent Poisson processes $\lambda_1 = 1.3\lambda_2$. Thereafter x_1 and x_2 are chosen as 10 each, and t_1 and t_2 are observed. What is the minimum ratio of t_1 to t_2 which will cause you to reject that hypothesis in favor of $H_a(\lambda_1 \neq 1.3\lambda_2)$ if $\alpha = 0.10$?

13.3   TESTING HYPOTHESES ABOUT POISSON PARAMETERS

Much of the general discussion in this section could have been given in one or both of the preceding sections, because it pertains to sampling concepts which also are useful in the computation of confidence intervals. But the existence of convenient tables of confidence intervals plus the fact that the ideas to be presented in this section really were not needed earlier has led to their postponement until now.

In view of the discussion of transformations of data given in Section 9.4 to normalize data, it is obvious that there will be experimental situations in which one might prefer to handle Poisson data (for which $\bar{x}$ and s^2 tend to be in direct proportion) by transforming the original data. When sampling mean and variance are so related, the square root transformation is likely to be helpful. More specifically, a transformation of the form

$$(13.31) \qquad Y_i = \sqrt{X_i + c}$$

has been suggested for trial. In fact, F. Anscombe (*Biometrika* 35: 246–54, 1948) has shown that the optimum value of c is $3/8 = 0.375$, as far as producing homogeneity of variance is concerned. As stated in Section 9.4, the assumptions and mathematical approximations used to derive the square root transformation, as well as the others, are sufficiently crude that one should always "prove" the success of any transformation used by determining whether or not it cured the difficulties which suggested the transformation in the first place. Of course, the data available may be insufficient to achieve this purpose. If so, one simply performs the best known transformation and goes ahead with normal analyses.

After other methods for handling Poisson data have been discussed, one can decide in a specific instance which procedure seems most appropriate and most likely to serve the purposes of the experiment best.

Given that two Poisson populations are to be sampled, one can take one of two different points of view looking toward a test of $H_0(\lambda_1 = \lambda_2)$, where λ_1 and λ_2 are the parameters of the two Poisson populations to be sampled. From one point of view, the experimenter can choose two specific positive integers, x_1 and x_2, as the respective numbers of events to be seen from each population in whatever times t_1 and t_2, respectively, it takes x_1 and x_2 events to occur. From this point of view, t_1 and t_2 are independent random variables. In view of Formula 13.15, $t_1 x_2/t_2 x_1$ has an $F(2x_1, 2x_2)$ distribution exactly, if $\lambda_1 = \lambda_2$. Thus, given an α and an alternative hypothesis, one can test $H_0(\lambda_1 = \lambda_2)$ by means of the tables of $F(2x_1, 2x_2)$. However, one needs to note what are the effects of false hypotheses, so that the best region of rejection can be chosen.

If one sets $F(2x_1, 2x_2) = (t_1 x_2)/(t_2 x_1)$, what sorts of sizes will this ratio have, on the average, if, in fact, $\lambda_1 > \lambda_2$? The answer to this question is more easily seen if the arbitrary x_1 and x_2 (which are to be chosen in advance anyway) are taken equal to a common value x. Clearly, the time t_1 required to observe x events in Population 1 should usually be *less* than the time t_2 required for x events to occur in Population 2, because the rate of occurrence (the λ) is greater in Population 1 than in Population 2 when $\lambda_1 > \lambda_2$. Hence, if we are supposing that $\lambda_1 = \lambda_2$, so that $t_1 x_2/t_2 x_1$ would be an $F(2x_1, 2x_2)$ variate, we shall tend to obtain excessively *small* values of $t_1 x_2/t_2 x_1$ as compared with a true $F(2x_1, 2x_2)$ distribution. This would call for a region of rejection at the left-hand end of the $F(2x_1, 2x_2)$ distribution, but tables for this part of the F distribution are rare. This suggests that a better approach is to redefine the F as

(13.32) $$F(2x_2, 2x_1) = t_2 x_1/t_1 x_2$$

when the alternative hypothesis is $H_a(\lambda_1 > \lambda_2)$. This leads to the use of the following region of rejection:

(13.33) ω: observed $F(2x_2, 2x_1) = t_2 x_1/t_1 x_2 > F_\alpha(2x_2, 2x_1)$

When the alternative hypothesis is $H_a(\lambda_1 \neq \lambda_2)$, the definition of F should be that it is the larger of $t_1 x_2 / t_2 x_1$ and $t_2 x_1 / t_1 x_2$, the region of rejection being

$$(13.34) \qquad \text{Observed F} > \begin{cases} F_{\alpha/2}(2x_1, 2x_2) & \text{for } t_1 x_2 / t_2 x_1 > 1 \\ F_{\alpha/2}(2x_2, 2x_1) & \text{for } t_2 x_1 / t_1 x_2 > 1 \end{cases}$$

To illustrate the uses of these last three expressions, consider a study in which one has chosen $x_1 = x_2 = 5$ and $\alpha = 0.05$ and in which, first, one wishes to test $H_0(\lambda_1 = \lambda_2)$ against $H_a(\lambda_1 > \lambda_2)$. $F(10, 10)$ is defined as t_2/t_1, and ω as $F(10, 10) > F_{0.05}(10, 10) = 2.98$. Suppose, now, that it turns out that $t_1 = 2.13$ hours and $t_2 = 5.35$ hours. Then $F(10, 10) = 5.35/2.13 = 2.49$, which is <2.98; therefore, $H_0(\lambda_1 = \lambda_2)$ is accepted. If H_a had been that $\lambda_1 \neq \lambda_2$, the F would have been defined in advance as that one of t_1/t_2 and t_2/t_1 which came out to be the larger. Also the region of rejection would have been ω; the observed $F(10, 10) > F_{0.025}(10, 10)$.

If the x_i had not been chosen equal for some reason, one would use a similar procedure. For example, suppose one chose $x_1 = 15$ and $x_2 = 20$ and thought the alternative hypothesis should be $H_a(\lambda_1 \neq \lambda_2)$, with $\alpha = 0.10$. The F would be defined as follows:

$$F(2x_1, 2x_2) = t_1 x_2 / t_2 x_1, \qquad \text{if this is } > 1$$
$$F(2x_2, 2x_1) = t_2 x_1 / t_1 x_2, \qquad \text{if this is } > 1$$

The region of rejection is:

$$\omega: \quad \begin{cases} \text{Observed } F(2x_1, 2x_2) > F_{0.05}(2x_1, 2x_2), & \text{and:} \\ \text{Observed } F(2x_2, 2x_1) > F_{0.05}(2x_2, 2x_1), & \text{if } \alpha = 0.10 \end{cases}$$

or, more specifically,

$$\omega: \quad \begin{cases} \text{Observed } F(30, 30) > F_{0.05}(30, 40) = 1.74, & \text{and} \\ \text{Observed } F(40, 30) > F_{0.05}(40, 30) = 1.79, & \text{with } \alpha = 0.10 \end{cases}$$

If it turns out that $t_1 = 4.75$ and $t_2 = 4.60$, then the observed F's are:

$$F(30, 40) = \frac{4.75(20)}{4.60(15)} = 1.38$$

which is greater than 1 but less than $F_{0.05}(30, 40) = 1.74$; hence, H_0 is accepted, and it is concluded that the rates of occurrence of Poisson events are approximately the same in the two populations supposedly sampled.

When x_i is fixed and t_i is observed, one is doing what is called inverse Poisson sampling, and this has just been discussed and illustrated with regard to $H_0(\lambda_1 = \lambda_2)$. Consider, next, direct Poisson sampling, in which the t_i are fixed and the numbers of Poisson events, x_i, are recorded. Obviously, the times t_i will not coincide exactly with the occurrences of the x_ith events. For example, if t_1 has been set at 10 units of time, the 18th event may occur 9.9 units of time and no other event occur before the expiration of time

$t_1 = 10$. For the direct sampling situation, Cox (*Biometrika* 40: 354–60, 1953) has suggested an approximate test of $H_0(\lambda_1 = \lambda_2)$, in which the discrete variates x_1 and x_2 are tentatively regarded as being continuous. On this basis, and using degrees of freedom halfway between $(2x_1, 2x_2)$ and $(2x_1 + 2, 2x_2 + 2)$ for the F ratio, Cox suggests that the following formula is close enough to being exact that it often may be used to test $H_0(\lambda_1 = \lambda_2)$ from direct Poisson sampling:

$$\textbf{(13.35)} \qquad \frac{t_1(2x_2 + 1)}{t_2(2x_1 + 1)} = F(2x_1 + 1, 2x_2 + 1)$$

This same formula was used in an earlier section, to compute confidence intervals on λ_1/λ_2.

Again one needs to choose a region of rejection by considering the effect of a false hypothesis on the ratio on the left-hand side of Equation 13.35. Suppose that the times t_1 and t_2 are fixed at t. Then $t_1(2x_2 + 1)/t_2(2x_1 + 1)$ becomes $= (2x_2 + 1)/(2x_1 + 1)$. If $\lambda_1 = \lambda_2$, this is approximately an $F(2x_1 + 1, 2x_2 + 1)$ variate, but if $\lambda_1 > \lambda_2$, the rate of occurrence of events whose final count is x_1 is greater than for the population from which x_2 is counted. Consequently, the ratio $(2x_2 + 1)/(2x_1 + 1)$ will tend to be less than unity. How much less it may be depends upon how much larger λ_1 is than λ_2 and, of course, upon chance. Thus, the region of rejection for testing $H_0(\lambda_1 = \lambda_2)$ against $H_a(\lambda_1 > \lambda_2)$ is in the extreme left-hand tail of the $F(2x_1 + 1, 2x_2 + 1)$ distribution. Again, considering the general lack of appropriate tables, it is preferable to so define the F ratio that it will tend to be larger than unity when H_0 is false. It is suggested that

(*a*)   If H_a is $\lambda_1 > \lambda_2$, define $F(2x_2 + 1, 2x_1 + 1) = \dfrac{t_2(2x_1 + 1)}{t_1(2x_2 + 1)}$.

(13.36)   (*b*)   If H_a is $\lambda_2 > \lambda_1$, define $F(2x_1 + 1, 2x_2 + 1) = \dfrac{t_1(2x_2 + 1)}{t_2(2x_1 + 1)}$.

(*c*)   If H_a is $\lambda_1 \neq \lambda_2$, define F so that the observed ratio is larger than unity, and use a two-part region of rejection, each region being of size $\alpha/2$.

To illustrate the preceding discussion, suppose that the numbers of telephone calls coming into two exchanges are thought to follow Poisson distributions with parameters λ_1 and λ_2. Choose $t_1 = 18$ and $t_2 = 24$ five-minute intervals, during which the two exchanges are to be observed. Suppose there is reason to believe that if $H_0(\lambda_1 = \lambda_2)$ is untrue, then $\lambda_1 > \lambda_2$. With $\alpha = 0.10$ and this alternative hypothesis, the F ratio is defined as follows:

$$F(2x_2 + 1, 2x_1 + 1) = \frac{t_2(2x_1 + 1)}{t_1(2x_2 + 1)} = \frac{4(2x_1 + 1)}{3(2x_2 + 1)}$$

Furthermore, the region of rejection becomes

$$\text{observed } \frac{4(2x_1 + 1)}{3(2x_2 + 1)} > F_{0.10}(2x_2 + 1, 2x_1 + 1)$$

If it is subsequently observed that during fixed times $t_1 = 18$, $t_2 = 24$, $x_1 = 60$, and $x_2 = 40$, then the specific region of rejection is

$$\omega: \qquad \text{Observed } \frac{4(2x_1 + 1)}{3(2x_2 + 1)} > F_{0.10}(81, 121) = 1.29$$

In fact, the observed $4(2x_1 + 1)/3(2x_2 + 1) = 1.99$; hence, $H_0(\lambda_1 = \lambda_2)$ is rejected, and it is concluded that the rate of incoming calls is greater for Exchange 1 than for Exchange 2.

If the alternative hypothesis in the preceding example were $H_a(\lambda_1 \neq \lambda_2)$, the F ratio would be defined so that the observed ratio would be greater than unity. Also, the region of rejection would be:

$$\text{Observed } F(81, 121) > F_{\alpha/2}(81, 121) = 1.38, \qquad \text{and}$$
$$\text{Observed } F(121, 81) > F_{\alpha/2}(121, 81) = 1.41, \qquad \text{for } \alpha = 0.10$$

Although it is obvious that $H_0(\lambda_1 = \lambda_2)$ also would have been rejected with this new region of rejection, this clearly is a different test, and it is one with less power against Type II error, when $\lambda_1 > \lambda_2$ is a reasonable alternative hypothesis, because half the two-tail region of rejection is being wasted when it is unreasonable that λ_1 could be $< \lambda_2$.

If three or more Poisson populations are to be sampled, so that the hypothesis $H_0(\lambda_1 = \lambda_2 = \cdots = \lambda_t = \lambda)$ can be tested against $H_a(\text{some } \lambda_i \text{ are unequal})$, one can take either of the following actions, among others:

(*a*) Do multiple F testing by pairs of λ_i. This is analogous to multiple t tests of $H_0(\mu_i = \mu_j)$. Obviously, this would create questions about the protection the test affords against Type I error, but in the presence of real differences among the λ_i it might be a powerful procedure for avoiding Type II error.

(*b*) Use the relationships

$$2\lambda_i t_i = \chi^2_{2x_i}, \qquad \text{when the } x_i \text{ is fixed}$$
$$= \frac{2x_i s_i^2}{\sigma_i^2} = \frac{S_i^2}{\sigma_i^2}, \qquad i = 1, 2, \cdots, t$$

where S_i^2 is the sum of squares for an s_i^2 with $2x_i$ DF, to make a test of $H_0(\lambda_1 = \lambda_2 = \cdots = \lambda_t = \lambda)$ correspond to a test of homogeneity of variance. Specifically, one merely substitutes t_i for S_i^2 on the assumption that all λ_i are equal and proceeds with a test for homogeneity of variance. Two such tests have been described earlier, namely Bartlett's χ^2 test and Hartley's $F_{\max}$ test.

To illustrate, suppose that all x_i have been chosen 10; that is, each Poisson process will be observed until 10 events have occurred and the times t_i have been recorded. In other words, inverse Poisson sampling is being done. If it turns out that $t_1 = 5.13$, $t_2 = 9.00$, $t_3 = 4.75$, $t_4 = 8.44$, and

$t_5 = 16.12$ units of time, one can apply Hartley's F_{max} test as follows: $F_{max} = 16.12/4.75 = 3.39$. Using Table XIV with $k = 5$ and $v = 20$ DF for each variance, it is learned that the region of rejection, ω, is $F_{max} > 3.54$, if $\alpha = 0.05$; therefore, the hypothesis $H_0(\lambda_1 = \cdots = \lambda_5 = \lambda)$ is accepted. It is concluded that the λ_i are essentially equal, so the rates of occurrences of events are approximately equal in the five Poisson populations so sampled.

In a summary of Poisson testing, one could say the following:

(a) If a sequence of random observations has been made on each of two or more Poisson populations and there are adequate data to use a transformation, apply the transformation $Y_i = \sqrt{X_i + 0.375}$ in the hope of normalizing the data so that normal analyses may be used.

(b) If only two Poisson populations are to be sampled and the x_i are fixed and the t_i are observed as random variables (inverse Poisson sampling), use the fact that $2\lambda_i t_i$ is a $\chi^2_{2x_i}$ variate, so that $t_1 x_2 / t_2 x_1$ is an $F\{2x_1, 2x_2\}$ variate. From this point of view one can either obtain confidence limits on one λ_i or test $H_0(\lambda_1 = \lambda_2)$ against an appropriate alternative.

(c) If but two Poisson populations are to be sampled and the times t_i are to be fixed, so that the observed discrete numbers of events, x_i, are to be the random variables (direct Poisson sampling), use the fact that

$$\frac{t_1(2x_2 + 1)}{t_2(2x_1 + 1)} = \text{an } F(2x_1 + 1, 2x_2 + 1) \text{ variate}$$

One can compute confidence limits on λ_1/λ_2 or can test $H_0(\lambda_1 = \lambda_2)$ against an appropriate alternative.

(d) If there are three or more Poisson populations to be sampled and the x_i are to be fixed, use the fact that $2\lambda_i t_i$ is a $2x_i s_i^2/\sigma^2 = S_i^2/\sigma_i^2$ variate, where S_i^2 is really the sum of squares from which the s_i^2 were computed, and that it can be replaced by λ_i. Thereafter either Bartlett's test or Hartley's F_{max} test for homogeneity of variance is applicable.

PROBLEMS

1. Suppose that five Poisson populations have been sampled with the following results (λ's in parentheses):

	Population			
1 (0.8)	2 (4.8)	3 (4.8)	4 (1.6)	5 (0.8)
2	6	6	1	0
2	9	10	2	0
0	7	6	0	1
0	4	7	2	2
1	5	6	2	3
0	5	10	2	0
Sum: 5	36	45	9	6
Mean: 0.83	6.00	7.50	1.5	1.0

Do an analysis of variance after transforming the data by $Y_i = \sqrt{X_i + 0.375}$. Draw appropriate conclusions.

2. Do Problem 1 without transformation of data, and compare the results obtained in these two ways.

3. Use the sums of the columns in Problem 1 as times t_i. Then, assuming all $x_i = 6$, apply Hartley's F_{max} test to $H_0(\lambda_1 = \cdots = \lambda_5 = \lambda)$.

4. Take the point of view of Problem 3 regarding Populations 1 and 2, and then compute a CI_{90} on λ_1/λ_2. Interpret your result.

5. Do Problem 3 by Bartlett's test of homogeneity of variance.

6. Toss five coins 100 times, recording the number of times in the 100 tosses that the coins were either all heads or all tails. Do the same with six coins and then with eight coins. Actually, $p = 1/16$ with five coins, $1/32$ with six coins, and $1/128$ with eight coins; so the results obtained should approximate the sampling of three Poisson populations. Let all t_i be 100 and the x_i be the observed numbers of times the coins fall all heads or all tails. Then test the hypothesis $H_0(\lambda_1 = \lambda_2 = \lambda_3 = \lambda)$ against its negation. Also obtain a CI_{90} on λ_2 and interpret it.

7. Suppose that $H_0(\lambda_1 = \lambda_2)$ is to be tested against $\lambda_2 > \lambda_1$ by direct Poisson sampling; that is, t_1 and t_2 are fixed and the random variates x_1 and x_2 observed. Let t_1 be 10 units and t_2 be 8 units, and suppose x_1 turns out to be 11 and x_2 turns out to be 12. Is H_0 acceptable with $\alpha = 0.10$?

8. Do Problem 7 with $H_a(\lambda_1 \neq \lambda_2)$.

9. Suppose that for four Poisson populations one wishes to test $H_0(\lambda_1 = \lambda_2 = \lambda_3 = \lambda_4 = \lambda)$ against H_a(some λ_i are unequal) with $\alpha = 0.10$. If all x_i are chosen as 5 in an inverse Poisson sampling procedure and it turns out that $t_1 = 15$, $t_2 = 8$, $t_3 = 4$, and $t_4 = 20$, is H_0 acceptable?

10. Change the t_i in Problem 9 (if necessary), so that H_0 is rejected at the 5 N level but not at the 1% level. Do likewise with all $x_i = 10$.

13.4 INTRODUCTION TO THE NEGATIVE BINOMIAL DISTRIBUTION

The negative binomial distribution has several forms, each applicable to a different type of experiment. From one point of view, the negative binomial variate is produced by a situation which apparently is Poisson, but the parameter λ is changing from observation to observation. Naturally, the way in which the parameter is changing must be describable mathematically, or such situations could not be handled by methods based on probability and mathematical statistics. For example, it has been observed that numbers of industrial accidents often have a negative binomial distribution, presumably because the accident rate for any particular employee is low and because this rate changes from person to person in a manner which is describable for groups of individuals. The way in which the λ changes from person to person may be approximately describable by what is called a Pearson Type III distribution function—of which chi-square is a familiar example—but this fact need not concern us unduly here. It simply turns out that if one mathematically combines a Poisson probability function with the fact that the parameter λ has a Type III distribution, one can derive one form of the negative binomial distribution.

A second point of view which produces a negative binomial distribution in another form is that of a waiting-time experiment under binomial sampling conditions. Instead of fixing the number of trials, n, and observing the number of events, x, on n trials, one fixes the number of occurrences of an event at some positive integer k and has x = the number of "failures" be the random variable. The total number of trials now is $k + x$, and the trials always end with the kth "success." For example, what is the probability that one will throw five tails with an unbiassed coin before throwing heads *once*? Or twice? Or k times? In the first instance, x is the number of tails thrown in succession from the start and k is 1 = the number of heads thrown. The probability of the sequence of events T T T T T H is easily calculated as follows:

$$\Pr\{\text{T T T T T}\} = \left(\tfrac{1}{2}\right)^5, \qquad \Pr\{\text{H on 6th throw}\} = \tfrac{1}{2}; \qquad \text{therefore,}$$

$$\Pr\{\text{T T T T T H}\} = \left(\tfrac{1}{2}\right)^5\left(\tfrac{1}{2}\right)^1 = \tfrac{1}{64}$$

If $k = 2$ and x still $= 5$, the tosses of the coin must produce five tails and one head, in *some* order, during the first six trials, and the seventh toss must result in heads. Hence, on the first $x + k - 1 = 6$ throws there must be five tails and one head. The probability of this outcome is just $\Pr\{5\text{T, 1H}\} = \binom{6}{1}\left(\tfrac{1}{2}\right)^1\left(\tfrac{1}{2}\right)^5$ by the binomial probability function. The probability that the seventh, and independent, event "heads" will follow this sequence is $1/2$; therefore, $\Pr\{5\text{T just before 2nd H}\} = \binom{6}{1}\left(\tfrac{1}{2}\right)^2\left(\tfrac{1}{2}\right)^5 = \tfrac{3}{64}$. It is noted that this is not just a binomial probability function, because the 6 in $\binom{6}{1}$ is not the sum of the powers on p and q, as it must be for $b(X; n, p)$. Note also that the fixed number is k rather than n.

For the general "waiting-time" problem, in which

p = the fixed probability of a "success"
k = the fixed number of "successes" chosen in advance
x = the random number of failures before the occurrence of the kth success

The probability function is obtained, as illustrated above, as the product of the binomial probability of exactly $k - 1$ successes in $x + k - 1$ trials.

The p is the probability of the prescribed success on the $(x + k)$th trial. Hence,

(13.41) $\Pr\{x$ failures before kth success$\} = \begin{pmatrix} x + k - 1 \\ x \end{pmatrix} \cdot q^x p^k,$ where

$$x = 0, 1, 2, \cdots, k \text{ and } p + q = 1$$

This is called the *Pascal form of the negative binomial probability function*. This function has two parameters: k and p. The true mean and variance for the variate x of Equation 13.41 are as follows:

(13.42) $\mu_x = \dfrac{kq}{p}$ and $\sigma_x^2 = \dfrac{kq}{p^2}$

Thus the variance here *exceeds* the mean, in contrast to the binomial (for which $\sigma^2 < \mu$) and the Poisson (for which $\sigma^2 = \mu$).

The name "negative binomial" appears to have come from the following facts:

(*a*) The x theoretically can become infinite, because there is some probability that the kth "success" will not occur within a finite number of trials. This makes it impossible for Equation 13.41 to be the general term of an ordinary, "positive," binomial.

(*b*) The binomial $(1 - q)^{-k}$ with a negative exponent has the following expansion:

$$(1 - q)^{-k} = (1)^{-k} - (-k)(1)^{-k-1}q^1$$

$$+ \frac{(-k)(-k - 1)}{2!}(1)^{-k-2}q^2 - \cdots \to \infty$$

$$= 1^{-k} + \frac{k}{1!}q^1 + \frac{k(k + 1)}{2!}q^2 + \cdots$$

$$+ \frac{k(k + 1)\cdots(k + x - 1)}{x!}q^x + \cdots \to \infty$$

The general term of this negative binomial series is as follows:

(13.43) $\dfrac{(k + x - 1)!}{(k - 1)!x!}q^x,$ which $= \begin{pmatrix} k + x - 1 \\ x \end{pmatrix}q^x$

which is the variable part of Equation 13.41; hence, the name *negative binomial probability* function for the variate x in Equation 13.41.

A third point of view regarding a negative binomial variate x displays another general type of experimental situation. This might be called a "contagious" model for the negative binomial, because it pertains to situations in which the observed occurrence of one event changes the probability of another event's occurrence.

Suppose that one starts with a binomial set-up consisting of an urn containing r red and w white marbles. At the start of this experiment the probability of drawing a red marble obviously is $r/(r + w)$ and of drawing a white marble is $w/(w + r)$. With a regular binomial model, these probabilities stay fixed at those values. Suppose, now, that the experiment is changed to be as follows:

(*a*) If a red marble is drawn, we shall add c red marbles to the urn before any other draw is made, and if a white marble is drawn we shall add c white marbles to the urn before the next draw.

(*b*) The procedure of (*a*) is repeated after each successive draw, so that after k draws the urn will contain $r + w + kc$ marbles. The numbers of red and of white marbles in the urn after k draws depend on what was drawn during the experiment, so the probabilities for red and white change from draw to draw.

This urn model often is called the Pólya-Eggenberger model.

If x is the number of red marbles drawn during n draws from a Pólya-Eggenberger model, what is the probability function for the random variable x? In this rather nonmathematical course, we shall only obtain $\Pr\{x\}$ for $n = 1$ and $n = 3$ and then generalize therefrom.

If $n = 1$,

$$\Pr\{x = 0\} = \frac{w}{w + r} \qquad \text{and} \qquad \Pr\{x = 1\} = \frac{r}{w + r}$$

If $n = 3$,

$$x \text{ can equal } 0, 1, 2, \text{ or } 3$$

In view of the probability laws of Chapter 1, the following should be reasonably clear;

(*a*) $\Pr\{x = 0\} = \Pr\{\text{white, white, white}\}$

$$= \binom{3}{0}\left(\frac{w}{w + r}\right)\left(\frac{w + c}{w + r + c}\right)\left(\frac{w + 2c}{w + r + 2c}\right)$$

which has the form $\displaystyle\binom{n}{x}\frac{w(w + c)\cdots[r + (n - x - 1)c]}{(w + r)(w + r + c)\cdots[w + r + (n - 1)c]}$

(*b*) $\Pr\{x = 1\} = \Pr\{\text{red, white, white}\} + \Pr\{\text{white, red, white}\}$
$$+ \Pr\{\text{white, white, red}\}$$

$$= \frac{r}{w + r}\cdot\frac{w}{w + r + c}\cdot\frac{w + c}{w + r + 2c} + \frac{w}{w + r}\cdot\frac{r}{w + r + c}\cdot\frac{w + c}{w + r + 2c}$$

$$+ \frac{w}{w + r}\cdot\frac{w + c}{w + r + c}\cdot\frac{r}{w + r + 2c}$$

which has the form $\displaystyle\binom{n}{x}\frac{r\cdot w\cdots[w + (n - x - 1)c]}{(w + r)(w + r + c)\cdots[w + r + (n - 1)c]}$

(c) $\Pr\{x = 2\} = \Pr\{\text{red, red, white}\} + \Pr\{\text{red, white, red}\}$
$$+ \Pr\{\text{white, red, red}\}$$

$$= \frac{r}{w+r} \cdot \frac{r+c}{w+r+c} \cdot \frac{w}{w+r+2c} + \frac{r}{w+r} \cdot \frac{w}{w+r+c} \cdot \frac{r+c}{w+r+2c}$$

$$+ \frac{w}{r+w} \cdot \frac{r}{w+r+c} \cdot \frac{r+c}{w+r+2c}$$

which has the form $\binom{n}{x} \dfrac{r \cdot w \cdots [r + (x-1)c]}{(r+w)(r+w+c)\cdots[r+w+(n-1)c]}$

(d) $\Pr\{x = 3\} = \Pr\{\text{red, red, red}\}$

$$= \frac{r}{r+w} \cdot \frac{r+c}{r+w+c} \cdot \frac{r+2c}{r+w+2c}$$

which has the form $\binom{n}{x} \dfrac{r(r+c)[r+(x-1)c]}{(r+w)(r+w+c)\cdots[r+w+(n-1)c]}$

It now should be easy to believe that for n draws the general probability function for x, the number of red marbles drawn on n draws under the Pólya-Eggenberger model, is

(13.44) $\Pr\{x \mid w, r, c, n\}$

$$= \binom{n}{x} \frac{r(r+c)\cdots[r+(x-1)c]w\cdots[w+(n-x-1)c]}{(w+r)(w+r+c)\cdots[w+r+(n-1)c]}$$

It can be shown by a mathematical process (well beyond the mathematical level of training assumed herein) that a limiting form of the Pólya-Eggenberger distribution as $n \to \infty$ and $p \to 0$ is just the negative binomial probability function of the term 13.43. The only interesting point here is that the "contagious" Pólya-Eggenberger model can turn into the negative binomial for very large samples and small p. Intuitively, this is simply saying that the number of occurrences of a rare event with a changing probability may have a negative binomial distribution—as was true when the Poisson parameter changed according to the Pearson Type III distribution function.

The quite diverse points of view and consequent experimental situations which lead to negative binomial distributions are associated with a broad field of applications of the negative binomial in general. The following brief descriptions of experimental situations which can produce a negative binomial variate may serve to illustrate this breadth of application.

(a) Counts of insects on experimental plots often conform to a negative binomial distribution, presumably because their gregariousness, or their hatching habits, introduce "contagion" in the sense that the location of one insect in a "plot" increases the probability that there are others in that plot.

(b) If the birth and death *rates* per individual within a living population are constant, and there is a constant rate of immigration, population size may conform to a negative binomial population (M. G. Kendall, *J. Roy. Stat. Soc.* (B) 11: 230, 1949).

(*c*) If chicks of a given age raised in the same environment are each given, say, 100 *A. galli* eggs, the counts of worms recovered in the digestive tract usually conform to a negative binomial distribution. Presumably, the varying resistance from chick to chick causes what is basically a Poisson distribution to become a negative binomial (J. I. Northam and U. F. Rocha, *Exptl. Parasitol.* 7: 428, 1958).

(*d*) The numbers of pinholes in 50-foot samples of enameled wire from numerous batches of such wire have been found by M. E. Wise (Suppl., *J. Roy. Stat. Soc.* 8: 202, 1046) to conform to a negative binomial distribution. Presumably, the rare event of a pinhole in such wire has a changing probability from batch to batch.

(*e*) Numbers of industrial accidents among workers during relatively short periods of time also may follow a negative binomial distribution. Apparently, the distribution over a number of periods of equal lengths of time and for the *i*th worker would be Poisson, but accident proneness from worker to worker varies in such a way that the numbers of accidents for a group of workers may follow a negative binomial distribution. This is one of the oldest applications for this distribution.

(*f*) If the number of "hits" with x-rays, cosmic rays, or whatever, has to reach a level, *k*, before some detectable effect, as death, mutation, etc., occurs, this waiting-time type of process will produce negative binomial data.

(*g*) Fisher (*Ann. Eugenics* 11: 182, 1941) illustrated the negative binomial by means of the number of sheep having 0, 1, 2, $\cdots$ ticks. He found that the frequency distribution of 0's, 1's, 2's, $\cdots$ closely followed a negative binomial frequency distribution. This, again, appears to be another basically Poisson situation but with a changing parameter, λ, from sheep to sheep. Note, however, that a different group of sheep in another region probably would have a negative binomial distribution with different parameters.

(*h*) In W. Feller, *Probability Theory and Its Applications* (Wiley, New York, 1950), an example is given from records of damage caused by lightning as observed during *n* time intervals each of length *t*. In this situation it seems that lightning strikes rarely enough to make a Poisson distribution applicable, but the damage caused varies from strike to strike in such a way that the total result is well fitted by a negative binomial function.

(*i*) There are various ways to sample populations of animals, fish, or insects, to estimate the number in the population involved. One way is to draw a random sample, tag or otherwise mark the individuals captured in the sample, and return them to their population. Then a second random sample is taken after the marked individuals have had time to disperse among the unmarked. The next step in the technique is to draw the members of a second random sample sequentially and with replacement, until a predetermined number of marked individuals is recaptured. This obviously simulates a Pascal waiting-time model with fixed k, x unmarked captures being a random variable and the total number $n = k + x$ being the random size of the second sample.

(*j*) J. Gurland (*Am. J. Public Health* 49: 1388, 1959) has found that the frequency distribution of numbers of children with $x = 0, 1, 2, \cdots$ cavities in their teeth also fits a negative binomial distribution. This situation could be visualized as either a waiting-time phenomenon, in which a series of bacteriological "events" is required before a cavity is produced, or a situation in which a cavity is a relatively rare event but in which there is a changing rate of formation of cavities from child to child.

The negative binomial distribution also has been found to be applicable to studies of infectious diseases, weather persistence, and other situations, but the preceding examples should point out the general nature of negative binomial frequency distributions and their wide usefulness.

Before leaving this introduction and discussing the usual two problems in statistics, estimation and testing hypotheses, it is well to indicate how the necessary tabular information can be obtained for negative binomial distributions.

The binomial probability function is $b(x; n, p) = \binom{n}{x} p^x q^{n-x}$, whereas the Pascal form of the negative binomial is $\Pr\{x \mid p, k\} = \binom{x + k - 1}{x} p^k q^x$. If the $b(x; n, p)$ is multiplied by p, one has the form of $\Pr\{x \mid p, k\}$ with $n = x + k - 1$ and the sum of the powers on p and q adding to more than the "n" of the formula for numbers of combinations. Thus, if $k = 4$, $p = 0.3$, and $x = 6$,

$$\Pr\{6 \mid 0.3, 4\} = \binom{9}{6}(0.3)^4(0.7)^6$$

with "n" $= 9$ and $k + x = 10$, but

$$\binom{9}{6}(0.3)^3(0.7)(0.7) = b(3; 0.3, 9)(0.7) = 0.2668(0.7) = 0.1868$$

from tables of $b(x; n, p)$, such as the *Tables of the Binomial Probability Distribution*, published by the Department of Commerce, 1950.

Usually one needs the cumulative distribution of a variate rather than its frequency distribution. E. S. Pearson and E. C. Fieller (*Biometrika* 25: 158–78, 1933) pointed out that existing tables of what is called the incomplete beta function can be used to obtain values of

$$F(y) = \sum_{x=0}^{y} \binom{x + k - 1}{x} p^k q^x$$

because of the following relationship:

$$(13.45) \qquad F(y) = \sum_{x=0}^{y} \binom{x + r - 1}{x} p^k q^x = I_p(k, y + 1)$$

Tables of $I_p(k, y + 1)$ are available in several places, including the *Biometrika Tables for Statisticians*, Vol. 1, Table 16.

The probability function for the Pascal form of the negative binomial distribution often is called the form for *inverse binomial sampling*, because it is derived from a binomial sampling model for which one fixes the number k of "successes" and observes the number of failures—and hence total sample size also—prior to the kth success. In *direct binomial sampling* one fixes the sample size and thereafter observes the number of "successes" which happen to occur on n trials.

There is another useful and somewhat more general form of a negative binomial distribution, for which the parameters still are k and p, but for which $q = 1 + p$ and k is not necessarily an integer. The probability function for this form is

$$(13.46) \quad \Pr\{x \mid p, k\} = \binom{x + k - 1}{x} p^x q^{-x-k}, \qquad q = 1 + p, \quad k > 0$$

This form derives most naturally from a situation which would be Poisson, if λ were fixed, but for which λ actually has a Pearson Type III distribution. Fisher (*Ann. Eugenics* 11: 182–87, 1941) showed how the Form 13.46 can be derived and what some uses of it are.

J. J. Bartko (*Virginia J. Sci.* 12: 18–37, 1961) gives a summary of the properties and some applications of the negative binomial both in the Pascal form and in Form 13.46. He also provides an extensive bibliography.

•

PROBLEMS

1. What Pascal probability function would give the probability that a biassed coin with $p_H = 0.4$ would need to be tossed x times to obtain the sixth appearance of Heads?

2. Evaluate the probability for Problem 1 if $x = 20$. Then compute $b(6; 21, 0.4)$ and discuss these two probabilities.

3. Expand the negative binomial $(1 - q)^{-6}$ for seven terms, and then give the general term from Formula 13.43.

4. Suppose that a box contains 10 blue and 15 red marbles, all alike in size, weight, and feel. One marble is to be drawn, its color noted, and then replaced, and three marbles of that same color added to the box. This process is to be repeated four times; that is, five draws are to be made. What is the probability of a blue marble's being drawn on the fifth draw? What is the probability of exactly three blue marbles being drawn during those five draws?

5. Construct the Pólya-Eggenberger model described in Problem 4 by marking lima beans with blue and red ink. Thereafter estimate empirically the probabilities required in Problem 4 by making 100 sets of five such draws.

6. Compute the true mean and variance for each part of Problem 2. What is the ratio of variance to mean for each part of that problem?

13.5 POINT ESTIMATION OF THE PARAMETERS OF A NEGATIVE BINOMIAL POPULATION

If the probability distribution function for a negative binomial population is put in the alternative Pascal form,

$$\text{(13.51)} \qquad \binom{n-1}{k-1} p^k \cdot q^x$$

which is Equation 13.41 with $n = x + k$, then, as J. B. S. Haldane (*Biometrika* 33: 222–25, 1943) has shown, an unbiassed estimator of the parameter, p, is obtained from

$$\text{(13.52)} \qquad \hat{p} = \frac{k-1}{n-1} = \frac{k-1}{x+k-1}$$

D. J. Finney (*Biometrika* 36: 233–35, 1949) has obtained the following formula for the unbiassed estimate of the variance of $\hat{p}$:

$$\text{(13.53)} \qquad s_{\hat{p}}^2 = \frac{\hat{p}(1-\hat{p})}{n-2} \quad \text{or} \quad = \frac{\hat{p}^2(1-\hat{p})}{k-1-\hat{p}}$$

To illustrate the last two equations, consider a sampling scheme for estimating the size of an animal population by tagging (or otherwise marking) v members of the population drawn at random and then resampling this same population until a predetermined number, k, of marked individuals is recaptured. D. G. Chapman (*Biometrics* 8: 286–306, 1952) has described such a procedure. All sampling is done with replacement, so that the proportion, p, of marked individuals remains constant for some useful period of time. Obviously, $p = v/N$, where N is the unknown population size. If it requires that $x + k = 300$ fish, say, be caught before $k = 25$ marked individuals are recaptured, then

$$\Pr\{n\} = \Pr\{x = 300 - 25 = 275 \text{ unmarked}\} = \binom{299}{24}\left(\frac{v}{N}\right)^{25}\left(1 - \frac{v}{N}\right)^{275}$$

The unbiassed estimate of p is 24/299, by Equation 13.52; therefore, the unbiassed estimate of N is $\hat{N} = 299v/24$, in which v is the known number of fish marked during the first sampling. If $v = 500$, then $\hat{N} = 6229$. In general,

$$\text{(13.54)} \qquad \hat{N} = \frac{(n-1)v}{k-1}$$

where:

> v = number marked during first sampling
> k = predetermined number of marked individuals which must be re-captured during the second sampling
> n = total number taken during second sampling at the time the kth marked individual is recaptured.

When a sampling situation is such that the Pascal form of the negative binomial does not apply, estimation of the parameters is more difficult and less precise. In the Form 13.46 the negative binomial simply is a mathematical expression for the probability distribution function for some two-parameter population which has been called a negative binomial population. The k is not predetermined, as for the Pascal form, and, in fact, k does not need to be an integer. Moreover, $p + q \neq 1$; in fact, $q = 1 + p$, so p and q are not probabilities, as in the binomial and Pascal negative binomial populations.

Two procedures have been employed to estimate p and k under the non-Pascal model. One is the method of maximum likelihood; the other is called the method of moments, because it is accomplished by setting the theoretical moments (mean and variance, for example) in their mathematical forms equal to the corresponding moments computed from sampling data. Neither method will be carried out here; only the results, $\hat{p}$ and $\hat{k}$, will be given and used.

R. A. Fisher (*Ann. Eugenics* 11: 182–87, 1941) used the method of moments to obtain the following estimates for p and k for the negative binomial in the non-Pascal form, 13.46:

(13.55)
$$\hat{p} = (s^2 - \bar{x})/\bar{x}, \qquad \hat{k} = \bar{x}^2/(s^2 - \bar{x})$$

where $\bar{x}$ and s^2 have their usual meaning. These estimates have larger sampling variances than the estimates made by the more difficult method of maximum likelihood. However, they probably are satisfactory for most experimental research.

The following data taken from Fisher's 1941 article (previous paragraph) on the negative binomial will be used to illustrate point estimation of p and k in Equation 13.46. These data were obtained originally by counting the numbers of ticks on sheep and thereafter making a frequency distribution table as follows:

												Sums
Numbers of ticks, x:	0	1	2	3	4	5	6	7	9	10		195
Frequency among sheep, f:	7	9	8	13	8	5	4	3	1	2		60

Thus, on a total of 60 sheep, 195 ticks were counted, so $\bar{x} = 195/60 = 3.250$. The variance $s^2 = \sum (x - \bar{x})^2/59 = 349.25/59 = 5.920$; therefore, $\hat{p} = (5.920 - 3.250)/3.250 = 0.822$, and $\hat{k} = (3.250)^2/(5.920 - 3.250) = 3.975$ are the estimates of p and k, respectively, by the method of moments. The method of maximum likelihood produces $\hat{p} = 0.867$ and $\hat{k} = 3.75$, according to J. J. Bartko (*Virgina J. Sci.* 12: 28, 1961). If an experimenter is anxious to have the utmost efficiency (lowest sampling error) for the estimators he uses, he should use the method of maximum likelihood, the formulas for which are given and illustrated by Bartko in the reference just cited.

PROBLEMS

1. Suppose that a wildlife conservationist wishes to estimate the number of large-mouth bass in a lake which, though fairly large, can be randomly sampled. Five hundred of this species of bass are caught, tagged, and returned to the lake. At a later date, after the tagged bass have completely intermingled in the population in the lake, a second sampling is done as follows: (*a*) Each large-mouth bass caught is recorded as tagged or not, added to the count, and returned to the lake. (*b*) When the 75th tagged large-mouth bass is recaptured, the sampling ceases. A total of $n = x + k = 2000$ large-mouth bass were caught in the second sample. Estimate N, the total number of large-mouth bass in this lake.

2. What is the probability function for x = number of tails tossed with an unbiassed coin before the fourth head is tossed? Put this function in two forms. Are there any parameters to be estimated?

3. Suppose that a biased coin has been flipped until the third head appeared, and that this required 20 tosses. Estimate p, the constant probability of a head with this coin. How reliable is this estimate?

4. What is the probability function for the random variable x, the number of tosses with two unbiassed dice, before the sixth sum = 7 is tossed? What are the values of p and k for this negative binomial variate?

5. Suppose that you wish to estimate the number of beans in a large container. This container is such that you can mix the beans well and sample randomly. How would you use a negative binomial process to estimate the number of beans?

6. R. A. Fisher (*Ann. Eugenics* 11: 186, 1941) gave the following frequency distribution of numbers of sheep with the indicated numbers of ticks on them:

Number, x:	0	1	2	3	4	5	6	7	8	9	10	11	12	13	14	15	16
Frequency, f:	4	5	11	10	9	11	3	5	3	2	2	5	—	2	2	1	1

Estimate the p and k for a negative binomial distribution which would be appropriate for this distribution.

7. Suppose that a large wire cage contains an unknown but large number of houseflies. You capture and mark 50 flies and return them to the cage. Assuming a process of random sampling is possible and that the previously marked flies are exactly as catchable as before their marking, suppose it takes a second sample of size 100 flies to obtain the tenth marked fly. Estimate the number of flies in this cage.

8. Suppose that for a Pascal model of the negative binomial the k is chosen as 10 and a coin has to be tossed 30 times to obtain the tenth Head. What is the unbiassed estimate of p_H? What is the unbiassed estimate of variance of $\hat{p}$? Would these results cause you to believe, somewhat superficially, that this coin is biassed? Explain.

9. Suppose that a rearing pond in a fish hatchery contains many six-inch channel catfish and that 25 are caught, marked, and returned unharmed to the pond. Then fish are caught one at a time, it merely being noted whether each one caught has been marked previously. This process is continued until five such fish are recaptured. If this second sampling required the catching of 100 fish to obtain the fifth recapture, what is the best estimate of the number of catfish in that pond?

10. Suppose that a random variate X has a negative binomial density function described by Equation 13.46. Write down the specific probability density, if $k = 5$ and $p = 0.3$, and plot this function for $X = 0, 1, 2, 3, 4$, and 5.

13.6   INTERVAL ESTIMATION OF THE PARAMETERS OF NEGATIVE BINOMIAL POPULATIONS

Two general forms of the negative binomial distribution have been considered, the Pascal, or Inverse, Binomial, for which

(13.61)
$$\Pr\{x\} = \binom{n-1}{k-1} p^k q^x$$

where

$$k + x = n, \quad p + q = 1, \quad \text{and } k = 1, 2, 3, \cdots \rightarrow \infty$$

or, the more general form, for which

(13.62) $\Pr\{x\} = \binom{x+k-1}{x} p^k q^{-x-k}, \qquad \text{where } k > 0 \quad \text{and } q = 1 + p$

It should be clear from the Pascal form that n is exactly the number of trials until the kth "success" has occurred, so the larger the p the smaller the n, if p is probability of "success" from trial to trial. Hence, the upper confidence limit p_U on p for a given result, k fixed and n observed, is that p such that the probability that the quota, k, will be attained in n *or more* trials is $\alpha/2$. Similarly, p_L, the lower confidence limit, is that p such that the probability of reaching the quota, k, in n *or fewer* trials is $\alpha/2$. J. J. Bartko (*Virginia J. Sci.* 12: 26, 1961), following D. J. Finney's procedure (*Biometrika* 36: 233, 1949), uses this reasoning to show that the confidence limits for the parameter p under inverse binomial sampling (Pascal form) can be obtained from tables or charts constructed for direct (Chapter 2) binomial confidence limits as follows:

(13.63)   (*a*) To find p_U for the Pascal negative binomial, use
$$\hat{p} = (k-1)/(n-1)$$
         (*b*) To find p_L, use $\hat{p} = k/n$

In view of the fact that all tables and charts for direct binomial CI's only include selected sample sizes, the determination of p_L and p_U will be approximate and often require interpolation. With direct binomial sampling, n is chosen in advance, but in inverse binomial sampling, n is random and k is fixed, so the n and $n - 1$ almost always fall between tabular values or between lines of charts.

The estimation of the parameters p and k for a non-Pascal negative binomial is quite different from that for Equation 13.61. In fact, there always are two parameters instead of one, and this appears to be the reason why such joint intervals are not normally computed.

PROBLEMS

1. Suppose that a coin of unknown bias is to be tossed until the fourteenth head appears; this requires a total of 40 tosses. Obtain a CI_{95} on p, the probability of heads from toss to toss. Does your CI lead you to believe the coin is biassed? Explain.

2. Take any pair of six-sided dice and roll them until you get the tenth sum of seven. Then compute the CI_{90} on p and decide whether this pair of dice is biassed. Explain.

3. Suppose that a dilute but homogeneous solution containing *E. coli* bacteria is at hand, along with an instrument for withdrawing 1-cc. samples at random from this solution. Also at hand is a large supply of Petri dishes containing a media optimal for the growth of this bacterium. The Petri dishes are numbered serially from 1 to n. You choose $k = 25$ and then plate out many 1-cc. samples. At a suitable time thereafter, when all *E. coli* present will have grown and become observable in the media, you find that you had to examine the first 90 plates to observe the twenty-fifth one showing *E. coli* growth. Compute a CI_{90} on p, the probability that a randomly drawn 1-cc. sample will contain at least one *E. coli* bacterium.

4. Suppose that a fairly large group of particles is a mixture of those particles with a fixed but very small amount of radioactivity of some sort and those particles with no radioactivity. Suppose also that the amount of radioactivity in any particle is so small that it takes 10 in a group to be recorded on the available instrument for measuring radioactivity. Particles are to be placed under this instrument one at a time and left there until radioactivity is first detected. Suppose this process requires that 150 particles be so placed. Compute a CI_{90} on p, the true proportion of radioactive particles in the material which was sampled.

13.7 TESTING HYPOTHESES ABOUT PARAMETERS OF NEGATIVE BINOMIAL POPULATIONS

If one is concerned with the Pascal form of inverse binomial sampling, for which k is an arbitrary positive integer, $p + q = 1$, and n is the total number of observations required to attain exactly k "successes," then a confidence interval on p can be used to test a hypothesis about p in the usual manner. For example, suppose that circumstances are such that one chooses

$k = 10$ and finds thereafter that it requires $n = 51$ observations to attain the tenth "success." The point estimate of p is $\hat{p} = (k - 1)/(n - 1) = 9/50 = 0.18$. As stated in Rules 13.63, we can use $(k - 1)/(n - 1) = 0.18$ as the $\hat{p}$ in direct binomial charts and tables to obtain p_U, the upper confidence limit on p, and can use $k/n = 0.0196 \simeq 0.02$ as p_L, the lower confidence limit. If α is chosen 0.05, Table IV yields $p_U = U = 0.31$ and $p_L = L = 0$. Hence, any H_0 which agrees with the confidence interval

$$\text{CI}_{95}: \qquad 0 < p < 0.31$$

is acceptable with a 5% two-sided region of rejection.

When more than one negative binomial population is involved or k is not an interger and $q = 1 + p$, the problems of testing hypotheses become very complex and, as they are used infrequently, they will not be presented here. However, the following information will be given as an aid to those who might be interested.

J. J. Bartko's summary article (*Virginia J. Sci.* 12: 18–37, 1961) points out several possibilities for some certain situations:

(a) If testing $H_0(p_1 = p_2)$, one can select k_1 and k_2, observe the corresponding n_1 and n_2, and thereafter use either the exact or the approximate procedure suggested by G. A. Barnard (*J. Roy. Stat. Soc.* (B) 1–26, 1946) and described by Bartko.

(b) It is occasionally preferable in a study which will lead to a contingency table analysis to fix the size of the frequency in one cell in advance. For example, one might feel certain that the cell in the lower right-hand corner of the contingency table would have the lowest frequency and wish to be sure it would not be too small. It would be set at a frequency of 10, say. One then has the inverse sampling situation and draws observations, until the frequency of this cell is 10. H. S. Steyn (*Statistica Neerlandica* 13: 433–44, 1959) has discussed this case both for 2×2 and for an $r \times c$ contingency tables.

PROBLEMS

1. Compute and interpret a CI_{90} for each of the following negative binomials of the Pascal type:
   (a) $k = 15$, $n = 20$ (b) $k = 28$, $n = 75$
   (c) $k = 10$, $n = 90$ (d) $k = 36$, $n = 200$.

2. Suppose that with $\alpha = 0.05$ and k set at 20, the n turns out to be 150; what is the least upper bound on p in the confidence interval sense? Use this result to test $H_0(p \leqslant 0.05)$ against $H_a(p > 0.05)$.

3. Suppose that an experiment is to be set up to test the unbiassedness of a pair of dice in terms of sums appearing on the pair when thrown simultaneously. It is decided that this pair of dice will be tossed until a sum of 7 appears for the twentieth time. It turns out that 130 sums other than 7 are tossed before the twentieth 7 occurs. Use a CI_{95} to decide whether this pair of dice probably is unbiassed.

REVIEW PROBLEMS

1. Suppose you wished to determine by samples whether the *relative* number of adverbs per sentence is the same for the seven sections of Chapter 13. Define the term "relative number of adverbs in a sentence" as the number of adverbs in a given sentence divided by the total number of words in the sentence. Thereafter conduct a sampling study of those seven sections, and draw appropriate conclusions regarding the question suggested in the first sentence of this problem.

2. Suppose that 3% of the mosquitoes in a certain area carry the organism which causes human encephalitis and that, if such a carrier bites a human being, that person will get encephalitis. If each of 50 people on a picnic in that area is bitten once by a mosquito and no mosquito bites more than one person, what is the probability that at least one of those picnickers will contact this encephalitis?

3. Describe how Problem 2 could be solved two ways, each using a different statistical distribution.

4. If Problem 2 had asked for the probability that exactly one picnicker will contact encephalitis, how would the solution to Problem 2 change? Could Problem 3 be done with this change?

5. What kind of statistical distribution would you judge each of the following random variables to have?
   (a) The weight of a robin's egg in Kansas four days after it is laid, measured to the nearest milligram.
   (b) The mean weight of 10 eggs under the conditions of part (a).
   (c) The number of fertile robins' eggs among 10 chosen at random from nests in Kansas.
   (d) The variate $w = \sum_{i=1}^{5} (v_i - a_i)^2$, where the v_i are NID(a_i, 1) variates.
   (e) The number of people per random sample of 1000 who have a rare blood disease.

6. Suppose that one of the even integers 2, 4, 6, 8, 10, and 12 is to be chosen at random. Thereafter an unbiassed coin is to be tossed a number of times equal to the number drawn at random. What is the probability of an equal number of Heads and Tails?

7. Do Problem 6 for the coin so biassed that $p_H = 0.4$.

8. Suppose that a group of university juniors in physical science have been classified two ways: (a) from high school of over 500 enrollment, 250–500 enrollment, or less than 250 enrollment, and (b) grade point average below 2.00, from 2.00 to 2.99, or at or above 3.00. The results of this two-way classification are:

High school enrollment:

GPA	Below 250	250–500	Over 500	Total
≥ 3.00	45	80	75	200
2.00–2.99	360	185	155	700
Below 2.00	35	45	20	100
Total:	440	310	250	1000

Do you accept the hypothesis that there is no association between the size of the high school and the grade point average of university juniors in physical science under the conditions sampled? Use $\alpha = 0.10$.

9. Make a line graph showing the relationship between number of tosses of an unbiassed coin, n, and the probability of tossing exactly $n/2$ Heads when $n = 2, 4, 6, 8, 10, 12, 14$, and 16.

10. Do Problem 9, given that $p_H = 0.7$ is the probability of Heads from toss to toss.

11. Suppose that a measurement X is known to have an N(2.85, 17) distribution. What number X_0 is such that $\Pr\{\bar{x} > X_0\} = 0.500$, no matter what size of sample is taken to obtain the mean, $\bar{x}$?

12. Given the following hypothetical data and computations therefrom, compute two unbiassed estimates of μ, and define one as being better than the other, in general, if these X's are from an N(μ, σ^2) population.

$$X: \quad 3.4, \ 5.6, \ 4.8, \ 4.3, \ 5.5, \ 5.1, \ 4.6, \ 6.7, \ \text{and} \ 5.0$$
$$\sum X = 45.0, \qquad \sum (X^2) = 231.76$$

13. Referring to Problem 12, compute a biassed estimate of μ. Of σ^2.

14. Compute the LUB_{90} on σ^2 for the population sampled in Problem 12. Then test $H_0(\sigma^2 \leqslant 2.0)$ against $H_a(\sigma^2 > 2.0)$. What is the decision if $H_0(\sigma^2 = 2.0)$ is tested against $H_a(\sigma^2 \neq 2.0)$?

15. Suppose that a bank has a free parking lot one block from it and wishes to find out the extent to which the lot is being used by nonpatrons of this bank. Which of the following sampling procedures would you prefer?
    (a) Have a trained interviewer ask each driver entering the lot whether he or she was going to the bank some time before returning to the car.
    (b) Tell each driver entering the lot that a survey was being conducted on the use of parking lots and on shopping habits, and thereafter ask what business establishments the occupants of the car intended to visit before leaving the parking lot.
    (c) Do as in (b), but interview the occupants of each car as they are about to leave the lot and ask what business establishments they had visited.
    (d) Surreptitiously record the license number of each car entering the lot, look up the ownership, and inquire later at the bank whether the car owner had been in the bank that day.

16. Suppose that a home economist wishes to study the strength of a certain type of cotton fabric as it may be affected by various amounts of exposure to light and after various degrees of mechanical wear. She also wishes to find out whether different brands of the same fabric differ importantly in strength. The strength, X, will be measured in a standard machine. The exposure to light will be made at four levels: L, $2L$, $3L$, and $4L$ by means of a standard Fade-O-Meter. The mechanical wear will be produced by subjecting each sample to 100, 200, 300, or 400 revolutions of a standard machine which wears by abrasion. Five brands will be selected at random from the many available, and four pieces of fabric will be tested at each combination of exposure, abrasion, and brand. Write down the statistical model for this experiment with a brief but accurate definition of *all* letter symbols.

17. Write down the outline for the analysis of variance for Problem 16, including *all* expected Mean Squares, being as specific as possible.

18. State all exact F tests one could use in reference to Problem 16, being as specific as possible. Also state what H_0 each F test tests.

19. Given the following plus-minus diagram, do as directed below, given that the symbol *ij* means the *i*th level of factor A and the *j*th level of factor B:

Comparison	Sum					
	00 (13)	01 (7)	02 (5)	10 (8)	11 (12)	12 (15)
	−1	−1	−1	+1	+1	+1
	+1	−2	+1	+1	−2	+1
	−1	0	+1	−1	0	+1
	−1	+2	−1	+1	−2	+1
	+1	0	−1	−1	0	+1

(*a*) Identify each comparison.
(*b*) Compute the Mean Square for the A × B$_Q$ interaction, given that $k = 3$ replications, where B$_Q$ is the quadratic part of the B effect.
(*c*) Show that this is an orthogonal set of comparisons.

20. Given the following graph of the least-squares regression line computed from a random sample, $(X_1, Y_1), \cdots (X_n, Y_n)$, and the observed pair, (X_4, Y_4) do as directed below.

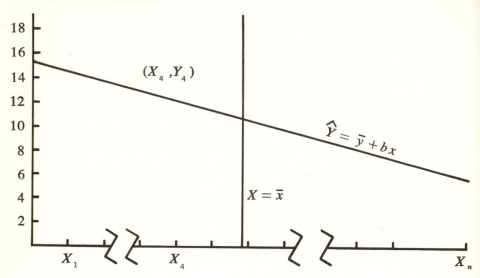

(*a*) Obtain an approximate *but specific* value for the adjusted Y_4, that is, Y_{a_4}.
(*b*) Obtain an approximate *but specific* value for $\hat{Y}_4$.
(*c*) Obtain an approximate *but specific* value for *b*.

21. Given the following computations from an RCB design with pairs of measurements (X_i, Y_i), perform an analysis of covariance through the F test of H_0(all $\tau_i = 0$) versus H_a(some $\tau_i \neq 0$), where τ_i is the adjusted effect of the *i*th Treatment:

Source of variation	DF	Σx^2	$\Sigma (xy)$	$\Sigma (y^2)$	$\Sigma y^2 - \dfrac{(\Sigma xy)^2}{\Sigma x^2}$	DF	Ms
Blocks	3	163.5	92.5	52.7			
Treats.	3	54.0	24.0	26.2			
Error	9	73.5	49.2	52.6	19.6		2.45
Total:	15	291.0	165.7	131.5			
Blocks + Error:		237.0	141.7	105.3	84.7		
Treats. + Error:		127.5	73.2	78.8	36.7		

22. A sampling box contains white, red, black, and green beads. There also is a sampling paddle design to take random samples of size $n = 50$ from the multinomial population. Four independent and random samples with $n = 50$ each time produced the following numbers: 125 white, 26 red, 40 black, and 9 green. Do these results agree satisfactorily with H_0(9 white : 3 red : 3 black : 1 green) versus its negation?

23. The following data are intended to simulate results from a study of fly sprays, the numbers being numbers of flies observed on individual dairy animals of the same sex, breed, and age.

Spray:

	1	2	3	4	5	6
	10	11	1	32	9	13
	92	3	2	18	24	9
	16	34	3	11	8	12
	21	25	10	26	17	5
	5	78	2	40	13	6
	60	17	6	17	13	3
Σ:	204	168	24	144	84	48
x_i:	34	28	4	24	14	8
s_i^2:	1190	716	11.6	115.6	34.4	16.0

Determine the best transformation of these data, apply it, and do the analysis of variance.

24. Do Problem 23, using a range of values of the constant "a" in the general transformation, and comment on the effect of this change in "a."

25. Make up a set of data presumably from an $N(\mu, \sigma^2)$ population such that $H_0(\mu = 0)$ will be accepted by a t test in preference to $H_a(\mu > 0)$. Use $n = 15$ and $\alpha = 0.10$. Next, change your data *without changing the mean*, so that H_0 will be rejected. Then change your data *without changing the variance*, so that H_0 will be rejected.

26. Make up a set of data presumably from an $N(\mu, \sigma^2)$ population which has $n = 10$ and $\bar{x} = 1.0$ and is such that $H_0(\mu = 0)$ is rejected with $\alpha = 0.10$. Then do the same with $\bar{x} = 0.10$.

27. Make up two sets of data with $n_1 = 12$ and $n_2 = 18$, such that Mood's Square Rank test will cause you to conclude that those two samples are from populations with different dispersions. Choose $\alpha = 0.10$.

28. Do Problem 27, but use Hartley's F_{max} test. What new assumptions did you have to make in this problem, as compared with Problem 27?

29. Make up two sets of data presumably from $N_1(\mu_1, \sigma^2)$ and $N_2(\mu_2, \sigma^2)$ and such that $H_0(\mu_1 = \mu_2)$ is rejected at the 10% level by the G test but that H_0 is accepted by the t test. Let $n_1 = n_2 = 10$.

30. Do as in Problem 20, but replace the t test by the Wilcoxon-Mann-Whitney test.

31. If a very large random sample from a Poisson population has produced $X = 6$, what is the CI_{80} on the parameter λ? What is the GLB_{90} on that parameter? What is the LUB_{95}? Interpret each result obtained in answer to these questions.

32. Plot the frequency distribution of the Poisson population with $\lambda = 4.5$.

33. Plot the frequency distribution of the Pascal negative binomial with $p = 0.6$ and $k = 3$.

Chapter 14

Introductory Discriminatory Analysis

14.1 INTRODUCTION

The reader already is familiar with the statistical problem of deciding whether two samples probably came from the same univariate population. The Student t test, the F test, or some alternative procedure is used to make this decision by dividing the t axis, say, into two nonoverlapping but all-inclusive regions known as the region of rejection and the region of acceptance of $H_0(\mu_1 = \mu_2)$. This sort of problem is in the field of testing hypotheses.

If three or more samples are drawn when $H_0(\mu_1 = \mu_2 \cdots = \mu_t)$ is to be tested, this is still a problem of testing hypotheses, and one still divides some axis into regions as the basis for decisions. The F test or some other procedure may be used as the basis for decision.

A natural extension of tests of significance regarding univariate populations is to consider tests of significance regarding multivariate populations. Varieties of plants and animals, species of insects, etc., may be quite similar, or even identical, with respect to some measurements, but quite different with respect to others, or they may not be different enough with respect to any one trait to make the populations distinguishable without excessively large samples. Hence, there is need for methods which take several measurements, $X_1, \cdots, X_p$, into account in making decisions about population differences. Something of this sort already has been done through multiple-regression analysis.

A statistical problem which is closely related to hypothesis testing but is importantly different can be described by the following situation:

(*a*) Three and only three species of a given sort of flower are known to exist in a certain geographical area.

(*b*) The frequency distributions of X_1 = sepal length, X_2 = sepal width, and X_3 = petal length either are well known for each species or can be estimated by means of samples from each species.

(*c*) The interrelations among X_1, X_2, and X_3 are known as well as their variances within each species, or they can be estimated by means of samples from each species.

(*d*) An individual flower, I, of unknown species has been found in this same area.

Question: How can one do the best job of classifying I into one of the three possible populations?

The answer to this question involves discriminatory analysis. There are many variations and ramifications of this problem, and it can become very complex. There also is much research yet to be done on the matter of discriminatory analysis. All that will be attempted herein is to introduce some interesting concepts and some useful practical procedures. The interested reader is referred to the following for additional information.

1. J. L. Hodges, Jr., "Discriminatory Analysis. 1. Survey of Discriminatory Analysis," published under Project Number 21-49-004, Report Number 1, by the United States Air Force School of Aviation Medicine, Randolph Field, Texas, 1950.

2. C. R. Rao, *Advanced Statistical Methods in Biometric Research*, Wiley, New York, 1952.

3. R. A. Fisher, "The use of multiple measurements in taxonomic problems," *Ann. Eugenics* 7: 179–88, 1936.

4. R. A. Fisher, "The statistical utilization of multiple measurements," *Ann. Eugenics* 8: 376–86, 1938.

5. R. A. Fisher, "The precision of discriminant functions," *Ann. Eugenics* 10: 422–29, 1940.

6. T. W. Anderson, *An Introduction to Multivariate Statistical Analysis*, Wiley, New York, 1958.

7. W. W. Cooley and P. R. Lohnes, *Multivariate Procedures for the Behavioral Sciences*, Wiley, New York, 1962.

8. R. A. Reyment, "Paleontological applicability of certain recent advances in multivariate statistical analysis," *Geol. Foren. Stockholm Forh.* 85: 236–65, 1963.

Those who are more mathematically inclined will find references in these publications to several important articles in the *Annals of Mathematical Statistics* and the *Journal of the Royal Statistical Society*, Series B.

14.2 TESTING THE HYPOTHESIS THAT TWO MULTIVARIATE SAMPLES CAME FROM THE SAME MULTIVARIATE POPULATION

In 1931 Harold Hotelling generalized Student's t test for univariate samples to the multivariate situation in which measurements $X_1, \cdots, X_p$ are taken on each member of each sample. The test criterion he developed for this purpose is called Hotelling's T^2. It is used to test $H_0(\mu_{1i} = \mu_{2i}, i = 1$ to $p \mid$ equal covariance matrices) against H_a(some means are different $\mid$ equal covariance matrices). The statement that the covariance matrices are equal essentially means that the variances and correlations are equal. Although this subject is not in the area of discriminatory analysis as that term customarily is used, or as used herein, it is related to discriminatory analysis and provides a useful statistical tool while also introducing concepts, notation, and procedures needed in discriminatory analysis.

To illustrate the definition and use of Hotelling's T^2, the data of Table 14.21 have been selected from Fisher's 1936 article (reference 3 above). For this example $p = 3$, because three measurements were taken on each flower, and $n_1 = 25$ and $n_2 = 27$ are the sample sizes.

The notation X_{aij} will denote the ith measurement for the jth member of the sample from the ath population. In the example of the table, $a = 1$ for *Iris versicolor* and $a = 2$ for *Iris virginica*. Also, $i = 1$ for sepal length, $i = 2$ for sepal width, and $i = 3$ for petal length. The index j is simply the counting index within each sample, and it varies from 1 to 25 for *I. versicolor* and from 1 to 27 for *I. virginica*. The X_{aij} come in sets of three measurements for each member of each sample. To illustrate specifically:

$$(X_{111}, X_{121}, X_{131}) \text{ is } (7.0, 3.2, 4.7)$$
$$(X_{112}, X_{122}, X_{132}) \text{ is } (6.4, 3.2, 4.5)$$
$$\vdots \qquad \vdots \qquad \vdots$$
$$(X_{1125}, X_{1225}, X_{1325}) \text{ is } (6.1, 3.0, 4.6)$$
$$(X_{211}, X_{221}, X_{231}) \text{ is } (5.8, 2.7, 5.1)$$
$$\vdots \qquad \vdots \qquad \vdots$$
$$(X_{2127}, X_{2227}, X_{2327}) \text{ is } (6.7, 3.3, 5.7)$$

The arithmetic means for each trait (sepal length, etc.) will be designated as follows:

$$\bar{x}_{11} = \text{the mean for sepal length of } I. \text{ versicolor}$$
$$= 6.256 \text{ from Table 14.21}$$

$$\bar{x}_{12} = 2.912, \quad \bar{x}_{13} = 4.636; \quad \bar{x}_{21} = 6.237, \quad \bar{x}_{22} = 2.900,$$

and

$$\bar{x}_{23} = 5.163 \text{ similarly}$$

Deviations from means *within* the same trait and population will be indicated by $x_{aij} = X_{aij} - \bar{x}_{ai}$.

When one is studying two populations and several measurements of traits within each population, it is necessary to give attention to matters of homogeneity of variance and of correlations (or, alternatively, covariances)

TABLE 14.21.   ILLUSTRATIVE DATA SELECTED FROM
Ann. Eugenics 7: 180, 1936

	Iris versicolor			*Iris virginica*		
	Sepal length	*Sepal width*	*Petal length*	*Sepal length*	*Sepal width*	*Petal length*
	7.0	3.2	4.7	5.8	2.7	5.1
	6.4	3.2	4.5	4.9	2.5	4.5
	6.9	3.1	4.9	6.5	3.2	5.1
	6.5	2.8	4.6	6.4	2.7	5.3
	5.7	2.8	4.5	6.8	3.0	5.5
	6.3	3.3	4.7	5.7	2.5	5.0
	6.6	2.9	4.6	5.8	2.8	5.1
	6.1	2.9	4.7	6.4	3.2	5.3
	6.7	3.1	4.4	6.5	3.0	5.5
	5.6	3.0	4.5	6.0	2.2	5.0
	6.2	2.2	4.5	5.6	2.8	4.9
	5.9	3.2	4.8	6.3	2.7	4.9
	6.3	2.5	4.9	6.2	2.8	4.8
	6.1	2.8	4.7	6.1	3.0	4.9
	6.6	3.0	4.4	6.3	2.8	5.1
	6.8	2.8	4.8	6.4	3.1	5.5
	6.7	3.0	5.0	6.0	3.0	4.8
	6.0	2.9	4.5	6.9	3.1	5.4
	6.0	2.7	5.1	6.9	3.1	5.1
	5.4	3.0	4.5	5.8	2.7	5.1
	6.0	3.4	4.5	6.7	3.0	5.2
	6.7	3.1	4.7	6.3	2.5	5.0
	6.3	2.3	4.4	6.5	3.0	5.2
	5.5	2.6	4.4	6.2	3.4	5.4
	6.1	3.0	4.6	5.9	3.0	5.1
				6.8	3.2	5.9
Sum:	156.4	72.8	115.9	6.7	3.3	5.7
				168.4	78.3	139.4
Mean:	6.256	2.912	4.636	6.237	2.900	5.163
n_i:	25	25	25	27	27	27

between populations, because the methods employed require the pooling of Sums of Squares and Products. Table 14.22 provides the Sums of Squares and Sums of Products for each species, as well as the variances and correlation coefficients.

It is apparent from this table that (*a*) there is little reason to worry about nonhomogeneity of variance, but (*b*) there is some reason to wonder whether the $\rho_{112} = \rho_{212}$, the $\rho_{113} = \rho_{213}$, or the $\rho_{123} = \rho_{223}$ in the populations of these measurements for *I. versicolor* and *I. virginica*. These individual hypotheses could be tested by methods presented in Chapter 6, but these would not be equivalent to a joint test of whether the covariances are equal.

TABLE 14.22. SUMS OF SQUARES, SUMS OF PRODUCTS, VARIANCES, AND CORRELATION COEFFICIENTS FOR THE DATA OF TABLE 14.21 AND WITHIN SPECIES

	Iris versicolor ($n = 25$)			*Iris virginica* ($n = 27$)		
	X_{11}	X_{12}	X_{13}	X_{21}	X_{22}	X_{23}
X_{i1}	4.6216	0.5332	0.6196	5.5430	1.9700	2.5470
	0.1926	0.17	0.30	0.2132	0.59	0.71
	(s_{11}^2)	(r_{112})	(r_{113})	(s_{21}^2)	(r_{212})	(r_{213})
		2.0264	0.0892		2.0400	1.3200
		0.0844	0.07		0.0785	0.60
		(s_{12}^2)	(r_{123})		(s_{22}^2)	(r_{223})
			0.9176			2.3430
			0.0382			0.0901
			(s_{13}^2)			(s_{23}^2)

It is necessary, in some of the procedures to be used shortly, to define and use a $p \times p$ *dispersion matrix*. The symbol S_{ij} will be used to denote the pooled Sum of Products and Squares:

$$\sum_{j=1}^{n_a} (x_{aij} x_{aij}), \qquad \text{where } a = 1, 2 \quad \text{and } i = 1, 2, 3$$

For example,

$$\sum_{j=1}^{25} (x_{11j} x_{11j}) + \sum_{j=1}^{27} (x_{21j} x_{21j}) = S_{11}$$

is the pooled Sum of Squares for sepal length for *I. versicolor* and *I. virginica*. Obviously, $S_{11} = 4.6216 + 5.5430 = 10.1646$, from Table 14.22. Similarly, $S_{12} = 2.5032$, etc. The *dispersion matrix* is defined by

(14.21)
$$(S_{ij}) = \begin{pmatrix} S_{11} & S_{12} & \cdots & S_{1p} \\ S_{21} & S_{22} & \cdots & S_{2p} \\ \vdots & \vdots & & \vdots \\ S_{p1} & S_{p2} & \cdots & S_{pp} \end{pmatrix}$$

in which $S_{ij} = S_{ji}$ when $i \neq j$. For Table 14.22, $p = 3$, and so (S_{ij}) is a matrix consisting of three rows and three columns as follows:

$$\textbf{(14.22)} \qquad (S_{ij}) = \begin{pmatrix} 10.1646 & 2.5032 & 3.1666 \\ 2.5032 & 4.0664 & 1.4097 \\ 3.1666 & 1.4097 & 3.2606 \end{pmatrix}$$

The reader already is familiar with the process of computing the inverse of a square matrix from the procedures used in Chapter 11 to secure (M_{ij}). For review, this process is repeated in Table 14.23 with the dispersion matrix of Equation 14.22. It should be noted that the process in Table 14.23 is applied to a dispersion matrix rather than to a correlation matrix, which makes some of the numbers look different, but the general procedure is the same. The notation (M_{ij}) will be used again for the inverse of the original matrix.

TABLE 14.23.   USE OF A BACKWARD DOOLITTLE PROCEDURE TO INVERT THE WITHIN-SPECIES DISPERSION MATRIX IN FORMULA 14.22, WHICH CAME FROM THE DATA OF TABLE 14.21

Dispersion matrix			Unit matrix		
X_1	X_2	X_3			
10.1646	2.5032	3.1666	1	0	0
2.5032	4.0664	1.4097	0	1	0
3.1666	1.4097	3.2606	0	0	1
10.1646	2.5032	3.1666	1	0	0
1	0.2463	0.3115	0.0984	0	0
	3.4499	0.6298	−0.2463	1	0
	1	0.1825	−0.0714	0.2899	0
		2.1593	−0.2666	−0.1825	1
		1	−0.1234	−0.0845	0.4631

$$(M_{ij}) = \begin{pmatrix} 0.1489 & -0.0489 & -0.1234 \\ -0.0489 & 0.3053 & -0.0845 \\ -0.1234 & -0.0845 & 0.4631 \end{pmatrix}$$

The computations in Table 14.23 can be checked as follows by matrix multiplication:

$$\begin{pmatrix} 0.1489 & -0.0489 & -0.1234 \\ -0.0489 & 0.3053 & -0.0845 \\ -0.1234 & -0.0845 & 0.4631 \end{pmatrix} \cdot \begin{pmatrix} 10.1646 & 2.5032 & 3.1666 \\ 2.5032 & 4.0664 & 1.4097 \\ 3.1666 & 1.4097 & 3.2606 \end{pmatrix}$$

$$= \begin{pmatrix} 1.0003 & -0.0001 & 0.0000 \\ -0.0001 & 0.9999 & 0.0000 \\ 0.0006 & 0.0003 & 1.0001 \end{pmatrix} \cong \begin{pmatrix} 1 & 0 & 0 \\ 0 & 1 & 0 \\ 0 & 0 & 1 \end{pmatrix}$$

where $(0.1489)(10.1666) + (-0.0489)(2.5032) + (0.1234)(3.1666) = 1.0003$, from the *first row* of (M_{ij}) and the first *column* of (S_{ij}), and so on.

As stated earlier, Hotelling generalized Student's t for two univariate populations to a T^2 for two multivariate populations. The definition of Hotelling's T^2 is as follows:

(14.23)
$$T^2 = \sum_{i=1}^{p} \sum_{j=1}^{p} \frac{n}{(1/n_1 + 1/n_2)} \cdot M_{ij} d_i d_j$$

where $n = n_1 + n_2 - 2$, $d_i = \bar{x}_{1i} - \bar{x}_{2i}$, $d_j = \bar{x}_{1j} - \bar{x}_{2j}$, and the M_{ij} are the elements of the inverse of the dispersion matrix (S_{ij}).

It turns out that

(14.24)
$$\frac{n_1 + n_2 - p - 1}{p(n_1 + n_2 - 2)} T^2 = F(p, n_1 + n_2 - p - 1)$$

where F is the familiar Snedecor F ratio of earlier chapters; hence, one can use readily available F tables to test the hypothesis that two multivariate samples are from the same multivariate population. This procedure will be illustrated by means of the iris example previously used.

It is readily seen that $p = 3$, $n_1 = 25$, and $n_2 = 27$; hence, the following computations should be evident:

$$n = 25 + 27 - 2 = 50 \quad \text{and} \quad 1/n_1 + 1/n_1 = 0.077037,$$

so

$$\frac{n}{(1/n_1 + 1/n_2)} = 649.039$$

$$d_1 = 6.256 - 6.237 = +0.019, \quad d_2 = 2.912 - 2.900 = +0.012,$$

and

$$d_3 = 4.636 - 5.163 = -0.527$$

Therefore, substituting into Formula 14.23,

$$T^2 = 649.04(M_{11} d_1^2 + 2 M_{12} d_1 d_2 + M_{22} d_2^2 + 2 M_{13} d_1 d_3 + 2 M_{23} d_2 d_3 + M_{33} d_3^2)$$
$$= 649.04[0.1489(+0.019)^2 + 2(-0.0489)(+0.019)(+0.012)$$
$$+ (0.3053)(0.012)^2 + 2(-0.1234)(+0.019)(-0.527)$$
$$+ 2(-0.0845)(+0.012)(-0.527) + 0.4631(-0.527)^2]$$
$$= 85.822$$

Because $\dfrac{n_1 + n_2 - p - 1}{p(n_1 + n_2 - 2)} = 0.32000$, the F ratio which corresponds to the $T^2 = 85.822$ just computed is $F(3, 48) = 27.46$. This $F(3, 48)$ would be significant even if α had been chosen much smaller than 0.001; hence, it is concluded that the *I. versicolor* and *I. virginica* species produce two different multivariate populations with respect to the three measurements $X_1 =$ sepal length, $X_2 =$ sepal width, and $X_3 =$ petal length. Before one attempts a discriminatory analysis involving two multivariate populations and certain proposed measurements $X_1, \cdots, X_p$, it is advisable to use the Hotelling T^2 to see whether the two populations are in fact distinguishable upon the basis of the proposed measurements.

It also is appropriate to ask whether the two populations in question could be distinguished from each other upon the basis of fewer than the p proposed measurements. This matter will not be pursued farther here, because (*a*) the procedure is analogous to methods used in multiple regression analyses, and can be easily understood by a reader who wishes to pursue this matter on his own, and (*b*) if an experimenter, say a taxonomist, believes that the measurements $X_1, \cdots, X_p$ are pertinent to the differentiation of two populations, it is not at all obvious that he should cut down the number p—possibly in several ways—to meet an arbitrary level of significance used to determine which X's should be retained. With digital computers so common, it might be as well to use all the information available from the study.

Hodges (previous citation) has pointed out an interesting relationship between the T^2 statistic and the Neyman-Pearson likelihood criterion, which is widely used in modern statistical theory. Hotelling seems to have devised the T^2 largely on the basis of intuition. S. S. Wilks (*Biometrika* 24: 471–94, 1932) used the likelihood-ratio principle to derive a test of the hypothesis that k p-variate samples came from the same multivariate normal population. His test statistic reduces to Hotelling's T^2 when $k = 2$.

Historically, the problem of distinguishing between two populations on the basis of p measurements, the problem of assigning an individual to the correct one of two multivariate populations, the t test, the chi-square test, and the F test have become somewhat intermingled. Pearson and his associates devised a *coefficient of racial likeness* (CRL) to be computed from multiple measurements on human skulls to facilitate studies of anthropology and evolution. To this end, Pearson used the following definition:

(14.25)
$$\text{CRL} = \frac{1}{p} \sum_{i=1}^{p} \left(\frac{d_i^2}{\dfrac{s_{1i}^2}{n_1} + \dfrac{s_{2i}^2}{n_2}} \right) - 1$$

where

$$s_{1i}^2 = \frac{1}{n_1} \sum_{j=1}^{n_1} (X_{1ij} - \bar{x}_{1i})^2$$

the estimated variance of the ith trait measured in population 1; similarly for s_{2i}^2. The early use of the CRL required the dubious (and so recognized) assumption that the p traits measured are statistically independent. After Pearson and others had taken proper account of the intercorrelations among the measurements $X_1, \cdots, X_p$, a more general and theoretically sound form of CRL was developed. It turns out that this generalized CRL is, aside from a constant factor, identical with Hotelling's T^2.

Starting in the mid nineteen-twenties P. C. Mahalanabis approached the problem of discrimination from the point of view of the "distance" between multivariate populations in p space. For example, if $p = 2$, one could have

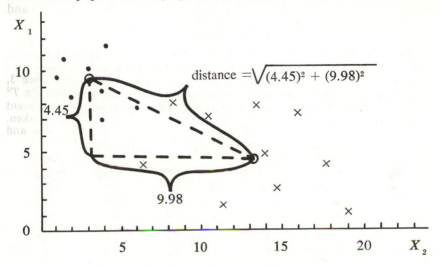

Figure 14.21.   Schematic illustration of "distance" between populations. Circled points are mean points for the respective populations.

the following picture of the X_1, X_2 sample space, as shown in Figure 14.21. Mahalanabis suggested using

(14.26)
$$D^2 = \frac{1}{p} \sum_{i=1}^{p} \left(\frac{\bar{x}_{1i} - \bar{x}_{2i}}{\sigma_i} \right)^2$$

which is called the *generalized distance* between any two populations. If, as is much more common, the populations sampled are different and the parameters only estimated, one obtains the so-called studentized distribution of D^2. The most general situation is that in which there also are correlations among the measurements, the X's. When R. C. Bose and S. N. Roy announced that they had obtained this most general distribution for D^2 in 1938, Fisher recognized and noted that this distribution was identical with the distribution he had published in 1928 for the multiple correlation coefficient. Fisher also pointed out that the distribution of the central studentized D^2 obtained by Bose and Roy was the same as for Hotelling's generalized t ratio, T^2. These comments point out how interrelated many seemingly different statistical problems actually are.

The reason for the term "generalized distance" can be suggested from the fact, shown in Figure 14.21, that $\sum_{i=1}^{2} (\bar{x}_{1i} - \bar{x}_{2i})^2$ is the square of the shortest distance between the mean points of the two sets of samples represented by the dots and crosses. In some sense, the divisors of p outside the summation and of σ_i^2 inside the summation merely take account of units and multiple measurements.

PROBLEMS

1. Given the following data from R. A. Fisher's 1936 article (reference 3, Section 14.1) and pertaining to the species *Iris setosa*, use Hotelling's T^2 to decide whether *I. setosa* and *I. versicolor* are associated with different multivariate populations with respect to the three measurements taken. Assume normal multivariate populations with the same variances and covariances.

Iris setosa:				*Iris setosa:*		
Sepal length	*Sepal width*	*Petal length*		*Sepal length*	*Sepal width*	*Petal length*
X_{31}	X_{32}	X_{33}		X_{31}	X_{32}	X_{33}
5.4	3.9	1.7		5.0	3.4	1.6
5.0	3.4	1.5		5.2	3.5	1.5
4.9	3.1	1.5		4.7	3.2	1.6
5.4	3.7	1.5		4.8	3.1	1.6
4.8	3.4	1.6		5.4	3.4	1.5
5.7	4.4	1.5		5.2	4.1	1.5
5.7	3.8	1.7		4.9	3.1	1.5
5.1	3.8	1.5		5.1	3.4	1.5
5.4	3.4	1.7		5.0	3.5	1.6
5.1	3.7	1.5		5.1	3.8	1.9
5.1	3.3	1.7		5.1	3.8	1.6
4.8	3.4	1.9		5.3	3.7	1.5
5.0	3.0	1.6				
		Sum:		128.2	88.3	39.8
		n:		25	25	25
		Mean:		$\bar{x}_{31} = 5.128$,	$\bar{x}_{32} = 3.532$,	$\bar{x}_{33} = 1.592$

2. Do as in Problem 1, but substitute *I. virginica* for *I. versicolor*.

3. With reference to Problem 1, compute the variances and linear correlation coefficients for *I. setosa* and compare with those for *I. versicolor* and *I. virginica*. Do you conclude that an assumption of equal variances and covariances is satisfactory in Problems 1 and 2 or not?

4. Compute the CRL for the data of *I. versicolor* and *I. setosa*.

5. Do as in Problem 4 for *I. virginica* and *I. setosa*.

6. Compute D^2 for *I. setosa* and *I. virginica*.

7. Given the following data which pertain to factors of interest in studies of sorghum, use Hotelling's T^2 to decide whether the two areas are associated with different multivariate normal populations:

	Area 1:			Area 2:	
X_1	X_2	X_3	X_1	X_2	X_3
30	244	180	39	308	322
30	345	209	22	284	311
65	522	418	23	397	243
34	279	180	40	381	322
41	444	209	91	625	406
67	544	418	71	579	195
34	279	180	45	463	322
59	524	209	91	625	406
86	652	418	71	579	195
38	334	180	45	463	322
65	561	209	91	655	406
98	687	418	71	580	195
34	279	180	40	340	322
34	396	209	43	473	406
67	544	418	71	579	195
34	278	180	39	311	322
32	367	209	40	354	406
65	522	418	23	386	195

8. Compute the D^2 for the data in Problem 7.

9. Compute the CRL for the data of Problem 7, even though the concept of "racial likeness" is not logical.

10. Do as in Problem 7 for the following data, which are similar to those of Problem 7:

	Area 3:			Area 4:	
X_1	X_2	X_3	X_1	X_2	X_3
97	16	351	109	136	838
98	58	523	111	389	1193
207	212	880	71	106	689
135	16	351	132	136	838
186	117	693	134	451	1280
237	286	991	75	85	664
135	16	351	135	136	838
209	117	693	134	451	1280
237	286	991	182	85	668
135	16	351	150	136	838
209	117	693	256	451	1280
237	286	991	193	85	684
97	130	441	132	140	860
149	278	959	135	430	1160
209	19	371	92	98	582
97	16	351	108	125	783
98	117	693	117	420	1206
228	286	991	79	92	683

14.3 DISCRIMINATORY ANALYSIS WHEN JUST TWO POPULATIONS ARE INVOLVED

As indicated in the Introduction, the true problem of discriminatory analysis, as the term is to be used herein, involves the classification of an individual into one of two or more populations. This needs to be done under one of two general circumstances: the types and parameters of the populations involved are known, or the type of the population is known but the parameters have to be estimated from samples known to be from single populations. Although the latter circumstance would seem to be the more common, it is not at all inconceivable that a taxonomist, for example, would have at hand so much information about the measurements $X_{a1}, \cdots, X_{ap}$ for each population that it would be sensible to assume that the parameters, such as μ_{a1}, σ_{a1}^2, etc., are known. In either case, there is an unknown individual I on which measurements $X_1, \cdots, X_p$ can be taken, and the problem is to classify I into the correct population.

It is obvious that every conceivable method which might be devised to assign I to either Population 1 (Π_1) or Population 2 (Π_2) can make a misclassification. With this fact admitted, there still is the matter of judging the degree of misclassification. To illustrate, suppose that an individual, I, has been found in an area where it must belong to one of only two possible normal populations. Suppose for simplification that only one measurement, X, is involved, so that $p = 1$. Suppose also that the populations are

$$\Pi_1 = N_1(5, 4) \qquad \text{and} \qquad \Pi_2 = N_2(7, 4)$$

If I turns out to have $X = 6.5$, how should it be classified? Of course, the answer appears obvious in this ultra-simple problem of discriminatory analysis, but this example will serve to illustrate some points.

The problem of classifying I into Π_1 or Π_2 will necessarily consist in dividing the X axis into two regions, as follows:

$$R_1: \qquad -\infty < X \leqslant \xi \qquad \text{and} \qquad R_2: \qquad \xi < X < +\infty$$

If X falls in R_1, I is assigned to Π_1; and if X falls into R_2, I is assigned to Π_2. What process should one use to determine ξ?

The probability of correctly classifying an I from Π_1 into Π_1 will be designated by $\Pr\{\Pi_1 \mid \Pi_1\}$. Similarly, $\Pr\{\Pi_2 \mid \Pi_2\}$ is the probability that an I from Π_2 will be assigned to Π_2. In a similar way, $\Pr\{\Pi_1 \mid \Pi_2\}$ is the probability of misclassifying a member of Π_2 into Π_1 and $\Pr\{\Pi_2 \mid \Pi_1\}$ is the probability of misclassifying a member of Π_1 into Π_2. The magnitudes of these four probabilities depend upon the choice of the point $X = \xi$. Table 14.31 has been constructed to show all four of the foregoing probabilities for a range of selections of ξ.

If the members of Π_1 and Π_2 are equally abundant in the area where I was found, and *if* one is as anxious to classify correctly an individual from Π_1 as one is to classify correctly an individual from Π_2, then the best choice of ξ would seem to be at 6. It might be, however, that members of Π_1 are not equally abundant in the area where I was found, or the consequences of a misclassification are not equally serious between $\Pi_1 \mid \Pi_2$ and $\Pi_2 \mid \Pi_1$.

TABLE 14.31. $\Pr\{\Pi_i \mid \Pi_j\}$, WITH $i, j = 1, 2$, FOR A SELECTED RANGE OF REGIONS OF CLASSIFICATION

$\Pr\{\Pi_i \mid \Pi_j\}$	$\xi = 5$	$\xi = 5.50$	$\xi = 5.75$	$\xi = 6.00$	$\xi = 6.25$	$\xi = 6.5$	$\xi = 7$
$\Pi_1 \mid \Pi_1$	0.50	0.60	0.65	0.69	0.73	0.77	0.84
$\Pi_2 \mid \Pi_2$	0.84	0.77	0.73	0.69	0.65	0.60	0.50
$\Pi_1 \mid \Pi_2$	0.16	0.23	0.27	0.31	0.35	0.40	0.50
$\Pi_2 \mid \Pi_1$	0.50	0.40	0.35	0.31	0.27	0.23	0.16

Returning to the choice $\xi = 6$ under the assumption that members of Π_1 and Π_2 are equally abundant in the area where I was found and that the consequences of the misclassifications $\Pi_1 \mid \Pi_2$ and $\Pi_2 \mid \Pi_1$ are equally serious, it is noted that no reason was given for saying that ξ should be 6. This was merely an appeal to intuition. How could one make this sort of decision more objectively? Actually, this problem is too mathematical for the mathematical sophistication assumed herein, but two partially clarifying statements may be made here:

(a) It is observed in Table 14.31 that for each value of ξ there is a larger and a smaller $\Pr\{\Pi_i \mid \Pi_i\}$ except at $\xi = 6$. One principle used in statistics in appropriate places is that the minimum probability of something desirable, such as correct classification of I, should be maximized by whatever choices are available. When $\xi = 5$, the minimum $\Pr\{\Pi_i \mid \Pi_i\}$ is 0.50. When $\xi = 5.5$, the minimum $\Pr\{\Pi_i \mid \Pi_i\}$ is 0.60. The minimum $\Pr\{\Pi_i \mid \Pi_i\}$ is a maximum when $\xi = 6$. This is a very simple illustration of what is called the *minimax principle* under the stated conditions and assumptions.

(b) The probability density functions for Π_1 and Π_2 are

$$\frac{1}{\sqrt{2\pi}(2)} e^{-(X-5)^2/8} \quad \text{and} \quad \frac{1}{\sqrt{2\pi}(2)} e^{-(X-7)^2/8}, \quad \text{respectively}$$

For a sample of one (as I is) these are also the *likelihoods for the X for I*, and their ratio is called *the likelihood ratio*. Neyman and Pearson introduced the use of the likelihood ratio to choose regions of rejection—or acceptance or classification, alternatively. Along the boundary between such regions the likelihood ratio is constant. For Π_1 and Π_2, the likelihood ratio is

$$(e^{-(X-5)^2/8})/(e^{-(X-7)^2/8}) = e^{-(4X-24)/8}$$

which is constant for $X = 6 = $ the ξ above.

The first truly discriminatory procedure for classifying I into Π_1 or Π_2 was devised by Fisher in his 1936 paper (reference 3, Section 14.1), although some related ideas were published by colleagues earlier in the nineteen-thirties. Fisher reduced the multivariate problem to a univariate problem by using a linear function of the $X_1, \cdots, X_p$. Specifically, he defined a *linear discriminant function* (LDF) as follows:

(14.31) $$y = \lambda_1 X_1 + \lambda_2 X_2 + \cdots + \lambda_p X_p$$

where the λ_i are to be so chosen that the ratio of the difference, $\bar{y}_1 - \bar{y}_2$, to the pooled within-sample estimate of the standard deviation is maximized. Or, put in symbols, the λ_i are to be so chosen that

(14.32) $$\frac{\bar{y}_1 - \bar{y}_2}{\sqrt{\sum_{i=1}^{n_1} (y_{1i} - \bar{y}_1)^2 + \sum_{j=1}^{n_2} (y_{2j} - \bar{y}_2)^2}}$$

is maximized, it being easier to dispense with the divisors in the denominator, which would not affect the maximizing process. Essentially this procedure is maximizing the ratio of the Between-Groups Mean Square to the Within-Groups Mean Square and, hence, tending to maximize the probability of detecting a true difference between the two multivariate populations.

It has been shown (in the Hodges reference, Section 14.1, for example) that the maximization of Ratio 14.32 is accomplished most efficiently by solving the following linear simultaneous equations in the unknown λ's:

(14.33) $$\begin{cases} S_{11}\lambda_1 + S_{12}\lambda_2 + \cdots + S_{1p}\lambda_p = d_1, \\ S_{21}\lambda_1 + S_{22}\lambda_2 + \cdots + S_{2p}\lambda_p = d_2, \\ \phantom{S_{21}\lambda_1}\cdot\cdot\cdot\cdot\cdot\cdot\cdot \\ S_{p1}\lambda_1 + S_{p2}\lambda_2 + \cdots + S_{pp}\lambda_p = d_p, \end{cases}$$

where the S_{ij} and the d_i are as used herein before; that is, the S_{ij} are pooled sums of squares and products, and the $d_i = \bar{x}_{1i} - \bar{x}_{2i}$. As is shown in matrix algebra, one can compute the λ_i by using the inverse of the dispersion matrix (S_{ij}). For example, the dispersion matrix for *I. versicolor* and *I. virginica* is given in Formula 14.22 as

$$(S_{ij}) = \begin{pmatrix} 10.1646 & 2.5032 & 3.1666 \\ 2.5032 & 4.0664 & 1.4097 \\ 3.1666 & 1.4097 & 3.2606 \end{pmatrix}$$

and its inverse is shown in Table 14.23 as

$$(M_{ij}) = \begin{pmatrix} 0.1489 & -0.0489 & -0.1234 \\ -0.0489 & 0.3053 & -0.0845 \\ -0.1234 & -0.0845 & 0.4631 \end{pmatrix}$$

The d_i are $d_1 = +0.019$, $d_2 = 0.012$, and $d_3 = -0.527$. It can be shown that

$$(14.34) \qquad (M_{ij}) \cdot \begin{pmatrix} d_1 \\ d_2 \\ \vdots \\ d_p \end{pmatrix} = \begin{pmatrix} \lambda_1 \\ \lambda_2 \\ \vdots \\ \lambda_p \end{pmatrix}$$

where matrix multiplication is required, as illustrated in Table 14.23. Specifically, for the iris problem

$$\begin{pmatrix} 0.1489 & -0.0489 & -0.1234 \\ -0.0489 & 0.3053 & -0.0845 \\ -0.1234 & -0.0845 & 0.4631 \end{pmatrix} \cdot \begin{pmatrix} +0.019 \\ +0.012 \\ -0.527 \end{pmatrix} = \begin{pmatrix} +0.0673 \\ +0.0473 \\ -0.2474 \end{pmatrix} = \begin{pmatrix} \lambda_1 \\ \lambda_2 \\ \lambda_3 \end{pmatrix}$$

Hence the linear discriminant function for these two species of iris, based on the sample data available, is

$$(14.35) \qquad y = 0.0673 X_1 + 0.0473 X_2 - 0.2474 X_3$$

where X_1 = sepal length, X_2 = sepal width, and X_3 = petal length. From this function one computes $\bar{y}_1$ and $\bar{y}_2$ using the $\bar{x}_{ai}$. The results are

$$\bar{y}_1 = 0.0673(6.256) + 0.0473(2.912) - 0.2474(4.636)$$
$$= -0.5883 \quad \text{for } I. \text{ versicolor}$$

$$\bar{y}_2 = 0.0673(6.237) + 0.0473(2.900) - 0.2474(5.163)$$
$$= -0.7206 \quad \text{for } I. \text{ virginica}$$

If an unknown iris, I, is found in an area where the only two possibilities are *I. versicolor* and *I. virginica*, and these are equally likely before that particular I is found, the y for the unknown I can be computed from Equation 14.35. The I is assigned to *I. versicolor* if y_I is closer to -0.5883 than to -0.7206, and to *I. virginica* if y_I is closer to -0.7206 than to -0.5883. For example, suppose that the unknown iris has $X_1 = 7.0$ cm, $X_2 = 3.1$ cm, and $X_3 = 5.0$ cm. It is found that $y_I = -0.6194$ by substituting those X's into Formula 14.35. The quantity -0.6194 is 0.0311 units from $\bar{y}_1$ and 0.1012 units from $\bar{y}_2$; therefore, this unknown iris is classified as *Iris versicolor*.

In a geometrical sense, the LDF procedure proposed by Fisher produces a maximum separation of the two populations in question. Fisher made no attempt to justify his LDF in terms of probabilities of misclassification. Under the assumption of multivariate normal populations with the same covariance matrix (equal variances and intercorrelations) the intuitively devised LDF has the optimum properties associated with the likelihood-ratio principle.

Hodges (reference 1, Section 14.1) points out that, although Fisher devised and used the LDF to solve the problem of assigning an individual I to the correct one of only *two* populations, others have used the LDF with more than two populations. It is recalled that the d_i in Equations 14.33 are $d_i = \bar{x}_{1i} - \bar{x}_{2i}$, where the subscripts 1 and 2 refer to the two populations.

Obviously, one set of d_i will lead to one LDF, and hence a single LDF could be used for more than two populations only if the d_i for Π_1 and Π_2, Π_1 and Π_3, Π_2 and Π_3, etc., are proportional. Even though much research remains to be done in this whole area of discriminatory analysis, it seems preferable to use other methods when more than two populations are involved.

To do a complete job of classifying an individual I into one of two populations, one needs to consider three matters simultaneously:

(*a*) The probabilities of misclassification, or of correct classification if preferable.

(*b*) The proportionate frequencies of members of Π_1 and Π_2 in the region in which I is found.

(*c*) The consequences of misclassification.

A completely satisfactory job of classification cannot be done unless more is known about the two populations than usually is known, but it is profitable to devise methods on those assumptions and do the best one can toward satisfying them.

Rao (reference 2, Section 14.1) points out that if π_i is the relative frequency of Π_i in an area, f_i is the probability density function for Π_i, and r_i is the loss sustained when a member of Π_i is assigned incorrectly to the one other population, then the best regions, R_1 and R_2, to use in classifying I are

(14.36)
$$
\begin{aligned}
R_1: & \quad \pi_1 r_1 f_1 \geqslant \pi_2 r_2 f_2 \\
R_2: & \quad \pi_2 r_2 f_2 \geqslant \pi_1 r_1 f_1
\end{aligned}
$$

To illustrate, suppose that the two possible populations are $\Pi_1 = N_1(5, 4)$ and $\Pi_2 = N_2(7, 4)$ and that $\pi_1 = 2/5$, so that $\pi_2 = 3/5$. If for some reason it is twice as serious to misclassify a member of Π_1 into Π_2 as it is to misclassify a member of Π_2 into Π_1, the $r_1 = 2/3$ and the $r_2 = 1/3$. Then the regions R_1 and R_2 require that

$$
(2/5)(2/3) \frac{1}{\sqrt{2\pi(2)}} \exp\{-\tfrac{1}{8}(X - 5)^2\}
$$

be

$$
\geqslant (3/5)(1/3) \frac{1}{\sqrt{2\pi(2)}} \exp\{-\tfrac{1}{8}(X - 7)^2\}
$$

for R_1. When this inequality is simplified, one obtains

$$
\exp\{-\tfrac{1}{8}(4X - 24)\} \geqslant 3/4, \qquad \text{whence } X \leqslant 6.576
$$

Thus, R_1 is $X \leqslant 6.576$ and R_2 is $X > 6.576$, arbitrarily assigning the equality to R_1. It is noted that the greater loss assumed for a misclassification of a member of Π_1 into Π_2 has outweighed the greater abundance of Π_2 in the area and caused the boundary of R_1 to be moved to the right on the X axis, as compared with the situation visualized in Table 14.31. The procedure just illustrated assures one that the expected loss from misclassification has been minimized, but it assumes one knows the π_i, the f_i, and the r_i, an assumption which may be unrealistic. However, one also could say that, unless enough information is available about the Π_i at least to make quite excellent estimates of the π_i, f_i, and r_i, perhaps one should not seriously try to classify an unknown individual at all.

Formulas 14.36 still apply if there are p measurements instead of the one used for illustration. The practical problem would be actually to determine the R_1 and R_2, if the probability density functions were in three or more dimensions.

It already has been said that if the two populations involved in a discriminatory analysis are multivariate normal with all variances and correlations equal—that is, equal covariance matrices—the Fisher LDF is the likelihood-ratio solution and is considered optimum. Rao (reference 2, Section 14.1) has given a formula for what he calls a *linear discriminant score* as follows (in the notation of this text):

$$(14.37) \quad L_r + \log_e \pi_r = \sum_{j=1}^{p}\left(\sum_{i=1}^{p} M_{ij} \cdot \mu_{ir}\right) X_j - \frac{1}{2}\sum_{j=1}^{p}\sum_{i=1}^{n} M_{ij}\mu_{ir}\mu_{jr} + \log_e \pi_r$$

where π_r is the proportion of all population members in the vicinity which belong to Π_r and the M_{ij}, μ_{ir} and μ_{jr} have their usual meanings. This formula applies to any number of populations but will be used in this section with $r = 1$ and 2 only. Rao's procedure is to assign an unknown individual, I, to that Π_r for which Formula 14.37 is maximum. If one knows the population parameters,

$$\mu_{11}, \cdots, \mu_{1p} \qquad \mu_{21}, \cdots, \mu_{2p} \qquad \sigma_{11}^2, \cdots, \sigma_{1p}^2 \qquad \sigma_{21}^2, \cdots, \sigma_{2p}^2$$

$$\rho_{11}, \cdots, \rho_{1p} \quad \text{and} \quad \rho_{21}, \cdots, \rho_{2p}$$

and if the corresponding σ_{ai}^2 and ρ_{ai} are equal, Formula 14.37 can be used as is. Only in that circumstance is it true that the constant likelihood ratio desired here corresponds to a constant difference in *linear discriminant scores*, which Rao uses as his criterion for recommending the use of $L_r + \log_e \pi_r$.

If the population parameters for Π_1 and Π_2 are unknown, one can use estimates from samples but cannot claim an optimum solution, only that nothing better seems to have been developed to a usable stage so far. Hence, the computation of the L_r will be illustrated with the data discussed previously on *I. versicolor* and *I. virginica*.

For $r = 1$, that is, for the linear discriminant score associated with *I. versicolor*,

$$L_1 = \sum_{j=1}^{3}\left(\sum_{i=1}^{3} M_{ij}\bar{x}_{1i}\right) X_j - \frac{1}{2}\sum_{j=1}^{3}\left(\sum_{i=1}^{3} M_{ij}\bar{x}_{1i}\right)\bar{x}_{1j}$$

The $(\sum_{i=1}^{3} M_{ij}\bar{x}_{1i})$ which appears in both terms of L_1 is readily determined by the following matrix product:

$$
\begin{pmatrix}
0.1489 & -0.0489 & -0.1234 \\
-0.0489 & 0.3053 & -0.0845 \\
-0.1234 & -0.0845 & 0.4631
\end{pmatrix}
\cdot
\begin{pmatrix}
6.256 \\
2.912 \\
4.636
\end{pmatrix}
=
\begin{pmatrix}
0.2170 \\
0.1914 \\
1.1289
\end{pmatrix}
$$

Hence, $L_1 = 0.2170X_1 + 0.1914X_2 + 1.1289X_3 - \frac{1}{2}\{0.2170(6.256) + 0.1914(2.912) + 1.1289(4.636)\} = 0.2170X_1 + 0.1914X_2 + 1.1289X_3 - 3.5742$, and the number associated with the multivariate population for *I. versicolor* is $L_1 + \log_e \pi_1$.

Similarly,

$$
\begin{pmatrix}
0.1489 & -0.0489 & -0.1234 \\
-0.0489 & 0.3053 & -0.0845 \\
-0.1234 & -0.0845 & 0.4631
\end{pmatrix}
\cdot
\begin{pmatrix}
6.237 \\
2.900 \\
5.163
\end{pmatrix}
=
\begin{pmatrix}
0.1498 \\
0.1441 \\
1.3763
\end{pmatrix}
$$

and $L_2 = 0.1498X_1 + 0.1441X_2 + 1.3763X_3 - 4.2119$ is the linear discriminant score associated with *I. virginica*; the number to be associated with *I. virginica* for purposes of classifying an unknown is $L_2 + \log_e \pi_2$.

Suppose, as in a previous example, an unknown iris, I, has been found with $X_1 = 7.0$ cm, $X_2 = 3.1$ cm, and $X_3 = 5.0$ cm. If *I. versicolor* and *I. virginica* are known to be equally abundant in the area where the unknown iris, I, was found, the $\log_e \pi_i$ can be ignored, because they only add the same constant to L_1 and L_2 and therefore add nothing to the process of discrimination. Then one computes for I:
$L_1 = 4.1326$ and $L_2 = 8.2978$. Therefore I is classified as *I. virginica* because $L_2 > L_1$. The reader should note that from inspection of the data on *I. versicolor* and *I. virginica* and of their discriminant scores it is apparent that petal length, X_3, is the major factor. When the unknown had a petal length much nearer to *I. virginica*'s average than to the average petal length of *I. versicolor*, its classification as *I. virginica* was pretty well settled. In practice this will seldom be true, or at least one would not use multivariate methods when one measurement does control the classification process.

If $\pi_1 \neq \pi_2$, the term $\log_e \pi_i$ must be added to L_r. For example, suppose *I. versicolor* is three times as prevalent in the area where the I was found as is *I. virginica*. Then, $\log_e 0.75 = -0.288$, whereas $\log_e 0.25 = -1.386$; $L_1 + \log_e \pi_1 = 3.8446$ and $L_2 + \log_e \pi_2 = 6.9118$. Hence, even though L_1 and L_2 are now closer together than when $\pi_1 = \pi_2$, I still is classified as *I. virginica* because $L_2 + \log_e \pi_2 > L_1 + \log_e \pi_1$.

Rao has suggested that one may wish to use regions of indecision in some circumstances, instead of always specifically assigning an I to one of two (or more) populations. The interested reader is referred to Rao (reference 2, Section 14.1) for further information on this matter.

Some progress also has been made in the matter of measuring probabilities of misclassification, but much remains to be done, and this is a complex computational process which will not be presented herein. The reader may wish to consult Hodges and Rao for more information on this topic also (references, Section 14.1).

PROBLEMS

1. Suppose that an unknown iris has been found in an area in which only *I. virginica* and *I. setosa* exist, and these species are equally abundant there. Suppose that the unknown, I, has the measurements: sepal length = 5.78 cm, sepal width = 3.21 cm, and petal length = 4.36 cm. Use Fisher's LDF to classify I on the basis of the multivariate samples given in Section 14.2.

2. Do as in Problem 1, but assume *I. versicolor* and *I. virginica* are the two possible species.

3. Assume that an unknown individual I has $X_1 = 5.81$, $X_2 = 3.25$, and $X_3 = 2.16$. Would you classify I as *I. versicolor* or as *I. setosa*, if these were the only two possibilities and *I. versicolor* were three times as prevalent as *Iris setosa* in the area where I was found?

4. Referring to the situation of Problem 7, Section 14.2, suppose that the area designation has been lost for the following set of data: $X_1 = 72$, $X_2 = 610$, and $X_3 = 210$. Would you conclude that these data are from Area 1 or from Area 2?

5. Referring to Problem 4, how would your answer change, if upon the basis of independent information of some sort you felt that those data were three times as likely to come from Area 1 as from Area 2?

6. Suppose that under the conditions of Problem 10, Section 14.2, the set of data $X_1 = 201$, $X_2 = 21$, and $X_3 = 1050$ has lost its area designation. To which area would you assign these data, if you had to assign it to one of them?

7. Do Problem 6 for $\pi_3 = 2.8\pi_4$.

14.4 DISCRIMINATORY ANALYSIS WHEN THREE OR MORE POPULATIONS ARE INVOLVED

Hotelling's T^2, Fisher's LDF, Pearson's CRL, and Mahalonabis's D^2 do not apply when more than two populations are involved, although there has been considerable pair-wise application of some of these procedures. Not only is the analysis more complex when more than two populations are involved, but also it is true that no completely satisfactory procedure exists unless the population density functions are completely known. Nevertheless, some useful procedures can be employed in some practical situations. It also is pointed out again that if only meager information exists about the multivariate populations which pertain to a problem of discriminatory analysis, one probably should not be attempting to assign an individual to a population at all.

As was true when but two multivariate populations, Π_1 and Π_2, were possible in a region in which an unknown I was found, one needs to determine for three or more Π_i if those Π_i can be distinguished by the available information. If the Π_i are multivariate normal, one can use Wilks's lambda (Λ) procedure to obtain either an approximate χ^2 test or an approximate F test. We shall first consider a simple between-group and within-group multivariate analysis of variance.

The reader already is familiar with the procedures for obtaining the dispersion matrix and can identify the various sums of squares and cross products in (S_{ij}). Using the dispersion matrix of Section 14.2, namely Equation 14.22, for Π_1 and Π_2, one obtains the information in Table 14.41.

TABLE 14.41.   A MULTIVARIATE ANALYSIS OF VARIANCE FOR *Iris versicolor* AND *Iris virginica* FROM TABLE 14.21 AND THE (S_{ij}) OF MATRIX 14.22

Source of variation	DF	$\sum x_1^2$	$\sum x_1 x_2$	$\sum x_2^2$	$\sum x_1 x_3$	$\sum x_2 x_3$	$\sum x_3^2$
Between species	1	0.0046	0.0030	0.0019	−0.1297	−0.0821	3.6046
Within species	50	10.1646	2.5032	4.0664	3.1666	1.4097	3.2606
Total	51	10.1692	2.5062	4.0683	3.0369	1.3286	6.8652

$$|W| = \begin{vmatrix} 10.1646 & 2.5032 & 3.1666 \\ 2.5032 & 4.0664 & 1.4097 \\ 3.1666 & 1.4097 & 3.2606 \end{vmatrix}$$

$$= [(10.1646)(4.0664)(3.2606) + 2(2.5032)(1.4097)(3.1666)]$$
$$- [3.1666^2(4.0664) + 1.4097^2(10.1646) + 2.5032^2(3.2606)]$$
$$= +75.71396, \quad \text{from the Within-Species data.}$$

Similarly,

$$|T| = \begin{vmatrix} 10.1692 & 2.5062 & 3.0369 \\ 2.5062 & 4.0683 & 1.3286 \\ 3.0369 & 1.3286 & 6.8652 \end{vmatrix} = +205.65480, \quad \text{from the Total data.}$$

Wilks's Λ is defined as $\dfrac{|W|}{|T|} = 0.36816.$

In the case of just two possible multivariate normal populations (so that $k = 2$) there is an exact F test defined as follows, but when $k > 2$, the test is not exact:

(14.41) $$F(2r, ms + 2\lambda) = \left(\frac{1-y}{y}\right) \cdot \left(\frac{ms + 2\lambda}{2r}\right)$$

where:

$$s = [p^2(k - 1)^2 - 4]/[p^2 + (k - 1)^2 - 5]$$
$$m = N - 1 - (p + k)/2$$
N = total number of observations on all populations
k = number of Π_i
p = number of X_j measured
$y = \Lambda^{1/s}$
$r = p(k - 1)/2$
$\lambda = [2 - p(k - 1)]/4$
Λ as in Table 14.41

From Table 14.41:

$$s = [9(1) - 4]/(9 + 1 - 5) = 1$$
$$p = 3$$
$$k = 2$$
$$N = 52$$
$$m = 51 - 5/2 = 48.5$$
$$\lambda = [2 - 3(1)]/4 = -0.25$$
$$r = 3(1)/2 = 1.5$$
$$y = (0.36816)^1$$

Hence $F(3, 48) = (0.63184/0.36816)(48/3) = 27.46$, $P \ll 0.001$. *The reader will note that this is precisely the same* F *ratio as was obtained in Section* 14.2 *with Hotelling's* T^2. Thus, it is seen that under the normality assumption and with $k = 2$, the F ratio from a simple between-group and within-group multivariate analysis of variance has a simple and exact relation to Hotelling's T^2, just as the corresponding F test in a univariate one-way analysis of variance has a simple and exact relation to the corresponding Student t test of the difference between two means.

Rao (book reference, Section 14.1) emphasizes use of a χ^2 test for the multivariate problem just solved by an F test. The chi-square is defined in terms of Wilks's lambda criterion, as follows:

(14.42) $$\chi_v^2 = -m \log_e \Lambda$$

where $v = p(k - 1)$ and the m and Λ are defined as above. Rao also gives procedures for computing the probability for such an approximate chi-square test. For the problem of Table 14.41, $\chi_3^2 = 48.46$ and $P \ll 0.001$.

Attention now is turned to a three-population multivariate analysis of variance, assuming normality of distribution. Table 14.42 was constructed from the previous data for *I. versicolor*, *I. virginica*, and *I. setosa*. The dispersion matrix of pooled Sums of Squares and Products is as follows:

(14.43) $$(S_{ij}) = \begin{pmatrix} 11.8350 & 3.9508 & 3.0922 \\ 3.9508 & 6.7808 & 1.3356 \\ 3.0922 & 1.3356 & 3.5990 \end{pmatrix}$$

The Between-Species Sums of Squares and cross products shown in Table 14.42 were computed in the usual way from the totals for the three species. For example,

$$\frac{(156.4)^2 + (128.2)^2}{25} + \frac{(168.4)^2}{27} - \frac{(453.0)^2}{77} = 21.1131$$

is the Between-Species $\sum (x_1^2)$.

TABLE 14.42.   A Multivariate Analysis of Variance for *Iris versicolor, Iris virginica,* and *Iris setosa,* with Three Measurements, X_1 = Sepal Length, X_2 = Sepal Width, and X_3 = Petal Length and Data from Dispersion Matrix 14.43

Source of variation	DF	$\sum x_1^2$	$\sum x_1 x_2$	$\sum x_2^2$	$\sum x_1 x_3$	$\sum x_2 x_3$	$\sum x_3^2$
Between species	2	21.1131	−11.8190	6.6528	60.4488	−36.5711	189.4298
Within species	74	11.8350	3.9508	6.7808	3.0922	1.3356	3.5990
Total	76	32.9481	−7.8682	13.4336	63.5410	−35.2355	193.0288

$$|W| = \begin{vmatrix} 11.8350 & 3.9508 & 3.0922 \\ 3.9508 & 6.7808 & 1.3356 \\ 3.0922 & 1.3356 & 3.5990 \end{vmatrix} = +179.33194$$

$$|T| = \begin{vmatrix} 32.9481 & -7.8682 & 63.5410 \\ -7.8682 & 13.4336 & -35.2355 \\ 63.5410 & -35.2355 & 193.0288 \end{vmatrix} = +13,574.85263$$

$$\Lambda = 179.33194/13,574.8526 = 0.01321060, \qquad -\log_e \Lambda = 4.32670$$

$$F(6, 146) \cong \frac{0.8851}{0.1149}\left(\frac{146}{6}\right) \cong 187.45, \qquad P \lll 0.001$$

$$\chi_6^2 \cong 73(4.32670) = 315.85, \qquad P \lll 0.001 \text{ also}$$

The symbol $\lll$ means "very much less than."

Either of the two approximate tests of significance in Table 14.42 should assure one that the hypothesis

(14.44) $H_0[(\mu_{11} = \mu_{21}; \mu_{12} = \mu_{22}; \text{etc.}) \mid (\text{equal covariance matrices})]$

should be rejected in favor of the conclusion that some of the means of the X_j are unequal. One then could feel that it was worth while to try to classify an unknown I into one of those quite different populations.

The reader is reminded that in this classic iris example based on an early article of Fisher's one *could* have used less than three X's to distinguish these populations. This historically important example is used herein solely to illustrate procedures and concepts.

It also is easy to see the importance of using as few X measurements as possible, because the labor involved in the multivariate analyses of variance illustrated in Tables 14.41 and 14.42 is not greatly increased if there are more than three populations possible, but it *is* greatly increased if there are more than three X's. However, on the bright side, high-speed computational facilities are becoming increasingly available to scientists, so less worry is justified over computational difficulties.

The problems of discriminatory analysis when more than two populations are possible will be considered specifically herein only for three populations, to maintain as much simplicity and clarity as possible.

If an individual I has been observed in an area where only populations Π_1, Π_2, and Π_3 are possible, discriminatory analysis requires that the p dimensional sample space, in which I is a point, shall have been divided into nonoverlapping but all-inclusive regions, R_1, R_2, and R_3, assuming no region of indecision, in such a way as to "best" classify I. There are two major questions, aside from computational difficulties: What do we know about Π_1, Π_2, and Π_3? With what we know about Π_1, Π_2, and Π_3 what criteria should we use to derive a "best" procedure for classifying I? As for only two populations, there is no truly satisfactory discriminatory procedure, unless the probability density functions for Π_1, Π_2, and Π_3 are completely known. Even then, there is trouble, unless they also have the same covariance matrix, that is, unless there is complete homogeneity of variance and covariance among populations for each trait measured.

Different points of view may be taken with regard to the choice of criteria for choosing R_1, R_2, and R_3 the best way. Table 14.43 has been constructed to illustrate this point, on the assumption that $p = 1$ and the three possible populations are

$$\Pi_1 = N_1(5, 4), \qquad \Pi_2 = N_2(7, 4), \qquad \Pi_3 = N_3(11, 4)$$

With only one X measurement there is no problem about the covariance matrices being equal when $\sigma^2 = 4$ in all cases.

Table 14.43 was constructed on the assumption that the probability that an individual I selected at random would be from Π_i is 1/3 for $i = 1, 2, 3$. In symbols, $\Pr\{$I will be from $\Pi_i\} = \pi_i = 1/3$. On that assumption the following points are illustrated with respect to the eight sets of (R_1, R_2, R_3) chosen for Table 14.43.

(a) If one wishes a set of regions which will maximize the $\sum_{i=1}^{3} \pi_i \Pr$ $\{\Pi_i/\Pi_i\}$ and consequently *minimize* the total probability of *misclassification*, one should choose $a = 6.0$ and $b = 9.0$. This is an extension of Regions

14.36, suggested by Rao, with all π_i equal and all r_i equal. Specifically, the regions for classifying I into Π_i are as follows:

$$
\begin{array}{llll}
& R_1: & f_1 \geqslant f_2 & \text{and} \quad f_1 \geqslant f_3 \\
\textbf{(14.45)} & R_2: & f_2 \geqslant f_1 & \text{and} \quad f_2 \geqslant f_3 \\
& R_3: & f_3 \geqslant f_1 & \text{and} \quad f_3 \geqslant f_2
\end{array}
$$

This is the maximum-likelihood method of classification.

(b) If one prefers to make the smallest probability of *correct* classification as high as possible, one chooses $a = 5.5$ and $b = 10$. This is an illustration of the general meaning of the *minimax principle*.

TABLE 14.43. PROBABILITIES OF CORRECT CLASSIFICATIONS AND OF MISCLASSIFICATIONS OF AN I WHEN $\Pi_1 = N(5, 4)$, $\Pi_2 = N(7, 4)$, AND $\Pi_3 = N(11, 4)$, AND FOR 8 SELECTED REGIONS $R_1(-\infty < X \leqslant a)$, $R_2(a < X \leqslant b)$, AND $R_3(X > b)$

$\Pr\{\Pi_i \mid \Pi_j\}$	$a = 6.0$ $b = 9.0$	$a = 5.5$ $b = 8.0$	$a = 5.5$ $b = 10.0$	$a = 5.0$ $b = 8.0$	$a = 5.0$ $b = 9.0$	$a = 6.5$ $b = 10.0$	$a = 7.0$ $b = 11.0$	$a = 7.0$ $b = 12.0$
$\Pi_1 \mid \Pi_1$	0.6915	0.5987	0.5987	0.5000	0.5000	0.7734	0.8413	0.8413
$\Pi_2 \mid \Pi_2$	0.5328	0.4649	0.7066	0.5328	0.6826	0.5319	0.4772	0.4938
$\Pi_3 \mid \Pi_3$	0.8413	0.9332	0.6915	0.9332	0.8413	0.6915	0.5000	0.3085
$\sum [\pi_i \Pr\{\Pi_i \mid \Pi_i\}]$ if π_i all $= 1/3$	0.6885 (max)	0.6656	0.6656	0.6553	0.6746	0.6656	0.6062	0.5479
Minimum $\Pr\{\Pi_i \mid \Pi_i\}$	0.5328	0.4649	0.5987 (max)	0.5000	0.5000	0.5319	0.4772	0.3085
$\Pi_2 \mid \Pi_1$	0.2857	0.3345	0.3951	0.4332	0.4772	0.2204	0.1572	0.1587
$\Pi_3 \mid \Pi_1$	0.0228	0.0668	0.0062	0.0668	0.0228	0.0062	0.0013	0.0002
$\Pi_1 \mid \Pi_2$	0.3085	0.2266	0.2266	0.1587	0.1587	0.4013	0.5000	0.5000
$\Pi_3 \mid \Pi_2$	0.1587	0.3085	0.0668	0.3085	0.1587	0.0668	0.0228	0.0062
$\Pi_1 \mid \Pi_3$	0.0062	0.0030	0.0030	0.0013	0.0013	0.0122	0.0228	0.0228
$\Pi_2 \mid \Pi_3$	0.1525	0.0638	0.3055	0.0655	0.1574	0.2963	0.4772	0.6687
$\sum [\pi_i \Pr\{\Pi_i \mid \Pi_j\}]$, if $i \neq j$ and all $\pi_i = 1/3$	0.3115 (min)	0.3344	0.3344	0.3447	0.3254	0.3344	0.3938	0.4521

If an individual I is found in an area which can be regarded as a mixture of three multivariate populations in the proportions

$$
f_1(X_1, \cdots, X_p) : f_2(X_1, \cdots, X_p) : f_3(X_1, \cdots, X_p) = \pi_1 : \pi_2 : \pi_3
$$

Rao (book reference Section 14.1) has shown that the maximum-likelihood regions are

$$R_1: \qquad \pi_1 f_1 \geqslant \pi_2 f_2 \quad \text{and} \quad \pi_1 f_1 \geqslant \pi_3 f_3$$

(14.46)
$$R_2: \qquad \pi_2 f_2 \geqslant \pi_1 f_1 \quad \text{and} \quad \pi_2 f_2 \geqslant \pi_3 f_3$$

$$R_3: \qquad \pi_3 f_3 \geqslant \pi_1 f_1 \quad \text{and} \quad \pi_3 f_3 \geqslant \pi_2 f_2$$

If in addition to the assumptions made for these it is assumed that the "loss" caused by misclassifying an I from Π_i is r_i, one obtains the following most general definitions of regions:

$$R_1: \qquad \pi_1 r_1 f_1 \geqslant \pi_2 r_2 f_2 \quad \text{and} \quad \pi_1 r_1 f_1 \geqslant \pi_3 r_3 f_3$$

(14.47)
$$R_2: \qquad \pi_2 r_2 f_2 \geqslant \pi_1 r_1 f_1 \quad \text{and} \quad \pi_2 r_2 f_2 \geqslant \pi_3 r_3 f_3$$

$$R_3: \qquad \pi_3 r_3 f_3 \geqslant \pi_1 r_1 f_1 \quad \text{and} \quad \pi_3 r_3 f_3 \geqslant \pi_2 r_2 f_2$$

Of course, the difficult problem in practice when the f_i are multivariate populations is to determine these regions.

Getting back more specifically to the problem of discriminatory analysis, what useful procedures are available for classifying an unknown individual I into one of several multivariate populations? Leaving aside possible ways to include regions of indecision, we shall again use Rao's *linear discriminant score* L_r for the rth population, on the assumption that the measurements $X_1, X_2, \cdots, X_p$ have a multivariate normal distribution within each population and that the covariance matrices of all populations are the same. This is quite a severe set of restrictions and is only excusable in the absence of some other useful procedure.

Rao's *linear discriminant score* was defined by Formula 14.37 and illustrated for $r = 1$ and 2. It now will be used in this section for general r. Under the assumptions stated, Rao has shown that $L_r + \log_e \pi_r$ gives a maximum-likelihood solution to the problem of discrimination, because the surfaces of equal likelihood can, in this case, be defined in terms of the L_r.

When the population parameters are unknown, it is suggested, as before, that one compute an L_r for each possible population in terms of the observed means and the dispersion matrix to obtain functions of $X_1, \cdots, X_p$. Then for an unknown individual, I, one computes each L_r and assigns I to that population for which $L_r + \log_e \pi_r$ is a maximum. This procedure will be illustrated by means of Table 14.44 and the procedures illustrated in Section 14.3, when r was limited to 1 and 2.

Using (M_{ij}) and the column matrices of species means one obtains the sample estimates of the $\sum_{i=1}^{p} (M_{ij}\mu_{ir})$ indicated in Formula 14.37 for L_r. Following Rao, these will be called the l_{ir}, where r will be 1, 2, and 3 in turn for *I. versicolor*, *I. virginica*, and *I. setosa*, and i will be 1, 2, and 3 for sepal length, sepal width, and petal length, respectively. When the means and the M_{ij} are substituted into Formula 14.37, one obtains for $p = 3$

$$L_r = \sum_{j=1}^{3} \left(\sum_{i=1}^{3} M_{ij}\bar{x}_{ir} \right) X_j - \frac{1}{2} \sum_{j=1}^{3} M_{ij}\bar{x}_{ir}x_{jr}$$

(14.48)
$$L_r = \sum_{j=1}^{3} l_{jr} X_j - \frac{1}{2} \sum_{j=1}^{3} (l_{jr}\bar{x}_{jr})$$

where $l_{jr} = \sum_{i=1}^{3} (M_{ij}\bar{x}_{ir})$, with $r = 1, 2,$ and 3.

The l_{ir} will be obtained by matrix multiplication as follows:

$$(M_{ij}) \cdot \begin{pmatrix} 6.256 \\ 2.912 \\ 4.636 \end{pmatrix} = (0.1261)(6.256) + (-0.0562)(2.912) + (-0.0875)(4.636)$$

$$= 0.2196 = l_{11}, \quad \text{using the first row of } (M_{ij})$$
$$= (-0.0562)(6.256) + (0.1842)(2.912) + (-0.0200)(4.636)$$
$$= 0.0921 = l_{21}, \quad \text{using the second row of } (M_{ij})$$
$$= (-0.0875)(6.256) + (-0.0200)(2.912) + (0.3605)(4.636)$$
$$= 1.0656 = l_{31}, \quad \text{using the third row of } (M_{ij})$$

TABLE 14.44.   DOOLITTLE INVERSION OF DISPERSION MATRIX OF SUMS
OF SQUARES AND PRODUCTS POOLED DATA OF 14.43

Dispersion matrix				Unit matrix	
X_1	X_2	X_3			
11.8350	3.9508	3.0922	1	0	0
	6.7808	1.3356	0	1	0
		3.5990	0	0	1
11.8350	3.9508	3.0922	1	0	0
1	0.3338	0.2613	0.0845	0	0
	5.4620	0.3034	−0.3338	1	0
	1	0.0555	−0.0611	0.1831	0
		2.7742	−0.2428	−0.0555	1
		1	−0.0875	−0.0200	0.3605

$$(M_{ij}) = \begin{pmatrix} 0.1261 & -0.0562 & -0.0875 \\ -0.0562 & 0.1842 & -0.0200 \\ -0.0875 & -0.0200 & 0.3605 \end{pmatrix}$$

Check: $(M_{ij}) \cdot \begin{pmatrix} r_{y1} \\ r_{y2} \\ r_{y3} \end{pmatrix} \cong \begin{pmatrix} 1 & 0 & 0 \\ 0 & 1 & 0 \\ 0 & 0 & 1 \end{pmatrix}$

Put more briefly and correctly,

$$(M_{ij}) \cdot \begin{pmatrix} \bar{x}_{11} \\ \bar{x}_{12} \\ \bar{x}_{13} \end{pmatrix} = \begin{pmatrix} l_{11} \\ l_{21} \\ l_{31} \end{pmatrix} = \begin{pmatrix} 0.2196 \\ 0.0921 \\ 1.0656 \end{pmatrix}$$

In a similar manner:

$$(M_{ij}) \cdot \begin{pmatrix} \bar{x}_{21} \\ \bar{x}_{22} \\ \bar{x}_{23} \end{pmatrix} = \begin{pmatrix} l_{12} \\ l_{22} \\ l_{32} \end{pmatrix} = \begin{pmatrix} 0.1717 \\ 0.0804 \\ 1.2575 \end{pmatrix}$$

$$(M_{ij}) \cdot \begin{pmatrix} \bar{x}_{31} \\ \bar{x}_{32} \\ \bar{x}_{33} \end{pmatrix} = \begin{pmatrix} l_{13} \\ l_{23} \\ l_{33} \end{pmatrix} = \begin{pmatrix} 0.3088 \\ 0.3306 \\ 0.0546 \end{pmatrix}$$

Furthermore, $\frac{1}{2} \sum_{i=1}^{3} l_{ir} \bar{x}_{ir} = 3.2911, 3.8933,$ and 1.4191 for $r = 1$ (*I. versicolor*), $r = 2$ (*I. virginica*), and $r = 3$ (*I. setosa*), respectively. If these values are used in Formula 14.44, one obtains the following linear discriminant scores for the three species of iris in the order maintained above:

$$L_1 = 0.2196X_1 + 0.0921X_2 + 1.0656X_3 - 3.2911, \quad \text{for } I. \text{ versicolor}$$
$$L_2 = 0.1717X_1 + 0.0804X_2 + 1.2575X_3 - 3.8933, \quad \text{for } I. \text{ virginica}$$
$$L_3 = 0.3088X_1 + 0.3306X_2 + 0.0546X_3 - 1.4191, \quad \text{for } I. \text{ setosa}$$

If the π_i are unknown, the last term of each $L_r + \log_e \pi_r$ is dropped, because all π_i would have to be taken equal and hence would add nothing to the linear discriminant score.

Now suppose an individual iris is obtained which is an unknown one of the three species discussed herein. Suppose also that the π_i are unknown and taken equal. If this individual I has $X_1 = 6.000$, $X_2 = 3.000$, and $X_3 = 3.000$ (for easy illustration), then $L_1 = 1.4996$, $L_2 = 1.1506$, and $L_3 = 1.5893$ when those X's are substituted in the L_r above. The largest of these L's for iris I is $L_3 = 1.5893$; therefore, this unknown I is classified as *I. setosa*.

Suppose next that upon the basis of good evidence it is judged that *I. versicolor* and *I. virginica* are about equally abundant in the area where I was found (and to which the data of Table 14.44 apply) and these two species are individually about twice as abundant as *I. setosa*. It then is reasonable to take $\pi_1 = \pi_2 = 0.4$ and $\pi_3 = 0.2$. Then it is found that $\log_e 0.4 = -0.916$ and $\log_{0.2} = -1.609$; whence $L_1 + \log_e \pi_1 = 0.5836$, $L_2 + \log_e \pi_2 = 0.2346$, and $L_3 + \log_e \pi_3 = -0.0197$ for the unknown I. Under these conditions, I would be classified as *I. versicolor*, because $L_1 + \log_e \pi_1$ is the largest $L_r + \log_e \pi_r$.

A natural question to ask after such an analysis is, How sure is one that the classification arrived at is correct? There are two reasons not to answer this question in any detail here: apparently the use of $L_r + \log_e \pi_r$ is as good a procedure as is presently known, and the procedure for computing the probabilities of wrong classifications is fairly complex even with $r = 3$. The reader is referred to Rao's book (references, Section 14.1) for additional information, if he wishes to perform these latter computations.

If $r > 3$, and one is satisfied to assume that the multivariate populations are reasonably close to normal and have the same variances and covariances for the $X_1, \cdots, X_p$, the procedure given above can be used with the confidence that the classifications made are as reliable as they can be made on the basis of present knowledge. If one feels that it is useful and worth while, one can use Rao's procedures for including regions of indecision and can also estimate the probabilities of misclassification if p is small.

PROBLEMS

1. It appears that the most important environmental factors influencing the rapidity with which grain sorghums mature are expressible as sets of temperature-summation variables. Given the following apparently different environments, determine whether they really are basically of the same environment, as far as the indicated set of temperature-summation variables is concerned.

Location 1:			Location 2:			Location 3:		
X_1	X_2	X_3	X_1	X_2	X_3	X_1	X_2	X_3
123	727	138	280	546	211	68	717	21
275	590	429	254	605	463	131	783	299
334	852	11	272	580	240	175	755	178
150	727	138	386	599	392	84	702	33
281	590	439	321	551	223	181	763	302
334	852	13	328	560	428	308	748	165
155	682	112	368	610	204	118	706	29
352	487	375	500	621	480	169	773	308
390	791	62	310	560	197	314	742	183
132	715	121	372	578	450	125	720	38
377	610	403	375	532	217	225	790	281
282	842	38	601	627	389	315	765	169
205	658	160	—	—	—	169	710	28
469	466	450				419	791	301
499	837	63				524	737	190
151	685	112				127	725	18
430	601	388				358	773	279
—	—	—				320	760	188

$X_1 =$ total accumulated degree-hours above 90°F. from 30 days after planting until maturity

$X_2 =$ accumulated degree-hours above 80°F. during first 20 days

$X_3 =$ accumulated degree-hours below 60°F. during first 20 nights.

2. The following data are the same as in Problem 1, but for three other locations:

Location 4:			Location 5:			Location 6:		
X_1	X_2	X_3	X_1	X_2	X_3	X_1	X_2	X_3
85	1004	12	60	308	175	124	614	43
203	554	239	38	337	376	89	357	397
301	637	215	165	367	3	65	690	400
88	982	37	65	298	200	130	598	57
279	487	250	46	310	297	92	471	411
312	598	192	170	350	14	115	702	408
117	995	26	72	281	182	132	626	37
360	529	261	126	347	382	195	368	372
494	628	212	181	380	43	220	681	391
188	1035	17	98	291	162	143	572	65
512	561	242	149	289	315	201	380	380
477	650	220	179	372	33	223	711	415
240	980	42	99	321	172	186	592	23
543	581	248	161	387	392	250	351	388
495	622	231	156	328	53	255	703	407
240	879	52	103	300	168	189	588	97
523	572	249	155	312	337	247	327	372
501	627	197	190	297	13	227	720	431

Decide whether these three locations constitute different multivariate normal populations with respect to these temperature-summation variables.

3. Suppose that the location designation for the set of data $X_1 = 110$, $X_2 = 580$, and $X_3 = 310$ has been lost. To which location would you assign it upon the basis of the evidence in Problem 2? In Problem 3?

4. Given the following data on two locations, compute Rao's L_r's, assuming $\pi_1 = \pi_2$:

Location 1:				Location 2:			
X_1	X_2	X_3	X_4	X_1	X_2	X_3	X_4
584	96	1432	204	604	283	742	1171
272	558	2129	24	1060	84	476	1619
17	482	1475	214	582	81	702	1210
754	541	1334	194	1664	1105	212	2709
272	938	2039	34	42	702	1190	559
31	1074	1375	196	106	130	2013	134
754	755	1452	224	115	680	2509	54
272	1207	2209	28	1892	1402	212	2513
46	1172	1502	172	214	1220	1312	729
769	950	1370	209	167	890	1977	210
272	1020	2017	8	230	1176	2731	82
833	1486	1528	162	2017	1533	347	2652
723	252	1397	186	280	1697	1068	810
272	819	1972	101	261	1002	2181	325
29	979	1610	182	540	1456	2077	49
665	158	1292	236	2120	1728	179	2828
				380	1470	988	785
				953	1836	2222	321
				1162	847	1897	87

5. Compute Hotelling's T^2 for Problem 4.

6. Compute Pearson's CRL for Problem 4.

7. Compute Rao's D^2 for Problem 4.

8. Do Problem 4 with $\pi_2 = 4\pi_1$.

9. Using only locations 1 and 2 of Problem 1, compute and interpret Hotelling's T^2.

10. Use Hotelling's T^2 to decide whether locations 2 and 3 of Problem 1 probably represent the same temperature-summation environment.

11. Use the F test of Equation 14.41 to test whether the multivariate normal populations of locations 1 and 2, Problem 4, probably are identical. How does this F ratio compare with the Hotelling T^2 required in Problem 5?

12. Use Wilks's Λ criterion to decide whether the three populations of Problem 1 are identical, making the assumptions necessary for this test. Is the test used an exact test?

REVIEW PROBLEMS

1. Suppose that it has been asserted that during the year 1963 a certain big-city newspaper averaged two misspellings per three column inches. You are assigned the job of testing this assertion by some sampling procedure. How would you take the sample?

2. Suppose that it is asserted that in a specific large bin of apples one apple in six has a rotten spot. How would you test this assertion by sampling, assuming the term "rotten spot" has been defined unambiguously?

3. Suppose it is asserted that in a certain large high school three boys out of five are at least five pounds overweight, according to a specific weight chart available in the principal's office. How would you test this assertion?

4. Assuming you had excellent samples from each of the samplings suggested in Problems 1, 2, and 3, what statistical test(s) would you use for each problem? Explain your choices.

5. Suppose that an insect trap has been properly operated in a certain location for a week in early June, and you are provided the counts obtained of each species of insect caught. What sorts of conclusion could you draw? What if you had such counts for 15 weeks during the summer? What if you had for the first week in June such counts from 10 different traps in the same general location? What if you had the latter situation and counts for 15 weeks?

6. Suppose it has been asserted that at any given time two people out of every three have at least one unfilled cavity in their teeth that should be filled. How would you test this hypothesis by a sampling procedure?

7. How large a sample must one take from a binomial population to be absolutely assured that the resulting CI_{90} will not exceed 10 units in length?

8. Write down the specific sizes of the true mean and variance for those populations for which the following are true:
   (a) The probability density function is $(1/\sqrt{2\pi})e^{-(y+1)^2/6}$, where $-\infty < y < +\infty$.
   (b) The constant probability of the event E is 0.35, 10 trials are made per set, and the variate is $X = $ number E's on 10 trials.

(c) The probability function is $\binom{15}{v} 2^v 3^{15-v}/5^{15}$, where $v = 0, 1, \cdots, 15$.

(d) The variate X is a Poisson variate with parameter $= 2.4$.

(e) The variate X is the number of nonoccurrences of event E before E occurs for the sixth time, and the probability of occurrence of E constantly is -0.7.

(f) X is a chi-square variate with five degrees of freedom.

(g) X is an F(4, 20) variate.

(h) W is a t variate with 11 degrees of freedom.

(i) The variate X is the ratio of two independent unbiassed estimates, s_1^2 and s_2^2, of the same normal variance, σ^2, with 12 and 18 DF, respectively.

(j) Y is a standard normal variate.

9. Suppose that you have the hypothesis $H_0(\mu \leqslant 2)$ for an $N(\mu_1, \sigma^2)$ population and seek to test this hypothesis against the alternative $H_a(\mu > 2)$ by means of a sample of size $n = 30$. The sample results are $\bar{x} = 3.8$ and $s^2 = 7.3842$. What is your decision, if you choose $\alpha = 0.10$?

10. Suppose you have the hypothesis $H_0(\rho \leqslant 0.5)$ and seek to test it against $H_a(\rho > 0.5)$ by means of 40 pair of observations from the normal bivariate population in question. If the product-moment coefficient of linear correlation turns out to be $r = 0.65$, what is your decision with a region of rejection of size 0.10?

11. Suppose that the hypothesis $H_0(\mu = 0)$ is to be tested for an $N(\mu, 9)$ population by means of a sample of size $n = 25$ and with $\alpha = 0.10$. If the alternative hypothesis is $H_a(\mu > 0)$ and the sample results are $\bar{x} = 1.1$ and $s^2 = 12.07$, what is your decision?

12. If w is an $N(10, 12)$ variate, what is the distribution of $w + 5$? Of $5w$? Of $2w - 3$?

13. Suppose that an experimenter is going to test $H_0(\mu = 0)$ against $H_a(\mu > 0)$. Also suppose that, unknown to the experimenter, of course, the population actually is $N(2, 9)$. Devise a graph which shows how the success of the experimenter in detecting the falseness of H_0 depends on sample size, if α is fixed at 0.10.

14. Suppose that a random sample from a binomial population produced the following confidence interval, CI_{90}: $21 < p < 36$. Make each of the tests of hypotheses indicated below and state the size of the region of rejection in each case:

(a) $H_0(p = 17)$ vs. $H_a(p \neq 17)$ (b) $H_0(p \leqslant 17)$ vs. $H_a(p > 17)$
(c) $H_0(p \geqslant 25)$ vs. $H_a(p < 25)$ (d) $H_0(p = 17)$ vs. $H_a(p > 17)$

15. Suppose that an experimenter is studying the effects of a certain specific exposure to a specific source of irradiation on the blood pH of laboratory mice. If he obtains 60 apparently identical female mice of the same age and origin, exposes 30 chosen at random to the radiation, and measures thereafter the blood pH of all 60 mice, what statistical analysis would you suggest? What information would you expect to be able to obtain thereby?

16. Suppose that Problem 15 were altered to state that the experimenter would measure protein-bound iodine as well as pH. How would you now answer the questions of Problem 15?

17. Suppose that Problem 16 were extended to include the measurement of blood cholesterol. How would you answer the questions asked?

18. Suppose Problem 17 is extended by assuming the experimenter has 90 mice, divides them at random into three groups of 30, irradiates one group at one level of intensity and a second group at another level of intensity, and leaves one group of 30 unexposed to radiation. What statistical analyses are possible and probably useful now? Clearly justify each analysis proposed.

19. Referring to Problem 15, suppose that the measurement of interest to the experimenter is the white cell count. What would you advise now in the way of statistical analyses, and why?

20. Sketch a graph which is appropriate for each of the following variates:

(a) $b(X; 15, 0.5)$ (b) $b(X; 15, 0.9)$ (c) $N(10, 6.25)$ (d) $N(10, 25)$,
(e) χ_5^2 (f) $F(3, 16)$ (g) t with 6 DF   (h) t with 20 DF
(i) Poisson with parameter 2.5
(j) Pascal Negative Binomial with $p = 0.4$ and $k = 3$

21. What is the true standard deviation for each variate of Problem 20?

22. Suppose that two Poisson populations with parameters λ_1 and λ_2 respectively each have been observed for $t_1 = t_2 = 8$ units of time. If it was observed that $x_1 = 4$ and $x_2 = 7$, is $H_0(\lambda_1 = \lambda_2)$ acceptable against the alternative $H_a(\lambda_1 < \lambda_2)$?

23. Compute and interpret the CI_{90} on λ_1/λ_2 for Problem 22.

24. Suppose that instead of the direct Poisson sampling described in Problem 22 the t's and x's are interchanged, so that one has inverse Poisson sampling. Now test $H_0(\lambda_1 = \lambda_2)$ against $H_a(\lambda_1 < \lambda_2)$.

25. Suppose that in an experiment involving inverse Poisson sampling from three populations the X_1, X_2, and X_3 have each been fixed at 5. It turns out that $t_1 = 8$, $t_2 = 3$, and $t_3 = 11$. Test $H_0(\lambda_1 = \lambda_2 = \lambda_3)$ against H_a(some λ_i are unequal). Let $\alpha = 0.10$.

26. Make up a set of 200 numbers whose frequency distribution displays most of the salient features of an $N(2.5, 1.69)$ population.

27. How would the solution to Problem 26 change if $N(2.5, 1.69)$ were replaced by $N(25, 169)$? By $N(1.5, 1.69)$?

28. Suppose that two binomial populations have been sampled with the following results:

$$\Pi_1: \quad n_1 = 100, \ X_1 = 28; \qquad \Pi_2: \quad n_2 = 75, \ X_2 = 23$$

Use the standard normal distribution to test $H_0(p_1 = p_2)$ against $H_a(p_1 < p_2)$ with $\alpha = 0.10$.

29. Suppose that a random sample of size $n = 100$ from $b(X; 100, p)$ has produced $X = 32$. Compute the GLB_{90} on p by means of the standard normal distribution. Compare with the GLB_{90} obtainable from Formula 2.31.

30. Given the following binomial frequency distributions for the indicated p's, determine an *approximate* CI_{80} therefrom, assuming that the random variate X was observed to be 4 in a sample of size $n = 12$.

$(.90 + .10)^{12} = .28 + .38 + .23 + .085 + .021 + .004 + .000 + \cdots$
$(.88 + .12)^{12} = .22 + .35 + .26 + .12 + .037 + .008 + .001$
$\qquad\qquad\qquad\qquad\qquad\qquad\qquad\qquad + .000 + \cdots$

$(.87 + .13)^{12} = .19 + .34 + .28 + .14 + .046 + .011 + .002$
$$+ .000 + \cdots$$
$(.85 + .15)^{12} = .14 + .30 + .29 + .17 + .068 + .019 + .004$
$$+ .001 + .000 + \cdots$$
$(.83 + .17)^{12} = .11 + .26 + .30 + .20 + .093 + .031 + .007$
$$+ .001 + .000 + \cdots$$
$(.80 + .20)^{12} = .069 + .21 + .28 + .24 + .13 + .053 + .016$
$$+ .003 + .001 + .000 + \cdots$$
$(.75 + .25)^{12} = .032 + .13 + .23 + .26 + .19 + .10 + .040$
$$+ .011 + .002 + .000 + \cdots$$
$(.50 + .50)^{12} = .000 + .003 + .016 + .054 + .12 + .19 + .23$
$$+ .19 + .12 + .054 + .016 + .003 + .000 + \cdots$$
$(.45 + .55)^{12} = .000 + .001 + .007 + .023 + .076 + .15 + .21$
$$+ .22 + .17 + .092 + .034 + .008 + .001 + \cdots$$
$(.44 + .56)^{12} = .000 + .001 + .006 + .024 + .068 + .14 + .21$
$$+ .23 + .18 + .10 + .039 + .009 + .001 + .000 + \cdots$$
$(.43 + .57)^{12} = .000 + .001 + .005 + .002 + .061 + .13 + .20$
$$+ .23 + .19 + .11 + .044 + .011 + .001 + .000 + \cdots$$
$(.40 + .60)^{12} = .000 + .000 + .002 + .012 + .042 + .10 + .18$
$$+ .23 + .21 + .14 + .064 + .017 + .002 + \cdots$$
$$X = 0, 1, 2, \cdots, 12, \text{ in order.}$$

31. Use the binomial series of Problem 30 to determine the GLB_{80} on p, given that X has been observed to be 3. Show how you obtained your answer.

32. Mark the following statements as true (t) or false (f) in the space ( ) provided at the right. If a statement definitely is partly false, mark it false.

    The point estimator midrange, MR, provides estimates of the parameter σ^2.   ( )

    The probability of equally many Heads and Tails on a toss of any *even* number of unbiassed coins is 1/2.   ( )

    Given $H_0(p = 0.50)$ versus $H_a(p \neq 0.50)$ and that the CI_{90} is $0.47 < p < 0.58$ on a subsequent random sample, H_0 would be accepted.   ( )

    Given two unbiassed coins and one unbiassed die, the probability of tossing an even number on the die and at least one Head on the coins is 1/2.   ( )

    The variance of the sample median for large normal samples is smaller than the variance of the MR but larger than the variance of the sample mean.   ( )

    If X is a random variable, $7 - (\bar{x})^2$ has a sampling distribution for samples of size $n = 10$, and this distribution is approximately normal.   ( )

    Two-tail regions of rejection are used when the alternative hypothesis is unknown.   ( )

    Any binomial frequency distribution is symmetrical if $p = 1/2$.   ( )

    A specific point estimate is always wrong, but an interval estimate had a specific and stated probability of including the parameter before the sample was drawn.   ( )

    The smaller the probability of a Type I error is taken, the larger is the probability of a Type II error, all else being the same.   ( )

33. Suppose that a geneticist wishes to test $H_0(9 \text{ dominants} : 7 \text{ recessives})$. He has good reason to believe that if this H_0 is false it is because there is an excess of dominants. On a random sample of size $n = 50$ he finds 35 dominants.

Show by a confidence interval argument what decision he should make about H_0.

34. Do Problem 33 by a chi-square test, and draw appropriate conclusions after changing H_a to $p_D \neq 9/16$.

35. Given the following binomial frequency distributions for the indicated p's, determine an *approximate* CI_{90} therefrom, assuming the random variate X was observed to be 7 on a sample of size $n = 12$.

$(.16 + .84)^{12} = .000 + .000 + .000 + .000 + .000 + .001 + .005$
$+ .025 + .080 + .19 + .30 + .28 + .12$
$(.18 + .82)^{12} = .000 + .000 + .000 + .000 + .000 + .002 + .010$
$+ .037 + .11 + .22 + .29 + .24 + .092$
$(.20 + .80)^{12} = .000 + .000 + .000 + .000 + .001 + .003 + .016$
$+ .053 + .13 + .24 + .28 + .21 + .069$
$(.70 + .30)^{12} = .014 + .017 + .17 + .24 + .23 + .16$
$+ .079 + .029 + .008 + .001 + .000$
$(.71 + .29)^{12} = .016 + .080 + .18 + .25 + .23 + .15$
$+ .070 + .025 + .006 + .001 + .000$
$(.72 + .28)^{12} = .019 + .091 + .19 + .25 + .22 + .14$
$+ .062 + .021 + .005 + .001 + .000$
$(.73 + .27)^{12} = .023 + .10 + .21 + .25 + .21 + .13$
$+ .054 + .017 + .004 + .001 + .000$
$(.75 + .25)^{12} = .032 + .13 + .23 + .26 + .19 + .10$
$+ .040 + .011 + .002 + .000$

36. Use the binomial series of Problem 35 to determine the GLB_{90} with $X = 6$.

37. Suppose that a psychiatrist believes that one person in 10 has some measurable degree of mental illness of a certain sort. If on a random sample of 100 persons, examined by a psychiatrist unassociated with the one who proposed the above hypothesis, seven are found to have the symptoms of this mental illness, would you accept the first psychiatrist's hypothesis with $\alpha = 0.10$? Use a confidence interval argument.

38. Do Problem 37 by a chi-square test, and draw appropriate conclusions.

39. Suppose that a very large random sample from a Poisson population has produced $X = 18$. What is the CI_{90} on the parameter λ? What is the LUB_{95}? The LUB_{90}?

40. Draw a random sample of 20 sentences from Chapters 1 and 7, count the number of adjectives in each sentence, and thereafter use Klotz's Normal Scores test to decide whether the variabilities in numbers of adjectives per sentence are different in the two chapters.

41. Suppose that a Poisson process is to be observed for $t = 10$ units of time. Graph the frequency distribution of X, the observed number of Poisson events, given that $\lambda = 1.4$ per unit of time.

42. Plot the frequency distribution of the number of tails appearing on tosses of an unbiassed coin before the sixth head is tossed.

43. Do Problem 42 for the coin so biassed that $p_H = 0.6$.

44. The following data are presumed to have been taken from an experiment involving three multivariate normal populations:

	Π_1:				Π_2:				Π_3:		
X_1	X_2	X_3	X_4	X_1	X_2	X_3	X_4	X_1	X_2	X_3	X_4
11.2	16.5	5.7	1.8	4.3	5.9	13.9	13.0	2.7	6.2	30.2	15.8
5.8	9.7	12.6	8.6	8.6	7.6	12.2	9.9	9.2	14.7	14.9	5.7
7.9	11.8	10.2	5.2	7.2	6.8	11.8	10.2	7.1	12.0	17.2	9.8
6.0	6.2	7.2	4.7	14.5	12.6	2.4	4.8	10.0	17.2	12.3	3.6
9.6	14.4	8.7	3.7	11.2	10.7	4.9	7.2	8.3	11.6	13.8	7.2
3.7	8.3	14.0	10.5	9.4	8.3	4.0	10.3	5.6	8.3	19.5	11.3
4.8	7.7	15.8	9.3	12.6	10.2	3.8	5.9	3.9	5.9	28.7	14.6

Perform a multivariate analysis of variance, to test $H_0[(\mu_{1i} = \mu_{2i} = \mu_{3i}) \mid$ (equal variance and covariances)] versus its negation, with $i = 1, 2, 3, 4$. Use $\alpha = 0.05$, and draw appropriate conclusions.

45. Perform Hotelling's T^2 test on Π_1 and Π_2 to see whether they differ significantly as multivariate populations. Use $\alpha = 0.10$, and draw appropriate conclusions.

46. Suppose an individual, I, has been observed, and it is known that I must be from one of the three populations visualized in Problem 44. If the measurements on I are

$$X_1 = 9.8, \qquad X_2 = 12.3, \qquad X_3 = 15.4, \qquad X_4 = 8.9$$

into which population would you classify I, assuming it initially was equally likely to be from each population?

47. Do Problem 46, supposing that members of Π_2 are twice as prevalent in the area as members of Π_1 but only half as prevalent as members of Π_3.

48. Graph the frequency distribution of the negative binomial population whose probability function is:

$$\Pr\{x \mid 0.4, 3\} = \binom{x + 2}{x}(0.4)^3(0.6)^x$$

49. Compute the mean and variance for the x of Problem 48.

50. Use Klotz's Normal Scores Test to decide whether the x_1 variances for Π_1 and Π_3 in Problem 44 probably are equal.

51. Use Mood's Square Rank Test to do Problem 50.

52. Test the X_1 data of Problem 44 for homogeneity of variance by means of Hartley's F_{max} procedure. Use $\alpha = 0.10$.

53. Use Hartley's range analysis of variance on the X_3 data of Problem 44 to test $H_0[(\mu_1 = \mu_2 = \mu_3) \mid (\sigma_1^2 = \sigma_2^2 = \sigma_3^2 = \sigma^2)]$ against its negation. Choose $\alpha = 0.10$.

54. Suppose that a Poisson process has been sampled by fixing the x at 8 and thereafter observing that it took $t = 20$ units of time until the eighth event occurred. What is the CI_{90} on $\lambda =$ true average number of events per unit of time?

55. Suppose that two separate Poisson processes are observed for fixed times: $t_1 = 12$ units and $t_2 = 16$ units. If the observed numbers of events are $x_1 = 7$ and $x_2 = 6$, what is the CI_{90} on λ_1/λ_2? Is $H_0(\lambda_1 = \lambda_2)$ acceptable in preference to $H_a(\lambda_1 \neq \lambda_2)$? What if $H_a(\lambda_1 > \lambda_2)$ is the alternative?

56. Suppose the following "game" is played: The words *twenty*, *every*, *household*, and *bonfire* are written on freely mixable and identical pieces of cardboard;

one word is drawn at random and all possible words written down from it; this process is repeated once. What is the probability that the sum of the two numbers of words so obtained will be at least 20? Less than 10? Use a convenient dictionary as your word standard.

57. Use the Method of Least Squares to fit a straight line to the X_1 and X_2 data of Problem 44 and Π_1, letting X_2 play the role of Y in Chapter 6 and making the necessary assumptions.

58. Make up a two-population multivariate problem with 4 measurements and 15 observations of each measurement in each population. Then apply Hotelling's T^2 test and Wilks's Λ criterion to show the equality of these two statistics in this case.

59. Graph the frequency distribution of the non-Pascal negative binomial with $k = 3$, $p = 0.6$ and $q = 1.6$.

Tables

TABLE I. SQUARES, SQUARE ROOTS, AND RECIPROCALS

n	$\sqrt{n}$	$\sqrt{10n}$	n^2	$1/n$		n	$\sqrt{n}$	$\sqrt{10n}$	n^2	$1/n$
0.1	0.32	1.00	0.01	10.00		2.1	1.45	4.58	4.41	0.48
0.2	0.45	1.41	0.04	5.00		2.2	1.48	4.69	4.84	0.45
0.3	0.55	1.73	0.09	3.33		2.3	1.52	4.80	5.29	0.43
0.4	0.63	2.00	0.16	2.50		2.4	1.55	4.90	5.76	0.42
0.5	0.71	2.24	0.25	2.00		2.5	1.58	5.00	6.25	0.40
0.6	0.77	2.45	0.36	1.67		2.6	1.61	5.10	6.76	0.38
0.7	0.84	2.65	0.49	1.43		2.7	1.64	5.20	7.29	0.37
0.8	0.89	2.83	0.64	1.25		2.8	1.67	5.29	7.84	0.36
0.9	0.95	3.00	0.81	1.11		2.9	1.70	5.39	8.41	0.34
1.0	1.00	3.16	1.00	1.00		3.0	1.73	5.48	9.00	0.33
1.1	1.05	3.32	1.21	0.91		3.1	1.76	5.57	9.61	0.32
1.2	1.10	3.46	1.44	0.83		3.2	1.79	5.66	10.24	0.31
1.3	1.14	3.61	1.69	0.77		3.3	1.82	5.74	10.89	0.30
1.4	1.18	3.74	1.96	0.71		3.4	1.84	5.83	11.56	0.29
1.5	1.22	3.87	2.25	0.67		3.5	1.87	5.92	12.25	0.29
1.6	1.26	4.00	2.56	0.62		3.6	1.90	6.00	12.96	0.28
1.7	1.30	4.12	2.79	0.59		3.7	1.92	6.08	13.69	0.27
1.8	1.34	4.24	3.24	0.56		3.8	1.95	6.16	14.44	0.26
1.9	1.38	4.36	3.61	0.53		3.9	1.97	6.24	15.21	0.26
2.0	1.41	4.47	4.00	0.50		4.0	2.00	6.32	16.00	0.25

(*cont.*)

TABLE I (*cont.*)

n	$\sqrt{n}$	$\sqrt{10n}$	n^2	$1/n$		n	$\sqrt{n}$	$\sqrt{10n}$	n^2	$1/n$
4.1	2.02	6.40	16.81	0.24		8.7	2.95	9.33	75.69	0.11
4.2	2.05	6.48	17.64	0.24		8.8	2.97	9.38	77.44	0.11
4.3	2.07	6.56	18.49	0.23		8.9	2.98	9.43	79.21	0.11
4.4	2.10	6.63	19.36	0.23		9.0	3.00	9.49	81.00	0.11
4.5	2.12	6.71	20.25	0.22		9.1	3.02	9.54	82.81	0.110
4.6	2.14	6.78	21.16	0.22		9.2	3.03	9.59	84.64	0.109
4.7	2.17	6.86	22.09	0.21		9.3	3.05	9.64	86.49	0.108
4.8	2.19	6.93	23.04	0.21		9.4	3.07	9.70	88.36	0.106
4.9	2.21	7.00	24.01	0.20		9.5	3.08	9.75	90.25	0.105
5.0	2.24	7.07	25.00	0.20		9.6	3.10	9.80	92.16	0.104
5.1	2.26	7.14	26.01	0.20		9.7	3.11	9.85	94.09	0.103
5.2	2.28	7.21	27.04	0.19		9.8	3.13	9.90	96.04	0.102
5.3	2.30	7.28	28.09	0.19		9.9	3.15	9.95	98.01	0.101
5.4	2.32	7.35	29.16	0.19		10.0	3.16	10.00	100.00	0.100
5.5	2.35	7.42	30.25	0.18		10.1	3.18	10.05	102.01	0.099
5.6	2.37	7.48	31.16	0.18		10.2	3.19	10.10	104.04	0.098
5.7	2.39	7.55	32.49	0.18		10.3	3.21	10.15	106.09	0.097
5.8	2.41	7.62	33.64	0.17		10.4	3.22	10.20	108.16	0.096
5.9	2.43	7.68	34.81	0.17		10.5	3.24	10.25	110.25	0.095
6.0	2.45	7.75	36.00	0.17		10.6	3.26	10.30	112.36	0.094
6.1	2.47	7.81	37.21	0.16		10.7	3.27	10.34	114.49	0.093
6.2	2.49	7.87	38.44	0.16		10.8	3.29	10.39	116.64	0.093
6.3	2.51	7.94	39.69	0.16		10.9	3.30	10.44	118.81	0.092
6.4	2.53	8.00	40.96	0.16		11.0	3.32	10.49	121.00	0.091
6.5	2.55	8.06	42.25	0.15		11.1	3.33	10.54	123.21	0.090
6.6	2.57	8.12	43.56	0.15		11.2	3.35	10.58	125.44	0.089
6.7	2.59	8.19	44.89	0.15		11.3	3.36	10.63	127.69	0.088
6.8	2.61	8.25	46.24	0.15		11.4	3.38	10.68	129.96	0.088
6.9	2.63	8.31	47.61	0.14		11.5	3.39	10.72	132.25	0.087
7.0	2.65	8.37	49.00	0.14		11.6	3.41	10.77	134.56	0.086
7.1	2.66	8.43	50.41	0.14		11.7	3.42	10.82	136.89	0.085
7.2	2.68	8.49	51.84	0.14		11.8	3.44	10.86	139.24	0.085
7.3	2.70	8.54	53.29	0.14		11.9	3.45	10.91	141.61	0.084
7.4	2.72	8.60	54.76	0.14		12.0	3.46	10.95	144.00	0.083
7.5	2.74	8.66	56.25	0.13		12.1	3.48	11.00	146.41	0.083
7.6	2.76	8.72	57.76	0.13		12.2	3.49	11.05	148.84	0.082
7.7	2.77	8.78	59.29	0.13		12.3	3.51	11.09	151.29	0.081
7.8	2.79	8.83	60.84	0.13		12.4	3.52	11.14	153.76	0.081
7.9	2.81	8.89	62.41	0.13		12.5	3.54	11.18	156.25	0.080
8.0	2.83	8.94	64.00	0.12		12.6	3.55	11.22	158.76	0.079
8.1	2.85	9.00	65.61	0.12		12.7	3.56	11.27	161.29	0.079
8.2	2.86	9.06	67.24	0.12		12.8	3.58	11.31	163.84	0.078
8.3	2.88	9.11	68.89	0.12		12.9	3.59	11.36	166.41	0.078
8.4	2.90	9.17	70.56	0.12		13.0	3.61	11.40	169.00	0.077
8.5	2.92	9.22	72.25	0.12		13.1	3.62	11.45	171.61	0.076
8.6	2.93	9.27	73.96	0.12		13.2	3.63	11.49	174.24	0.076

(*cont.*)

TABLE I (*cont.*)

n	$\sqrt{n}$	$\sqrt{10n}$	n^2	$1/n$		n	$\sqrt{n}$	$\sqrt{10n}$	n^2	$1/n$
13.3	3.65	11.53	176.89	0.075		17.9	4.23	13.38	320.41	0.056
13.4	3.66	11.58	179.56	0.075		18.0	4.24	13.42	324.00	0.056
13.5	3.67	11.62	182.25	0.074		18.1	4.25	13.45	327.61	0.055
13.6	3.69	11.66	184.96	0.074		18.2	4.27	13.49	331.24	0.055
13.7	3.70	11.70	187.69	0.073		18.3	4.28	13.53	334.89	0.055
13.8	3.72	11.75	190.44	0.072		18.4	4.29	13.56	338.56	0.054
13.9	3.73	11.79	193.21	0.072		18.5	4.30	13.60	342.25	0.054
14.0	3.74	11.83	196.00	0.071		18.6	4.31	13.64	345.96	0.054
14.1	3.76	11.87	198.81	0.071		18.7	4.32	13.67	349.69	0.053
14.2	3.77	11.92	201.64	0.070		18.8	4.34	13.71	353.44	0.053
14.3	3.78	11.96	204.49	0.070		18.9	4.35	13.75	357.21	0.053
14.4	3.79	12.00	207.36	0.069		19.0	4.36	13.78	361.00	0.053
14.5	3.81	12.04	210.25	0.069		19.1	4.37	13.82	364.81	0.052
14.6	3.82	12.08	213.16	0.068		19.2	4.38	13.86	368.64	0.052
14.7	3.83	12.12	216.09	0.068		19.3	4.39	13.89	372.49	0.052
14.8	3.85	12.17	219.04	0.068		19.4	4.40	13.93	376.36	0.052
14.9	3.86	12.21	222.01	0.067		19.5	4.42	13.96	380.25	0.051
15.0	3.87	12.25	225.00	0.067		19.6	4.43	14.00	384.16	0.051
15.1	3.89	12.29	228.01	0.066		19.7	4.44	14.04	388.09	0.051
15.2	3.90	12.33	231.04	0.066		19.8	4.45	14.07	392.04	0.050
15.3	3.91	12.37	234.09	0.065		19.9	4.46	14.11	396.01	0.050
15.4	3.92	12.41	237.16	0.065		20.0	4.47	14.14	400.00	0.050
15.5	3.94	12.45	240.25	0.065		20.1	4.48	14.18	404.01	0.050
15.6	3.95	12.49	243.36	0.064		20.2	4.49	14.21	408.04	0.050
15.7	3.96	12.53	246.49	0.064		20.3	4.51	14.25	412.09	0.049
15.8	3.97	12.57	249.64	0.063		20.4	4.52	14.28	416.16	0.049
15.9	3.99	12.61	252.81	0.063		20.5	4.53	14.32	420.25	0.049
16.0	4.00	12.65	256.00	0.062		20.6	4.54	14.35	424.36	0.049
16.1	4.01	12.69	259.21	0.062		20.7	4.55	14.39	428.49	0.048
16.2	4.02	12.73	262.44	0.061		20.8	4.56	14.42	432.64	0.048
16.3	4.04	12.77	265.69	0.061		20.9	4.57	14.46	436.81	0.048
16.4	4.05	12.81	268.96	0.061		21.0	4.58	14.49	441.00	0.048
16.5	4.06	12.85	272.25	0.061		21.1	4.59	14.53	445.21	0.047
16.6	4.07	12.88	275.56	0.060		21.2	4.60	14.56	449.44	0.047
16.7	4.09	12.92	278.89	0.060		21.3	4.62	14.59	453.69	0.047
16.8	4.10	12.96	282.24	0.060		21.4	4.63	14.63	457.96	0.047
16.9	4.11	13.00	285.61	0.059		21.5	4.64	14.66	462.25	0.047
17.0	4.12	13.04	289.00	0.059		21.6	4.65	14.70	466.56	0.046
17.1	4.14	13.08	292.41	0.058		21.7	4.66	14.73	470.89	0.046
17.2	4.15	13.11	295.84	0.058		21.8	4.67	14.76	475.24	0.046
17.3	4.16	13.15	299.29	0.058		21.9	4.68	14.80	479.61	0.046
17.4	4.17	13.19	302.76	0.057		22.0	4.69	14.83	484.00	0.045
17.5	4.18	13.23	306.25	0.057		22.1	4.70	14.87	488.41	0.045
17.6	4.20	13.27	309.76	0.057		22.2	4.71	14.90	492.84	0.045
17.7	4.21	13.30	313.29	0.056		22.3	4.72	14.93	497.29	0.045
17.8	4.22	13.34	316.84	0.056		22.4	4.73	14.97	501.76	0.045

(*cont.*)

TABLE I (*cont.*)

n	$\sqrt{n}$	$\sqrt{10n}$	n^2	$1/n$		n	$\sqrt{n}$	$\sqrt{10n}$	n^2	$1/n$
22.5	4.74	15.00	506.25	0.044		23.8	4.88	15.43	566.44	0.042
22.6	4.75	15.03	510.76	0.044		23.9	4.89	15.46	571.21	0.042
22.7	4.76	15.07	515.29	0.044		24.0	4.90	15.49	576.00	0.042
22.8	4.77	15.10	519.84	0.044		24.1	4.91	15.52	580.81	0.041
22.9	4.79	15.13	524.41	0.044		24.2	4.92	15.56	585.64	0.041
23.0	4.80	15.17	529.00	0.043		24.3	4.93	15.59	590.49	0.041
23.1	4.81	15.20	533.61	0.043		24.4	4.94	15.62	595.36	0.041
23.2	4.82	15.23	538.24	0.043		24.5	4.95	15.65	600.25	0.041
23.3	4.83	15.26	542.89	0.043		24.6	4.96	15.68	605.16	0.041
23.4	4.84	15.30	547.56	0.043		24.7	4.97	15.72	610.09	0.040
23.5	4.85	15.33	552.25	0.043		24.8	4.98	15.75	615.04	0.040
23.6	4.86	15.36	556.96	0.042		24.9	4.99	15.78	620.01	0.040
23.7	4.87	15.39	561.69	0.042		25.0	5.00	15.81	625.00	0.040

TABLE II. MANTISSAS FOR COMMON LOGARITHMS

N	0	1	2	3	4	5	6	7	8	9
1.0	0000	0043	0086	0128	0170	0212	0253	0294	0334	0374
1.1	0414	0453	0492	0531	0569	0607	0645	0682	0719	0755
1.2	0792	0828	0864	0899	0934	0969	1004	1038	1072	1106
1.3	1139	1173	1206	1239	1271	1303	1335	1367	1399	1430
1.4	1461	1492	1523	1553	1584	1614	1644	1673	1703	1732
1.5	1761	1790	1818	1847	1875	1903	1931	1959	1987	2014
1.6	2041	2068	2095	2122	2148	2175	2201	2227	2253	2279
1.7	2304	2330	2355	2380	2405	2430	2455	2480	2504	2529
1.8	2553	2577	2601	2625	2648	2672	2695	2718	2742	2765
1.9	2788	2810	2833	2856	2878	2900	2923	2945	2967	2989
2.0	3010	3032	3054	3075	3096	3118	3139	3160	3181	3201
2.1	3222	3243	3263	3284	3304	3324	3345	3365	3385	3404
2.2	3424	3444	3464	3483	3502	3522	3541	3560	3579	3598
2.3	3617	3636	3655	3674	3692	3711	3729	3747	3766	3784
2.4	3802	3820	3838	3856	3874	3892	3909	3927	3945	3962
2.5	3979	3997	4014	4031	4048	4065	4082	4099	4116	4133
2.6	4150	4166	4183	4200	4216	4232	4249	4265	4281	4298
2.7	4314	4330	4346	4362	4378	4393	4409	4425	4440	4456
2.8	4472	4487	4502	4518	4533	4548	4564	4579	4594	4609
2.9	4624	4639	4654	4669	4683	4698	4713	4728	4742	4757
3.0	4771	4786	4800	4814	4829	4843	4857	4871	4886	4900
3.1	4914	4928	4942	4955	4969	4983	4997	5011	5024	5038
3.2	5051	5065	5079	5092	5105	5119	5132	5145	5159	5172
3.3	5185	5198	5211	5224	5237	5250	5263	5276	5289	5302
3.4	5315	5328	5340	5353	5366	5378	5391	5403	5416	5428
3.5	5441	5453	5465	5478	5490	5502	5514	5527	5539	5551
3.6	5563	5575	5587	5599	5611	5623	5635	5647	5658	5670
3.7	5682	5694	5705	5717	5729	5740	5752	5763	5775	5786
3.8	5798	5809	5821	5832	5843	5855	5866	5877	5888	5899
3.9	5911	5922	5933	5944	5955	5966	5977	5988	5999	6010
4.0	6021	6031	6042	6053	6064	6075	6085	6096	6107	6117
4.1	6128	6138	6149	6160	6170	6180	6191	6201	6212	6222
4.2	6232	6243	6253	6263	6274	6284	6294	6304	6314	6325
4.3	6335	6345	6355	6365	6375	6385	6395	6405	6415	6425
4.4	6435	6444	6454	6464	6474	6484	6493	6503	6513	6522
4.5	6532	6542	6551	6561	6571	6580	6590	6599	6609	6618
4.6	6628	6637	6646	6656	6665	6675	6684	6693	6702	6712
4.7	6721	6730	6739	6749	6758	6767	6776	6785	6794	6803
4.8	6812	6821	6830	6839	6848	6857	6866	6875	6884	6893
4.9	6902	6911	6920	6928	6937	6946	6955	6964	6972	6981
5.0	6990	6998	7007	7016	7024	7033	7042	7050	7059	7067
5.1	7076	7084	7093	7101	7110	7118	7126	7135	7143	7152
5.2	7160	7168	7177	7185	7193	7202	7210	7218	7226	7235
5.3	7243	7251	7259	7267	7275	7284	7292	7300	7308	7316
5.4	7324	7332	7340	7348	7356	7364	7372	7380	7388	7396
5.5	7404	7412	7419	7427	7435	7443	7451	7459	7466	7474

(cont.)

TABLE II (*cont.*)

N	0	1	2	3	4	5	6	7	8	9
5.6	7482	7490	7497	7505	7513	7520	7528	7536	7543	7551
5.7	7559	7566	7574	7582	7589	7597	7604	7612	7619	7627
5.8	7634	7642	7649	7657	7664	7672	7679	7686	7694	7701
5.9	7709	7716	7723	7731	7738	7745	7752	7760	7767	7774
6.0	7782	7789	7796	7803	7810	7818	7825	7832	7839	7846
6.1	7853	7860	7868	7875	7882	7889	7896	7903	7910	7917
6.2	7924	7931	7938	7945	7952	7959	7966	7973	7980	7987
6.3	7993	8000	8007	8014	8021	8028	8035	8041	8048	8055
6.4	8062	8069	8075	8082	8089	8096	8102	8109	8116	8122
6.5	8129	8136	8142	8149	8156	8162	8169	8176	8182	8189
6.6	8195	8202	8209	8215	8222	8228	8235	8241	8248	8254
6.7	8261	8267	8274	8280	8287	8293	8299	8306	8312	8319
6.8	8325	8331	8338	8344	8351	8357	8363	8370	8376	8382
6.9	8388	8395	8401	8407	8414	8420	8426	8432	8439	8445
7.0	8451	8457	8463	8470	8476	8482	8488	8494	8500	8506
7.1	8513	8519	8525	8531	8537	8543	8549	8555	8561	8567
7.2	8573	8579	8585	8591	8597	8603	8609	8615	8621	8627
7.3	8633	8639	8645	8651	8657	8663	8669	8675	8681	8686
7.4	8692	8698	8704	8710	8716	8722	8727	8733	8739	8745
7.5	8751	8756	8762	8768	8774	8779	8785	8791	8797	8802
7.6	8808	8814	8820	8825	8831	8837	8842	8848	8854	8859
7.7	8865	8871	8876	8882	8887	8893	8899	8904	8910	8915
7.8	8921	8927	8932	8938	8943	8949	8954	8960	8965	8971
7.9	8976	8982	8987	8993	8998	9004	9009	9015	9020	9025
8.0	9031	9036	9042	9047	9053	9058	9063	9069	9074	9079
8.1	9085	9090	9096	9101	9106	9112	9117	9122	9128	9133
8.2	9138	9143	9149	9154	9159	9165	9170	9175	9180	9186
8.3	9191	9196	9201	9206	9212	9217	9222	9227	9232	9238
8.4	9243	9248	9253	9258	9263	9269	9274	9279	9284	9289
8.5	9294	9299	9304	9309	9315	9320	9325	9330	9335	9340
8.6	9345	9350	9355	9360	9365	9370	9375	9380	9385	9390
8.7	9395	9400	9405	9410	9415	9420	9425	9430	9435	9440
8.8	9445	9450	9455	9460	9465	9469	9474	9479	9484	9489
8.9	9494	9499	9504	9509	9513	9518	9523	9528	9533	9538
9.0	9542	9547	9552	9557	9562	9566	9571	9576	9581	9586
9.1	9590	9595	9600	9605	9609	9614	9619	9624	9628	9633
9.2	9638	9643	9647	9652	9657	9661	9666	9671	9675	9680
9.3	9685	9689	9694	9699	9703	9708	9713	9717	9722	9727
9.4	9731	9736	9741	9745	9750	9754	9759	9763	9768	9773
9.5	9777	9782	9786	9791	9795	9800	9805	9809	9814	9818
9.6	9823	9827	9832	9836	9841	9845	9850	9854	9859	9863
9.7	9868	9872	9877	9881	9886	9890	9894	9899	9903	9908
9.8	9912	9917	9921	9926	9930	9934	9939	9943	9948	9952
9.9	9956	9961	9965	9969	9974	9978	9983	9987	9991	9996

TABLE III. FREQUENCY AND RELATIVE CUMULATIVE FREQUENCY DISTRIBUTIONS
FOR THE STANDARD NORMAL POPULATION FOR THE ABSCISSAS FROM
$\lambda = -3.00$ TO $\lambda = +3.00$

Abscissas λ	Ordinates y	R.C.F.	Abscissas λ	Ordinates y	R.C.F.	Abscissas λ	Ordinates y	R.C.F.
−3.00	0.004	0.001	−1.14	0.208	0.127	−0.30	0.381	0.382
−2.90	0.006	0.002	−1.12	0.213	0.131	−0.28	0.384	0.390
−2.80	0.008	0.003	−1.10	0.218	0.136	−0.26	0.386	0.397
−2.70	0.010	0.003	−1.08	0.223	0.140	−0.24	0.388	0.405
−2.60	0.014	0.005	−1.06	0.227	0.145	−0.22	0.389	0.413
−2.50	0.018	0.006	−1.04	0.232	0.149	−0.20	0.391	0.421
−2.40	0.022	0.008	−1.02	0.237	0.154	−0.18	0.393	0.429
−2.30	0.028	0.011	−1.00	0.241	0.159	−0.16	0.394	0.436
−2.25	0.032	0.012	−0.98	0.247	0.164	−0.14	0.395	0.444
−2.20	0.035	0.014	−0.96	0.252	0.169	−0.12	0.396	0.452
−2.15	0.040	0.016	−0.94	0.256	0.174	−0.10	0.397	0.460
−2.10	0.044	0.018	−0.92	0.261	0.179	−0.08	0.398	0.468
−2.05	0.049	0.020	−0.90	0.266	0.184	−0.06	0.398	0.476
−2.00	0.054	0.023	−0.88	0.271	0.189	−0.04	0.399	0.484
−1.95	0.060	0.026	−0.86	0.276	0.195	−0.02	0.399	0.492
−1.90	0.066	0.029	−0.84	0.280	0.200	0.00	0.399	0.500
−1.85	0.072	0.032	−0.82	0.285	0.206	+0.02	0.399	0.508
−1.80	0.079	0.036	−0.80	0.290	0.212	0.04	0.399	0.516
−1.75	0.086	0.040	−0.78	0.294	0.218	0.06	0.398	0.524
−1.70	0.094	0.045	−0.76	0.299	0.224	0.08	0.398	0.532
−1.66	0.101	0.048	−0.74	0.303	0.230	0.10	0.397	0.540
−1.62	0.107	0.053	−0.72	0.308	0.236	0.12	0.396	0.548
−1.58	0.114	0.057	−0.70	0.312	0.242	0.14	0.395	0.556
−1.54	0.122	0.062	−0.68	0.317	0.248	0.16	0.394	0.564
−1.50	0.130	0.067	−0.66	0.321	0.255	0.18	0.393	0.571
−1.48	0.133	0.069	−0.64	0.325	0.261	0.20	0.391	0.579
−1.46	0.137	0.072	−0.62	0.329	0.268	0.22	0.389	0.587
−1.44	0.141	0.075	−0.60	0.333	0.274	0.24	0.388	0.595
−1.42	0.146	0.078	−0.58	0.337	0.281	0.26	0.386	0.603
−1.40	0.150	0.081	−0.56	0.341	0.288	0.28	0.384	0.610
−1.38	0.154	0.084	−0.54	0.345	0.295	0.30	0.381	0.618
−1.36	0.158	0.087	−0.52	0.348	0.302	0.32	0.379	0.626
−1.34	0.163	0.090	−0.50	0.352	0.309	0.34	0.377	0.633
−1.32	0.167	0.093	−0.48	0.356	0.316	0.36	0.374	0.641
−1.30	0.171	0.097	−0.46	0.359	0.323	0.38	0.371	0.648
−1.28	0.176	0.100	−0.44	0.362	0.330	0.40	0.368	0.655
−1.26	0.180	0.104	−0.42	0.365	0.337	0.42	0.365	0.663
−1.24	0.185	0.107	−0.40	0.368	0.345	0.44	0.362	0.670
−1.22	0.190	0.111	−0.38	0.371	0.352	0.46	0.359	0.677
−1.20	0.194	0.115	−0.36	0.374	0.359	0.48	0.356	0.684
−1.18	0.199	0.119	−0.34	0.377	0.367	0.50	0.352	0.691
−1.16	0.204	0.123	−0.32	0.379	0.374	0.52	0.348	0.698

(*cont.*)

TABLE III (*cont.*)

Abscissas λ	Ordinates y	R.C.F.	Abscissas λ	Ordinates y	R.C.F.	Abscissas λ	Ordinates y	R.C.F.
0.54	0.345	0.705	1.04	0.232	0.851	1.54	0.122	0.938
0.56	0.341	0.712	1.06	0.227	0.855	1.58	0.114	0.943
0.58	0.337	0.719	1.08	0.223	0.860	1.62	0.107	0.947
0.60	0.333	0.726	1.10	0.218	0.864	1.66	0.101	0.952
0.62	0.329	0.732	1.12	0.213	0.869	1.70	0.094	0.955
0.64	0.325	0.739	1.14	0.208	0.873	1.75	0.086	0.960
0.66	0.321	0.745	1.16	0.204	0.877	1.80	0.079	0.964
0.68	0.317	0.752	1.18	0.199	0.881	1.85	0.072	0.968
0.70	0.312	0.758	1.20	0.194	0.885	1.90	0.066	0.971
0.72	0.308	0.764	1.22	0.190	0.888	1.95	0.060	0.974
0.74	0.303	0.770	1.24	0.185	0.893	2.00	0.054	0.977
0.76	0.299	0.776	1.26	0.180	0.896	2.05	0.049	0.980
0.78	0.294	0.782	1.28	0.176	0.900	2.10	0.044	0.982
0.80	0.290	0.788	1.30	0.171	0.903	2.15	0.040	0.984
0.82	0.285	0.794	1.32	0.167	0.907	2.20	0.035	0.986
0.84	0.280	0.800	1.34	0.163	0.910	2.25	0.032	0.988
0.86	0.276	0.805	1.36	0.158	0.913	2.30	0.028	0.989
0.88	0.271	0.811	1.38	0.154	0.916	2.40	0.022	0.992
0.90	0.266	0.816	1.40	0.150	0.919	2.50	0.018	0.994
0.92	0.261	0.821	1.42	0.146	0.922	2.60	0.014	0.995
0.94	0.256	0.826	1.44	0.141	0.925	2.70	0.010	0.997
0.96	0.252	0.831	1.46	0.137	0.928	2.80	0.008	0.997
0.98	0.247	0.836	1.48	0.133	0.931	2.90	0.006	0.998
1.00	0.241	0.841	1.50	0.130	0.933	3.00	0.004	0.999
1.02	0.237	0.846						

TABLE IV.   90% CONFIDENCE INTERVALS ON THE BINOMIAL PARAMETER, p

X	n = 20 L	n = 20 U	n = 50 L	n = 50 U	X/n	n = 100 L	n = 100 U	n = 200 L	n = 200 U	n = 300 L	n = 300 U	n = 500 L	n = 500 U
0	0	14	0	6	0.00	0	3	0	1	0	1	0	0+
1	0	22	0	9	0.01	0	5	0	3	0	2	0	2
2	2	28	1	12	0.02	0	6	1	5	1	4	1	3−
3	4	34	2	15	0.03	1	8	1	6	2	5	2	5
4	7	40	3	17	0.04	1	9	2	7	2	6	3	6
5	10	46	4	20	0.05	2	10	3	8	3	8	3	7
6	14	51	5	22	0.06	3	12	4	10	4	9	4	8
7	18	56	7	25	0.07	3	13	4	11	5	10	5	9
8	22	61	8	27	0.08	4	14	5	12	6	11	6	10
9	26	65	11	29	0.09	5	15	6	13	6	12	7	11
10	30	70	11	32	0.10	6	16	7	14	7	13	8	12
11	35	74	13	34	0.11	6	18	8	15	8	14	9	14
12	39	78	14	36	0.12	7	19	8	16	9	16	10	15
13	44	82	16	38	0.13	8	20	9	18	10	17	11	16
14	49	86	18	40	0.14	9	21	10	19	11	18	12	17
15	54	90	20	42	0.15	9	22	11	20	12	19	13	18
16	60	93	21	44	0.16	10	23	12	21	13	20	13	19
17	66	96	23	47	0.17	11	24	13	22	14	21	14	20
18	72	98	25	49	0.18	12	26	13	23	14	22	15	21
19	78	100	26	51	0.19	13	27	14	24	15	23	16	22
20	86	100	28	53	0.20	14	28	15	25	16	24	17	23
21			30	55	0.21	14	29	16	26	17	25	18	24
22			32	57	0.22	15	30	17	27	18	27	19	25
23			34	59	0.23	16	31	18	29	19	27	20	26
24			36	60	0.24	17	32	19	29	20	29	21	27
25			38	62	0.25	18	33	20	31	21	30	22	28
26			40	64	0.26	19	34	21	32	22	31	23	29
27			41	66	0.27	20	35	22	33	23	32	24	30
28			43	68	0.28	21	36	23	34	24	33	25	31
29			45	70	0.29	22	37	24	35	25	34	26	32
30			47	72	0.30	22	38	25	36	26	35	27	33
31			49	74	0.31	23	40	25	37	27	36	28	34
32			51	75	0.32	24	41	26	38	27	37	29	36
33			53	77	0.33	25	42	27	39	28	38	30	37
34			56	79	0.34	26	43	28	40	29	39	31	38
35			58	80	0.35	27	44	29	41	30	40	32	39
36			60	82	0.36	28	45	30	42	31	41	33	40
37			62	84	0.37	29	46	31	43	32	42	34	41
38			64	86	0.38	30	47	32	44	33	43	34	42
39			66	87	0.39	31	48	33	45	34	44	36	43
40			68	89	0.40	32	49	34	46	35	45	37	44
41			71	90	0.41	33	50	35	47	36	46	38	45
42			73	92	0.42	34	51	36	48	37	47	39	46
43			75	93	0.43	35	52	37	49	38	48	40	47
44			78	95	0.44	36	53	38	50	39	49	41	48
45			80	96	0.45	36	54	39	51	40	50	41	49
46			83	97	0.46	37	55	40	52	41	51	42	50
47			85	98	0.47	38	56	41	53	42	52	43	51
48			88	99	0.48	39	57	42	54	43	53	44	52
49			91	100	0.49	40	58	43	55	44	54	45	53
50			94	100	0.50	41	59	44	56	45	55	46	54

Computed by means of Tables of Binomial Probability Distribution published by the Department of Commerce, National Bureau of Standards, Applied Mathematics Series, 6, 1950.

TABLE V.   95% CONFIDENCE INTERVALS ON THE BINOMIAL PARAMETER, p

X	n = 20		n = 50		X/n	n = 100		n = 200		n = 300		n = 500	
	L	U	L	U		L	U	L	U	L	U	L	U
0	0	17	0	7	0.00	0	4	0	2	0	2	0	0+
1	0	25	0	11	0.01	0	5	0	4	0	3	0	2
2	1	32	1	14	0.02	0	7	1	5	1	4	1	4
3	3	38	1	17	0.03	1	9	1	6	1	6	2	5
4	6	44	2	19	0.04	1	10	2	8	2	7	3	6
5	9	49	3	22	0.05	2	11	2	9	3	8	3	7
6	12	54	5	24	0.06	2	13	3	10	4	9	4	9
7	15	59	6	27	0.07	3	14	4	12	4	11	5	10
8	19	64	7	29	0.08	4	15	5	13	5	12	6	11
9	23	68	9	31	0.09	4	16	6	14	6	13	7	12
10	27	73	10	34	0.10	5	18	6	15	7	14	8	13
11	32	77	11	36	0.11	6	19	7	17	8	15	8	14
12	36	81	13	38	0.12	6	20	8	18	9	16	9	15
13	41	85	15	40	0.13	7	21	9	19	9	17	10	16
14	46	88	16	43	0.14	8	22	10	20	10	19	11	17
15	51	91	18	45	0.15	9	24	11	21	11	20	12	18
16	56	94	19	47	0.16	9	25	11	23	12	21	13	19
17	62	97	21	49	0.17	10	26	12	24	13	22	14	21
18	68	99	23	51	0.18	11	27	13	25	14	23	15	22
19	75	100	25	53	0.19	12	28	14	26	15	24	16	23
20	83	100	26	55	0.20	13	29	15	27	16	25	17	24
21			28	57	0.21	14	30	16	28	17	26	18	25
22			30	59	0.22	14	31	17	29	17	27	19	26
23			32	61	0.23	15	33	18	30	18	28	19	27
24			33	63	0.24	16	34	18	31	19	29	20	28
25			35	65	0.25	17	35	19	32	20	30	21	29
26			37	67	0.26	18	36	20	33	21	31	22	30
27			39	68	0.27	18	37	21	34	22	32	23	31
28			41	70	0.28	19	38	22	35	23	34	24	32
29			43	72	0.29	20	39	23	36	24	35	25	33
30			45	74	0.30	21	40	24	37	25	36	26	34
31			47	75	0.31	22	41	25	38	26	37	27	35
32			49	77	0.32	23	42	26	39	27	38	28	36
33			51	79	0.33	24	43	27	40	28	39	29	37
34			53	81	0.34	25	44	28	41	29	40	30	38
35			55	82	0.35	26	45	29	42	30	41	31	39
36			57	84	0.36	26	46	30	43	30	42	32	40
37			60	85	0.37	27	47	31	44	31	43	33	41
38			62	87	0.38	28	48	32	45	32	44	34	42
39			64	89	0.39	29	49	33	46	33	45	35	43
40			66	90	0.40	30	50	34	47	34	46	36	44
41			69	91	0.41	31	51	35	48	35	47	37	45
42			71	93	0.42	32	52	36	49	36	48	38	46
43			73	94	0.43	33	53	37	50	37	49	39	47
44			76	95	0.44	34	54	38	51	38	50	40	48
45			78	97	0.45	35	55	39	52	39	51	41	49
46			81	99	0.46	36	57	40	53	40	52	42	50
47			83	99	0.47	36	58	41	54	41	53	43	51
48			86	100	0.48	37	59	42	55	42	54	44	52
49			89	100	0.49	38	60	43	56	43	55	45	53
50			93	100	0.50	39	61	43	57	44	56	46	54

Computed as indicated for Table IV.

TABLE VI. 99% CONFIDENCE INTERVALS ON THE BINOMIAL PARAMETER, p

X	n = 20 L	n = 20 U	n = 50 L	n = 50 U	X/n	n = 100 L	n = 100 U	n = 200 L	n = 200 U	n = 300 L	n = 300 U	n = 500 L	n = 500 U
0	0	23	0	10	0.00	0	5	0	3	0	2	0	1
1	0	32	0	14	0.01	0	7	0	5	0	4	0	3
2	1	39	0	17	0.02	0	9	1	6	1	5	1	4
3	2	45	1	20	0.03	0	10	1	8	1	7	1	6
4	4	51	1	23	0.04	1	12	2	9	2	8	2	7
5	6	56	2	26	0.05	1	13	3	10	2	9	3	8
6	8	61	3	28	0.06	2	15	3	12	3	11	4	9
7	11	66	4	31	0.07	2	16	4	13	3	12	4	11
8	15	70	5	33	0.08	3	17	5	14	4	13	5	12
9	18	74	7	36	0.09	3	19	5	15	5	14	6	13
10	22	78	8	38	0.10	4	20	6	17	6	15	7	14
11	26	82	9	40	0.11	4	21	7	18	7	16	8	15
12	30	85	10	43	0.12	5	23	8	19	7	18	9	16
13	34	89	12	45	0.13	6	24	9	20	8	19	9	17
14	39	92	13	47	0.14	7	25	9	21	9	20	10	19
15	44	94	15	49	0.15	7	26	10	22	10	21	11	20
16	49	96	16	51	0.16	8	27	11	24	11	22	12	21
17	55	98	18	53	0.17	9	29	12	25	12	23	13	22
18	61	99	19	55	0.18	9	30	13	26	13	25	14	23
19	68	100	21	57	0.19	10	31	13	27	13	26	15	24
20	77	100	23	59	0.20	11	32	14	28	14	27	16	25
21			24	61	0.21	12	33	15	29	15	28	17	26
22			26	63	0.22	12	34	16	30	16	29	17	27
23			28	65	0.23	13	35	17	31	17	30	18	28
24			30	67	0.24	14	36	18	32	18	31	19	29
25			32	68	0.25	15	37	19	33	19	32	20	30
26			33	70	0.26	16	39	20	35	20	33	21	31
27			35	72	0.27	17	40	20	36	21	34	22	32
28			37	74	0.28	17	41	21	37	21	35	23	33
29			39	76	0.29	18	42	22	38	22	36	24	35
30			41	77	0.30	19	43	23	39	23	37	25	36
31			43	79	0.31	20	44	24	40	24	38	26	37
32			45	81	0.32	21	45	25	41	25	39	27	38
33			46	82	0.33	22	46	26	42	26	41	28	39
34			48	84	0.34	22	47	27	43	27	42	29	40
35			50	85	0.35	23	48	28	44	28	43	30	41
36			53	87	0.36	24	49	29	45	29	44	31	42
37			55	88	0.37	25	50	30	46	30	45	32	43
38			57	90	0.38	26	51	31	47	31	46	33	44
39			59	91	0.39	27	52	32	48	32	47	34	45
40			61	92	0.40	28	53	33	49	33	48	34	46
41			64	93	0.41	28	54	33	50	34	49	35	47
42			66	95	0.42	29	55	34	51	35	50	36	48
43			69	96	0.43	30	56	35	52	36	51	37	49
44			71	97	0.44	31	57	36	53	36	52	38	50
45			74	98	0.45	32	58	37	54	37	53	39	51
46			76	99	0.46	33	59	38	55	38	54	40	52
47			80	99	0.47	34	60	39	56	39	55	41	53
48			83	100	0.48	35	61	40	57	40	56	42	54
49			86	100	0.49	36	62	41	58	41	57	43	55
50			90	100	0.50	37	63	41	59	42	58	44	56

Computed as indicated for Table IV.

TABLE VII. RELATIVE CUMULATIVE FREQUENCY DISTRIBUTION OF t, SHOWING PROPORTIONS OF ALL SAMPLING t_i WITH SAME DEGREES OF FREEDOM WHICH ARE LESS THAN t SHOWN IN COLUMN 1 ON THE LEFT

t	Degrees of freedom											
	8	9	10	11	12	14	16	18	20	22	26	30
−5.0	0.001	0.000										
−4.6	0.001	0.001	0.000	0.000	0.000							
−4.2	0.002	0.001	0.001	0.001	0.001	0.000	0.000	0.000	0.000			
−3.8	0.003	0.002	0.002	0.001	0.001	0.001	0.001	0.001	0.001	0.000	0.000	0.000
−3.4	0.005	0.004	0.003	0.003	0.003	0.002	0.002	0.002	0.001	0.001	0.001	0.001
−3.0	0.009	0.007	0.007	0.006	0.006	0.005	0.004	0.004	0.004	0.003	0.003	0.003
−2.8	0.012	0.010	0.009	0.009	0.008	0.007	0.006	0.006	0.006	0.005	0.005	0.004
−2.6	0.016	0.014	0.013	0.012	0.012	0.010	0.010	0.009	0.009	0.008	0.008	0.007
−2.4	0.022	0.020	0.019	0.018	0.017	0.015	0.014	0.014	0.013	0.013	0.012	0.011
−2.2	0.030	0.028	0.026	0.025	0.024	0.023	0.021	0.021	0.020	0.019	0.019	0.018
−2.0	0.040	0.038	0.037	0.035	0.034	0.033	0.031	0.030	0.030	0.029	0.028	0.027
−1.8	0.055	0.053	0.051	0.050	0.049	0.047	0.045	0.044	0.043	0.043	0.042	0.041
−1.6	0.074	0.072	0.070	0.069	0.068	0.066	0.065	0.064	0.063	0.062	0.061	0.060
−1.4	0.100	0.098	0.096	0.095	0.093	0.092	0.090	0.089	0.088	0.088	0.087	0.086
−1.2	0.132	0.130	0.129	0.128	0.127	0.125	0.124	0.123	0.122	0.121	0.121	0.120
−1.0	0.173	0.172	0.170	0.169	0.169	0.167	0.166	0.165	0.165	0.164	0.163	0.163
−0.8	0.223	0.222	0.221	0.220	0.220	0.219	0.218	0.217	0.217	0.216	0.216	0.215
−0.6	0.283	0.282	0.281	0.280	0.280	0.279	0.278	0.278	0.278	0.277	0.277	0.277
−0.4	0.350	0.349	0.349	0.348	0.348	0.348	0.347	0.347	0.347	0.347	0.346	0.346
−0.2	0.423	0.423	0.423	0.423	0.422	0.422	0.422	0.422	0.422	0.422	0.421	0.421
0	0.500	0.500	0.500	0.500	0.500	0.500	0.500	0.500	0.500	0.500	0.500	0.500
0.2	0.577	0.577	0.577	0.577	0.578	0.578	0.578	0.578	0.578	0.578	0.579	0.579
0.4	0.650	0.651	0.651	0.652	0.652	0.652	0.653	0.653	0.653	0.653	0.654	0.654
0.6	0.717	0.718	0.719	0.720	0.720	0.721	0.722	0.722	0.722	0.723	0.723	0.723
0.8	0.777	0.778	0.779	0.780	0.780	0.781	0.782	0.783	0.783	0.784	0.784	0.785
1.0	0.827	0.828	0.830	0.831	0.831	0.833	0.834	0.835	0.835	0.836	0.837	0.837
1.2	0.868	0.870	0.871	0.872	0.873	0.875	0.876	0.877	0.878	0.879	0.879	0.880
1.4	0.900	0.902	0.904	0.905	0.907	0.908	0.910	0.911	0.912	0.912	0.913	0.914
1.6	0.926	0.928	0.930	0.931	0.932	0.934	0.935	0.936	0.937	0.938	0.939	0.940
1.8	0.945	0.947	0.949	0.950	0.951	0.953	0.955	0.956	0.957	0.957	0.958	0.959
2.0	0.960	0.962	0.963	0.965	0.966	0.967	0.969	0.970	0.970	0.971	0.972	0.973
2.2	0.970	0.972	0.974	0.975	0.976	0.977	0.979	0.979	0.980	0.981	0.981	0.982
2.4	0.978	0.980	0.981	0.982	0.983	0.985	0.986	0.986	0.987	0.987	0.988	0.989
2.6	0.984	0.986	0.987	0.988	0.988	0.990	0.990	0.991	0.991	0.992	0.992	0.993
2.8	0.988	0.990	0.991	0.991	0.992	0.993	0.994	0.994	0.994	0.995	0.995	0.996
3.0	0.991	0.993	0.993	0.994	0.994	0.995	0.996	0.996	0.996	0.997	0.997	0.997
3.4	0.995	0.996	0.997	0.997	0.997	0.998	0.998	0.998	0.999	0.999	0.999	0.999
3.8	0.997	0.998	0.998	0.999	0.999	0.999	0.999	0.999	0.999	1.000	1.000	1.000
4.2	0.998	0.999	0.999	0.999	0.999	1.000	1.000	1.000	1.000			
4.6	0.999	0.999	1.000	1.000	1.000							
5.0	0.999	1.000										

TABLE VII-A. SOME FREQUENTLY USED t'S CORRESPONDING TO PREASSIGNED PROBABILITIES OF OCCURRENCE DURING RANDOM SAMPLING

$P(t > t_0)$	Degrees of freedom												
	8	9	10	11	12	14	16	18	20	22	26	30	120
0.100	1.86	1.83	1.81	1.80	1.78	1.76	1.75	1.73	1.72	1.72	1.71	1.70	1.66
0.050	2.31	2.26	2.23	2.20	2.18	2.14	2.12	2.10	2.09	2.07	2.06	2.04	1.98
0.010	3.36	3.25	3.17	3.11	3.06	2.98	2.92	2.88	2.84	2.82	2.78	2.75	2.62
0.001	5.04	4.78	4.59	4.44	4.32	4.14	4.02	3.92	3.85	3.79	3.71	3.65	3.37

TABLE VIII. BINOMIAL COEFFICIENTS, $\binom{n}{x} = n!/x!(n-x)!$

x	5	6	7	8	9	10	11	12	13	14	15	16	17	18	19	20
0	1	1	1	1	1	1	1	1	1	1	1	1	1	1	1	1
1	5	6	7	8	9	10	11	12	13	14	15	16	17	18	19	20
2	10	15	21	28	36	45	55	66	78	91	105	120	136	153	171	190
3	10	20	35	56	84	120	165	220	286	364	455	560	680	816	969	1140
4	5	15	35	70	126	210	330	495	715	1001	1365	1820	2380	3060	3876	4845
5	1	6	21	56	126	252	462	792	1287	2002	3003	4368	6188	8568	11628	15504
6		1	7	28	84	210	462	924	1716	3003	5005	8008	12376	18564	27132	38760
7		1	1	8	36	120	330	792	1716	3432	6435	11440	19448	31824	50388	77520
8			1	1	9	45	165	495	1287	3003	6435	12870	24310	43758	75582	125970
9				1	1	10	55	220	715	2002	5005	11440	24310	48620	92378	167960
10					1	1	11	66	286	1001	3003	8008	19448	43758	92378	184756
11						1	1	12	78	364	1365	4368	12376	31824	75582	167960
12							1	1	13	91	455	1820	6188	18564	50388	125970
13								1	1	14	105	560	2380	8568	27132	77520
14									1	1	15	120	680	3060	11628	38760
15										1	1	16	136	816	3876	15504
16											1	1	17	153	969	4845
17												1	1	18	171	1140
18													1	1	19	190
19														1	1	20
20															1	1

TABLE IX.   PERCENTAGE POINTS OF THE DISTRIBUTION OF $G = (\bar{x} - \mu)/R$
(R = RANGE IN SAMPLE, n = SAMPLE SIZE)

	α			
n	0.10	0.05	0.02	0.01
5	0.388	0.507	0.685	0.843
6	0.312	0.399	0.523	0.628
7	0.263	0.333	0.429	0.507
8	0.230	0.288	0.366	0.429
9	0.205	0.255	0.322	0.374
10	0.186	0.230	0.288	0.333
11	0.170	0.210	0.262	0.302
12	0.158	0.194	0.241	0.277
13	0.147	0.181	0.224	0.256
14	0.138	0.170	0.209	0.239
15	0.131	0.160	0.197	0.224
16	0.124	0.151	0.186	0.212
17	0.118	0.144	0.177	0.201
18	0.113	0.137	0.168	0.191
19	0.108	0.131	0.161	0.182
20	0.104	0.126	0.154	0.175

From E. Lord, "The use of the range in place of the standard deviation in the t test," *Biometrika* 34: 66, 1947. Reproduced with the permission of the author and the Biometrika trustees.

TABLE X.   PERCENTAGE POINTS OF THE DISTRIBUTION OF $G = \dfrac{\bar{x}_1 - \bar{x}_2}{(R_1 + R_2)/2}$
(R_i = RANGE IN iTH SAMPLE, WITH i = 1,2; n = COMMON SAMPLE SIZE)

	α			
n	0.10	0.05	0.02	0.01
5	0.493	0.613	0.772	0.896
6	0.405	0.499	0.621	0.714
7	0.347	0.426	0.525	0.600
8	0.306	0.373	0.459	0.521
9	0.275	0.334	0.409	0.464
10	0.250	0.304	0.371	0.419
11	0.233	0.280	0.340	0.384
12	0.214	0.260	0.315	0.355
13	0.201	0.243	0.294	0.331
14	0.189	0.228	0.276	0.311
15	0.179	0.216	0.261	0.293
16	0.170	0.205	0.247	0.278
17	0.162	0.195	0.236	0.264
18	0.155	0.187	0.225	0.252
19	0.149	0.179	0.216	0.242
20	0.143	0.172	0.207	0.232

From E. Lord, "The use of the range in place of the standard deviation in the t test," *Biometrika* 34: 67, 1947. Reproduced with the permission of the author and the Biometrika trustees.

TABLE XI. RELATIVE CUMULATIVE DISTRIBUTION OF χ^2_ν, THE CHI-SQUARE DISTRIBUTION WITH ν DEGREES OF FREEDOM (THE NUMBER IN THIS TABLE IS THE χ^2_0 SUCH THAT FOR THE INDICATED NUMBER, ν, OF DF, $\Pr\{\text{RANDOM } \chi^2_\nu > \chi^2_0\} = $ PROBABILITY AT TOP OF COLUMN)

ν						Probability					
	0.99	0.95	0.90	0.75	0.50	0.25	0.11	0.10	0.06	0.05	0.01
1	0.000	0.000	0.016	0.102	0.455	1.323	2.56	2.706	3.54	3.841	6.635⁻
2	0.020	0.103	0.211	0.575	1.386	2.773	4.42	4.605	5.63	5.991	9.210
3	0.115	0.352	0.584	1.213	2.366	4.108	6.04	6.251	7.40	7.815	11.345
4	0.297	0.711	1.064	1.923	3.357	5.385	7.53	7.779	9.04	9.488	13.277
5	0.554	1.145	1.610	2.675	4.351	6.626	8.98	9.236	10.59	11.070	15.086
6	0.872	1.635	2.204	3.455	5.348	7.841	10.38	10.645	12.10	12.592	16.812
7	1.239	2.167	2.833	4.255	6.346	9.037	11.74	12.017	13.55	14.067	18.475
8	1.646	2.733	3.490	5.071	7.344	10.219	13.06	13.362	14.95	15.507	20.090
9	2.088	3.325	4.168	5.899	8.343	11.389	14.38	14.684	16.35	16.919	21.666
10	2.568	3.940	4.865	6.737	9.342	12.549	15.67	15.987	17.72	18.307	23.209
12	3.571	5.226	6.304	8.438	11.340	14.845	18.20	18.549	20.21	21.026	26.217
14	4.660	6.571	7.790	10.165	13.339	17.117	20.71	21.064	23.02	23.685	29.141
16	5.812	7.962	9.312	11.912	15.338	19.369	23.17	23.542	25.62	26.296	32.000
18	7.015	9.390	10.865	13.675	17.338	21.605	25.60	25.989	28.14	28.869	34.805
20	8.260	10.851	12.443	15.452	19.337	23.828	27.96	28.412	30.67	31.410	37.566
25	11.524	14.611	16.473	19.939	24.337	29.338	33.61	34.382	36.86	37.652	44.314
30	14.954	18.493	20.599	24.478	29.336	34.800	39.76	40.256	43.00	43.773	50.892
50	29.707	34.764	37.689	42.942	49.335	56.334	62.58	63.167	66.44	67.505⁻	76.154

Interpolated linearly from *Biometrika Tables for Statisticians*, Vol. 1, Cambridge Univ. Press, London, 1958, Tables 7 and 8, with the permission of the authors and the Biometrika Trustees.

TABLE XII. RELATIVE CUMULATIVE DISTRIBUTION OF $F(\nu_1, \nu_2)$ (THE NUMBER GIVEN IN THE TABLE FOR A PARTICULAR COMBINATION OF DEGREES OF FREEDOM, (ν_1, ν_2), IS THE F_0 SUCH THAT $\Pr\{\text{RANDOM } F(\nu_1, \nu_2) > F_0(\nu_1, \nu_2)\}$ = THE NUMBER IN THE LEFT-HAND COLUMN UNDER P)

ν_2	P^a	The number of degrees of freedom for the numerator, ν_1																
		1	2	3	4	5	6	7	8	9	10	12	15	20	30	40	60	120
6	0.500	0.51	0.78	0.89	0.94	0.98	1.00	1.02	1.03	1.04	1.05	1.06	1.07	1.08	1.10	1.10	1.11	1.12
	0.250	1.62	1.76	1.78	1.79	1.79	1.78	1.78	1.78	1.76	1.77	1.77	1.76	1.76	1.75	1.75	1.74	1.74
	0.200	2.07	2.13	2.11	2.09	2.08	2.06		2.04			2.02						
	0.100	3.78	3.46	3.29	3.18	3.11	3.05	3.01	2.98	2.96	2.94	2.90	2.87	2.84	2.80	2.78	2.76	2.74
	0.050	5.99	5.14	4.76	4.53	4.39	4.28	4.21	4.15	4.10	4.06	4.00	3.94	3.87	3.81	3.77	3.74	3.70
	0.025	8.81	7.26	6.60	6.23	5.99	5.82	5.70	5.60	5.52	5.46	5.37	5.27	5.17	5.06	5.01	4.96	4.90
	0.010	13.74	10.92	9.78	9.15	8.75	8.47	8.26	8.10	7.98	7.87	7.72	7.56	7.40	7.23	7.14	7.06	6.97
	0.005	18.64	14.54	12.92	12.03	11.46	11.07	10.79	10.57	10.39	10.25	10.03	9.81	9.59	9.36	9.24	9.12	9.00
7	0.500	0.51	0.77	0.87	0.93	0.96	0.98	1.00	1.01	1.02	1.03	1.04	1.05	1.07	1.08	1.08	1.09	1.10
	0.250	1.57	1.70	1.72	1.72	1.71	1.71	1.70	1.70	1.69	1.69	1.68	1.68	1.67	1.66	1.66	1.65	1.65
	0.200	2.00	2.04	2.02	1.99	1.97	1.96		1.93			1.91						
	0.100	3.59	3.26	3.07	2.96	2.88	2.83	2.78	2.75	2.72	2.70	2.67	2.63	2.59	2.56	2.54	2.51	2.49
	0.050	5.59	4.74	4.35	4.12	3.97	3.87	3.79	3.73	3.68	3.64	3.57	3.51	3.44	3.38	3.34	3.30	3.27
	0.025	8.07	6.54	5.89	5.52	5.29	5.12	4.99	4.90	4.82	4.76	4.67	4.57	4.47	4.36	4.31	4.25	4.20
	0.010	12.25	9.55	8.45	7.85	7.46	7.19	6.99	6.84	6.72	6.62	6.47	6.31	6.16	5.99	5.91	5.82	5.74
	0.005	16.24	12.40	10.88	10.05	9.52	9.16	8.89	8.68	8.51	8.38	8.18	7.97	7.75	7.53	7.42	7.31	7.19
8	0.500	0.50	0.76	0.86	0.91	0.95	0.97	0.99	1.00	1.01	1.02	1.03	1.04	1.05	1.07	1.07	1.08	1.08
	0.250	1.54	1.66	1.67	1.66	1.66	1.65	1.64	1.64	1.64	1.63	1.62	1.62	1.61	1.60	1.59	1.59	1.58
	0.200	1.95	1.98	1.95	1.92	1.90	1.88		1.86			1.83						
	0.100	3.46	3.11	2.92	2.81	2.73	2.67	2.62	2.59	2.56	2.54	2.50	2.46	2.42	2.38	2.36	2.34	2.32
	0.050	5.32	4.46	4.07	3.84	3.69	3.58	3.50	3.44	3.39	3.35	3.28	3.22	3.15	3.08	3.04	3.01	2.97
	0.025	7.57	6.06	5.42	5.05	4.82	4.65	4.53	4.43	4.36	4.30	4.20	4.10	4.00	3.89	3.84	3.78	3.73
	0.010	11.26	8.65	7.59	7.01	6.63	6.37	6.18	6.03	5.91	5.81	5.67	5.52	5.36	5.20	5.12	5.03	4.95
	0.005	14.69	11.04	9.60	8.81	8.30	7.95	7.69	7.50	7.34	7.21	7.01	6.81	6.61	6.40	6.29	6.18	6.06

df	P																	
9	0.500	1.07	1.07	1.06	1.05	1.04	1.03	1.02	1.01	1.00	0.99	0.98	0.96	0.94	0.91	0.85	0.75	0.49
	0.250	1.53	1.54	1.54	1.55	1.56	1.57	1.58	1.59	1.59	1.60	1.60	1.61	1.62	1.63	1.63	1.62	1.51
	0.200							1.76			1.80		1.83	1.85	1.87	1.90	1.94	1.91
	0.100	2.18	2.21	2.23	2.25	2.30	2.34	2.38	2.42	2.44	2.47	2.51	2.55	2.61	2.69	2.81	3.01	3.36
	0.050	2.75	2.79	2.83	2.86	2.94	3.01	3.07	3.14	3.18	3.23	3.29	3.37	3.48	3.63	3.86	4.26	5.12
	0.025	3.39	3.45	3.51	3.56	3.67	3.77	3.87	3.96	4.03	4.10	4.20	4.32	4.48	4.72	5.08	5.71	7.21
	0.010	4.40	4.48	4.57	4.65	4.81	4.96	5.11	5.26	5.35	5.47	5.61	5.80	6.06	6.42	6.99	8.02	10.56
	0.005	5.30	5.41	5.52	5.62	5.83	6.03	6.23	6.42	6.54	6.69	6.88	7.13	7.47	7.96	8.72	10.11	13.61
10	0.500	1.06	1.06	1.05	1.05	1.03	1.02	1.01	1.00	0.99	0.98	0.97	0.95	0.93	0.90	0.85	0.74	0.49
	0.250	1.49	1.50	1.51	1.51	1.52	1.53	1.54	1.55	1.56	1.56	1.57	1.58	1.59	1.59	1.60	1.60	1.49
	0.200							1.72			1.75		1.78	1.80	1.83	1.86	1.90	1.88
	0.100	2.08	2.11	2.13	2.16	2.20	2.24	2.28	2.32	2.35	2.38	2.41	2.46	2.52	2.61	2.73	2.92	3.28
	0.050	2.58	2.62	2.66	2.70	2.77	2.84	2.91	2.98	3.02	3.07	3.14	3.22	3.33	3.48	3.71	4.10	4.96
	0.025	3.14	3.20	3.26	3.31	3.42	3.52	3.62	3.72	3.78	3.85	3.95	4.07	4.24	4.47	4.83	5.46	6.94
	0.010	4.00	4.08	4.17	4.25	4.41	4.56	4.71	4.85	4.94	5.06	5.20	5.39	5.64	5.99	6.55	7.56	10.04
	0.005	4.75	4.86	4.97	5.07	5.27	5.47	5.66	5.85	5.97	6.12	6.30	6.54	6.87	7.34	8.08	9.43	10.83
11	0.500	1.06	1.05	1.05	1.04	1.03	1.02	1.01	0.99	0.99	0.98	0.97	0.95	0.93	0.89	0.84	0.74	0.49
	0.250	1.46	1.47	1.47	1.48	1.49	1.50	1.51	1.52	1.53	1.53	1.54	1.55	1.56	1.57	1.58	1.58	1.47
	0.200							1.68			1.72		1.75	1.77	1.80	1.83	1.87	1.86
	0.100	2.00	2.03	2.05	2.08	2.12	2.17	2.21	2.25	2.27	2.30	2.34	2.39	2.45	2.54	2.66	2.86	3.23
	0.050	2.45	2.49	2.53	2.57	2.65	2.72	2.79	2.85	2.90	2.95	3.01	3.09	3.20	3.36	3.59	3.98	4.84
	0.025	2.94	3.00	3.06	3.12	3.23	3.33	3.43	3.53	3.59	3.66	3.76	3.88	4.04	4.28	4.63	5.26	6.72
	0.010	3.69	3.78	3.86	3.94	4.10	4.25	4.40	4.54	4.63	4.74	4.89	5.07	5.32	5.67	6.22	7.21	9.65
	0.005	4.34	4.44	4.55	4.65	4.86	5.05	5.24	5.42	5.54	5.68	5.86	6.10	6.42	6.88	7.60	8.91	12.23
12	0.500	1.05	1.05	1.04	1.03	1.02	1.01	1.00	0.99	0.98	0.97	0.96	0.94	0.92	0.89	0.84	0.73	0.48
	0.250	1.43	1.44	1.45	1.45	1.47	1.48	1.49	1.50	1.51	1.51	1.52	1.53	1.54	1.55	1.56	1.56	1.46
	0.200							1.65			1.69		1.72	1.74	1.77	1.80	1.85	1.84
	0.100	1.93	1.96	1.99	2.01	2.06	2.10	2.15	2.19	2.21	2.24	2.28	2.33	2.39	2.48	2.61	2.81	3.18
	0.050	2.34	2.38	2.43	2.47	2.54	2.62	2.69	2.75	2.80	2.85	2.91	3.00	3.11	3.26	3.49	3.89	4.75
	0.025	2.79	2.85	2.91	2.96	3.07	3.18	3.28	3.37	3.44	3.51	3.61	3.73	3.89	4.12	4.47	5.10	6.55
	0.010	3.45	3.54	3.62	3.70	3.86	4.01	4.16	4.30	4.39	4.50	4.64	4.82	5.06	5.41	5.95	6.93	9.33
	0.005	4.01	4.12	4.23	4.33	4.53	4.72	4.91	5.09	5.20	5.35	5.52	5.76	6.07	6.52	7.23	8.51	11.75

(cont.)

TABLE XII (cont.)

The number of degrees of freedom for the numerator, v_1

v_2	P	1	2	3	4	5	6	7	8	9	10	12	15	20	30	40	60	120
13	0.500	0.48	0.73	0.83	0.88	0.92	0.94	0.96	0.97	0.98	0.98	1.00	1.01	1.02	1.03	1.04	1.04	1.05
	0.250	1.45	1.55	1.55	1.53	1.52	1.51	1.50	1.49	1.49	1.48	1.47	1.46	1.45	1.43	1.42	1.42	1.41
	0.200	1.82	1.83	1.78	1.75	1.72	1.69		1.66			1.62						
	0.100	3.14	2.76	2.56	2.43	2.35	2.28	2.23	2.20	2.16	2.14	2.10	2.05	2.01	1.96	1.93	1.90	1.88
	0.050	4.67	3.81	3.41	3.18	3.03	2.92	2.83	2.77	2.71	2.67	2.60	2.53	2.46	2.38	2.34	2.30	2.25
	0.025	6.41	4.97	4.35	4.00	3.77	3.60	3.48	3.39	3.31	3.25	3.15	3.05	2.95	2.84	2.78	2.72	2.66
	0.010	9.07	6.70	5.74	5.21	4.86	4.62	4.44	4.30	4.19	4.10	3.96	3.82	3.66	3.51	3.43	3.34	3.25
	0.005	11.37	8.19	6.93	6.23	5.79	5.48	5.25	5.08	4.94	4.82	4.64	4.46	4.27	4.07	3.97	3.87	3.76
14	0.500	0.48	0.73	0.83	0.88	0.91	0.94	0.95	0.96	0.97	0.98	0.99	1.00	1.01	1.03	1.03	1.04	1.04
	0.250	1.44	1.53	1.53	1.52	1.51	1.50	1.49	1.48	1.47	1.46	1.45	1.44	1.43	1.41	1.41	1.40	1.39
	0.200	1.81	1.81	1.76	1.73	1.70	1.67		1.64			1.60						
	0.100	3.10	2.73	2.52	2.39	2.31	2.24	2.19	2.15	2.12	2.10	2.06	2.01	1.96	1.91	1.89	1.86	1.83
	0.050	4.60	3.74	3.34	3.11	2.96	2.85	2.76	2.70	2.65	2.60	2.53	2.46	2.39	2.31	2.27	2.22	2.18
	0.025	6.30	4.86	4.24	3.89	3.66	3.50	3.38	3.29	3.21	3.15	3.05	2.95	2.84	2.73	2.67	2.61	2.55
	0.010	8.86	6.51	5.56	5.04	4.70	4.46	4.28	4.14	4.03	3.94	3.80	3.66	3.51	3.35	3.27	3.18	3.09
	0.005	11.06	7.92	6.68	6.00	5.56	5.26	5.03	4.86	4.72	4.60	4.43	4.25	4.06	3.86	3.76	3.66	3.55
15	0.500	0.48	0.73	0.83	0.88	0.91	0.93	0.95	0.96	0.97	0.98	0.99	1.00	1.01	1.02	1.03	1.03	1.04
	0.250	1.43	1.52	1.52	1.51	1.49	1.48	1.47	1.46	1.46	1.45	1.44	1.43	1.41	1.40	1.39	1.38	1.37
	0.200	1.80	1.79	1.75	1.71	1.68	1.66		1.62			1.58						
	0.100	3.07	2.70	2.49	2.36	2.27	2.21	2.16	2.12	2.09	2.06	2.02	1.97	1.92	1.87	1.85	1.82	1.79
	0.050	4.54	3.68	3.29	3.06	2.90	2.79	2.71	2.64	2.59	2.54	2.48	2.40	2.33	2.25	2.20	2.16	2.11
	0.025	6.20	4.77	4.15	3.80	3.58	3.41	3.29	3.20	3.12	3.06	2.96	2.86	2.76	2.64	2.58	2.52	2.46
	0.010	8.68	6.36	5.42	4.89	4.56	4.32	4.14	4.00	3.89	3.80	3.67	3.52	3.37	3.21	3.13	3.05	2.96
	0.005	10.80	7.70	6.48	5.80	5.37	5.07	4.85	4.67	4.54	4.42	4.25	4.07	3.88	3.69	3.58	3.48	3.37

16

	1	2	3	4	5	6	7	8	9	10	11	12	13	14	15	16	17
0.500	0.48	0.72	0.82	0.88	0.91	0.93	0.95	0.96	0.97	0.97	0.99	1.00	1.01	1.02	1.03	1.03	1.04
0.250	1.42	1.51	1.51	1.50	1.48	1.47	1.46	1.45	1.44	1.44	1.43	1.41	1.40	1.38	1.37	1.36	1.35
0.200	1.79	1.78	1.74	1.70	1.67	1.64		1.61			1.56						
0.100	3.05	2.67	2.46	2.33	2.24	2.18	2.13	2.09	2.06	2.03	1.99	1.94	1.89	1.84	1.81	1.78	1.75
0.050	4.49	3.63	3.24	3.01	2.85	2.74	2.66	2.59	2.54	2.49	2.42	2.35	2.28	2.19	2.15	2.11	2.06
0.025	6.12	4.69	4.08	3.73	3.50	3.34	3.22	3.12	3.05	2.99	2.89	2.79	2.68	2.57	2.51	2.45	2.38
0.010	8.53	6.23	5.29	4.77	4.44	4.20	4.03	3.89	3.78	3.69	3.55	3.41	3.26	3.10	3.02	2.93	2.84
0.005	10.58	7.51	6.30	5.64	5.21	4.91	4.69	4.52	4.38	4.27	4.10	3.92	3.73	3.54	3.44	3.33	3.22

17

	1	2	3	4	5	6	7	8	9	10	11	12	13	14	15	16	17
0.500	0.47	0.72	0.82	0.87	0.91	0.93	0.94	0.96	0.96	0.97	0.98	0.99	1.01	1.02	1.02	1.03	1.03
0.250	1.42	1.51	1.50	1.49	1.47	1.46	1.45	1.44	1.43	1.43	1.41	1.40	1.39	1.37	1.36	1.35	1.34
0.200	1.78	1.77	1.72	1.68	1.65	1.63		1.59			1.55						
0.100	3.03	2.64	2.44	2.31	2.22	2.15	2.10	2.06	2.03	2.00	1.96	1.91	1.86	1.81	1.78	1.75	1.72
0.050	4.45	3.59	3.20	2.96	2.81	2.70	2.61	2.55	2.49	2.45	2.38	2.31	2.23	2.15	2.10	2.06	2.01
0.025	6.04	4.62	4.01	3.66	3.44	3.28	3.16	3.06	2.98	2.92	2.82	2.72	2.62	2.50	2.44	2.38	2.32
0.010	8.40	6.11	5.18	4.67	4.34	4.10	3.93	3.79	3.68	3.59	3.46	3.31	3.16	3.00	2.92	2.83	2.75
0.005	10.38	7.35	6.16	5.50	5.07	4.78	4.56	4.39	4.25	4.14	3.97	3.79	3.61	3.41	3.31	3.21	3.10

18

	1	2	3	4	5	6	7	8	9	10	11	12	13	14	15	16	17
0.500	0.47	0.72	0.82	0.87	0.90	0.93	0.94	0.95	0.96	0.97	0.98	0.99	1.00	1.02	1.02	1.03	1.03
0.250	1.41	1.50	1.49	1.48	1.46	1.45	1.44	1.43	1.42	1.42	1.40	1.39	1.38	1.36	1.35	1.34	1.33
0.200	1.77	1.76	1.71	1.67	1.64	1.62		1.58			1.53						
0.100	3.01	2.62	2.42	2.29	2.20	2.13	2.08	2.04	2.00	1.98	1.93	1.89	1.84	1.78	1.75	1.72	1.69
0.050	4.41	3.55	3.16	2.93	2.77	2.66	2.58	2.51	2.46	2.41	2.34	2.27	2.19	2.11	2.06	2.02	1.97
0.025	5.98	4.56	3.95	3.61	3.38	3.22	3.10	3.01	2.93	2.87	2.77	2.67	2.56	2.44	2.38	2.32	2.26
0.010	8.29	6.01	5.09	4.58	4.25	4.01	3.84	3.71	3.60	3.51	3.37	3.23	3.08	2.92	2.84	2.75	2.66
0.005	10.21	7.21	6.03	5.37	4.96	4.66	4.44	4.28	4.14	4.03	3.86	3.68	3.50	3.30	3.20	3.10	2.99

19

	1	2	3	4	5	6	7	8	9	10	11	12	13	14	15	16	17
0.500	0.47	0.72	0.82	0.87	0.90	0.92	0.94	0.95	0.96	0.97	0.98	0.99	1.00	1.01	1.02	1.02	1.03
0.250	1.41	1.49	1.49	1.47	1.46	1.44	1.43	1.42	1.41	1.41	1.40	1.38	1.37	1.35	1.34	1.33	1.32
0.200	1.76	1.75	1.70	1.66	1.63	1.61		1.57			1.52						
0.100	2.99	2.61	2.40	2.27	2.18	2.11	2.06	2.02	1.98	1.96	1.91	1.86	1.81	1.76	1.73	1.70	1.67
0.050	4.38	3.52	3.13	2.90	2.74	2.63	2.54	2.48	2.42	2.38	2.31	2.23	2.16	2.07	2.03	1.98	1.93
0.025	5.92	4.51	3.90	3.56	3.33	3.17	3.05	2.96	2.88	2.82	2.72	2.62	2.51	2.39	2.33	2.27	2.20
0.010	8.18	5.93	5.01	4.50	4.17	3.94	3.77	3.63	3.52	3.43	3.30	3.15	3.00	2.84	2.76	2.67	2.58
0.005	10.07	7.09	5.92	5.27	4.85	4.56	4.34	4.18	4.04	3.93	3.76	3.59	3.40	3.21	3.11	3.00	2.89

(*cont.*)

TABLE XII (cont.)

The number of degrees of freedom for the numerator, v_1

v_2	P	1	2	3	4	5	6	7	8	9	10	12	15	20	30	40	60	120
20	0.500	0.47	0.72	0.82	0.87	0.90	0.92	0.94	0.95	0.96	0.97	0.98	0.99	1.00	1.01	1.02	1.02	1.03
	0.250	1.40	1.49	1.48	1.47	1.45	1.44	1.43	1.42	1.41	1.40	1.39	1.37	1.36	1.34	1.33	1.32	1.31
	0.200	1.76	1.75	1.70	1.65	1.62	1.60		1.56			1.51						
	0.100	2.97	2.59	2.38	2.25	2.16	2.09	2.04	2.00	1.96	1.94	1.89	1.84	1.79	1.74	1.71	1.68	1.64
	0.050	4.35	3.49	3.10	2.87	2.71	2.60	2.51	2.45	2.39	2.35	2.28	2.20	2.12	2.04	1.99	1.95	1.90
	0.025	5.87	4.46	3.86	3.51	3.29	3.13	3.01	2.91	2.84	2.77	2.68	2.57	2.46	2.35	2.29	2.22	2.16
	0.010	8.10	5.85	4.94	4.43	4.10	3.87	3.70	3.56	3.46	3.37	3.23	3.09	2.94	2.78	2.69	2.61	2.52
	0.005	9.94	6.99	5.82	5.17	4.76	4.47	4.26	4.09	3.96	3.85	3.68	3.50	3.32	3.12	3.02	2.92	2.81
21	0.500	0.47	0.72	0.81	0.87	0.90	0.92	0.94	0.95	0.96	0.96	0.98	0.99	1.00	1.01	1.02	1.02	1.03
	0.250	1.40	1.48	1.48	1.46	1.44	1.43	1.42	1.41	1.40	1.39	1.38	1.37	1.35	1.33	1.32	1.31	1.30
	0.200	1.75	1.74	1.69	1.65	1.61	1.59		1.55			1.50						
	0.100	2.96	2.57	2.36	2.23	2.14	2.08	2.02	1.98	1.94	1.92	1.88	1.83	1.78	1.72	1.69	1.66	1.62
	0.050	4.32	3.47	3.07	2.84	2.68	2.57	2.49	2.42	2.37	2.32	2.25	2.18	2.10	2.01	1.96	1.92	1.87
	0.025	5.83	4.42	3.82	3.48	3.25	3.10	2.97	2.87	2.80	2.73	2.64	2.53	2.42	2.31	2.25	2.18	2.11
	0.010	8.02	5.78	4.87	4.37	4.04	3.81	3.64	3.51	3.40	3.31	3.17	3.03	2.88	2.72	2.64	2.55	2.46
	0.005	9.83	6.89	5.73	5.09	4.68	4.39	4.18	4.01	3.88	3.77	3.60	3.43	3.24	3.05	2.95	2.84	2.73
22	0.500	0.47	0.72	0.81	0.87	0.90	0.92	0.93	0.95	0.96	0.96	0.97	0.99	1.00	1.01	1.01	1.02	1.03
	0.250	1.40	1.48	1.47	1.45	1.44	1.42	1.41	1.40	1.39	1.39	1.37	1.36	1.34	1.32	1.31	1.30	1.29
	0.200	1.75	1.73	1.68	1.64	1.61	1.58		1.54			1.49						
	0.100	2.95	2.56	2.35	2.22	2.13	2.06	2.01	1.97	1.93	1.90	1.86	1.81	1.76	1.70	1.67	1.64	1.60
	0.050	4.30	3.44	3.05	2.82	2.66	2.55	2.46	2.40	2.34	2.30	2.23	2.15	2.07	1.98	1.94	1.89	1.84
	0.025	5.79	4.38	3.78	3.44	3.22	3.05	2.93	2.84	2.76	2.70	2.60	2.50	2.39	2.27	2.21	2.14	2.08
	0.010	7.95	5.72	4.82	4.31	3.99	3.76	3.59	3.45	3.35	3.26	3.12	2.98	2.83	2.67	2.58	2.50	2.40
	0.005	9.73	6.81	5.65	5.02	4.61	4.32	4.11	3.94	3.81	3.70	3.54	3.36	3.18	2.98	2.88	2.77	2.66

The following is a continuation of a table of critical values of the F-distribution. For each denominator degrees of freedom (ν₂ = 23, 24, 25, 27) the rows give the upper-tail probability (0.500, 0.250, 0.200, 0.100, 0.050, 0.025, 0.010, 0.005) and the columns give increasing numerator degrees of freedom (numerator df heading is cut off at the top of the page).

ν₂ = 23

P																		
0.500	1.02	1.02	1.01	1.01	1.01	1.00	0.98	0.97	0.96	0.95	0.95	0.93	0.92	0.90	0.86	0.81	0.71	0.47
0.250	1.28	1.30	1.31	1.32	1.34	1.35	1.37	1.38	1.39	1.40	1.41	1.42	1.43	1.45	1.47	1.47	1.47	1.39
0.200							1.49			1.53		1.57	1.60	1.63	1.68	1.73	1.73	1.74
0.100	1.59	1.62	1.66	1.69	1.74	1.80	1.84	1.89	1.92	1.95	1.99	2.05	2.11	2.21	2.34	2.55	2.55	2.94
0.050	1.81	1.86	1.91	1.96	2.05	2.13	2.20	2.27	2.32	2.37	2.44	2.53	2.64	2.80	3.03	3.42	3.42	4.28
0.025	2.04	2.11	2.18	2.24	2.36	2.47	2.57	2.67	2.73	2.81	2.90	3.02	3.18	3.41	3.75	4.35	4.35	5.75
0.010	2.35	2.45	2.54	2.62	2.78	2.93	3.07	3.21	3.30	3.41	3.54	3.71	3.94	4.26	4.76	5.66	5.66	7.88
0.005	2.60	2.71	2.82	2.92	3.12	3.30	3.47	3.64	3.75	3.88	4.05	4.26	4.54	4.95	5.58	6.66	6.73	9.63

ν₂ = 24

P																		
0.500	1.02	1.02	1.01	1.01	0.99	0.98	0.97	0.96	0.95	0.94	0.94	0.93	0.92	0.90	0.86	0.81	0.71	0.47
0.250	1.28	1.29	1.30	1.31	1.33	1.35	1.36	1.38	1.38	1.39	1.39	1.40	1.41	1.43	1.44	1.46	1.47	1.39
0.200			1.53				1.48			1.53		1.57	1.59	1.62	1.66	1.67	1.72	1.74
0.100	1.57	1.61	1.64	1.67	1.73	1.78	1.83	1.88	1.91	1.94	1.98	2.04	2.10	2.19	2.33	2.54	2.54	2.93
0.050	1.79	1.84	1.89	1.94	2.03	2.11	2.18	2.25	2.30	2.36	2.42	2.51	2.62	2.78	3.01	3.40	3.40	4.26
0.025	2.01	2.08	2.15	2.21	2.33	2.44	2.54	2.64	2.70	2.78	2.87	2.99	3.15	3.38	3.72	4.32	4.32	5.72
0.010	2.31	2.40	2.49	2.58	2.74	2.89	3.03	3.17	3.26	3.36	3.50	3.67	3.90	4.22	4.72	5.61	5.61	7.82
0.005	2.55	2.66	2.77	2.87	3.06	3.25	3.42	3.59	3.69	3.83	3.99	4.20	4.49	4.89	5.52	6.60	6.66	9.55

ν₂ = 25

P																		
0.500	1.02	1.02	1.01	1.01	1.00	0.99	0.98	0.97	0.96	0.95	0.95	0.94	0.93	0.92	0.89	0.86	0.81	0.71	0.47
0.250	1.27	1.28	1.29	1.31	1.33	1.34	1.36	1.37	1.38	1.38	1.39	1.40	1.41	1.42	1.44	1.46	1.47	1.39
0.200					1.47				1.52		1.56	1.58	1.61	1.62	1.66	1.66	1.72	1.73
0.100	1.56	1.59	1.63	1.66	1.72	1.77	1.82	1.87	1.89	1.93	1.97	2.01	2.09	2.18	2.32	2.53	2.53	2.92
0.050	1.77	1.82	1.87	1.92	2.01	2.09	2.16	2.24	2.28	2.34	2.41	2.49	2.60	2.76	2.99	3.39	3.39	4.24
0.025	1.98	2.05	2.12	2.18	2.30	2.41	2.51	2.61	2.68	2.75	2.85	2.97	3.13	3.35	3.69	4.29	4.29	5.69
0.010	2.27	2.36	2.45	2.54	2.70	2.85	2.99	3.13	3.22	3.32	3.46	3.63	3.85	4.18	4.68	5.57	5.57	7.77
0.005	2.50	2.61	2.72	2.82	3.01	3.20	3.37	3.54	3.64	3.78	3.94	4.15	4.43	4.84	5.46	6.60	6.60	9.47

ν₂ = 27

P																		
0.500	1.02	1.01	1.01	1.01	1.00	0.99	0.98	0.97	0.96	0.95	0.94	0.93	0.91	0.91	0.89	0.86	0.81	0.71	0.47
0.250	1.26	1.27	1.28	1.30	1.32	1.33	1.35	1.36	1.37	1.38	1.38	1.40	1.40	1.42	1.43	1.45	1.46	1.38
0.200					1.46				1.51		1.55	1.55	1.58	1.61	1.66	1.66	1.71	1.73
0.100	1.53	1.57	1.60	1.64	1.70	1.75	1.80	1.85	1.87	1.91	1.95	2.00	2.07	2.17	2.30	2.51	2.51	2.90
0.050	1.73	1.79	1.84	1.88	1.97	2.06	2.13	2.20	2.25	2.31	2.37	2.46	2.57	2.73	2.96	3.35	3.35	4.21
0.025	1.93	2.00	2.07	2.13	2.25	2.36	2.47	2.57	2.63	2.71	2.80	2.92	3.08	3.31	3.65	4.24	4.24	5.63
0.010	2.20	2.29	2.38	2.47	2.63	2.78	2.93	3.06	3.15	3.26	3.39	3.56	3.78	4.11	4.60	5.49	5.49	7.68
0.005	2.41	2.52	2.63	2.73	2.93	3.11	3.28	3.45	3.56	3.69	3.85	4.06	4.34	4.74	5.36	6.49	6.49	9.34

(cont.)

TABLE XII (*cont.*)

The number of degrees of freedom for the numerator, v_1

v_2	P	1	2	3	4	5	6	7	8	9	10	12	15	20	30	40	60	120
30	0.500	0.47	0.71	0.81	0.86	0.89	0.91	0.93	0.94	0.95	0.96	0.97	0.98	0.99	1.00	1.01	1.01	1.02
	0.250	1.38	1.45	1.44	1.42	1.41	1.39	1.38	1.37	1.36	1.35	1.34	1.32	1.30	1.28	1.27	1.26	1.24
	0.200	1.72	1.70	1.64	1.60	1.57	1.54		1.50			1.45						
	0.100	2.88	2.49	2.28	2.14	2.05	1.98	1.93	1.88	1.85	1.82	1.77	1.72	1.67	1.61	1.57	1.54	1.50
	0.050	4.17	3.32	2.92	2.69	2.53	2.42	2.33	2.27	2.21	2.16	2.09	2.01	1.93	1.84	1.79	1.74	1.68
	0.025	5.57	4.18	3.59	3.25	3.03	2.87	2.75	2.65	2.57	2.51	2.41	2.31	2.20	2.07	2.01	1.94	1.87
	0.010	7.56	5.39	4.51	4.02	3.70	3.47	3.30	3.17	3.07	2.98	2.84	2.70	2.55	2.39	2.30	2.21	2.11
	0.005	9.18	6.35	5.24	4.62	4.23	3.95	3.74	3.58	3.34	3.18	3.01	2.82	2.73	2.63	2.52	2.42	2.30
40	0.500	0.46	0.71	0.80	0.85	0.98	0.91	0.92	0.93	0.94	0.95	0.96	0.97	0.98	0.99	1.00	1.01	1.01
	0.250	1.36	1.44	1.42	1.40	1.39	1.37	1.36	1.35	1.34	1.33	1.31	1.30	1.28	1.26	1.24	1.22	1.21
	0.200	1.70	1.68	1.62	1.57	1.54	1.51		1.47			1.41						
	0.100	2.84	2.44	2.23	2.09	2.00	1.93	1.87	1.83	1.79	1.76	1.71	1.66	1.61	1.54	1.51	1.47	1.42
	0.050	4.08	3.23	2.84	2.61	2.45	2.34	2.25	2.18	2.12	2.08	2.00	1.92	1.84	1.74	1.69	1.64	1.58
	0.025	5.42	4.05	3.46	3.13	2.90	2.74	2.62	2.53	2.45	2.39	2.29	2.18	2.07	1.94	1.88	1.80	1.72
	0.010	7.31	5.18	4.31	3.83	3.51	3.29	3.12	2.99	2.89	2.80	2.66	2.52	2.37	2.20	2.11	2.02	1.92
	0.005	8.83	6.07	4.98	4.37	3.99	3.71	3.51	3.35	3.22	3.12	2.95	2.78	2.60	2.40	2.30	2.18	2.06
120	0.500	0.46	0.70	0.79	0.84	0.88	0.90	0.91	0.92	0.93	0.94	0.95	0.96	0.97	0.98	0.99	0.99	1.00
	0.250	1.34	1.40	1.39	1.37	1.35	1.33	1.31	1.30	1.29	1.28	1.26	1.24	1.22	1.19	1.18	1.16	1.13
	0.200	1.66	1.63	1.57	1.52	1.48	1.45		1.41			1.35						
	0.100	2.75	2.35	2.13	1.99	1.90	1.82	1.77	1.72	1.68	1.65	1.60	1.54	1.48	1.41	1.37	1.32	1.26
	0.050	3.92	3.07	2.68	2.45	2.29	2.18	2.09	2.02	1.96	1.91	1.82	1.75	1.66	1.55	1.50	1.43	1.35
	0.025	5.15	3.80	3.23	2.89	2.67	2.52	2.39	2.30	2.22	2.16	2.05	1.94	1.82	1.69	1.61	1.53	1.43
	0.010	6.85	4.79	3.95	3.48	3.17	2.96	2.79	2.66	2.56	2.47	2.34	2.19	2.03	1.86	1.76	1.66	1.53
	0.005	8.18	5.54	4.50	3.92	3.54	3.28	3.09	2.93	2.81	2.71	2.54	2.37	2.19	1.98	1.87	1.75	1.61

	0.45	0.69	0.79	0.84	0.87	0.89	0.91	0.92	0.93	0.93	0.95	0.96	0.97	0.98	0.98	0.99	1.00
0.500	0.45	0.69	0.79	0.84	0.87	0.89	0.91	0.92	0.93	0.93	0.95	0.96	0.97	0.98	0.98	0.99	1.00
0.250	1.32	1.39	1.37	1.35	1.33	1.31	1.29	1.28	1.27	1.25	1.24	1.22	1.19	1.16	1.14	1.12	1.08
0.200	1.64	1.61	1.55	1.50	1.46	1.43		1.38			1.32						
0.100	2.71	2.30	2.08	1.94	1.85	1.77	1.72	1.67	1.63	1.60	1.55	1.49	1.42	1.34	1.30	1.24	1.17
0.050	3.84	3.00	2.60	2.37	2.21	2.10	2.01	1.94	1.88	1.83	1.75	1.67	1.57	1.46	1.39	1.32	1.22
0.025	5.02	3.69	3.12	2.79	2.57	2.41	2.29	2.19	2.11	2.05	1.94	1.83	1.71	1.57	1.48	1.39	1.27
0.010	6.63	4.61	3.78	3.32	3.02	2.80	2.64	2.51	2.41	2.32	2.18	2.04	1.88	1.70	1.59	1.47	1.32
0.005	7.88	5.30	4.28	3.72	3.35	3.09	2.90	2.74	2.62	2.52	2.36	2.19	2.00	1.79	1.67	1.53	1.36

∞

I am indebted to the late Professor Sir Ronald A. Fisher, F.R.S., Cambridge, and to Dr. Frank Yates, F.R.S., Rothamsted, also to Messrs Oliver and Boyd Ltd., Edinburgh, for permission to use parts of Table V from their *Statistical Tables for Biological, Agricultural and Medical Research.* I also am indebted to the authors and the Biometrika Trustees for permission to use portions of "Tables of the percentage points of the inverted Beta (F) distribution" by M. Merrington and C. Thompson in *Biometrika*: 33, 74, 1943.

TABLE XIII. CRITICAL VALUES FOR DUNCAN'S NMRT, WITH SPECIAL
PROTECTION LEVELS AGAINST TYPE I ERRORS, $(1 - \alpha)^{p-1}$

n_2	α	p									
		2	3	4	5	6	7	8	9	10	15
10											
	0.10	2.56	2.68	2.75	2.79	2.81	2.83	2.83	2.84	2.84	2.84
	0.05	3.15	3.29	3.38	3.43	3.46	3.49	3.50	3.52	3.52	3.52
	0.01	4.48	4.67	4.79	4.87	4.93	4.98	5.01	5.04	5.06	5.11
12											
	0.10	2.52	2.64	2.71	2.76	2.79	2.81	2.82	2.83	2.83	2.83
	0.05	3.08	3.22	3.31	3.37	3.41	3.44	3.46	3.47	3.48	3.50
	0.01	4.32	4.50	4.62	4.71	4.77	4.82	4.85	4.88	4.91	4.98
15											
	0.10	2.48	2.60	2.68	2.73	2.76	2.79	2.81	2.82	2.82	2.83
	0.05	3.01	3.16	3.25	3.31	3.36	3.39	3.41	3.43	3.45	3.48
	0.01	4.17	4.35	4.46	4.55	4.61	4.66	4.70	4.73	4.76	4.85
18											
	0.10	2.45	2.58	2.66	2.71	2.75	2.78	2.80	2.81	2.82	2.84
	0.05	2.97	3.12	3.21	3.27	3.32	3.36	3.38	3.40	3.42	3.46
	0.01	4.07	4.25	4.36	4.44	4.51	4.56	4.60	4.64	4.66	4.76
20											
	0.10	2.44	2.57	2.65	2.70	2.74	2.77	2.79	2.81	2.82	2.85
	0.05	2.95	3.10	3.19	3.26	3.30	3.34	3.37	3.39	3.41	3.46
	0.01	4.02	4.20	4.31	4.40	4.46	4.51	4.55	4.59	4.62	4.72
24											
	0.10	2.42	2.55	2.63	2.69	2.73	2.76	2.78	2.80	2.82	2.85
	0.05	2.92	3.07	3.16	3.23	3.28	3.32	3.34	3.37	3.39	3.45
	0.01	3.96	4.13	4.24	4.32	4.39	4.44	4.48	4.52	4.55	4.65
30											
	0.10	2.40	2.53	2.62	2.67	2.72	2.75	2.78	2.80	2.81	2.86
	0.05	2.89	3.04	3.13	3.20	3.25	3.29	3.32	3.35	3.37	3.44
	0.01	3.89	4.06	4.17	4.25	4.31	4.37	4.41	4.44	4.48	4.59
60											
	0.10	2.36	2.50	2.58	2.65	2.69	2.73	2.76	2.79	2.81	2.87
	0.05	2.83	2.98	3.07	3.14	3.20	3.24	3.28	3.31	3.33	3.42
	0.01	3.76	3.92	4.03	4.11	4.17	4.23	4.37	4.31	4.34	4.46
120											
	0.10	2.34	2.48	2.57	2.63	2.68	2.72	2.75	2.78	2.80	2.88
	0.05	2.80	2.95	3.04	3.12	3.17	3.22	3.25	3.29	3.31	3.41
	0.01	3.70	3.86	3.96	4.04	4.11	4.16	4.20	4.24	4.27	4.39

From tables by H. L. Harter in *Biometrics* 16: 675–79, 1960. Reproduced
from *Biometrics* with the permission of the author and editor.

TABLE XIV. UPPER 5% AND 1% POINTS OF $F_{max} = $ (LARGEST s^2)/(SMALLEST s^2)
FOR k SAMPLES FROM NORMAL POPULATIONS, EACH PROVIDING ν DEGREES
OF FREEDOM FOR s^2

ν	2	3	4	5	6	7	8	9	10	11	12
					5% points						
2	39.0	87.5	142	202	266	333	403	475	550	626	704
3	15.4	27.8	39.2	50.7	62.0	72.9	83.5	93.9	104	114	124
4	9.60	15.5	20.6	25.2	29.5	33.6	37.5	41.1	44.6	48.0	51.4
5	7.15	10.8	13.7	16.3	18.7	20.8	22.9	24.7	26.5	28.2	29.9
6	5.82	8.38	10.4	12.1	13.7	15.0	16.3	17.5	18.6	19.7	20.7
7	4.99	6.94	8.44	9.70	10.8	11.8	12.7	13.5	14.3	15.1	15.8
8	4.43	6.00	7.18	8.12	9.03	9.78	10.5	11.1	11.7	12.2	12.7
9	4.03	5.34	6.31	7.11	7.80	8.41	8.95	9.45	9.91	10.3	10.7
10	3.72	4.85	5.67	6.34	6.92	7.42	7.87	8.28	8.66	9.01	9.34
12	3.28	4.16	4.79	5.30	5.72	6.09	6.42	6.72	7.00	7.25	7.48
15	2.86	3.54	4.01	4.37	4.68	4.95	5.19	5.40	5.59	5.77	5.93
20	2.46	2.95	3.29	3.54	3.76	3.94	4.10	4.24	4.37	4.49	4.59
30	2.07	2.40	2.61	2.78	2.91	3.02	3.12	3.21	3.29	3.36	3.39
60	1.67	1.85	1.96	2.04	2.11	2.17	2.22	2.26	2.30	2.33	2.36
∞	1.00	1.00	1.00	1.00	1.00	1.00	1.00	1.00	1.00	1.00	1.00
					1% points						
2	199	448	729	1036	1362	1705	2063	2432	2813	3204	3605
3	47.5	85	120	151	184	21(6)	24(9)	28(1)	31(0)	33(7)	36(1)
4	23.2	37	49	59	69	79	89	97	106	113	120
5	14.9	22	28	33	38	42	46	50	54	57	60
6	11.1	15.5	19.1	22	25	27	30	32	34	36	37
7	8.89	12.1	14.5	16.5	18.4	20	22	23	24	26	27
8	7.50	9.9	11.7	13.2	14.5	15.8	16.9	17.9	18.9	19.8	21
9	6.54	8.5	9.9	11.1	12.1	13.1	13.9	14.7	15.3	16.0	16.6
10	5.85	7.4	8.6	9.6	10.4	11.1	11.8	12.4	12.9	13.4	13.9
12	4.91	6.1	6.1	7.6	8.2	8.7	9.1	9.5	9.9	10.2	10.6
15	4.07	4.9	5.5	6.0	6.4	6.7	7.1	7.3	7.5	7.8	8.0
20	3.32	3.8	4.3	4.6	4.9	5.1	5.3	5.5	5.6	5.8	5.9
30	2.63	3.0	3.3	3.4	3.6	3.7	3.8	3.9	4.0	4.1	4.2
60	1.96	2.2	2.3	2.4	2.4	2.5	2.5	2.6	2.6	2.7	2.7
∞	1.00	1.0	1.0	1.0	1.0	1.0	1.0	1.0	1.0	1.0	1.0

Taken from H. O. Hartley, *Biometrika* 39: 424 (1952).

Values in the column $k = 2$ and in the rows $\nu = 2$ and $\nu = \infty$ are exact. Elsewhere the third digit may be in error by a few units for the 5% points and several units for the 1% points. The third-digit figures in parentheses for $\nu = 3$ are the most uncertain.

See also E. S. Pearson and H. O. Hartley, *Biometrika Tables for Statisticians*, Vol. 1, Cambridge Univ. Press, London, 1962, Table 31, p. 179. Reproduced with the permission of the authors and the Biometrika Trustees.

TABLE XV. SELECTED PORTIONS OF KLOTZ'S NORMAL SCORES

DISTRIBUTION, $S = \sum_{i=1}^{N} (W_{Ni}Z_i)$

		Probability of a larger S					Probability of a larger S		
N	m	0.10	0.05	0.025	N	m	0.10	0.05	0.025
10	3	2.974	3.578	3.687	17	5	5.705	6.378	6.913
10	4	3.809	4.404	4.512	17	6	6.554	7.178	7.688
10	5	4.525	4.878	5.122	17	7	7.340	7.948	8.454
11	4	4.011	4.466	4.806	17	8	8.110	8.689	9.174
11	5	4.806	5.216	5.402	18	5	5.850	6.489	7.051
12	4	4.200	4.656	5.151	18	6	6.675	7.356	7.905
12	5	4.909	5.446	5.736	18	7	7.496	8.155	8.692
12	6	5.698	5.988	6.410	18	8	8.272	8.915	9.422
13	5	5.187	5.681	6.074	18	9	9.046	9.637	10.121
13	6	5.898	6.380	6.708	19	5	5.943	6.587	7.216
14	5	5.285	5.869	6.300	19	6	6.788	7.491	8.061
14	6	6.054	6.577	6.989	19	7	7.639	8.333	8.902
14	7	6.763	7.231	7.602	19	8	8.442	9.105	9.632
15	5	5.386	6.024	6.440	19	9	9.204	9.843	10.382
15	6	6.197	6.758	7.204	20	5	6.083	6.769	7.431
15	7	6.931	7.443	7.864	20	6	6.954	7.701	8.294
16	5	5.567	6.236	6.653	20	7	7.817	8.561	9.144
16	6	6.416	7.000	7.494	20	8	8.651	9.362	9.938
16	7	7.179	7.751	8.184	20	9	9.438	10.126	10.688
16	8	7.892	8.438	8.886	20	10	10.193	10.864	11.407

Derived from Table 4, *Ann. Math. Stat.* 33: 509–12, 1962, with permission of the author and the editor.

TABLE XVI. NORMAL SCORES WEIGHTS, W_{Ni}, FOR USE IN KLOTZ'S NORMAL SCORES TEST FOR SCALE W_{Ni} = SQUARE OF STANDARD NORMAL ABSCISSA CORRESPONDING TO A CUMULATIVE FREQUENCY OF $i/(N + 1)$

N	i									
	1	2	3	4	5	6	7	8	9	10
10	1.783	0.825	0.366	0.122	0.013					
11	1.913	0.936	0.455	0.186	0.044	0				
12	2.034	1.040	0.542	0.252	0.086	0.009				
13	2.146	1.141	0.627	0.320	0.134	0.032	0			
14	2.253	1.234	0.708	0.378	0.186	0.064	0.007			
15	2.353	1.322	0.787	0.388	0.239	0.102	0.024	0		
16	2.451	1.409	0.863	0.521	0.293	0.142	0.050	0.005		
17	2.538	1.491	0.936	0.585	0.347	0.186	0.080	0.020	0	
18	2.624	1.568	1.006	0.647	0.402	0.230	0.134	0.040	0.004	
19	2.706	1.644	1.074	0.708	0.455	0.275	0.148	0.064	0.016	0
20	2.824	1.714	1.133	0.768	0.508	0.320	0.186	0.092	0.032	0.004

Derived from Table 3, *Ann. Math. Stat.* 33: 505, 1962, with the permission of the author and the editor.

TABLE XVII. CONFIDENCE LIMITS FOR THE EXPECTATION OF A POISSON VARIABLE
WITH $\alpha = 0.20, 0.10, 0.05,$ AND 0.01. CONFIDENCE COEFFICIENT,
$100(1 - \alpha)\%$

X	80 Lower	80 Upper	90 Lower	90 Upper	95 Lower	95 Upper	99 Lower	99 Upper
0	0	1.819	0	2.436	0	3.285	0	4.771
1	0.223	3.546	0.105	4.532	0.051	5.323	0.010	6.914
2	0.824	4.758	0.532	5.976	0.355	6.686	0.149	8.727
3	1.535	5.882	1.102	7.512	0.818	8.102	0.436	10.473
4	1.819	7.564	1.745	8.597	1.366	9.598	0.823	12.347
5	2.645	8.529	2.433	9.716	1.970	11.177	1.279	13.793
6	3.546	9.922	2.436	11.342	2.613	12.817	1.785	15.277
7	3.914	10.969	3.589	12.531	3.285	13.765	2.330	16.801
8	4.758	12.481	4.532	13.553	3.285	14.921	2.906	18.362
9	5.696	13.243	4.532	15.298	4.460	16.768	3.507	19.462
10	5.882	15.205	5.976	15.985	5.323	17.633	4.130	20.676
11	7.564	15.438	5.976	17.810	5.323	19.050	4.771	22.042
12	7.564	16.914	7.512	18.403	6.686	20.335	4.771	23.765
13	8.529	18.537	7.512	20.054	6.686	21.364	5.829	24.925
14	9.922	18.938	8.597	21.035	8.102	22.945	6.668	25.992
15	9.922	20.414	9.484	22.258	8.102	23.762	6.914	27.718
16	10.969	22.037	9.716	23.824	9.598	25.400	7.756	28.852
17	12.481	22.326	11.342	24.452	9.598	26.306	8.727	29.900
18	12.481	23.744	11.342	26.158	11.177	27.735	8.727	31.839
19	13.243	25.707	12.531	26.935	11.177	28.966	10.009	32.547
20	15.205	25.707	13.553	28.092	12.817	30.017	10.473	34.183
21	15.205	26.972	13.553	29.988	12.817	31.675	11.242	35.204
22	15.438	28.469	15.298	30.179	13.765	32.277	12.347	36.544
23	16.914	29.983	15.795	31.639	14.921	34.048	12.347	37.819
24	18.537	30.152	15.985	33.444	14.921	34.665	13.793	38.939
25	18.537	31.507	17.810	33.643	16.768	36.030	13.793	40.373
26	18.94	33.03	18.28	35.08	16.77	37.67	15.28	41.39
27	20.41	34.42	18.40	37.00	17.63	38.16	15.28	42.85
28	22.04	34.58	20.05	37.04	19.05	39.76	16.80	43.91
29	22.04	35.92	21.03	38.44	19.05	40.94	16.80	45.26
30	22.33	37.39	21.03	40.10	20.33	41.75	18.36	46.50

(*cont.*)

If X is the observed frequency or count and m_L and m_U are the lower and upper $100(1 - \alpha)\%$ confidence limits for its expectation, m, then $\Pr\{m_L \leq m \leq m_U\} \geq 1 - \alpha$.

Reproduced from E. L. Crow and R. S. Gardiner, "Confidence intervals for the expectation of a Poisson variable," *Biometrika* 46: 448–53, 1959, by permission of the authors and the Biometrika Trustees.

TABLE XVII (*cont.*)

X	80		90		95		99	
	Lower	*Upper*	*Lower*	*Upper*	*Lower*	*Upper*	*Lower*	*Upper*
31	23.74	39.07	22.26	40.99	21.36	43.45	18.36	47.62
32	25.71	39.07	23.82	41.74	21.36	44.26	19.46	49.13
33	25.71	40.23	23.82	43.22	22.94	45.28	20.28	49.96
34	25.71	41.62	24.45	44.87	23.76	47.02	20.68	51.78
35	26.97	43.25	26.16	45.00	23.76	47.69	22.04	52.28
36	28.47	44.20	26.93	46.38	25.40	48.74	22.04	54.03
37	29.98	44.48	26.93	47.97	26.31	50.42	23.76	54.74
38	29.98	45.79	28.09	49.12	26.31	51.29	23.76	56.14
39	30.15	47.20	29.99	49.56	27.73	52.15	24.92	57.61
40	31.51	48.99	29.99	50.96	28.97	53.72	25.83	58.35
41	33.03	49.46	30.18	52.64	28.97	54.99	25.99	60.39
42	34.42	49.94	31.64	53.46	30.02	55.51	27.72	60.59
43	34.42	51.25	33.44	54.05	31.67	56.99	27.72	62.13
44	34.58	52.64	33.44	55.44	31.67	58.72	28.85	63.63
45	35.92	54.29	33.64	57.10	32.28	58.84	29.90	64.26
46	37.39	55.16	35.08	57.99	34.05	60.24	29.90	65.96
47	39.07	55.33	37.00	58.48	34.66	61.90	31.84	66.81
48	39.07	56.61	37.00	59.85	34.66	62.81	31.84	67.92
49	39.07	57.95	37.04	61.41	36.03	63.49	32.55	69.83
50	40.23	59.44	38.44	62.69	37.67	64.95	34.18	70.05
51	41.62	61.02	40.10	62.86	37.67	66.76	34.18	71.56
52	43.25	61.02	40.99	64.19	38.16	66.76	35.20	73.20
53	44.20	61.90	40.99	65.64	39.76	68.10	36.54	73.62
54	44.20	63.19	41.74	67.45	40.94	69.62	36.54	75.16
55	44.48	64.56	43.22	67.45	40.94	71.09	37.82	76.61
56	45.79	66.12	44.87	68.49	41.75	71.28	38.94	77.15
57	47.20	67.33	44.87	69.86	43.45	72.66	38.94	78.71
58	48.99	67.33	45.00	71.42	44.26	74.22	40.37	80.06
59	49.46	68.38	46.38	72.67	44.26	75.49	41.39	80.65
60	49.46	69.67	47.97	72.76	45.28	75.78	41.39	82.21
61	49.94	71.04	49.12	74.07	47.02	77.16	42.85	83.56
62	51.25	72.58	49.12	75.47	47.69	78.73	43.91	84.12
63	52.64	73.87	49.56	77.15	47.69	79.98	43.91	85.65
64	54.29	73.87	50.96	77.94	48.74	80.25	45.26	87.12
65	55.16	74.79	52.64	78.27	50.42	81.61	46.50	87.55
66	55.16	76.07	53.46	79.59	51.29	83.14	46.50	89.05
67	55.33	77.40	53.46	80.99	51.29	84.57	47.62	90.72
68	56.61	78.85	54.05	82.72	52.15	84.67	49.13	90.96
69	57.95	80.60	55.44	83.37	53.72	86.01	49.13	92.42
70	59.44	80.60	57.10	83.73	54.99	87.48	49.96	94.34

(*cont.*)

TABLE XVII (*cont.*)

X	80		90		95		99	
	Lower	*Upper*	*Lower*	*Upper*	*Lower*	*Upper*	*Lower*	*Upper*
71	61.02	81.13	57.99	85.04	54.99	89.23	51.78	94.35
72	61.02	82.38	57.99	86.43	55.51	89.23	51.78	95.76
73	61.02	83.67	58.48	88.05	56.99	90.37	52.28	97.42
74	61.90	85.04	59.85	89.04	58.72	91.78	54.03	98.36
75	63.19	86.58	61.41	89.15	58.72	93.48	54.74	99.09
76	64.56	87.87	62.69	90.44	58.84	94.23	54.74	100.61
77	66.12	87.87	62.69	91.79	60.24	94.70	56.14	102.16
78	67.33	88.64	62.86	93.29	61.90	96.06	57.61	102.42
79	67.33	89.89	64.19	94.80	62.81	97.54	57.61	103.84
80	67.33	91.19	65.64	94.80	62.81	99.17	58.35	105.66
81	68.38	92.55	67.45	95.78	63.49	99.17	60.39	106.12
82	69.67	94.11	67.45	97.10	64.95	100.32	60.39	107.10
83	71.04	95.34	67.45	98.51	66.76	101.71	60.59	108.61
84	72.58	95.34	68.49	100.28	66.76	103.31	62.13	110.16
85	73.87	96.08	69.86	100.81	66.76	104.40	63.63	110.37
86	73.87	97.32	71.42	101.09	68.10	104.58	63.63	111.78
87	73.87	98.60	72.67	102.38	69.62	105.90	64.26	113.45
88	74.79	99.95	72.67	103.71	71.09	107.32	65.96	114.33
89	76.07	101.43	72.76	105.17	71.09	109.11	66.81	114.99
90	77.40	103.02	74.07	106.92	71.28	109.61	66.81	116.44
91	78.85	103.02	75.47	106.92	72.66	110.11	67.92	118.33
92	80.60	103.45	77.15	107.63	77.22	111.44	69.83	118.33
93	80.60	104.68	77.94	108.91	75.49	112.87	69.83	119.59
94	80.60	105.94	77.94	110.26	75.49	114.84	70.05	121.09
95	81.13	107.24	78.27	111.75	75.78	114.84	71.56	122.69
96	82.38	108.63	79.59	113.35	77.16	115.60	73.20	122.78
97	83.67	110.27	80.99	113.35	78.73	116.93	73.20	124.16
98	85.04	111.18	82.72	114.11	79.98	118.35	73.62	125.70
99	86.58	111.18	83.37	115.40	79.98	120.36	75.16	127.07
100	87.87	111.98	83.37	116.74	80.25	120.36	76.61	127.31
101	87.88	113.21	83.73	118.21	81.61	121.06	76.61	128.70
102	87.88	114.47	85.04	119.88	83.14	122.37	77.15	130.27
103	88.64	115.79	86.43	119.88	84.57	123.77	78.71	131.50
104	89.89	117.19	88.05	120.55	84.57	125.46	80.06	131.82
105	91.19	118.95	89.04	121.82	84.67	126.26	80.06	133.21
106	92.55	119.50	89.04	123.15	86.01	126.48	80.65	134.79
107	94.11	119.50	89.15	124.57	87.48	127.78	82.21	135.99
108	95.34	120.44	90.44	126.52	89.23	129.14	83.56	136.30
109	95.34	121.67	91.79	126.52	89.23	130.68	83.56	137.68
110	95.34	122.92	93.29	126.94	89.23	132.03	84.12	139.24

(*cont.*)

TABLE XVII (*cont.*)

X	80		90		95		99	
	Lower	*Upper*	*Lower*	*Upper*	*Lower*	*Upper*	*Lower*	*Upper*
111	96.08	124.23	94.80	128.20	90.37	132.03	85.65	140.54
112	97.32	125.61	94.80	129.50	91.78	133.14	87.12	140.76
113	98.60	127.22	94.80	130.87	93.48	134.48	87.12	142.12
114	99.95	128.23	95.78	132.44	94.23	135.92	87.55	143.64
115	101.43	128.23	97.10	133.66	94.23	137.79	89.05	145.13
116	103.02	128.84	98.51	133.66	94.70	137.79	90.72	145.19
117	103.02	130.06	100.28	134.54	96.06	138.49	90.72	146.54
118	103.02	131.30	100.81	135.81	97.54	139.79	90.96	148.01
119	103.45	132.57	100.81	137.13	99.17	141.16	92.42	149.76
120	104.68	133.91	101.09	138.55	99.17	142.70	94.34	149.76
121	105.94	135.37	102.38	140.54	99.17	144.01	94.34	150.93
122	107.24	137.08	103.71	140.54	100.32	144.01	94.35	152.35
123	108.63	137.08	105.17	140.85	101.71	145.08	95.76	154.18
124	110.27	137.18	106.92	142.09	103.31	146.39	97.42	154.60
125	111.18	138.38	106.92	143.47	104.40	147.80	98.36	155.31
126	111.18	139.60	106.92	144.71	104.40	149.53	98.36	156.69
127	111.18	140.85	107.63	146.16	104.58	150.19	99.09	158.25
128	111.98	142.14	108.91	147.94	105.90	150.36	100.61	159.53
129	113.21	143.49	110.26	147.94	107.32	151.63	102.16	159.67
130	114.47	145.01	111.75	148.35	109.11	152.96	102.16	161.01
131	115.79	146.45	113.35	149.60	109.61	154.39	102.42	162.46
132	117.19	146.45	113.35	150.88	109.61	156.32	103.84	164.31
133	118.95	146.66	113.35	152.21	110.11	156.32	105.66	164.31
134	119.50	147.86	114.11	153.67	111.44	156.87	106.12	165.33
135	119.50	149.08	115.40	155.43	112.87	158.15	106.12	166.71
136	119.50	150.33	116.74	155.43	114.84	159.48	107.10	168.29
137	120.44	151.61	118.21	155.81	114.84	160.92	108.61	169.49
138	121.67	152.96	119.88	157.05	114.84	162.79	110.16	169.64
139	122.92	154.45	119.88	158.33	115.60	162.79	110.16	170.98
140	124.23	156.01	119.88	159.65	116.93	163.35	110.37	172.41
141	125.61	156.01	120.55	161.07	118.35	164.63	111.78	174.36
142	127.22	156.09	121.82	163.02	120.36	165.96	113.45	174.36
143	128.23	157.28	123.15	163.02	120.36	167.39	114.33	175.25
144	128.23	158.49	124.57	163.24	120.36	169.33	114.33	176.61
145	128.23	159.73	126.52	164.47	121.06	169.33	114.99	178.11
146	128.84	160.99	126.52	165.73	122.37	169.80	116.44	179.67
147	130.06	162.31	126.52	167.03	123.77	171.07	118.33	179.67
148	131.30	163.72	126.94	168.41	125.46	172.38	118.33	180.84
149	132.57	165.68	128.20	170.00	126.26	173.79	118.33	182.22
150	133.91	165.77	129.50	171.09	126.26	175.48	119.59	183.81

(*cont.*)

TABLE XVII (*cont.*)

X	80 Lower	80 Upper	90 Lower	90 Upper	95 Lower	95 Upper	99 Lower	99 Upper
151	135.37	165.77	130.87	171.09	126.48	176.23	121.09	184.97
152	137.08	166.64	132.44	171.84	127.78	176.23	122.69	185.08
153	137.08	167.84	133.66	173.08	129.14	177.48	122.69	186.40
154	137.08	169.06	133.66	174.36	130.68	178.77	122.78	187.81
155	137.18	170.30	133.66	175.69	132.03	180.14	124.16	189.50
156	138.38	171.58	134.54	177.13	132.03	181.67	125.70	190.28
157	139.60	172.92	135.81	178.96	132.03	183.05	127.07	190.61
158	140.85	174.39	137.13	178.96	133.14	183.05	127.07	191.94
159	142.14	176.06	138.55	179.18	134.48	183.86	137.31	193.36
160	143.49	176.06	140.54	180.40	135.92	185.13	128.70	195.19
161	145.01	176.06	140.54	181.65	137.79	186.46	130.27	195.59
162	146.45	177.14	140.54	182.94	137.79	187.89	131.50	196.13
163	146.45	178.34	140.85	184.30	137.79	189.82	131.50	197.46
164	146.45	179.56	142.09	185.80	138.49	189.83	131.82	198.88
165	146.66	180.80	143.37	187.30	139.79	190.21	133.21	200.84
166	147.86	182.08	144.71	187.30	141.16	191.46	134.79	200.94
167	149.08	183.42	146.16	187.70	142.70	192.76	135.99	201.62
168	150.33	184.89	147.94	188.93	144.01	194.11	135.99	202.94
169	151.61	186.56	147.94	190.18	144.01	195.63	136.30	204.36
170	152.96	186.56	147.94	191.47	144.01	197.09	137.68	206.19
171	154.45	186.56	148.35	192.83	145.08	197.09	139.24	206.60
172	156.01	187.59	149.60	194.36	146.39	197.78	140.54	207.08
173	156.01	188.78	150.88	195.73	147.80	199.04	140.54	208.04
174	156.01	189.99	152.21	195.73	149.53	200.35	140.76	209.81
175	156.09	191.23	153.67	196.18	150.19	201.73	142.12	211.50
176	157.28	192.49	155.43	197.40	150.19	203.35	143.64	212.29
177	158.49	193.81	155.43	198.65	150.36	204.36	145.13	212.53
178	159.73	195.22	155.43	199.94	151.63	204.36	145.13	213.84
179	160.99	197.12	155.81	201.30	152.96	205.31	145.19	215.22
180	162.31	197.33	157.05	202.80	154.39	206.58	146.54	216.80
181	163.72	197.33	158.33	204.30	156.32	207.90	148.01	217.98
182	165.68	197.97	159.65	204.30	156.32	209.30	149.76	217.98
183	165.77	199.16	161.07	204.62	156.32	211.03	149.76	219.25
184	165.77	200.36	163.02	205.84	156.87	211.69	149.76	220.61
185	165.77	201.58	163.02	207.08	158.15	211.69	150.93	222.10
186	166.64	202.82	163.02	208.36	159.48	212.28	152.35	223.67
187	167.84	204.11	163.24	209.69	160.92	214.09	154.18	223.67
188	169.06	205.45	164.47	211.13	162.79	215.40	154.60	224.65
189	170.30	206.94	165.73	212.96	162.79	216.81	154.60	225.98
190	171.58	208.52	167.03	212.96	162.79	218.56	155.31	227.41

(*cont.*)

TABLE XVII (*cont.*)

X	80		90		95		99	
	Lower	Upper	Lower	Upper	Lower	Upper	Lower	Upper
271	248.47	292.03	242.85	298.73	239.00	303.22	229.37	314.75
272	249.70	293.57	244.09	300.36	240.45	304.48	230.03	316.11
273	250.96	294.88	245.37	300.36	242.27	305.77	231.33	317.60
274	252.27	294.88	246.70	300.36	242.27	307.13	232.71	319.19
275	253.67	294.88	248.15	301.44	242.27	308.64	234.28	319.19
276	255.39	295.66	249.94	302.64	242.53	310.07	235.50	319.84
277	256.07	296.82	249.94	303.86	243.76	310.07	235.50	321.11
278	256.07	298.00	249.94	305.10	245.02	310.38	235.50	322.43
279	256.07	299.18	249.94	306.38	246.32	311.60	236.68	323.84
280	256.19	300.39	251.09	307.71	247.70	312.83	238.01	325.58
281	257.36	301.61	252.30	309.16	249.28	314.10	239.46	326.21
282	258.54	302.86	253.54	310.94	250.43	315.42	241.32	326.21
283	259.73	304.15	254.81	310.94	250.43	316.83	241.32	327.46
284	260.94	305.51	256.13	310.94	250.43	318.63	241.32	328.75
285	262.17	307.03	257.55	311.88	251.11	319.09	242.01	330.10
286	263.42	308.42	259.50	313.07	252.35	319.09	243.31	331.59
287	264.73	308.42	259.60	314.29	253.63	319.95	244.69	333.20
288	266.11	308.42	259.60	315.52	254.95	321.17	246.24	333.20
289	267.73	309.10	259.60	316.78	256.37	322.42	247.54	333.80
290	268.73	310.26	260.51	318.10	258.34	323.70	247.54	335.06
291	268.73	311.43	261.72	319.50	258.34	325.04	247.54	336.37
292	268.73	312.62	262.95	321.24	258.34	326.50	248.62	337.76
293	268.73	313.81	264.20	321.86	258.45	328.21	249.94	339.38
294	269.79	315.03	265.50	321.86	259.67	328.21	251.35	340.41
295	270.96	316.27	266.87	322.29	260.92	328.28	253.14	340.41
296	272.14	317.54	268.42	323.47	262.20	329.49	253.65	341.38
297	273.34	318.87	269.67	324.68	263.54	330.72	253.65	342.65
298	274.56	320.31	269.67	325.90	265.00	331.97	253.92	343.98
299	275.81	322.14	269.67	327.15	266.71	333.26	255.20	345.41
300	277.09	322.15	269.90	328.43	266.71	334.62	256.54	347.37

TABLE XVII (*cont.*)

X	80		90		95		99	
	Lower	*Upper*	*Lower*	*Upper*	*Lower*	*Upper*	*Lower*	*Upper*
191	172.92	208.52	168.41	213.03	163.35	219.16	156.69	229.37
192	174.39	208.52	170.00	214.24	164.63	219.16	158.25	229.37
193	176.06	209.49	171.09	215.47	165.96	220.29	159.53	230.03
194	176.06	210.67	171.09	216.73	167.39	221.56	159.53	231.33
195	176.06	211.88	171.09	218.03	169.33	222.86	159.67	232.71
196	176.06	213.10	171.84	219.40	169.33	224.26	161.01	234.28
197	177.14	214.35	173.08	221.00	169.33	225.90	162.46	235.50
198	178.34	215.63	174.36	222.10	169.80	226.81	164.31	235.50
199	179.56	216.98	175.69	222.10	171.07	226.81	164.31	236.68
200	180.90	218.49	177.13	222.60	172.38	227.73	164.31	238.01
201	182.08	219.96	178.96	223.82	173.79	228.99	165.33	239.46
202	183.42	219.96	178.96	225.05	175.48	230.28	166.71	241.32
203	184.89	219.96	178.96	226.33	176.23	231.65	168.29	241.32
204	186.56	220.95	179.18	227.65	176.23	233.19	169.49	242.01
205	186.56	222.13	180.40	229.07	176.23	234.53	169.49	243.31
206	186.56	223.33	181.65	231.02	177.48	234.53	169.64	244.69
207	186.56	224.55	182.94	231.02	178.77	235.14	170.98	246.24
208	187.59	225.79	184.30	231.02	180.14	236.39	172.41	247.54
209	188.78	227.07	185.80	232.14	181.67	237.67	174.36	247.54
210	189.99	228.40	187.30	233.35	183.05	239.00	174.36	248.62
211	191.23	229.85	187.30	234.60	183.05	240.45	174.36	249.94
212	192.49	231.60	187.30	235.88	183.05	242.27	175.25	251.35
213	193.81	231.60	187.70	237.21	183.86	242.27	176.61	253.14
214	195.22	231.60	188.93	238.66	185.13	242.53	178.11	253.65
215	197.12	232.36	190.18	240.43	186.46	243.76	179.67	253.92
216	197.22	233.53	191.47	240.43	187.89	245.02	179.67	255.20
217	197.33	234.72	193.83	240.43	189.83	246.32	179.67	256.26
218	197.33	235.93	194.36	241.63	189.83	247.70	180.84	258.00
219	197.97	237.16	195.73	242.85	189.83	249.28	182.22	259.78
220	199.16	238.41	195.73	244.09	190.21	250.43	183.81	259.78
221	200.36	239.71	195.73	245.37	191.46	250.43	184.97	260.47
222	201.58	241.09	196.18	246.70	192.76	251.11	184.97	261.77
223	202.82	242.69	197.40	248.15	194.11	252.35	185.08	263.12
224	204.11	243.76	198.65	249.94	195.63	253.63	186.40	264.63
225	205.45	243.76	199.94	249.94	197.09	254.95	187.81	266.15
226	206.94	243.76	201.30	249.94	197.09	256.37	189.50	266.15
227	208.52	244.88	202.80	251.09	197.09	258.34	190.28	267.01
228	208.52	246.06	204.30	252.30	197.78	258.34	190.28	268.31
229	208.52	247.26	204.30	253.54	199.04	258.45	190.61	269.68
230	208.52	248.47	204.30	254.81	200.35	259.67	191.94	271.22

(*cont.*)

TABLE XVII (*cont.*)

X	80		90		95		99	
	Lower	Upper	Lower	Upper	Lower	Upper	Lower	Upper
231	209.49	249.70	204.62	256.13	201.73	260.92	193.36	272.56
232	210.67	250.96	205.84	257.55	203.35	262.20	195.19	272.56
233	211.88	252.27	207.08	259.50	204.36	263.54	195.59	273.53
234	213.10	253.67	208.36	259.60	204.36	265.00	195.59	274.83
235	214.35	255.39	209.69	259.60	204.36	266.71	196.13	276.20
236	215.63	256.07	211.13	260.51	205.31	266.71	197.46	277.77
237	216.98	256.07	212.96	261.72	206.58	266.97	198.88	279.01
238	218.49	256.19	212.96	262.95	207.90	268.19	200.84	279.01
239	219.96	257.36	212.96	264.20	209.30	269.44	200.94	280.02
240	219.96	258.54	213.03	265.50	211.03	270.73	200.94	281.32
241	219.96	259.73	214.24	266.87	211.69	272.08	201.62	282.70
242	219.96	260.94	215.47	268.42	211.69	273.57	202.94	284.25
243	220.95	262.17	216.73	269.67	211.69	275.15	204.36	285.53
244	222.13	263.42	218.03	269.67	212.82	275.15	206.19	285.53
245	223.33	264.73	219.40	269.90	214.09	275.46	206.60	286.50
246	224.55	266.11	221.00	271.10	215.40	276.69	206.60	287.79
247	225.79	267.73	222.10	272.31	216.81	277.94	207.08	289.16
248	227.07	268.73	222.10	273.55	218.56	279.22	208.40	290.68
249	228.40	268.73	222.10	274.82	219.16	280.57	209.81	292.10
250	229.85	268.73	222.60	276.14	219.16	282.05	211.50	292.10
251	231.60	269.79	223.82	277.57	219.16	283.67	212.29	292.95
252	231.60	270.96	225.05	279.53	220.29	283.67	212.29	294.24
253	231.60	272.14	226.33	279.53	221.56	283.93	212.53	295.59
254	231.60	273.34	227.65	279.53	222.86	285.15	213.84	297.07
255	232.36	274.56	229.07	280.45	224.26	286.40	215.22	298.71
256	233.53	275.81	231.02	281.65	225.90	287.68	216.80	298.71
257	234.72	277.09	231.02	282.87	226.81	289.01	217.98	299.?
258	235.93	278.43	231.02	284.12	226.81	290.46	217.98	300
259	237.16	279.90	231.02	285.40	226.81	292.26	217.98	30
260	238.41	281.56	232.14	286.73	227.73	292.26	219.25	?
261	239.71	281.56	233.35	288.20	228.99	292.37	220.61	
262	241.09	281.56	234.60	289.90	230.28	293.59	222.1	
263	242.69	282.16	235.88	289.90	231.65	294.82	223.	
264	243.76	283.33	237.21	289.90	233.19	296.09	22?	
265	243.76	284.51	238.66	290.96	234.53	297.41	2?	
266	243.76	285.69	240.43	292.16	234.53	298.81		
267	243.76	286.90	240.43	293.38	234.53	300.56		
268	244.88	288.12	240.43	294.63	235.14	301.1?		
269	246.06	289.37	240.43	295.91	236.39	301.?		
270	247.26	290.67	241.63	297.26	237.67	30?		

Table XVIII. Upper 10% Points of the Studentized Range

r, number of observations per treatment

v	2	3	4	5	6	7	8	9	10	11	12	13	14	15	16	17	18	19	20
1	8.93	13.44	16.36	18.49	20.15	20.51	22.64	23.62	24.48	25.24	25.92	26.54	27.10	27.62	28.10	28.54	28.96	29.35	29.71
2	4.13	5.73	6.77	7.54	8.14	8.63	9.05	9.41	9.72	10.01	10.26	10.49	10.70	10.98	11.07	11.24	11.39	11.54	11.68
3	3.33	4.47	5.20	5.74	6.16	6.51	6.81	7.06	7.29	7.49	7.67	7.83	7.98	8.12	8.25	8.37	8.48	8.58	8.68
4	3.01	3.98	4.59	5.03	5.39	5.68	5.93	6.14	6.33	6.49	6.65	6.78	6.91	7.02	7.13	7.23	7.33	7.41	7.50
5	2.85	3.72	4.26	4.66	4.98	5.24	5.46	5.65	5.82	5.97	6.10	6.22	6.34	6.44	6.54	6.63	6.71	6.79	6.86
6	2.75	3.56	4.07	4.44	4.73	4.97	5.17	5.34	5.50	5.64	5.76	5.87	5.98	6.07	6.16	6.25	6.32	6.40	6.47
7	2.68	3.45	3.93	4.28	4.55	4.78	4.97	5.14	5.28	5.41	5.53	5.64	5.74	5.83	5.91	5.99	6.06	6.13	6.19
8	2.63	3.37	3.83	4.17	4.43	4.65	4.83	4.99	5.13	5.25	5.36	5.46	5.56	5.64	5.72	5.80	5.87	5.93	6.00
9	2.59	3.32	3.76	4.08	4.34	4.54	4.72	4.87	5.01	5.13	5.23	5.33	5.42	5.51	5.58	5.66	5.72	5.79	5.85
10	2.56	3.27	3.70	4.02	4.26	4.47	4.64	4.78	4.91	5.03	5.13	5.23	5.32	5.40	5.47	5.54	5.61	5.67	5.73
11	2.54	3.23	3.66	3.96	4.20	4.40	4.57	4.71	4.84	4.95	5.05	5.15	5.23	5.31	5.38	5.45	5.51	5.57	5.63
12	2.52	3.20	3.62	3.92	4.16	4.35	4.51	4.65	4.78	4.89	4.99	5.08	5.16	5.24	5.31	5.37	5.44	5.49	5.55
13	2.50	3.18	3.59	3.88	4.12	4.30	4.46	4.60	4.72	4.83	4.93	5.02	5.10	5.18	5.25	5.31	5.37	5.43	5.48
14	2.49	3.16	3.56	3.85	4.08	4.27	4.42	4.56	4.68	4.79	4.88	4.97	5.05	5.12	5.19	5.26	5.32	5.37	5.43
15	2.48	3.14	3.54	3.83	4.05	4.23	4.39	4.52	4.64	4.75	4.84	4.93	5.01	5.08	5.15	5.21	5.27	5.32	5.38
16	2.47	3.12	3.52	3.80	4.03	4.21	4.36	4.49	4.61	4.71	4.81	4.89	4.97	5.04	5.11	5.17	5.23	5.28	5.33
17	2.46	3.11	3.50	3.78	4.00	4.18	4.33	4.46	4.58	4.68	4.77	4.86	4.93	5.01	5.07	5.13	5.19	5.24	5.30
18	2.45	3.10	3.49	3.77	3.98	4.16	4.31	4.44	4.55	4.65	4.75	4.83	4.90	4.98	5.04	5.10	5.16	5.21	5.26
19	2.45	3.09	3.47	3.75	3.97	4.14	4.29	4.43	4.53	4.63	4.72	4.80	4.88	4.95	5.01	5.07	5.13	5.18	5.23
20	2.44	3.08	3.46	3.74	3.95	4.12	4.27	4.40	4.51	4.61	4.70	4.78	4.85	4.92	4.99	5.05	5.10	5.16	5.20
24	2.42	3.05	3.42	3.69	3.90	4.07	4.21	4.34	4.44	4.54	4.63	4.71	4.78	4.85	4.91	4.97	5.02	5.07	5.12
30	2.40	3.02	3.39	3.65	3.85	4.02	4.16	4.28	4.38	4.47	4.56	4.64	4.71	4.77	4.83	4.89	4.94	4.99	5.03
40	2.38	2.99	3.35	3.60	3.80	3.96	4.10	4.21	4.34	4.41	4.49	4.56	4.63	4.69	4.75	4.81	4.86	4.90	4.95
60	2.36	2.96	3.31	3.56	3.75	3.91	4.04	4.16	4.25	4.34	4.42	4.49	4.56	4.62	4.67	4.73	4.78	4.82	4.86
120	2.34	2.93	3.28	3.52	3.71	3.86	3.99	4.10	4.19	4.28	4.35	4.42	4.48	4.54	4.60	4.65	4.69	4.74	4.78
∞	2.33	2.90	3.24	3.48	3.66	3.81	3.93	4.04	4.13	4.21	4.28	4.35	4.41	4.47	4.52	4.57	4.61	4.65	4.69

TABLE XVIII (cont.). UPPER 5% POINTS

r, number of observations per treatment

v	2	3	4	5	6	7	8	9	10	11	12	13	14	15	16	17	18	19	20
1	17.97	26.98	32.82	37.08	40.41	43.12	45.40	47.36	49.07	50.59	51.96	53.20	54.33	55.36	56.32	57.22	58.04	58.83	59.56
2	6.08	8.33	9.80	10.88	11.74	12.44	13.03	13.54	13.99	14.39	14.75	15.08	15.38	15.65	15.91	16.14	16.37	16.57	16.77
3	4.50	5.91	6.82	7.50	8.04	8.48	8.85	9.18	9.46	9.72	9.95	10.15	10.35	10.52	10.69	10.84	10.98	11.11	11.24
4	3.93	5.04	5.76	6.29	6.71	7.05	7.35	7.60	7.83	8.03	8.21	8.37	8.52	8.66	8.79	8.91	9.03	9.13	9.23
5	3.64	4.60	5.22	5.67	6.03	6.33	6.58	6.80	6.99	7.17	7.32	7.47	7.60	7.72	7.83	7.93	8.03	8.12	8.21
6	3.46	4.34	4.90	5.30	5.63	5.90	6.12	6.32	6.49	6.65	6.79	6.92	7.03	7.14	7.24	7.34	7.43	7.51	7.59
7	3.34	4.16	4.68	5.06	5.36	5.61	5.82	6.00	6.16	6.30	6.43	6.55	6.66	6.76	6.85	6.94	7.02	7.10	7.17
8	3.26	4.04	4.53	4.89	5.17	5.40	5.60	5.77	5.92	6.05	6.18	6.29	6.39	6.48	6.57	6.65	6.73	6.80	6.87
9	3.20	3.95	4.41	4.76	5.02	5.24	5.43	5.59	5.74	5.87	5.98	6.09	6.19	6.28	6.36	6.44	6.51	6.58	6.64
10	3.15	3.88	4.33	4.65	4.91	5.12	5.30	5.46	5.60	5.72	5.83	5.93	6.03	6.11	6.19	6.27	6.34	6.40	6.47
11	3.11	3.82	4.26	4.57	4.82	5.03	5.20	5.35	5.49	5.61	5.71	5.81	5.90	5.98	6.06	6.13	6.20	6.27	6.33
12	3.08	3.77	4.20	4.51	4.75	4.95	5.12	5.27	5.39	5.51	5.61	5.71	5.80	5.88	5.95	6.02	6.09	6.15	6.21
13	3.06	3.73	4.15	4.45	4.69	4.88	5.05	5.19	5.32	5.43	5.53	5.63	5.71	5.79	5.86	5.93	5.99	6.05	6.11
14	3.03	3.70	4.11	4.41	4.64	4.83	4.99	5.13	5.25	5.36	5.46	5.55	5.64	5.71	5.79	5.85	5.91	5.97	6.03
15	3.01	3.67	4.08	4.37	4.59	4.78	4.94	5.08	5.20	5.31	5.40	5.49	5.57	5.65	5.72	5.78	5.85	5.90	5.96
16	3.00	3.65	4.05	4.33	4.56	4.74	4.90	5.03	5.15	5.26	5.35	5.44	5.52	5.59	5.66	5.73	5.79	5.84	5.90
17	2.98	3.63	4.02	4.30	4.52	4.70	4.86	4.99	5.11	5.21	5.31	5.39	5.47	5.54	5.61	5.67	5.73	5.79	5.84
18	2.97	3.61	4.00	4.28	4.49	4.67	4.82	4.96	5.07	5.17	5.27	5.35	5.43	5.50	5.57	5.63	5.69	5.74	5.79
19	2.96	3.59	3.98	4.25	4.47	4.65	4.79	4.92	5.04	5.14	5.23	5.29	5.39	5.46	5.53	5.59	5.65	5.70	5.75
20	2.95	3.58	3.96	4.23	4.45	4.62	4.77	4.90	5.01	5.11	5.20	5.28	5.36	5.43	5.49	5.55	5.61	5.66	5.71
24	2.92	3.53	3.90	4.17	4.37	4.54	4.68	4.81	4.92	5.01	5.10	5.18	5.25	5.32	5.38	5.44	5.49	5.55	5.59
30	2.89	3.49	3.85	4.10	4.30	4.46	4.60	4.72	4.82	4.92	5.00	5.08	5.15	5.21	5.27	5.33	5.38	5.43	5.47
40	2.86	3.44	3.79	4.04	4.23	4.39	4.52	4.63	4.73	4.82	4.90	4.98	5.04	5.11	5.16	5.22	5.27	5.31	5.36
60	2.83	3.40	3.74	3.98	4.16	4.31	4.44	4.55	4.65	4.73	4.81	4.88	4.94	5.00	5.06	5.11	5.15	5.20	5.24
120	2.80	3.36	3.68	3.92	4.10	4.24	4.36	4.47	4.56	4.64	4.71	4.78	4.84	4.90	4.95	5.00	5.04	5.09	5.13
∞	2.77	3.31	3.63	3.86	4.03	4.17	4.29	4.39	4.47	4.55	4.62	4.68	4.74	4.80	4.85	4.89	4.93	4.97	5.01

TABLE XVIII (cont.).   UPPER 1% POINTS

r, number of observations per treatment

v	2	3	4	5	6	7	8	9	10	11	12	13	14	15	16	17	18	19	20
1	90.03	135.0	164.3	185.6	202.2	215.8	227.2	237.0	245.6	253.2	260.0	266.2	271.8	277.0	281.8	286.3	290.4	294.3	298.0
2	14.04	19.02	22.29	24.72	26.63	28.20	29.53	30.68	31.69	32.59	33.40	34.13	34.81	35.43	36.00	36.53	37.03	37.50	37.95
3	8.26	10.62	12.17	13.33	14.24	15.00	15.64	16.20	16.69	17.13	17.53	17.89	18.22	18.52	18.81	19.07	19.32	19.55	19.77
4	6.51	8.12	9.17	9.96	10.58	11.10	11.55	11.93	12.27	12.57	12.84	13.09	13.32	13.53	13.73	13.91	14.08	14.24	14.40
5	5.70	6.98	7.80	8.42	8.91	9.32	9.67	9.98	10.24	10.48	10.70	10.89	11.08	11.24	11.40	11.55	11.68	11.81	11.93
6	5.24	6.33	7.03	7.56	7.97	8.32	8.61	8.87	9.10	9.30	9.48	9.65	9.81	9.95	10.08	10.21	10.32	10.43	10.54
7	4.95	5.92	6.54	7.01	7.37	7.68	7.94	8.17	8.37	8.55	8.71	8.86	9.00	9.12	9.24	9.35	9.46	9.55	9.65
8	4.75	5.64	6.20	6.62	6.96	7.24	7.47	7.68	7.86	8.03	8.18	8.31	8.44	8.55	8.66	8.76	8.85	8.94	9.03
9	4.60	5.43	5.96	6.35	6.66	6.91	7.13	7.33	7.49	7.65	7.78	7.91	8.03	8.13	8.23	8.33	8.41	8.49	8.57
10	4.48	5.27	5.77	6.14	6.43	6.67	6.87	7.05	7.21	7.36	7.49	7.60	7.71	7.81	7.91	7.99	8.08	8.15	8.23
11	4.39	5.15	5.62	5.97	6.25	6.48	6.67	6.84	6.99	7.13	7.25	7.36	7.46	7.56	7.65	7.73	7.81	7.88	7.95
12	4.32	5.05	5.50	5.84	6.10	6.32	6.51	6.67	6.81	6.94	7.06	7.17	7.26	7.36	7.44	7.52	7.59	7.66	7.73
13	4.26	4.96	5.40	5.73	5.98	6.19	6.37	6.53	6.67	6.79	6.90	7.01	7.10	7.19	7.27	7.35	7.42	7.48	7.55
14	4.21	4.89	5.32	5.63	5.88	6.08	6.26	6.41	6.54	6.66	6.77	6.87	6.96	7.05	7.13	7.20	7.27	7.33	7.39
15	4.17	4.84	5.25	5.56	5.80	5.99	6.16	6.31	6.44	6.55	6.66	6.76	6.84	6.93	7.00	7.07	7.14	7.20	7.26
16	4.13	4.79	5.19	5.49	5.72	5.92	6.08	6.22	6.35	6.46	6.56	6.66	6.74	6.82	6.90	6.97	7.03	7.09	7.15
17	4.10	4.74	5.14	5.43	5.66	5.85	6.01	6.15	6.27	6.38	6.48	6.57	6.66	6.73	6.81	6.87	6.94	7.00	7.05
18	4.07	4.70	5.09	5.38	5.60	5.79	5.94	6.08	6.20	6.31	6.41	6.50	6.58	6.65	6.73	6.79	6.85	6.91	6.97
19	4.05	4.67	5.05	5.33	5.55	5.73	5.89	6.02	6.14	6.25	6.34	6.43	6.51	6.58	6.65	6.72	6.78	6.84	6.89
20	4.02	4.64	5.02	5.29	5.51	5.69	5.84	5.97	6.09	6.19	6.28	6.37	6.45	6.52	6.59	6.65	6.71	6.77	6.82
24	3.96	4.55	4.91	5.17	5.37	5.54	5.69	5.81	5.92	6.02	6.11	6.19	6.26	6.33	6.39	6.45	6.51	6.56	6.61
30	3.89	4.45	4.80	5.05	5.24	5.40	5.54	5.65	5.76	5.85	5.93	6.01	6.08	6.14	6.20	6.26	6.31	6.36	6.41
40	3.82	4.37	4.70	4.93	5.11	5.26	5.39	5.50	5.60	5.69	5.76	5.83	5.90	5.96	6.02	6.07	6.12	6.16	6.21
60	3.76	4.28	4.59	4.82	4.99	5.13	5.25	5.36	5.45	5.53	5.60	5.67	5.73	5.78	5.84	5.89	5.93	5.97	6.01
120	3.70	4.20	4.50	4.71	4.87	5.01	5.12	5.21	5.30	5.37	5.44	5.50	5.56	5.61	5.66	5.71	5.75	5.79	5.83
∞	3.64	4.12	4.40	4.60	4.76	4.88	4.99	5.08	5.16	5.23	5.29	5.35	5.40	5.45	5.49	5.54	5.57	5.61	5.65

Table XIX.   Moment Constants of the Mean Deviation and of the Range

n	Mean deviation, m/σ					Range, $W = w/\sigma$						
	Expectation	S.D.	V_n variance	β_1	β_2	$\epsilon(W_n) = d_r$	S.D.	V_n variance	β_1	β_2	d_n/V_n	d_n/V_n
2	0.564 190	0.4263	0.1816	0.9919	3.869	1.12838	0.8525	0.72676	0.9906	3.869	1.55	1.75
3	0.651 470	0.3419	0.11692	0.417	3.286	1.69257	0.8884	0.78922	0.4174	3.286	2.14	3.63
4	0.690 988	0.2970	0.08822	0.298	3.252	2.05875	0.8798	0.77407	0.2735	3.188	2.66	5.48
5	0.713 650	0.2663	0.07094	0.230	3.197	2.32593	0.8641	0.74661	0.2174	3.169	3.12	7.25
6	0.725 366	0.2436	0.05934	0.187	3.161	2.53441	0.8480	0.71916	0.1892	3.168	3.52	8.93
7	0.738 698	0.2258	0.05101	0.157	3.136	2.70436	0.8332	0.69424	0.1742	3.174	3.90	10.53
8	0.746 353	0.2115	0.04473	0.136	3.118	2.84720	0.8198	0.67213	0.1657	3.184	4.24	12.06
9	0.752 253	0.1996	0.03982	0.119	3.104	2.97003	0.8078	0.65262	0.1608	3.191	4.55	13.52
10	0.756 940	0.1894	0.03589	0.106	3.0927	3.07751	0.7971	0.63531	0.1580	3.200	4.84	14.91
11	0.760 753	0.1807	0.03266	0.0961	3.0838	3.17287	0.7873	0.61984	0.1564	3.205	5.12	16.2
12	0.763 916	0.1731	0.02997	0.0876	3.0765	3.25846	0.7785	0.60601	0.1560	3.213	5.38	17.5
13	0.766 583	0.1664	0.02769	0.0805	3.0703	3.33598	0.7704	0.59353	0.1559	3.220	5.62	18.8
14	0.768 861	0.1604	0.02573	0.0744	3.0650	3.40676	0.7630	0.58217	0.1561	3.225	5.85	19.9
15	0.770 830	0.1550	0.02403	0.0692	3.0605	3.47183	0.7562	0.57186	0.1568	3.231	6.07	21.1
16	0.772 548	0.1501	0.02254	0.0647	3.0566	3.53198	0.7499	0.56237	0.1576	3.237	6.28	22.2
17	0.774 062	0.1457	0.02122	0.0607	3.0531	3.58788	0.7441	0.55363	0.1588	3.242	6.48	23.3
18	0.775 404	0.1416	0.02005	0.0572	3.0501	3.64006	0.7386	0.54554	0.1598	3.248	6.67	24.3
19	0.776 604	0.1378	0.01900	0.0541	3.0473	3.68896	0.7335	0.53802	0.1612	3.254	6.86	25.3
20	0.777 682	0.1344	0.01806	0.0513	3.0449	3.73495	0.7287	0.53097	0.1627	3.259	7.03	26.3
30	0.784 474	0.1098	0.01206	0.0338	3.0296							
60	0.791 208	0.0777	0.00604	0.0167	3.0146							

TABLE XX. TABLES FOR AN ANALYSIS OF VARIANCE BASED ON RANGE

A. Scale factor, c, and equivalent degrees of freedom, v, appropriate to a one-way classification into t groups of r observations each

t:	2		3		4		5		...	10		Constant at ∞ difference	
r	v	c	v	c	v	c	v	c		v	c	v	c
2	1.9	1.28	2.8	1.23	3.7	1.21	4.6	1.19		9.0	1.16	0.88	1.13
3	3.8	1.81	5.7	1.77	7.5	1.75	9.3	1.74		18.4	1.72	1.82	1.69
4	5.7	2.15	8.4	2.12	11.2	2.11	13.9	2.10		27.6	2.08	2.74	2.06
5	7.5	2.40	11.1	2.38	14.7	2.37	18.4	2.36		36.5	2.34	3.62	2.33
6	9.2	2.60	13.6	2.58	18.1	2.57	22.6	2.56		44.9	2.55	4.47	2.53
7	10.8	2.77	16.0	2.75	21.3	2.74	26.6	2.73		52.9	2.72	5.27	2.70
8	12.3	2.91	18.3	2.89	24.4	2.88	30.4	2.87		60.6	2.86	6.03	2.85
9	13.8	3.02	20.5	3.01	27.3	3.00	34.0	2.99		67.8	2.98	6.76	2.97
10	15.1	3.13	22.6	3.11	30.1	3.10	37.5	3.10		74.8	3.09	7.45	3.08

B. Scale factor, c, and equivalent degrees of freedom, v, for an analysis of variance for a two-way classification with t Treatments and r Blocks (account is taken of the correlation between the ranges of residuals)

t:	2		3		4		5		6		7		8		9	
r	v	c	v	c	v	c	v	c	v	c	v	c	v	c	v	c
2	1.0	1.00	2.0	1.35	2.9	1.58	3.8	1.75	4.7	1.89	5.5	2.00	6.3	2.10	7.0	2.18
3	1.9	1.05	3.7	1.48	5.6	1.76	7.4	1.96	9.3	2.12	11.3	2.26	13.4	2.37	15.7	2.46
4	2.7	1.07	5.4	1.54	8.2	1.84	11.0	2.06	13.9	2.23	16.9	2.38	20.1	2.50	23.6	2.60
5	3.6	1.08	7.2	1.57	10.9	1.88	14.6	2.12	18.5	2.30	22.4	2.45	26.6	2.57	31.1	2.68
6	4.5	1.09	8.9	1.59	13.6	1.91	18.2	2.15	23.0	2.34	27.9	2.49	33.0	2.62	38.2	2.73
7	5.4	1.09	10.7	1.61	16.3	1.93	21.8	2.18	27.6	2.37	33.3	2.52	39.3	2.65	45.4	2.76
8	6.3	1.10	12.5	1.62	19.0	1.95	25.4	2.20	32.1	2.39	38.7	2.55	45.6	2.68	52.5	2.79
9	7.1	1.10	14.3	1.63	21.7	1.96	29.0	2.21	36.6	2.41	44.0	2.57	51.8	2.70	59.6	2.81
10	8.1	1.10	16.1	1.63	24.4	1.97	32.6	2.22	41.0	2.42	49.3	2.58	57.9	2.71	66.6	2.83
20	16.7	1.11	33.9	1.66	51.5	2.02	68.8	2.28	86.0	2.48	103	2.64	119	2.78	134	2.90
C at ∞		1.13		1.69		2.06		2.33		2.53		2.70		2.85		2.97
Const. diff.	0.87		1.80		2.71		3.62		4.50		5.33		6.10		6.79	

Derived from E. S. Pearson and H. O. Hartley, *Biometrika Tables for Statisticians*, Vol. 1, Cambridge Univ. Press, London, 1960, Tables 30A and 30B, with the permission of the authors and publisher, on behalf of the Biometrika Trustees.

TABLE XXI.   10, 5, and 1% Regions of Rejection for the Product Moment
Coefficient of Correlation with ν Degrees of Freedom

ν	ω: $r \geq$ number shown for stated α		
	$\alpha = 0.10$	$\alpha = 0.05$	$\alpha = 0.01$
3	0.805	0.878	0.959
4	0.729	0.811	0.917
5	0.669	0.755†	0.875
6	0.622*	0.707	0.834
7	0.582	0.666	0.798
8	0.549	0.632	0.765
9	0.521	0.602	0.735
10	0.498*	0.576	0.708
11	0.476	0.553	0.684
12	0.458*	0.533*	0.661
13	0.441	0.514	0.641
14	0.426	0.497	0.623
15	0.412	0.482	0.605†
16	0.400	0.468	0.590
17	0.389	0.455†	0.575
18	0.379*	0.444	0.562*
19	0.369	0.433	0.549
20	0.360	0.423	0.537
25	0.323	0.381	0.487
30	0.296	0.349	0.449
40	0.257	0.304	0.393
60	0.211	0.250	0.325
120	0.150	0.178	0.232

Critical r calculated from $r_\alpha = \sqrt{F_\alpha(1,\nu)/[\nu + F_\alpha(1,\nu)]}$,
using three-digit values of F.

* is one unit larger in third decimal place than value in
Biometrika Tables, Vol. 1.

† is one unit smaller in third decimal place than value in
Biometrika Tables, Vol. 1.

Index